Advances in

VIRUS RESEARCH

VOLUME 16

CONTRIBUTORS TO THIS VOLUME

J. B. Bancroft
Gerald A. Cole
Nancy L. Couse
Donald J. Cummings
Gerald L. Forrest
Robert R. Granados
Hiroyuki Hirumi
Barbara Hohn
Thomas Hohn
A. F. Howatson
George L. Le Bouvier
Robert W. McCollum
Karl Maramorosch
Seiichi Matsumoto
Neal Nathanson
George Poste

Advances in
VIRUS RESEARCH

Edited by

KENNETH M. SMITH
Cambridge, England

MAX A. LAUFFER
Department of Biophysics
and Microbiology
University of Pittsburgh
Pittsburgh, Pennsylvania

FREDERIK B. BANG
Department of Pathobiology
The Johns Hopkins University
Baltimore, Maryland

VOLUME 16

1970

ACADEMIC PRESS
NEW YORK AND LONDON

ACADEMIC PRESS, INC.
111 Fifth Avenue, New York, New York 10003

United Kingdom Edition published by
ACADEMIC PRESS, INC. (LONDON) LTD.
Berkeley Square House, London W1X 6BA

LIBRARY OF CONGRESS CATALOG CARD NUMBER: 53-11559

PRINTED IN THE UNITED STATES OF AMERICA

CONTENTS

Vesicular Stomatitis and Related Viruses

A. F. HOWATSON

Rabies Virus

SEIICHI MATSUMOTO

Virus-Induced Polykaryocytosis and the Mechanism of Cell Fusion

GEORGE POSTE

Australia (Hepatitis-Associated) Antigen: Physicochemical and Immunological Characteristics

GEORGE L. LE BOUVIER AND ROBERT W. MCCOLLUM

Immunosuppression and Experimental Virus Infection of the Nervous System

NEAL NATHANSON AND GERALD A. COLE

CONTRIBUTORS TO VOLUME 16

Numbers in parentheses indicate the pages on which the authors' contributions begin.

J. B. BANCROFT, *Department of Botany and Plant Pathology, Purdue University, Lafayette, Indiana (99)*

GERALD A. COLE, *Department of Epidemiology, School of Hygiene and Public Health, The Johns Hopkins University, Baltimore, Maryland (397)*

NANCY L. COUSE, *Department of Microbiology, University of Colorado Medical Center, Denver, Colorado (1)*

DONALD J. CUMMINGS, *Department of Microbiology, University of Colorado Medical Center, Denver, Colorado (1)*

GERALD L. FORREST, *Department of Microbiology, University of Colorado Medical Center, Denver, Colorado (1)*

ROBERT R. GRANADOS, *Boyce Thompson Institute for Plant Research, Yonkers, New York (135)*

HIROYUKI HIRUMI, *Boyce Thompson Institute for Plant Research, Yonkers, New York (135)*

BARBARA HOHN, *Departments of Biochemistry and Pathology, Stanford University School of Medicine, Stanford, California (43)*

THOMAS HOHN, *Departments of Biochemistry and Pathology, Stanford University School of Medicine, Stanford, California (43)*

A. F. HOWATSON, *Ontario Cancer Institute and Department of Medical Biophysics, University of Toronto, Toronto, Canada (195)*

GEORGE L. LE BOUVIER, *Department of Epidemiology and Public Health, Yale University School of Medicine, New Haven, Connecticut (357)*

ROBERT W. MCCOLLUM, *Department of Epidemiology and Public Health, Yale University School of Medicine, New Haven, Connecticut (357)*

KARL MARAMOROSCH, *Boyce Thompson Institute for Plant Research, Yonkers, New York (135)*

SEIICHI MATSUMOTO, *Institute for Virus Research, Kyoto University, Kyoto, Japan (257)*

NEAL NATHANSON, *Department of Epidemiology, School of Hygiene and Public Health, The Johns Hopkins University, Baltimore, Maryland (397)*

GEORGE POSTE, *Department of Virology, Royal Postgraduate Medical School, London, England (303)*

STRUCTURAL DEFECTS OF T-EVEN BACTERIOPHAGES

Donald J. Cummings, Nancy L. Couse, and Gerald L. Forrest

Department of Microbiology, University of Colorado Medical Center, Denver, Colorado

I. Introduction

Bacterial viruses were discovered independently by Twort (1915) and d'Herelle (1917) and the history of their discovery has already been well described (Stent, 1963). We will concern ourselves with some of the bacteriophages of *Escherichia coli* designated T- (for type): T1, T2, T3, T4, T5, T6, and T7 (Demerec and Fano, 1945); in particular, the serologically related bacteriophages T2, T4, and T6. The pioneering work of Schlesinger (1932, 1934, 1936), who took the view that viruses were amenable to study by simple physicochemical methods, indicated that these viruses had a uniform size of about 0.1 μ, a mass of 4×10^{-16} gm and that they were composed of roughly equal amounts of DNA and protein. With the advent of electron microscopy, Luria and Anderson (1942) were able to show that T-even bacteriophage were tadpole-shaped particles and the DNA appeared to be confined within the head structure. Further refinement of techniques (Brenner and Horne, 1959) has led to the elucidation of the detailed structure represented in Fig. 1. These viruses are indeed complex, composed of many substructural components linked together to form the complete particle. As suggested by Schlesinger, the total length of the T-even bacteriophage is about 2000 Å, with a head 1000 by 700 Å and a tail structure 1000 Å long. This particle is composed of several substructures. Proceeding from the point of attachment to the host bacterium, there are six tail fibers (Williams and Fraser, 1956; Brenner *et al.*, 1959), a tail plate having sixfold symmetry to which the six tail fibers are attached (Brenner *et al.*, 1959), a hollow tail tube through which the DNA is injected (Kellenberger and Arber, 1955; Brenner *et al.*, 1959), a contractile tail sheath surrounding the tail tube (Brenner *et al.*, 1959; Kozloff and Lute, 1959), a tail collar (Anderson, 1961; Daems *et al.*, 1961), a neck (Cummings *et al.*, 1968) or connector (King, 1968) connecting the head to the tail tube and sheath, and, finally, the voluminous head substructure which encloses the double-stranded DNA. In addition there is a so-called internal protein (Levine *et al.*, 1958) which may lie at the central region of the super-coiled DNA (Cummings and Wanko, 1963). Sedimentation and diffusion studies (Cummings and Kozloff, 1960) on the intact particles of T2L indicated that the particle weight was 215×10^6 daltons. The molecular weight of the DNA has been determined by various physical techniques and was found to be about 120×10^6 daltons (Rubenstein *et al.*, 1961; Davison *et al.*, 1961). Therefore, the particle weight of all the protein components can be calculated to be about 95×10^6 daltons. These substructures are all linked together both physically and functionally. Simon and Anderson (1967a, b) have carefully examined the steps in the attachment of the virus to the host cell. First, there is reversible binding of the tail fiber to the cell wall, then an irreversible attachment of the tail plate involving a conformational change in the tail plate, the sheath contracts, and the DNA is injected into the host. Cummings and Kozloff (1962) reported that for T2L, at least, there may be a head conformational change necessary for successful injection of the DNA. The role of the collar in this process is unknown but it may be involved in the reversible extension of the tail fibers (Cummings, 1964; Kanner and Kozloff, 1964; Kellenberger *et al.*, 1965; Cummings *et al.*, 1969).

In recent years, Edgar and his collaborators (see later) made the important discovery that some bacteriophage mutants are defective and cannot manufacture normal substructures. This and other aspects of phage morphology have been the subject of many reviews. We will limit our review primarily to the study of the structure and composition of the head. Special attention will be directed at examining the various models which have been presented to elucidate the assembly of both normal and aberrant heads.

II. Properties of the Substructural Components

The limiting factor in studying these substructures involves the isolation, in the undegraded state, of sufficient quantities for analysis. An estimation of the relative amounts of these components can be readily made; these estimates are presented in Table I. The collar, neck, and plate, collectively, account for about 2.5% of the protein mass of the particle and have not yet been characterized to any great extent. Moreover, these substructures appeared to be labile to the isolation procedures employed (see later). Similarly, tail fibers were also labile and were not isolated successfully. Recently, in our laboratory we have found that dimethyl sulfoxide disrupts the bonds connecting the various substructures (Cummings *et al.*, 1968) and free heads, fibers, and sheaths are obtainable; tail tubes appear to remain attached to the tail plate and have not yet been separated.

An elegant alternative approach to studying these substructures has been the use of amber mutants of T4D bacteriophage (Epstein *et al.*, 1963). When certain mutants are grown on the restrictive host, only particular substructures are made and they can be isolated directly from the bacterial lysate. Kellenberger (1968) has studied heads extensively in this manner (we will discuss this later) and King and Wood (1969) have recently reported on some of the properties of tail fibers. From the wild type phage, however, only heads, tubes, and sheaths have been characterized.

TABLE I
RELATIVE AMOUNTS OF SUBSTRUCTURES

Substructure	Percent of total protein	Reference
Head	75	Cummings (1963a)
Internal protein	7	Minagawa (1961)
Fibers (6)	2–4	Calculated
Sheath	9–12	Brenner *et al.* (1959)
		Sarkar *et al.* (1964a)
		Our laboratory
Tube	0.5	Sarker *et al.* (1964b)
Collar, neck, and plate	2.5	Estimated

A. Tail Sheath and Tail Tube Substructures

The chemical properties of these substructures have been recently reviewed by Kozloff (1968). Briefly, both substructures were isolated taking advantage of their resistance to proteolytic enzyme treatment following acid denaturation of the intact particle (Brenner *et al.*, 1959). Head protein, neck, collar, plate, and fibers were dissociated to some extent by this treatment and were not recovered as intact substructures. The molecular weight of the contracted sheath was determined by light scattering (Sarkar *et al.*, 1964a) and was found to be 8.0×10^6 daltons. Amino acid analysis indicated that, compared with the total amino acid content of phage protein, sheath subunits were low in histidine. A subunit molecular weight, assuming one histidine per subunit, was calculated to be about 55,000 daltons. Moody (1967a, b) critically examined electron micrographs of this substructure and determined that it had sixfold symmetry in its rotation axis and further predicted that there may be two types of subunits. Farid and Kozloff (1968) later found two C-terminal end groups in sheath protein and confirmed that the N-terminal end group was blocked. The fact that there are two types of subunits may weaken the argument (Sarkar *et al.*, 1964a) that the molecular weight of the sheath subunits is 55,000 daltons and further work is necessary on isolated subunits.

Sarkar *et al.* (1964b) isolated the tail tubes using the same methods for sheath isolation and found that the intact tube had a molecular weight of 500,000 daltons and contained only five cysteine residues. From this they estimated that there were five subunits each of molecular weight 100,000. These authors made a model of the tube in which there were five asymmetric subunits twisted about each other to form a cable, having a central hole, with fivefold symmetry. It may be that this model is incorrect since sixfold symmetry may be necessary for attachment to the sheath and tail plate, each of which has sixfold symmetry axes. In addition, the tail tube was found to have a high amount of proline (6.5 %) and the significance of this will be considered later.

B. Head Substructure

A major obstacle to understanding the structure of the polyhedral head of the T-even bacteriophage is that no morphological subunits are observable by electron microscopy. Many attempts have been made (Bradley, 1967; Moody, 1965) to fit the morphology of this substructure into the well-developed scheme established for spherical viruses (Caspar and Klug, 1962). As is well known, the morphology of spherical viruses has been shown to have icosahedral symmetry in which the protein subunits are arranged in groups or capsomeres such that they are readily visible in the electron microscope. T-even bacteriophage, and other tailed phages (Bradley, 1967) differ from these spherical viruses in two respects: (1) the head is not isometric, and (2) the head protein is arranged in a shell, 100 to 120 Å thick, surrounding the DNA (Anderson *et al.*, 1953). Referring back to Fig. 1, the head here is pictured as having sixfold symmetry throughout, i.e., six triangular faces at each apex and six rectangular sides. This model is clearly distinguishable from the modified icosahedral symmetry models (Moody, 1965) in which the apices necessarily have fivefold symmetry. A prediction from the completely sixfolded symmetry model would be that in thin sections of phage heads, no five-sided figure would be observed. On the other hand, thin sections of icosahedra would yield about 15 % of the sections having five regular sides. In Fig. 2A are electron micrographs of thin sections of T2 embedded in epon and stained with osmium tetroxide. It can be observed that five-sided figures are simply not detectable if they are present. Figure 2B is an overlay diagram of many of the smallest structures in the field; all have, as can best be determined, six regular sides.

A more direct approach to understanding the structure of the head would be to analyze the protein subunits themselves. Van Vunakis and co-workers (1958) dissociated T2 bacteriophage using sodium dodecyl sulfate at alkaline pH and found that the vast majority of the isolated protein, i.e., the head protein, had a molecular weight of 85,000 daltons and an axial ratio of 28:1. Using these parameters, Cummings (1959) attempted to construct a model of the head and was unable to fit these protein subunits into the known dimensions of the shell. An obvious possibility was that

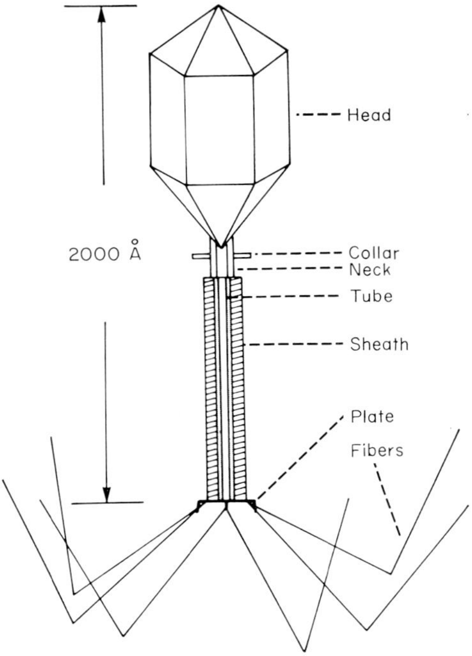

FIG. 1. Schematic diagram of the structural components of T-even bacteriophage.

these protein subunits were actually dimers of a 42,000 molecular weight protein. Cummings (1963a) reinvestigated the physicochemical properties of head protein of T2L and found that by using the glacial acetic acid treatment introduced by Fraenkel-Conrat (1957) for dissociating tobacco mosaic virus (TMV), protein subunits of molecular weight 42,000 daltons with physical dimensions of 270 × 19 Å could be isolated. A subunit of this molecular weight was also found later for the major protein subunits of T4 (Cummings, 1964).

Dissociation was also accomplished under the same alkaline conditions used by Van Vunakis *et al.* (1958) and a subunit of 85,000 molecular weight was isolated. The 42,000-dalton subunit could be dimerized to the 85,000

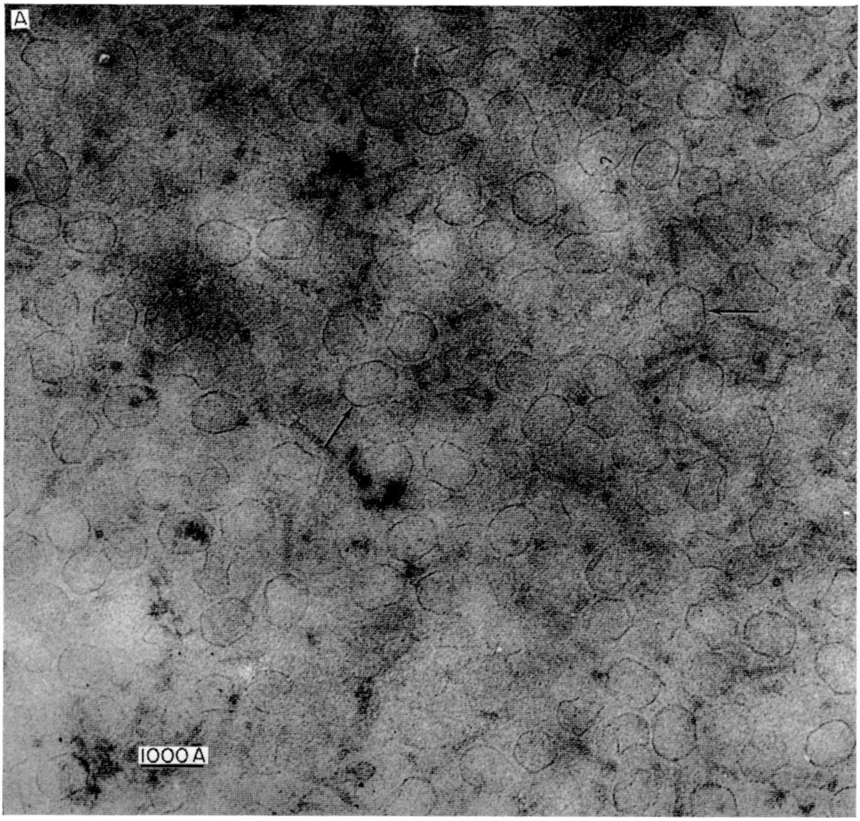

FIG. 2. (A). An electron micrograph of a thin section of the protein coats of T2L bacteriophage. Note that all of the heads have six sides or at least appear to have the appearance of six-sided figures. The arrows refer to those heads which have been sectioned such that their tails are also visible; *i.e.*, a direct longitudinal section. (B). An overlay schematic diagram of Fig. 2A in which the smallest hexagonal heads have been reproduced. Some of these small heads necessarily have the same width, 700 Å, as a direct longitudinal section (arrow). However, many are only 500–550 Å in diameter and these are presumably apical sections. All the sections of heads displayed sixfold symmetry.

subunit in the presence of Zn^{2+} and this property was related to the sedimentation changes observed in T2L. It was concluded that the monomeric subunit of T-even heads was a protein of 42,000 molecular weight and an axial ratio of 14:1 and subunits dimerized readily, both end-to-end and side-by-side. Van Vunakis *et al.* (1958) also determined the N- and C-terminal amino acids of this protein and found that alanine was the only N-terminal amino acid and using carboxypeptidase suggested that leucine was the C-terminal residue. Cummings (1964) later found, using the more reliable hydrazine method, that glycine was the only C-terminal residue. From the number of N-terminal residues per phage particle and from the mass (Table I) of the phage, it can be estimated that there are between 1500 and 2000 subunits of 42,000 molecular weight in the phage head. These

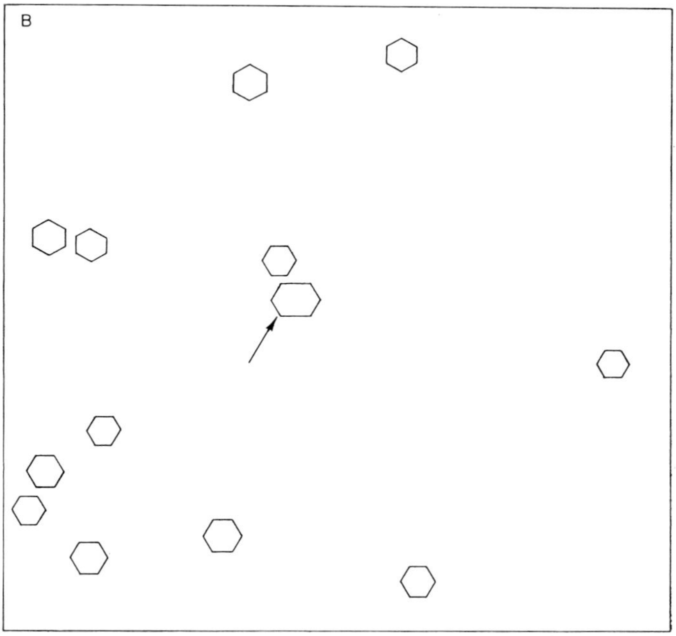

FIG. 2B

subunits can be arranged in the phage head in the manner depicted in Fig. 3. The rectangular sides have the majority of the subunits and the length of each side is 500 Å, just enough to accommodate two subunits end-to-end with a slight overlap. This overlap demands that the adjacent subunits be offset, and the most practical arrangement is a close packed array of alternating rows such that there are 168 subunits in each face resulting in a depth of the protein shell of 114 Å. Placing these subunits in each of the 12 triangular faces, 6 in each apex, presents the problem of attaining subunit interaction with the subunits in the rectangular faces and at the same time of allowing subunits to come to an apex at the top and bottom of the head. The simplest way of visualizing this was to double the area of the region containing one subunit and still have alternating rows. This permits considerable overlap of the subunits such that not all the overlapping row of subunits need extend to the apex. There are a total of 26 subunits in each row of the triangular face for a total of 52 in each face.

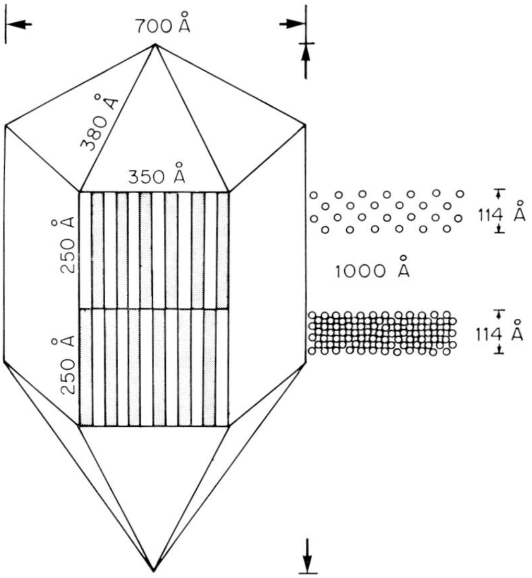

FIG. 3. A schematic diagram of the head indicating a proposed arrangement of the protein subunits. Each rectangular face is depicted as being divided into two sections of subunits. The shaded areas indicate that subunits in the same level do not touch. On the right side of the head, a cross section of the subunits is presented for both the rectangular face and the triangular apical face.

In the entire head, 12 × 52 in the triangular faces and 6 × 168 in the rectangular faces, there are 1632 subunits of 42,000 molecular weight.

For an alternate icosahedral model of the head to be correct, this number of physical subunits demands that the T-number* related to quasiico-

* A perfect icosahedron has 20 triangular faces with 5:3:2 symmetry in its isometric axes. Caspar and Klug (1962) postulated that quasiicosahedra could be generated whereby only certain multiples of twenty faces, with three subunits in each face, were allowed. This multiple, the triangulation number T, was given by

sahedra (Caspar and Klug, 1962) must be either 27 or 28. Consequently, the head would be subdivided into either 540 or 560 triangular faces with three subunits in each face. How one would place three such subunits in these necessarily smaller faces is not obvious. For example, dividing the total area depicted (Fig. 3) into 540 to 560 triangles yields equivalent equilateral triangles having dimensions of only 88 Å. Moody (1965) and Boy de la Tour and Kellenberger (1965) presented a prolate icosahedron-type model in which all the faces had dimensions similar to the apical triangular faces in Fig. 3 and an extra row of such triangular faces was inserted in the mid-portion of the head. This model retained some elements of icosahedral symmetry and yielded a structure which was nonisometric; in fact, this structure is more nonisometric than phage heads actually appear. In particular, these investigators were concerned with the observations that phage heads could have up to four tails attached (Smith and Trousdale, 1965; see also Fig. 7), suggesting that tails could attach at any apex. A prolate icosahedron would have the property that all corners or apices would be equivalent in that all would be formed by the union of five sides. The bipyramidal hexagonal model we have proposed has two types of apices, those distal which are formed by six sides and those lateral which are formed by four sides. This difficulty may be only apparent; what we are concerned with is subunit interaction and the end-to-end arrangement of subunits postulated may still generate almost equivalent corners depending on overlap. Moreover, the length of each side of the prolate icosahedral triangular faces is only 250 Å and while this could possibly allow one 42,000 subunit along each side, packing all the required subunits into the triangular faces is most difficult. The major geometric evidence that the T-even head does not conform to icosahedral symmetry is the observation previously stated that five-sided figures were not detected in thin sections of heads. It may be noted here that Bradley (1967) has reviewed these types of structure and, in addition, proposes a model, similar to ours, in which the head is a twisted bipyramidal hexagon, which allows triangular faces (two per twisted rectangular face), end-to-end subunit interaction and sixfold symmetry throughout. The insistence on triangular faces throughout in these other models was due to the theoretical reasons discussed and to what could be construed as triangles observed in electron micrographs. These observed triangles are difficult to interpret, however, since they are not consistently

---

$$T = H^2 + HK + K^2$$

where H and K are any two integers. Therefore, quasiicosahedra, such as adenovirus, would have $20T$ faces and a total of $60T$ subunits.

oriented and may be artifacts resulting from drying and staining during the electron microscopy.

What further evidence supports the bipyramidal hexagonal model we have proposed in addition to the absence of five-sided figures? This model accounts for the head conformational changes observed in T2L (Cummings and Kozloff, 1960, 1962; Cummings, 1963a, b, 1964; Cummings *et al.*, 1969). A 15% change in head length was reported which resulted in a concomitant change in sedimentation coefficient. In the shorter head, a band of greater protein density was noted at the middle of the phage head; overlap of interdigitating subunits would yield this pattern (Cummings, 1963a, b). Divalent cations had a marked effect on the transition between long head and short head. Cummings (1963a) found that Zn^{2+} effected a dimerization of the monomeric subunits yielding an end-to-end dimer of 85,000 molecular weight. In addition, there is suggestive chemical evidence. Photooxidation of histidine residues (Cummings, 1963b) eliminated the short head form. Polyglucose sulfuric acid, a polyanion, binds to heads (Young and Mora, 1960) and polylysine, a polycation, also binds to phage heads and its binding is inhibited by the polyanion, polyaspartic acid (Shalitin *et al.*, 1962). The amino acid composition of the 42,000 molecular weight subunits (see later) for all T-even phages has not been done, but some characterization of the terminal amino acids has been reported. Table II is a composite of the data collected for total amino acids and for those amino acids near both termini of the 42,000 molecular weight protein. Stretton and Brenner (1965) determined the sequence of the N-terminal tryptic peptide and Cummings (1964) looked at the amino acids released during stepwise carboxypeptidase treatment. The sequence of the N-terminal, for 13 residues, and an approximate proposed C terminal, for 10 residues, sequence is as follows:

N—Ala·Gly·(Val,Phe)·Asp·Phe·Gln·Asp·Pro·Ile·Asp·Ile·Arg·
C—Gly·(Leu,Val)·(Ala,Lys,Thr,Lys)·(His,Arg,Asp).

The parentheses indicate that the sequence in that region is in doubt. It is obvious from the table that the distribution near the ends of the head protein subunit is grossly different from the total amino acid composition. The C-terminal end is rich in basic amino acids and the N-terminal region is rich in acidic amino acids. Both ends have semirepresentative amounts of nonpolar residues. Looking at the apparent partial sequences we see that, in general, nonpolar residues can be aligned and that the basic residues of the C-terminal region can be aligned opposite or near the aspartic residues of the N-terminal region. In addition, histidine is near the C-terminal end (relative to the total residues contained in a 42,000 molecular weight protein, about 330). With this arrangement, subunit interaction could readily occur end-to-end and polyions could interact with the acid or basic groups. Moreover, head configurational changes should be markedly sensitive to variations in the ionic environment both with respect to the polar and non-polar groups and such has recently been shown to be the case (Cummings *et al.*, 1969).

TABLE II

TERMINAL AMINO ACIDS OF T-EVEN HEAD PROTEIN

Side chain	Amino acid[a]	Percent of whole phage protein[a]	Head protein distribution of terminal residues	
			N(13)[b]	C(10)[c]
Basic	Arginine	4.2	1	1
	Histidine	3.9		1
	Lysine	5.8		1 or 2
Acid	Glutamic acid	10.1		
	Aspartic acid	10.3	3	1
Polar	Asparagine	—		
	Glutamine	—	1	
	Serine	5.3		
	Threonine	5.9		1
	Tyrosine	3.9		
	Tryptophan	1.5		
	Half-cystine	1.0		
	Methionine	2.2		
Nonpolar	Glycine	9.2	1	1
	Alanine	10.7	1	1
	Valine	6.7	1	1
	Leucine	6.0		1
	Isoleucine	6.7	2	
	Proline	3.6	1	
	Phenylalanine	4.3	2	

[a] Fitch and Susman (1965); Fraser (1957); and Kozloff (1968).
[b] Stretton and Brenner (1965).
[c] Cummings (1964).

III. ABERRANT SUBSTRUCTURES

As indicated earlier, mutant bacteriophages exist which grow normally on permissive suppressor hosts but not on restrictive nonsuppressor hosts. Such mutants have been termed conditionally lethal and were named amber mutants (Epstein *et al.*, 1963). These mutants have been used in a most elegant manner to study phage morphogenesis (Edgar and Wood, 1966; Edgar and Lielausis, 1968; King, 1968; King and Wood, 1969). Their results indicated that the substructures were made independently of each other and that the assembly of the different substructures to form the mature virion was a well-defined and stepwise process. The genes controlling the formation of the various substructures have been determined (Edgar *et al.*, 1964) and their role in the morphogenetic pathway has been recently reviewed by Levine (1969). The reader is referred to that review

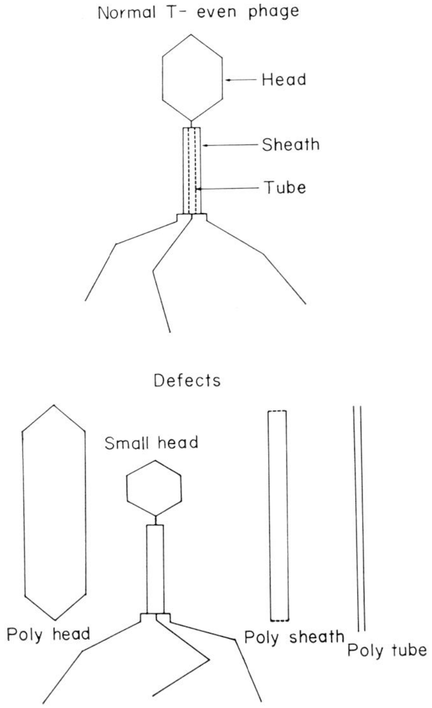

FIG. 4. Schematic diagram of the types of aberrant substructure obtained in defective amber bacteriophage lysates. (Reprinted with the permission of the copyright owner, the American Society for Microbiology.)

for additional information on this important topic. For the purposes of the present review, the significant result on these amber bacteriophages was that not only were some substructures not made but that aberrant substructures were made. As illustrated in Fig. 4, so-called polyheads, small heads, polysheath, and polytail tubes were visible in the electron microscope (Epstein *et al.*, 1963).

A. Aberrant Substructures in Amber Bacteriophages

Kellenberger and his co-workers have worked extensively on the morphology and some chemical characteristics of the aberrant head substruc-

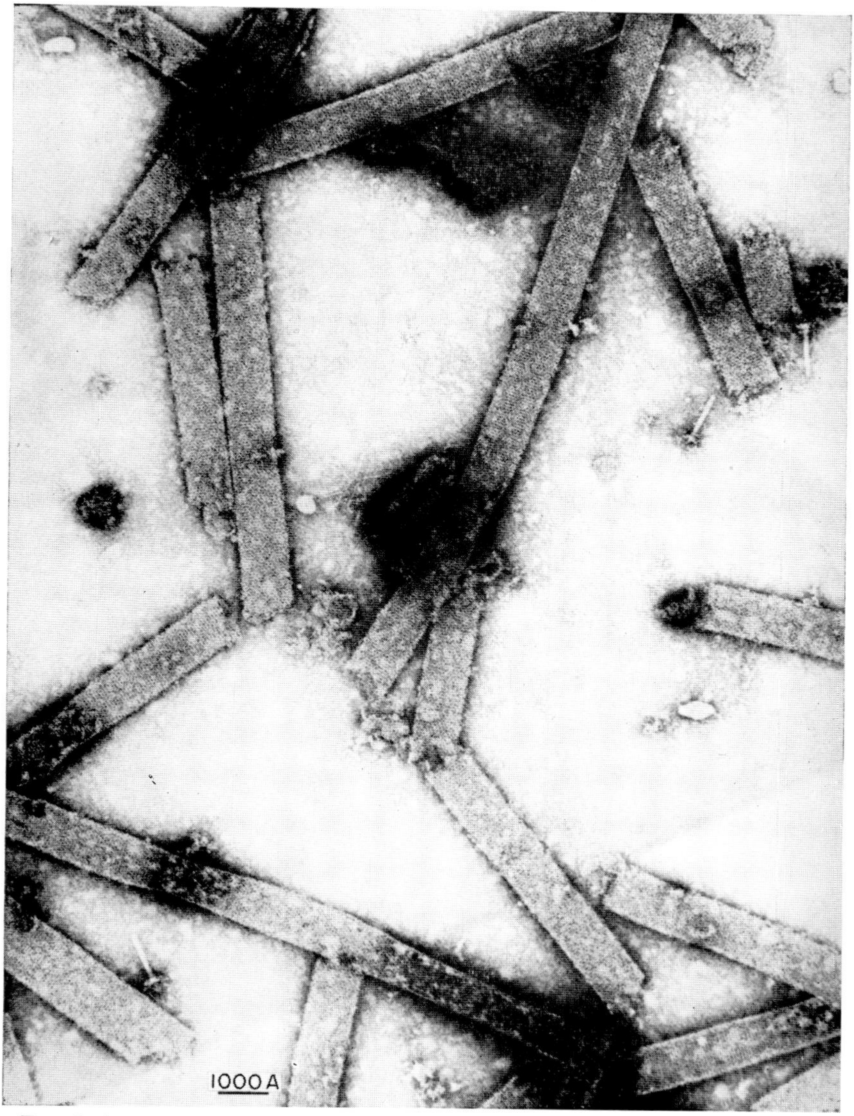

FIG. 5. An electron micrograph of T4D amber bacteriophage, gene 20 polyheads. Note that the edges of the polyhead do not show the characteristic thickening observed in normal protein coats and that morphological subunits or capsomeres are readily visualized. (Supplied through the courtesy of E. Kellenberger.)

tures found in lysates of some amber bacteriophages. Morphologically, polyheads are quite different from normal heads (Figs. 5 and 6). There appear to be readily visible capsomeres arranged in a Moire hexagonal

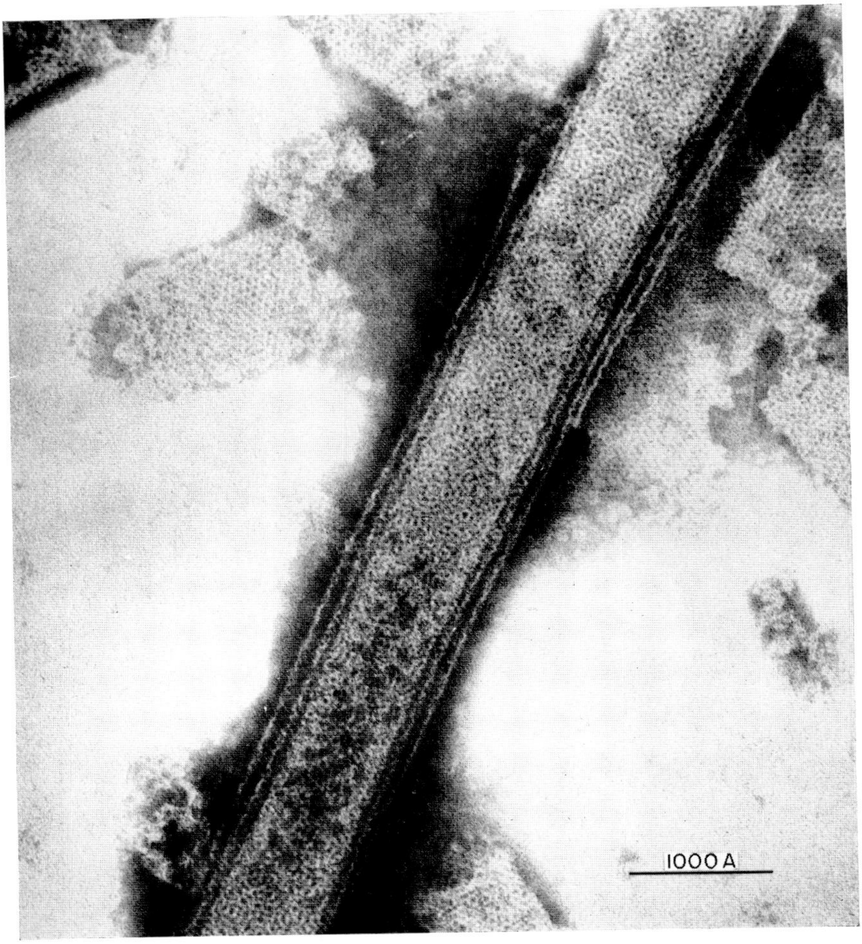

FIG. 6. An electron micrograph of T4D amber bacteriophage, gene 22 "layered" polyheads. Note that there appear to be layers of protein and that capsomeres are readily visible. (Supplied through the courtesy of E. Kellenberger.)

pattern in polyheads which are not observable in normal empty heads. In addition, some mutants give rise to "layered" polyheads in which there are multiple layers of protein comprising the structure (Fig. 6). Small-headed phage are also generated in some mutants (Fig. 7) and Mosig

(1966) has demonstrated that these mutants have a reduced amount of DNA and are nonviable unless several such particles infect the same host simultaneously, i.e., multiplicity reactivation of the small-headed phage was required for growth of the phage. Levinthal *et al.* (1967) and Kellenberger (1968) have analyzed the protein components of both normal and aberrant structures on polyacrylamide gels and have found that there are three different proteins in the head of bacteriophage T4D: a major M protein containing at least 80% of the total head protein, and an *l* and a *k* protein comprising the remaining 10–20%. The small-headed phage, which appear normal except for their shortened length, have the same distribution of these protein components as do normal heads (Kellenberger, 1968). However, Kellenberger reported that isolated polyheads have primarily the M protein, as judged by acrylamide gel electrophoresis, and very little *k* or *l* protein. As far as understanding the assembly of the head, it may well be that the capsomeric structure of amber polyheads bears little relation to the amorphous surface of normal, or small-headed, phage heads.

Kellenberger (1966) has interpreted these protein components in terms of their morphopoietic properties. The M protein is the product of gene 23 and is the major structural protein of 40,000 molecular weight (Cummings, 1963a). However, the information contained in gene 23 is not fully space specifying and some other products such as those from gene 20 (rounding-up factor) or gene 66 (elongating factor) must supply additional information. Neither the *k* nor the *l* proteins have been identified with the product of any of the known head genes and it is not clear what these proteins contribute to the determination of symmetry in the head structure. Kellenberger suggests that their apparent absence in polyheads is the result and not the cause of polyhead formation. One possible explanation for the absence of these proteins in amber polyheads could be that the M proteins in amber polyheads are not identical with the M proteins in normal or small-headed phage heads. If this were so, then the aberrant M protein could have a different tertiary structure and consequently, subunit interactions with this protein would be altered. While M proteins isolated from normal head and polyheads appear to have the same electrophoretic behavior in acrylamide gels, there is no chemical evidence available which would unambiguously establish identity. It is clear that the surface morphology of amber polyheads is grossly different from normal heads and the reason for this difference must lie in the physicochemical properties of the protein subunits. Molecular weight determinations, amino acid composition, and end group analyses must be performed before the symmetry relations of these aberrant substructures can be properly evaluated.*

* While this review was in press, U. Laemmli and J. King (personal communication) discovered that the M protein in extracts of polyheads had a molecular weight of

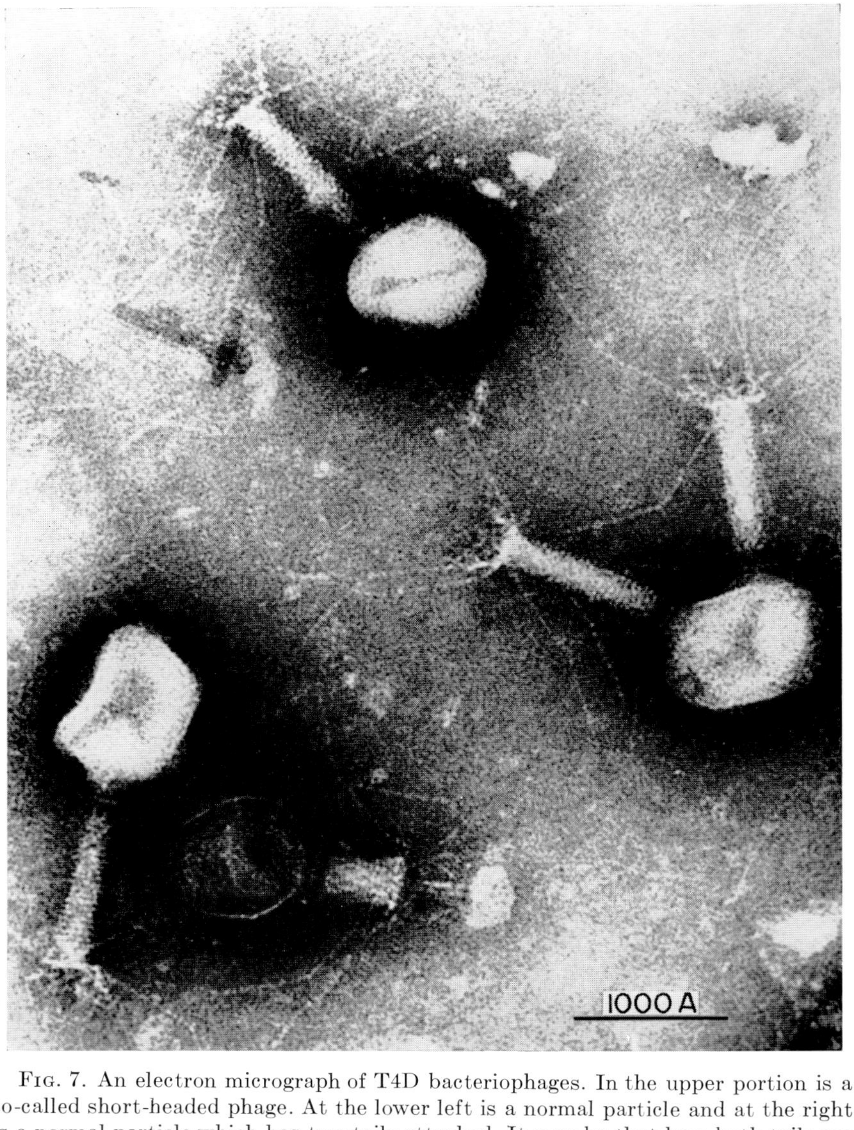

FIG. 7. An electron micrograph of T4D bacteriophages. In the upper portion is a so-called short-headed phage. At the lower left is a normal particle and at the right is a normal particle which has two tails attached. It may be that here both tails are attached to lateral apices. (This micrograph was taken by F. A. Eiserling and supplied through the courtesy of E. Kellenberger.)

57,000 daltons. We have also found that the M protein in isolated polyheads has a molecular weight of 54,000 daltons compared with the 42,000 dalton protein found in both normal and short heads. In addition, we have also observed that both the 18,000 and 11,000 dalton proteins were either absent or greatly decreased in isolated polyheads.

Recently, Forrest and Cummings (1969) reported a comparative study of the protein components of wild-type T-even heads in which they obtained results that have some bearing on Kellenberger's findings. Bacteriophages T2H, T2L, T4B, T4B01, T4D, and T6 were grown and purified and protein coats were obtained in the usual manner (see Cummings *et al.*, 1968). Free heads of some of these phages were obtained using the dimethyl sulfoxide disruption procedure (Cummings *et al.*, 1968) and amber T4D heads, which appear to have the same surface morphology as normal heads, were obtained by growth of T4Dam H21 (gene 54; see King, 1968) on the restrictive host. The protein substructures were then dissociated into their

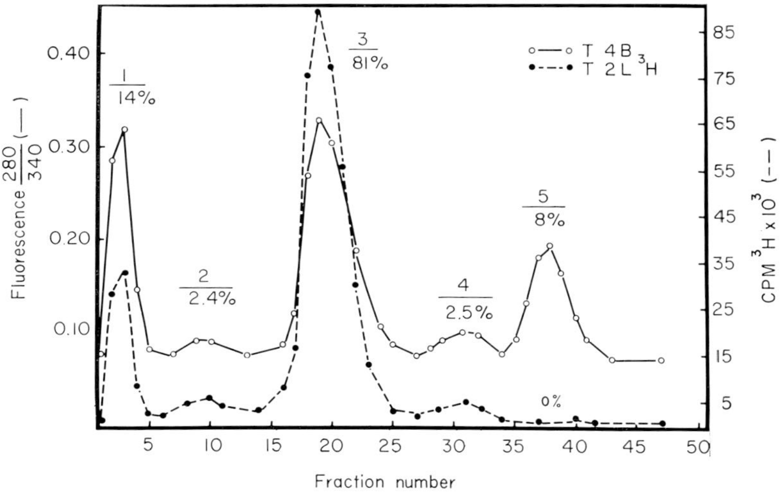

FIG. 8. Chromatographic profile of T-even bacteriophage structural proteins. The proteins of unlabeled T4B were mixed with ^3H-labeled T2L proteins and examined on a 6% agarose column. Note that there is no detectable 11,000 dalton protein present among the structural proteins of T2L.

component subunits in 6 *M* guanidinium chloride and these subunits were then separated on an agarose column containing 5 *M* guanidinium chloride and 5 m*M* Clelands reagent (dithiothreitol) (Davison, 1968). This procedure allows separation of a mixture of proteins according to their molecular weight and shape of the protein does not influence the separation since the proteins are completely denatured by the guanidinium chloride. A composite pattern of the coat proteins is presented in Fig. 8 and the profile obtained from just the head substructure is given in Fig. 9. T2H, T4B, T4B01, T4D, and T6 all contained three proteins in their head structure: a 40,000 molecular weight protein representing about 85–90% of the total head protein; an 11,000 molecular weight protein, representing about 9%

of the head protein; and an 18,000 molecular weight protein representing about 2% of the head protein. Presumably, the 40,000 protein corresponds to the M protein; the 11,000 to the *l* protein; and the 18,000 to the *k* protein. Identification of the *k* and *l* proteins is, of course, only tentative and must be determined by acrylamide gel electrophoresis but the relative concentrations of these proteins is consistent with these assignations. An 11,000 molecular weight protein in the heads of T4D has also been reported by Larcom and Bendet (1968), but they reported that there were three times as many 11,000 subunits as there were 40,000 subunits whereas we find just the opposite: about twice as many 40,000 subunits as there are

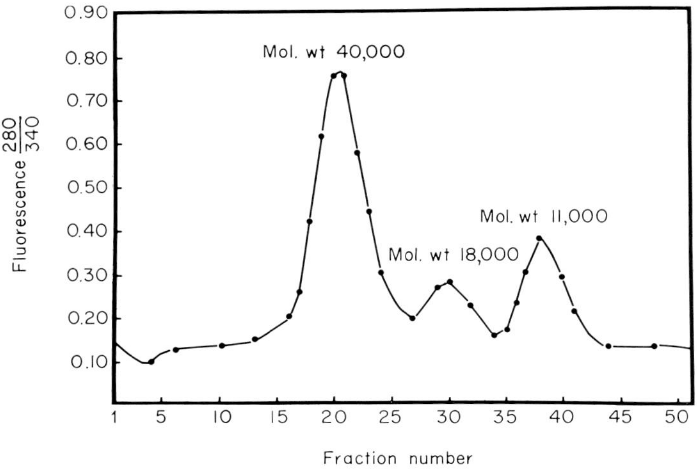

FIG. 9. Chromatographic profile of the proteins obtained from T4D amber gene 54 heads on a 6% agarose column. The high molecular weight proteins obtained in Fig. 8 but absent here are presumably tail proteins. The same type pattern was also obtained using T6 heads purified by the DMSO procedure (Cummings *et al.*, 1968).

11,000 subunits. What this discrepancy means is not clear; we arrived at our values using radioactive labeling of the proteins, which agreed qualitatively with the results using fluorescence assay, and Larcom and Bendet (1968) reached their values by osmotic pressure studies.

It is pertinent that T2L had no detectable 11,000 molecular weight subunit and yet its head structure appears to be the same as T4 or T6; were it missing half its structural protein, as Larcom and Bendet's results would suggest, one would have expected some difference in head morphology. All the phages examined had about the same amount of the 18,000 molecular weight subunit. Preliminary amino acid analyses of these three proteins from T4 (Table III) have indicated that we are dealing with three distinct proteins and that they are not subunits of one another. The 18,000 subunit appears to be different from the 40,000 subunit in serine, alanine, phenylalanine, and possibly lysine and arginine and the 11,000 subunit is grossly different from the other two structural proteins. Distinct differences appeared in methionine, tryptophan, and especially lysine and histidine. The 11,000 subunit seems to be rich in basic amino acids and this may be significant in ascertaining its role. It is clear that

TABLE III

AMINO ACID COMPOSITION[a] OF HEAD PROTEIN SUBUNITS OF T4B BACTERIOPHAGE

Amino acid	Protein subunit (μmoles %)		
	40,000	18,000	11,000
Aspartic + Asparagine	10.6	10.5	8.9
Threonine	6.5	6.6	7.2
Serine	5.8	5.0	7.3
Glutamic + Glutamine	11.2	11.2	14.0
Glycine	10.7	8.7	6.9
Alanine	13.4	10.2	9.6
Valine	6.7	7.2	6.8
Methionine	2.7	2.1	0.2
Isoleucine	7.1	6.4	6.4
Leucine	5.9	5.0	4.5
Tyrosine	4.3	4.0	5.9
Phenylalanine	4.7	4.0	4.2
Lysine	5.4	7.0	10.0
Histidine	0.9	0.8	2.3
Arginine	4.2	5.2	3.1
Tryptophan	0.4	0.3	3.3
Cys-SO_3	0.3	0.4	0.0

[a] This is a partial analysis of the amino acid composition and does not include all the amino acids. For example, 5.4% proline has been determined for the 40,000 dalton protein but this amino acid has not yet been analyzed in the 11,000 and 18,000 dalton proteins.

further work is necessary on these proteins to determine completely their characteristics. Moreover, it would be of interest to ascertain what differences exist between the proteins isolated from T4 and those from T2, or T6, serologically related phages.

In terms of structure, it is not clear where the 11,000 and 18,000 molecular weight proteins fit within the framework of the 40,000 subunit presented in our model. Kellenberger (1968) reported that some, if not all, of the *k* and *l* bands were leached out of the phage heads by treatment with urea so perhaps these proteins fill in the surface spaces. However, T2L and presumably amber polyheads have no 11,000 subunit and yet polyheads clearly show capsomere arrangements and T2L heads do not. Perhaps these low molecular weight proteins are simply space filling or they may lie at specific regions of the head. For example, per phage head there could be only about 100 of the 18,000 molecular weight proteins. Such a small number suggests that these proteins may be distributed in a nonrandom fashion and may serve a special role, such as closure of the head at the distal apices. There are many more of the 11,000 molecular weight proteins, approximately 700, and these may be distributed randomly. However, no such subunit was detected in T2L and therefore the possible role of this protein in maintaining the head structure cannot be evaluated at the present time.

B. Induced Aberrant Substructures

Kellenberger (1966) envisions the assembly process of individual protein subunits into a phage substructure as a sequential triggering of subprocesses induced by different morphopoietic factors. From the known properties of the individual subunits of the various substructures, we felt that it should be possible to interfere with the assembly of subunits during growth in host cells infected with normal wild-type bacteriophages. For example, the end terminating residues of the 40,000 molecular weight protein subunits of the head appeared to be rich in either acid or basic residues and the last four or five residues at each end had nonpolar groups. As indicated by Sarkar *et al.* (1964b), the tail tube protein appeared to have an unusual amino acid composition in that proline was present in such high amounts. Consequently, we chose to study the maturation process of the substructure by investigating what effect, if any, amino acid analogs or antimetabolites had on phage assembly.

Our first attempt at inducing aberrant substructures (Cummings *et al.*, 1967) indicated that some analogs led to the appearance of many defects and other analogs led to specific aberrations. Analogs such as *p*-fluorophenylalanine (Fruton, 1963) can be regarded as rather gross inhibitors of cell growth and these were chosen to determine what structural defects could arise in phage grown in their presence. Many defects (Fig. 10) such as polyheads, small heads, polysheaths, and polytail tubes were obtained without any notable preference for a particular substructure. These aberrant substructures were identified by virtue of their morphology and their occasional association with other phage substructures. Once it had been observed that aberrant substructures do occur in a normal bacteriophage system, the question arose as to whether particular compounds would give rise to preferential defects. Table IV catalogs the various amino acid analogs and antimetabolites which were first employed (Cummings *et al.*, 1967) and the substructural defects which were produced. In determining the aberrant substructures induced, care was taken that a sufficient number of particles were counted, a total of 2000 normal whole phage and ghosts, in order that we could be certain of the degree of induction of the aberrant substructure. Moreover, intact phage and protein coats, with and without

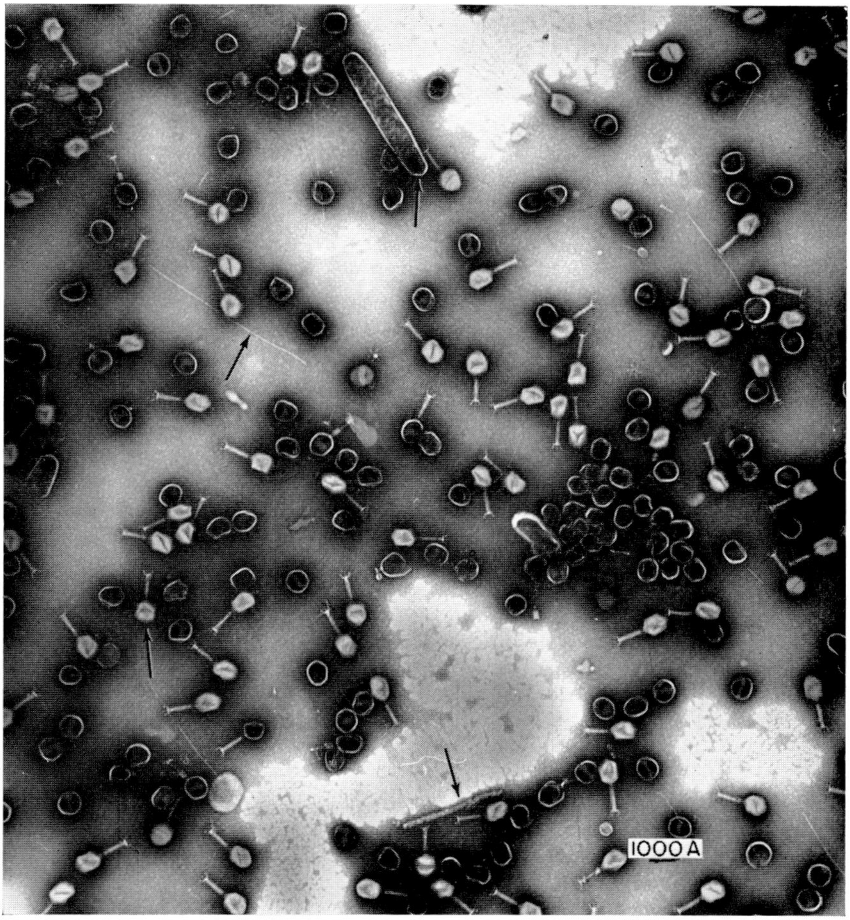

FIG. 10. Electron micrograph of a purified T2L lysate obtained during growth in the presence of *p*-fluorophenylalanine. The arrows indicate the various aberrant substructures obtained, such as polyheads, polysheaths, polytail tubes, and small heads, and these correspond to those depicted in Fig. 4. (Reprinted with the permission of the copyright owner, The American Society for Microbiology.)

attached tails, were differentiated so that we could have a separate indication of interference with maturation. As can be noted, gross inhibitors of cell growth greatly depress the yield of viable phage and give rise to a variety of structural defects. Polysheaths were obtained to some degree with all the analogs and antimetabolites used and we were not able to specifically induce these aberrant substructures. This may be because sheath is the only phage substructure known to have a helical configuration (Moody, 1967a, b) and that it may be relatively easy to continue adding subunits to a helical structure without restriction. An obvious consequence

TABLE IV

DISTRIBUTION OF INDUCED DEFECTS IN T-EVEN BACTERIOPHAGE

Compound		Viability (fraction of normal)	Bacteriophage		Poly-head	Poly-sheath	Poly-tail tube	Small heads
Amino acid	Analog		Whole	Ghost				
L-Tyrosine, L-Tryptophan, L-Phenylalanine	p-Fluorophenylalanine, 5-Methyl-DL-tryptophan, DL-7-Azatryptophan	1×10^{-4}	830	1170	6	33	32	30
L-Arginine	L-Canavanine							
	6–14 minutes	1.5×10^{-3}	270	1730	54	22	90	4
	18 minutes	4×10^{-3}	1170	930	2	8	3	8
L-Histidine	Triazole-3-alanine							
	T2L	3×10^{-2}	1870	130	0	1	1	110
	T6	0.5	1470	530	2	7	2	580
L-Proline	L-Azetidine-2-carboxylic acid	6×10^{-4}	920	1080	2	5	180	2
Antimetabolites	Phage							
Actinomycin D	T2L	1.5×10^{-2}	1390	610	0	10	1	40
	T4	7×10^{-2}	1020	980	1	10	4	370
	T6	0.4						
Proflavin	T2L	5×10^{-2}	1110	890	0	3	0	150
	T4 or T6	2×10^{-5}	30	1970	2	5	2	750

of the nonspecific appearance of polysheath is that there must be some event which terminates addition of sheath subunits during normal maturation and this could involve binding to the tail tube.

Other aberrant substructures appeared to be induced specifically, depending on the analog used. Polyheads were obtained with a relatively high frequency, considering their mass, when L-canavanine, an arginine analog was used (Fig. 11) and the ability to induce these polyheads was diminished when L-canavanine was added 18 minutes or later after infection. At this time, presumably, normal maturation had already occurred

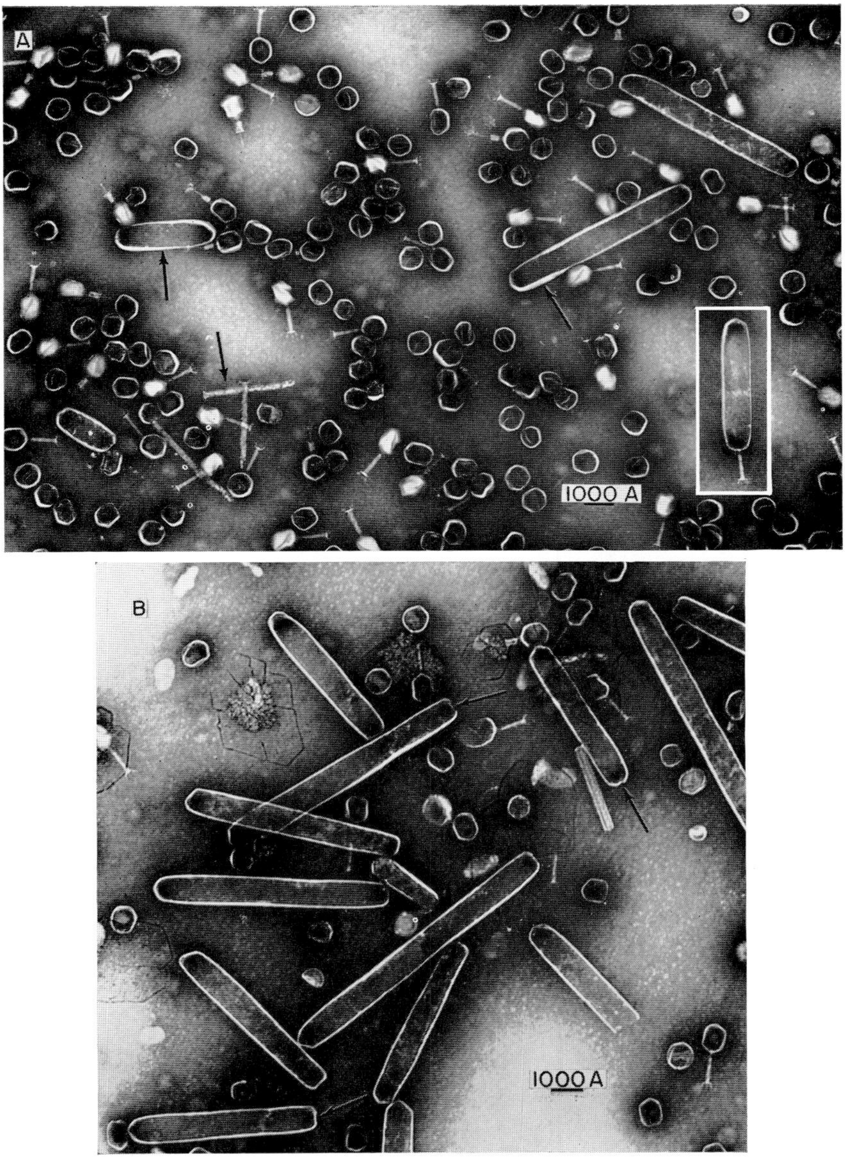

FIG. 11. Electron micrograph demonstrating the polyheads induced when the phage was grown in the presence of L-canavanine. (A) L-Canavanine was added 14 minutes after infection of *E. coli* B with T2L. Notice that the polyheads obtained are of varying lengths, and that the insert has a polyhead with a tail attached. Such polyheads with attached tails were observed in 1 to 2% of the polyheads and primarily on the shorter polyheads. (B) These particles resulted from a T4B lysate where L-Canavanine was added 10 minutes after infection. This micrograph illustrates a cluster of polyheads on the electron microscope grid. Note the apparent rigidity of these heads; the fact that most are closed and have indentations at one end, where possibly the neck could fit, is also evident. (Reprinted with the permission of the copyright owner, The American Society for Microbiology.)

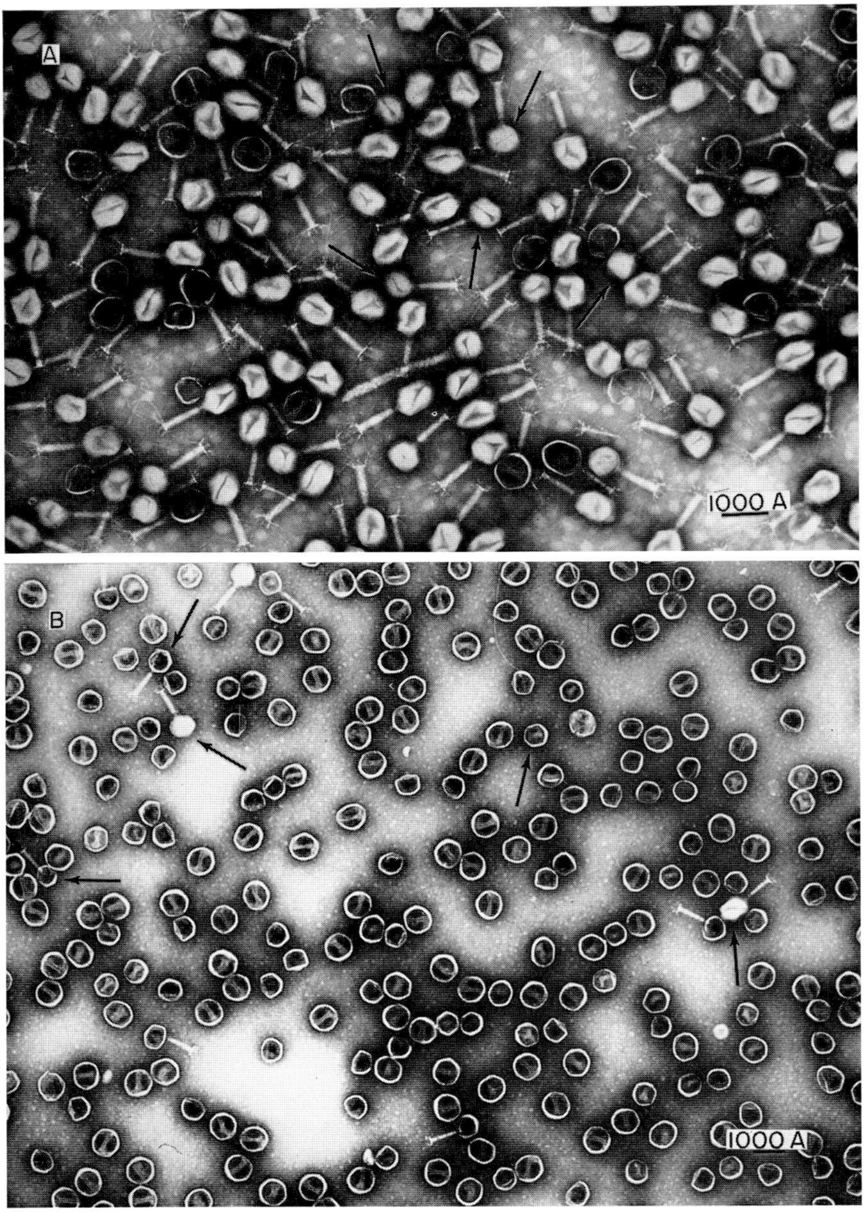

FIG. 12. Electron micrographs illustrating the effects of adding proflavine to a growing phage culture. (A) T2L, proflavin added at 8 minutes after infection. The only aberration noted was small heads (arrows) and primarily whole phage were recovered whether the proflavin was added at 8, 11, or 14 minutes. (B) T4B, proflavin added at 11 minutes. Again small heads were obtained, but with very few tails or whole phage. (Reprinted with the permission of the copyright owner, the American Society for Microbiology.)

and the analog had no effect on the completed heads. The polyheads obtained here are grossly different from the polyheads obtained from the amber phage mutants (Figs. 5 and 6). It can be observed that the induced polyheads more closely resemble normal heads in that no capsomeres are visible; the edges of the polyheads are well defined, as they are in empty normal phage, indicating that the depth of the protein shell is the same and that the arrangement of the subunits is probably the same; and most of the polyheads here have closed ends, which again resemble normal phage heads. The histidine analog, triazole-3-alanine, also exerted its effect on the head but instead of inducing polyheads, small heads were generated in as much as 30% of the population. The number of other aberrant substructures was not significantly increased. The small heads obtained were both filled with DNA and empty, with and without tails. All the small heads appeared to be about the same length (about 700 Å) and no apparent surface morphology could be observed in the empty small heads. Other substances also gave rise to small heads. Actinomycin D and proflavin, both known to inhibit phage maturation presumably by virtue of being inhibitors of nucleic acid synthesis (Korn *et al.*, 1965; DeMars *et al.*, 1953; Piechowski and Susman, 1966), also yielded an increased number of small heads. The effect of proflavin, a well-known inhibitor of phage maturation (DeMars *et al.*, 1953) was particularly interesting (Table IV and Figure 12B) in that for T2L, filled or empty heads attached to tails were obtained whereas for T4 or T6, primarily empty tailless heads were found. Luftig and Wood (1969) have recently shown that certain T4 amber mutants defective in genes 16, 17, or 49 accumulate structures which appear to resemble empty or unfilled head membranes. Their evidence suggests that these structures are precursors or intermediates in head formation and that gene 43 (T4 DNA polymerase) is necessary for packaging to proceed. Perhaps the step involved in closure of the head of T2L differs from that step in T4 or T6 or it may be that proflavin has a modified effect on T2L DNA polymerase which does not prevent packaging but does lead to small heads.

The only other aberrant substructure which was induced preferentially was polytail tubes. When any of the T-even bacteriophages were grown in the presence of L-azetidine-2-carboxylic acid, a proline analog, polytail tubes were produced to a relatively high degree and no other aberrations were noted. These polytail tubes (Fig. 13A) were identified by virtue of their overall appearance and by the fact that some were attached to baseplate at one end and head at the other. However, some ambiguity existed both in their identification and in their specific induction. These aberrant substructures did resemble one of the classes of bacterial pili (Brinton, 1965) and they did arise occasionally when other analogs (Table IV, L-canava-

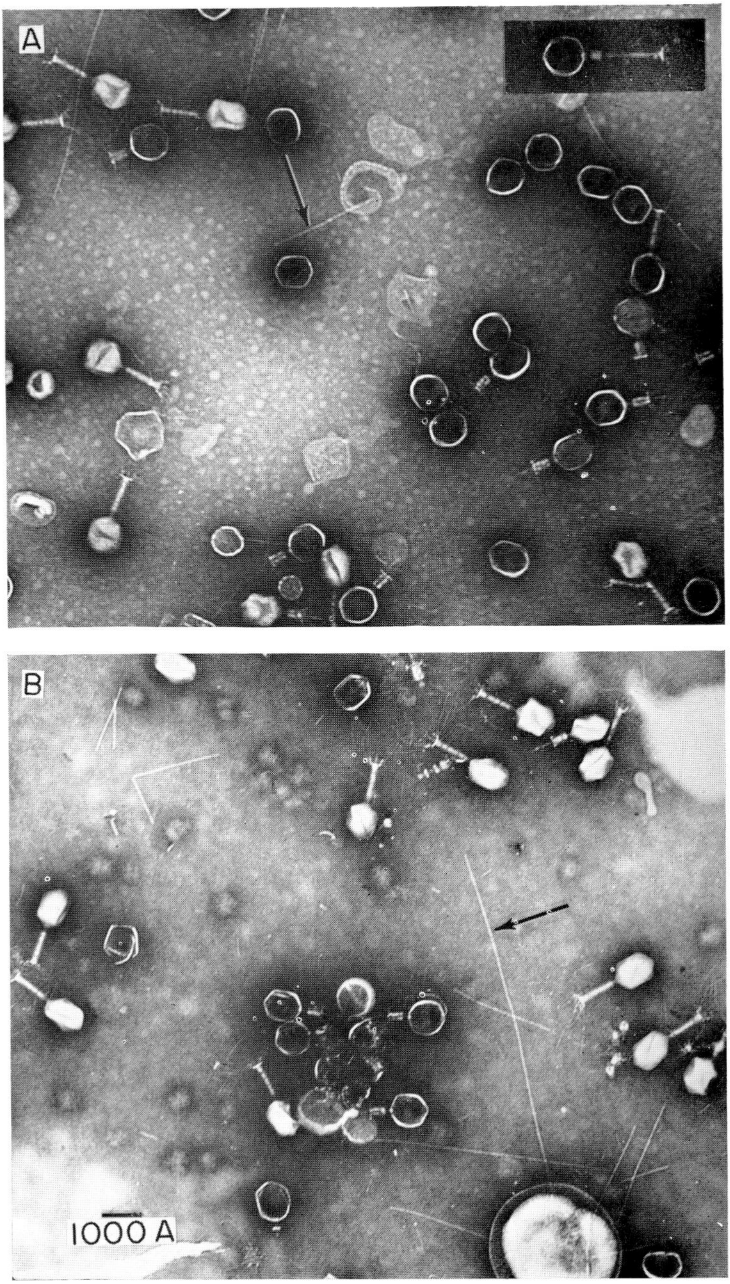

FIG. 13.

nine) were used. We decided that if polytail tubes were specifically induced by L-proline analogs, then the effect could be enhanced by using L-proline-requiring mutants of the host cell, *E. coli* B. Such was found to be the case (Table V and Fig. 13B). The number of polytail tubes was increased about eightfold when proline-requiring *E. coli* B was infected in the presence of a low concentration (1 μg/ml) of proline and L-azetidine-2-carboxylic acid (150 μg/ml) was added at various times after infection. The number of polytail tubes isolated remained essentially constant until at least 14 minutes after infection and then decreased precipitously at 18 minutes. Readdition of L-proline rather than the analog gave rise to essentially a

TABLE V
EFFECT OF L-AZETIDINE-2-CARBOXYLIC ACID WITH *E. coli* B PRO⁻

Experiment[a]	Viability	Bacteriophage		Poly-head	Poly-sheath	Polytail tube	Small head
		Whole	Ghost				
L-Azetidine-2-carboxylic acid							
@ 6 minutes, T2L	3×10^{-5}	350	1650	0	0	1620	0
10 minutes, T2L	1.3×10^{-4}	270	1730	0	0	1010	2
T6	3×10^{-5}	190	1810	0	9	1330	0
14 minutes, T2L	4×10^{-4}	610	1390	0	0	1240	0
18 minutes, T2L	2×10^{-3}	1470	530	0	0	63	7
L-Proline							
@ 8 minutes, T2L	1.0	1940	60	0	2	0	2

[a] The times indicated (@ 6 min, etc.) refer to the time after infection at which the analog was added.

normal phage population with very few aberrant substructures of any kind. We concluded that these substructures were indeed polytail tubes and that the proline analog induced their formation. It may be significant that the proline analog led to polytail tubes since proline represents a rather high amount (6.5%) of the amino acid composition of normal tail tubes (Sarkar *et al.*, 1964b). Whether the amount of a particular amino acid in a substructure is involved in determining the induction of an aberrant substructure is not clear, but it should be pointed out that in λ bacterio-

FIG. 13. Electron micrographs of T2L lysates after administration of L-azetidine-2-carboxylic acid. (A) The proline analog was added to the lysate 14 minutes after infection, and while the overall phage yield was depressed greatly, the only aberration obtained was polytail tubes. The insert contains a particle with a tail tube, about two times its normal length, still attached to the head at one end and a tail plate at the other. (B) The enhanced effect of this proline analog when a proline-requiring mutant of *E. coli* B was used as the host. (Reprinted with the permission of the copyright owner, the American Society for Microbiology.)

phage (Shuve and Howatson, personal communication), L-azetidine-2-carboxylic acid induced the formation of polyheads. The amount of proline in the structural proteins of λ bacteriophage is also relatively high (5.5%; Dyson and Van Holde, 1967).

C. Other Compounds Which Induce Structural Aberrations

It was clear from these studies that aberrant substructures of T-even bacteriophage could be induced and that particular compounds induced particular aberrant substructures. L-canavanine led to polyheads, 1,2,4-triazole-3-alanine led to small heads, and L-azetidine-2-carboxylic acid led to polytail tubes. Since so-called basic compounds, or at least compounds which accepted protons, gave rise to aberrations which affected the head, we investigated the effect of a variety of compounds, including some which could not be considered analogs of any known amino acids. For example, in Table VI and Fig. 14 and Table VII and Fig. 15, we can see that guanidinium hydrochloride, at concentrations exceeding 2 gm/liter or 20 mM, and dimethyl sulfoxide (DMSO), at 10%/volume, gave rise to polyheads and these were the only aberrations noted. Guanidinium was chosen because of its being a structural moiety of arginine and canavanine; dimethyl sulfoxide was used since it was shown to interfere with the bonds holding the head to the tail (Cummings *et al.*, 1968). Structurally, these compounds could not be more dissimilar and yet both gave rise to the same aberration—polyheads. The only common feature shared by these compounds is that both are capable of accepting protons (MacGregor, 1967; Rammler

TABLE VI

EFFECT OF GUANIDINIUM HYDROCHLORIDE[a] ON FORMATION OF POLYHEADS[b]

	Polyheads	Titer
Control[c]	0.8	1.0
T2L	8	0.8
T4B	7	1.0
T6	28	1.0

[a] Guanidium hydrochloride was effective only when added early during the lytic cycle and at concentrations greater than 2 gm/liter. These results were obtained using 6 gm/liter guanidinium hydrochloride added at 1.5 minutes after infection.

[b] The number of polyheads reported here is a total per grid opening in the electron microscope. This is essentially equivalent, under these conditions, to the evaluation used in Table IV. In addition, no other aberration was noted; a few small heads were in every field but not exceeding those obtained in the absence of guanidinum hydrochloride.

[c] The control number of polyheads given here is an average obtained from all three phages; T2L always had the least number of polyheads and T6 the greatest in normal lysates.

and Zaffaroni, 1967) and, in that sense, are able to disrupt the water structure surrounding the protein substructures. Evidence from studies on viability following freeze-thawing of T-even bacteriophage (Leibo, personal communication) also indicates that maintenance of the water structure around the protein substructures is essential for the persistence of viability. In comparing Figs. 14 and 15 with Fig. 11, it can be seen that polyheads obtained in the presence of guanidine or DMSO appear to be more fragile than those obtained using L-canavanine. Part of the problem here is that the polyheads obtained in the presence of either guanidine or DMSO are extremely long and simply break up during preparation for electron microscopy. For example, Fig. 16 shows some of the polyheads obtained in T2L

TABLE VII

EFFECT OF DIMETHYL SULFOXIDE ON FORMATION OF POLYHEADS[a]

Percent[b] DMSO	T2L		T4B		T6	
	Polyheads	Titer	Polyheads	Titer	Polyheads	Titer
0	0.2	1.0	0.4	1.0	1.0	1.0
7	5	0.6	1.6	0.76	12	0.45
10	49	0.1	72	0.09	82	0.06
15	0.3	2×10^{-5}	1.6	2×10^{-5}	4	3×10^{-5}

[a] As in Table VI, the number of polyheads is per grid opening in the electron microscope. The numbers reported both here and in Table VI were obtained following growth of the phage in enriched medium (casamino acids, see Cummings, 1963a); fewer polyheads were obtained (by about a factor of 2) in unsupplemented medium but the controls also yielded fewer polyheads.

[b] DMSO was added at 10 to 20 minutes after infection and little difference was noted in the number of polyheads obtained when DMSO was added early or late. Note that the number of polyheads decreases when the DMSO concentration reaches 15%. However, the yield of viable phage decreases markedly and this may indicate that DMSO is affecting other processes at high concentrations, such as the disruption of the secondary structure of transfer RNA (Gillchriest and Nelson, 1969).

during growth in the presence of DMSO; many of these polyheads are 50 times as long as a normal phage head. Another feature of these polyheads which warrants mention is that not all appear to have the same width. In Fig. 14B and C are two areas of the identical field, i.e., the magnification is the same. Yet, the width of the polyhead in Fig. 14C appears to be between 900 and 1000 Å and in Fig. 14B, about 700 Å, the normal width of a phage head. This difference may be due to flattening on the electron microscope grid or it may be real and will be considered later. It should be noted that all the polyheads observed here have well-defined sides and have no apparent surface morphology.

Another question which arose in the course of this work was whether the analogs of the amino acids chosen were the only analogs which could induce an aberrant substructure or whether any analog of that particular amino acid would have the same effect. We investigated, and are in the

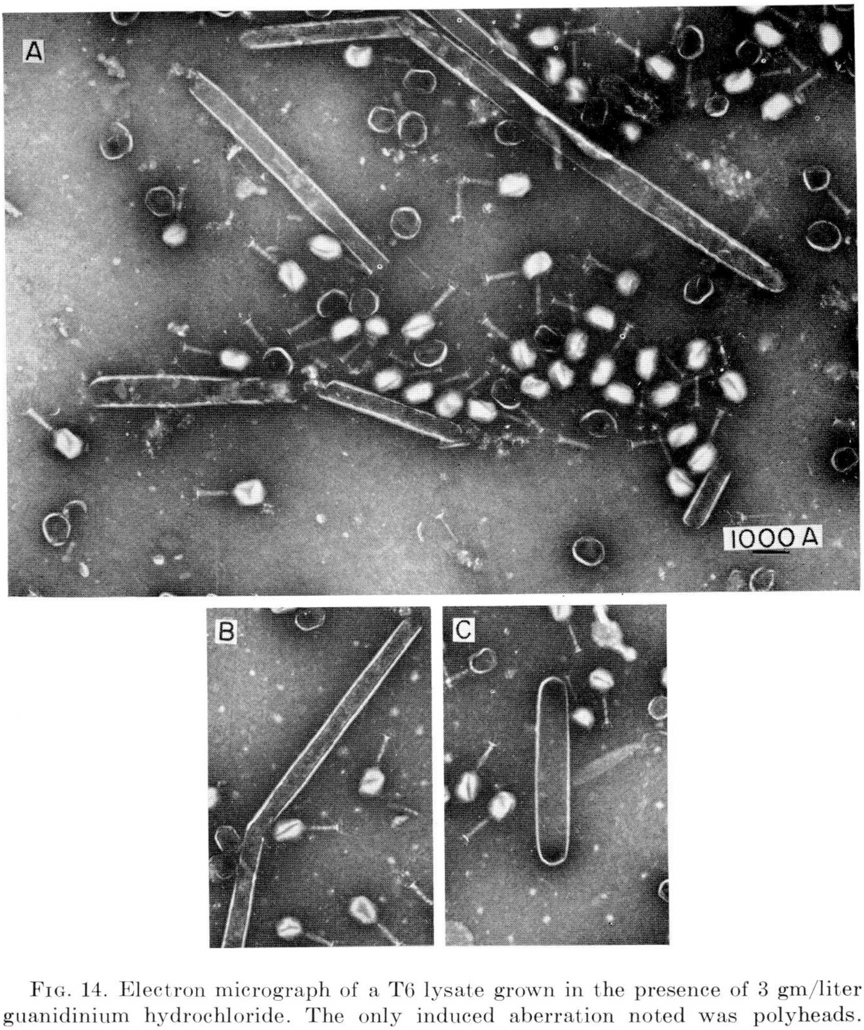

FIG. 14. Electron micrograph of a T6 lysate grown in the presence of 3 gm/liter guanidinium hydrochloride. The only induced aberration noted was polyheads. Note the difference in width of the polyheads in B and C.

process of further study of, many analogs of the amino acids mentioned as well as those from additional amino acids. A few words on the procedure used are necessary here. Before embarking on this extensive study, we

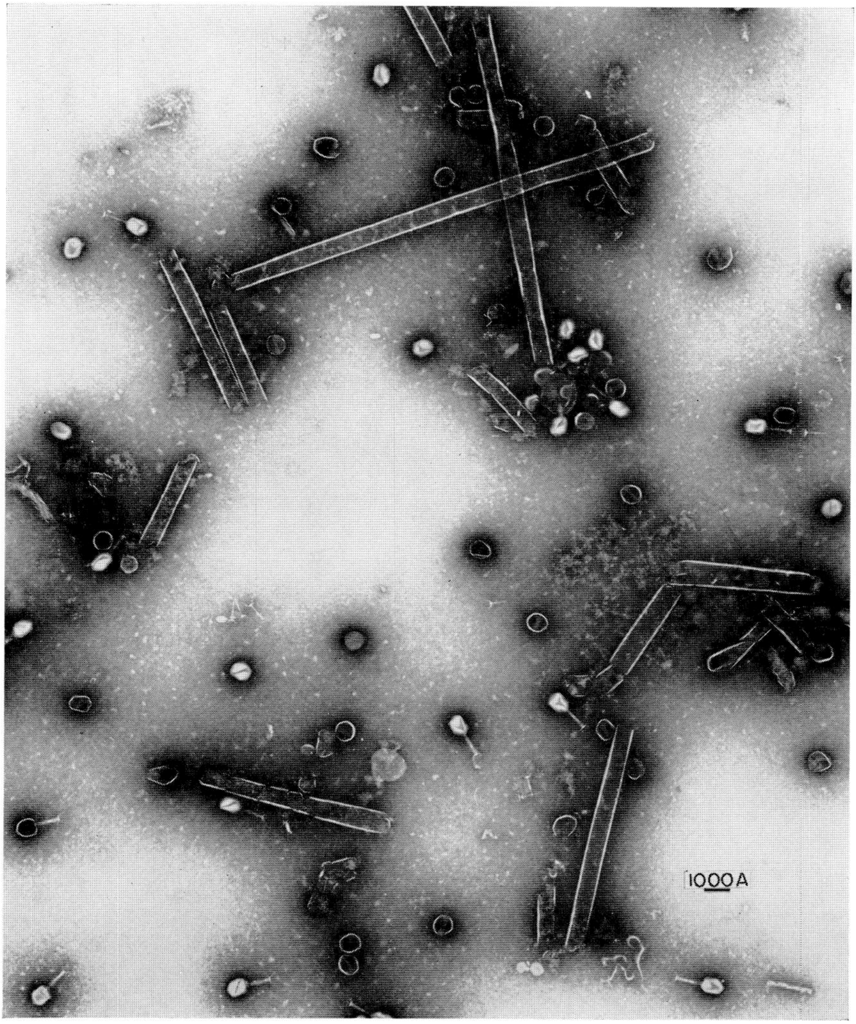

FIG. 15. Electron micrograph of a T6 lysate grown in the presence of 10% dimethyl sulfoxide. Many of the polyheads obtained appear to have been broken but all have well-defined sides and no surface morphology was noted.

elected to standardize the procedure in a manner which differed from that previously utilized (Cummings *et al.*, 1967). Essentially, this was done from two viewpoints: (1) To be certain all the infecting phage initiated new phage synthesis simultaneously, we infected the bacteria under nongrowing conditions and then transferred the infected cells to growth medium.

FIG. 16. Electron micrograph of a T2L lysate grown in the presence of 10% DMSO. Note the length of the polyheads and that the width of a particular polyhead does not appear to be constant. Constrictions are often visible indicating possibly that closure of the head was attempted but not completed.

These cells then went through the usual lytic cycle and yielded mature phage when expected. In some cases, the growth medium was supplemented with a mixture of fifteen amino acids, each at a concentration of 50 μg/ml in order to increase the overall yield of bacteriophage. (2) We changed the method of counting aberrant substructures. As noted previously, the length of an aberrant substructure varied considerably for polyheads, polysheath, and polytail tubes. Consequently, we measured the number of polysubstructures in terms of equivalent lengths. If an aberrant substruc-

TABLE VIII

DISTRIBUTION OF INDUCED ABERRATIONS IN SUPPLEMENTED MEDIA[a]

Compound	Bacteriophage	Viability[c]	Bacteriophage[b]		Polyhead	Polysheath	Polytail tube	Small heads	
			Whole	Ghost				Whole	Ghost
None	T6	1.0	900	1100	64	260	360	100	300
	T2L	1.0	1620	380	0	25	58	2	35
	T4B	1.0	1590	410	14	210	220	190	180
Group I[d]									
L-Canavanine									
200 μg/ml, 5 minutes	T6	5×10^{-3}	200	1800	620	180	3730	7	170
Putrescine									
125 m*M*, 5–10 minutes	T6	0.18	360	1640	20	670	730	170	1290
125 m*M*, 120 minutes	T6	0.86	850	1150	32	450	1010	90	390
125 m*M*, 5–10 minutes	T2L	0.32	1040	960	2	120	420	50	230
125 m*M*, 120 minutes	T2L	1.6	1950	50	0	8	31	8	0
125 m*M*, 5–10 minutes	T4B	0.17	840	1160	0	860	1130	940	1660
Homoarginine[e]									
2 mg/ml	T6	0.92	1240	760	54	429	715	256	467
Hydroxylysine									
4 mg/ml, 5 minutes	T6	0.32	1000	1000	0	12	1570	10	40
Group II[d]									
L-Azetidine-2-carboxylic acid 100 μg/ml									
10 minutes	T6	7×10^{-3}	210	1790	29	100	20310	13	290
L-Thiazolidine-4-carboxylic acid									
600 μg/ml, 10 minutes	T6	0.22	240	1760	53	420	1030	3	110

[a] Minimal medium was supplemented with 50 μg/ml of L-valine, L-histidine, L-isoleucine, L-proline, glycine, L-serine, L-lysine, L-tryptophan, L-alanine, L-cysteine, L-leucine, L-phenylalanine, L-threonine, and L-methionine. Whenever an amino acid analog was added, that corresponding amino acid was deleted.

[b] The numbers given here were normalized to a total of 2000 particles, even though many more particles were counted. These numbers are not meant to appear precise; in fact there was about a 20% variation in counting duplicate lysates.

[c] It should be pointed out here that whenever an aberrant substructure was increased in number, an effect on the overall phage yield was also noted. Wherever a test compound had little or no effect on viability, no additional aberrations were observed.

[d] Group I contains those compounds which are basic and could lead to head aberrations. Group II consists of two proline analogs.

[e] Recent experiments with homoarginine have indicated that as high as 20 mg/ml had little apparent effect on the maturation of T2L, T4B, or T6.

ture was 10 times as long as a normal substructure, it was counted as 10 aberrant substructures. This procedure greatly increased the numbers determined but we feel it reflects the proportion of aberrations in a phage preparation more realistically than simply counting structures. Recall for example, the results obtained in the presence of DMSO where many of the polyheads were at least 5 μ long.

We reexamined the effects of L-canavanine, L-azetidine-2-carboxylic acid, and triazole-3-alanine using these new conditions. In addition, other compounds were tested for their effects on maturation and the results are reported in Tables VIII and IX. Two main observations can be noted. The basal levels of aberrant substructures were found to be much higher than previously noted, indicating that mistakes in assembly readily occur during normal growth. These naturally occurring aberrations were all of the types described in that the surface morphology of aberrant heads was similar to that of normal heads; the number of induced aberrant substructures

TABLE IX

DISTRIBUTION OF INDUCED ABERRATIONS IN UNSUPPLEMENTED MEDIA[a]

Compound	Bacteriophage	Viability	Bacteriophage		Polyhead	Polysheath	Polytail tube	Small Heads	
			Whole	Ghost				Whole	Ghost
None	T6	1.0	1700	300	21	140	690	260	100
	T2L	1.0	1870	130	0	120	130	65	7
	T4B	1.0	1270	730	63	340	970	690	390
Group III[b]									
Triazolealanine									
400 μg/ml, 10 minutes	T6	0.24	1520	480	27	63	910	300	120
200 μg/ml, 10 minutes	T2L	0.27	850	1150	28	400	350	250	280
400 μg/ml, 10 minutes	T4B	0.037	1590	410	120	240	420	3200	570
Thiazolealanine									
400 μg/ml, 10 minutes	T6	0.80	1900	100	0	54	330	270	31
200 μg/ml, 10 minutes	T2L	0.10	430	1570	25	1430	1980	80	150
400 μg/ml, 10 minutes	T4B	0.11	1360	640	140	1460	2040	2580	330

[a] As stated in this section, the bacteria were infected in the nongrowing state and then transferred into growth medium. Some experiments indicated that fewer small heads were obtained with histidine analogs in supplemented medium (but lacking histidine). Consequently, no amino acids were added here.

[b] Group III refers to the two histidine analogs.

depends strongly on the analog used. In Table VIII, it can be seen that L-canavanine, as before, increased the number of polyheads about tenfold. These polyheads were similar in morphology to those induced before. However, homoarginine and hydroxylysine, compounds which can also be considered as analogs of arginine (see Meister, 1965), had no apparent effect on the maturation process both with respect to the induction of aberrant substructures and to affecting the number of phages produced even when added at very high concentrations. The threefold reduction in viability indicated for hydroxylysine is only apparent; when the host cells were grown in the complete supplemental medium and then infected with any of the T-even bacteriophages and the phage grown in the absence of both lysine and the analog, the overall phage yield was also reduced three-fold. These differences in the effects on maturation of arginine analogs may reflect the manner in which arginine biosynthetic pathways are affected. For example, Maas (1961) concluded that canavanine competes with arginine for incorporation into proteins and acts as a repressor, whereas, Peyru and Maas (1967) concluded that in *E. coli* B, the host cell used here, homoarginine does not act as a repressor in the arginine biosynthetic pathway.

Examination of the two proline analogs, L-azetidine-2-carboxylic acid and L-thiazolidine-4-carboxylic acid, revealed that only the former had a dramatic effect on the induction of tail tubes. The number of tail tubes was increased about 100-fold when the phage was grown in the presence of L-azetidine-2-carboxylic acid whereas there was an increase of only three-fold when L-thiazolidine-4-carboxylic acid was used. This may be because L-thiazolidine-4-carboxylic acid has the same stereo configuration as does proline in terms of affecting the α-helix (Unger and DeMoss, 1966) and may indicate that the protein subunits of polytail tubes differ from the protein subunits of normal tail tubes. Putrescine, a polyamine, also affected the maturation of bacteriophage, but only at high concentrations. When the putrescine concentration exceeded 60 mM, and only when added early, the number of small heads in the phage population increased about sevenfold for all the phages examined. The overall effect on the number of viable phages produced was the same as that previously reported (Shalitin and Sarid, 1967) where it was shown that 125 mM putrescine was necessary to affect maturation of T4D. The requirement for such high concentrations of putrescine may be due to the fact that putrescine is normally synthesized during phage growth (Cohen *et al.*, 1967) and that additional putrescine leads to an increased number of small heads. It has been suggested that putrescine is involved in the neutralization of the DNA inside the phage head (Ames and Dubin, 1960) and it may be that excess putrescine has an effect on the packaging of DNA into the preformed heads. Other polyamines, for example, steroid diamines (Mahler and Baylor, 1967), also affect phage maturation and it may be that this is a general effect of polyamines and is not limited to putrescine.

In studying the effect of the histidine analogs, 1,2,4-triazolealanine and 2-thiazolealanine (Moyed, 1961), it was noted that fewer small heads were induced by triazolealanine in T6 than was previously noted (Table IV). Consequently, we examined the effect of the histidine analogs in unsupplemented media but still infected the host cells in the nongrowth state so that phage growth could be initiated synchronously. In Table IX, we see that both histidine analogs increased the number of small-headed phage, as before, by about three- to sevenfold in T2L and T4B but had little effect on T6. This is in contrast to those results reported previously (Cummings *et al.*, 1967) for the effect of triazolealanine on T2L and T6 when an exponentially growing population of *E. coli* B was infected without any interruption in the growth state. In ascertaining a reason for this difference, it should be noted that here the histidine analogs had much less of an effect on the overall viability of T6 than on either T2L or T4B. It may be that T6 renders the host cell impermeable, or less permeable, to these analogs

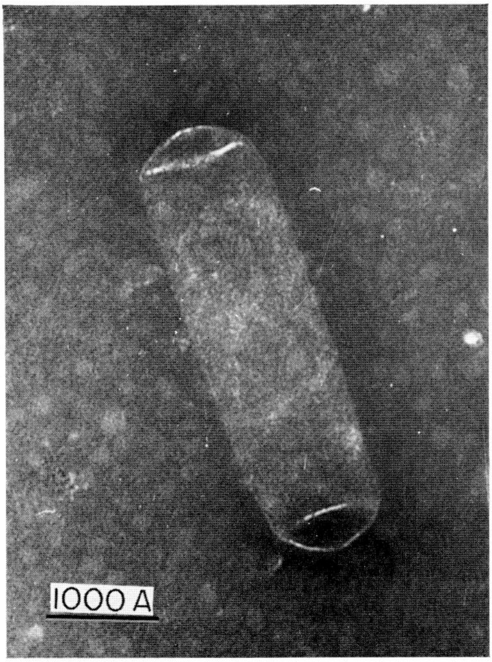

FIG. 17. An electron micrograph of a different type of polyhead. This polyhead was obtained whenever L-canavanine was used during growth and represented about 1% of all the polyheads obtained. Note that the ends of the polyhead have well-defined edges but that the long sides do not. In addition, this polyhead, whenever obtained, was always wider than the width of normal phage; in fact they appear to be about 1100 Å, i.e., wider than normal phage is long.

than do T2L or T4B and the effect of the analogs cannot be expressed. It is clear, however, that both histidine analogs lead to the formation of small heads.

IV. ABERRANT HEAD MODELS

Before considering the types of models which could simulate the head aberrations reported, another head aberration should first be presented. In reinvestigating the effects of L-canavanine on phage maturation, many preparations were analyzed and a different type of polyhead was observed (Fig. 17) in about 0.5 to 1 % of all the polyheads. In this polyhead, the ends appear to have the well-defined shell morphology and the extended length of the polyhead have sides which appear to have little definition. The width of these heads (see Fig. 14 for polyheads which are wide but have well-defined edges) is greater (by about 100 Å) than normal heads are long.

Any model for head substructures must therefore account for four types of head aberrations: (1) a short head; (2) a polyhead with well-defined edges and a uniform width; (3) a polyhead with well-defined edges but an undulating width, often with constrictions about one head length apart;

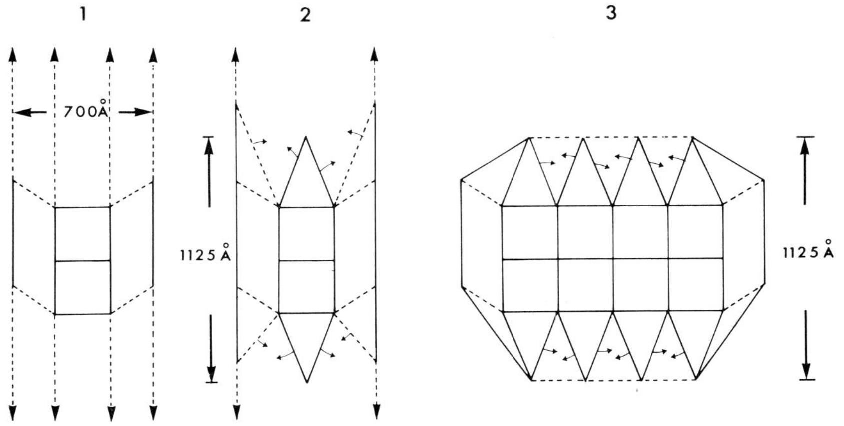

Fig. 18. A schematic diagram of the possible types of polyheads predictable by the type of head model presented in Fig. 3. The dotted lines indicate the extension of the heads leading to polyheads and the arrows indicate that some interplay of subunits must occur for the triangular apical faces to form a continuous structure. The dimensions given are for the flattened head and correspond to the 1000 Å given for the closed head.

and (4) a polyhead where only the ends are well-defined and the width is greater than normal heads are long. These structures can all be related to the bipyramidal hexagon model presented in Fig. 3. Generating a short-headed phage is comparatively simple; one need only remove one section of the rectangular faces to generate a head 750 × 700 Å. The prolate icosahedral model discussed can also give rise to a small head by the removal of the extra row of triangular faces which were inserted to account for nonisometric symmetry. Schematic diagrams of the three types of polyheads are presented in Fig. 18. Type 1 could occur by simple extension of the rows of subunits in the rectangular faces; type 2 could occur if the subunits somehow attempted closure of the head but failed leading to polyheads with undulating widths. Type 3 could occur by a lateral extension of the head leading to the type of polyhead where only the ends are well-defined. As is well known, defects in maturation of icosahedra often lead to polyheads in which longitudinal extension occurs (Caspar and Klug, 1962). Thus, the prolate icosahedral model could also account for type 1 polyhead and probably type 2. However, it is difficult for this model to account for type 3 where apparently a lateral extension occurs. No attempt will be made to fit the amber type polyhead (Figs. 5 and 6) into this scheme since it is not clear whether such polyheads have any relation to normal phage morphology.

V. Conclusion and Perspectives

We have investigated the effects of a variety of compounds on the maturation of bacteriophages. Table X represents a summary of the compounds

TABLE X
Summary of Induced Aberrations

Small heads	Polyheads	Polytail tubes	Polysheath
Triazolealanine	Canavanine	Azetidine-2-carboxylic acid	(Thiazolealanine)
Thiazolealanine	Guanidine		
Putrescine	DMSO		
Proflavine			
Actinomycin D			

and the aberrations they induce. In considering any mechanism for protein subunit interaction which could account for these aberrant substructures, it is necessary to take into account the diversity of compounds which can affect the production of that substructure. Triazolealanine, thiazolealanine, putrescine, proflavin, and actinomycin all affect the production of short-headed phage. Canavanine, guanidine, and dimethyl sulfoxide all affect the production of polyheads. It is unlikely, with the diversity of compounds involved, that incorporation of the compound is required to produce these aberrant substructures. In the case of polytail tubes, it may well be that incorporation or some direct effect on the protein subunits is necessary. Only L-azetidine-2-carboxylic acid had a gross effect on the production of polytail tubes. Taken with the finding that tail tubes are rich in proline (Sarkar *et al.*, 1964b) and the fact that this analog has a different effect on the α-helix than proline (Unger and DeMoss, 1966), this suggests that some alteration has taken place in the protein subunits which ultimately affects their assembly into a substructure. In Table X, thiazolealanine is parenthetically indicated as having an effect on polysheaths. This is not at all certain, but this analog was the only one tested which had any significant effect on the number of polysheaths. Obviously in order to understand the mechanism(s) involved in aberrant substructure assembly, the aberrant substructures must be isolated and their protein subunits examined.

Since some success with interfering with maturation in T-even bacteriophages has been achieved, it is important to determine whether or not other viral systems are affected. Shuve and Howatson (personal communication) have demonstrated that polyheads can be induced in λ bacteriophage when azetidine-2-carboxylic acid is present during growth. More important, what effect would such compounds have on the growth of animal viruses? Some of these compounds can and should be tested. For example, 10% dimethyl sulfoxide, the concentration used here, has little effect on bacterial viability and yet has a marked effect on the organization of phage heads. It would be interesting to determine what effect dimethyl sulfoxide had on, for example, the growth of adenovirus, or herpes simplex virus.

Acknowledgments

Much of our work reported in this review was supported by Public Health Service Research Grants AI 08265 and AI 06472.

The authors express their appreciation to V. A. Chapman and S. S. DeLong for their assistance in the electron microscopy.

References

Ames, B. N., and Dubin, D. T. (1960). *J. Biol. Chem.* **235,** 769.

Anderson, T. F. (1961). *Proc. European Regional Conf. Electron Microscopy, Delft, 1960* **2,** 1008.

Anderson, T. F., Rappaport, C., and Muscatine, N. A. (1953). *Ann. Inst. Pasteur* **84,** 5.

Boy de la Tour, E., and Kellenberger, E. (1965). *Virology* **27,** 222.

Bradley, D. E. (1967). *Bacteriol. Rev.* **31,** 230.

Brenner, S., and Horne, R. W. (1959). *Biochim. Biophys. Acta.* **34,** 103.

Brenner, S., Streisinger, G., Horne, R. W., Champe, S. P., Barnett, L., Benzer, S., and Rees, H. W. (1959). *J. Mol. Biol.* **1,** 281.

Brinton, C. C., Jr. (1965). *Trans. N.Y. Acad. Sci.* **27,** 1003.

Caspar, D. L. D., and Klug, A. (1962). *Cold Spring Harbor Symp. Quant. Biol.* **27,** 1.

Cohen, S. S., Hoffner, N., Jansen, M., Moore, M., and Raine, A. (1967). *Proc. Natl. Acad. Sci. U.S.* **57,** 721.

Cummings, D. J. (1959). Ph.D. Thesis, Univ. of Chicago, Chicago, Illinois.

Cummings, D. J. (1963a). *Biochim. Biophys. Acta* **68,** 472.

Cummings, D. J. (1963b). *Virology* **19,** 536.

Cummings, D. J. (1964). *Virology* **23,** 408.

Cummings, D. J., and Kozloff, L. M. (1960). *Biochim. Biophys. Acta* **44,** 445.

Cummings, D. J., and Kozloff, L. M. (1962). *J. Mol. Biol.* **5,** 50.

Cummings, D. J., and Wanko, T. (1963). *J. Mol. Biol.* **7,** 658.

Cummings, D. J., Chapman, V. A., DeLong, S. S., and Mondale, L. (1967). *J. Virol.* **1**, 193.
Cummings, D. J., Chapman, V. A., and DeLong, S. S. (1968). *J. Virol.* **2**, 610.
Cummings, D. J., Chapman, V. A., and DeLong, S. S. (1969). *Virology* **37**, 94.
Daems, W. T., Van de Pol, J. H., and Cohen, J. A. (1961). *J. Mol. Biol.* **3**, 225.
Davison, P. F. (1968). *Science* **161**, 906.
Davison, P. F., Freifelder, D., Hede, R., and Levinthal, C. (1961). *Proc. Natl. Acad. Sci. U.S.* **47**, 1123.
DeMars, R. I., Luria, S. E., Fisher, H., and Levinthal, C. (1953). *Ann. Inst. Pasteur* **84**, 113.
Demerec, M., and Fano, U. (1945). *Genetics* **30**, 119.
d'Herelle, F. (1917). *Compt. Rend.* **165**, 373.
Dyson, R. D., and Van Holde, K. E. (1967). *Virology* **33**, 559.
Edgar, R. S., and Lielausis, I. (1968). *J. Mol. Biol.* **32**, 263.
Edgar, R. S., and Wood, W. B. (1966). *Proc. Natl. Acad. Sci. U.S.* **55**, 598.
Edgar, R. S., Denhardt, G. H., and Epstein, R. H. (1964). *Genetics* **49**, 635.
Epstein, R. H., Bolle, A., Steinberg, C. M., Kellenberger, E., Boy de la Tour, E., Chevalley, R., Edgar, R. S., Susman, M., Denhardt, G. H., and Lielausis, A. (1963). *Cold Spring Harbor Symp. Quant. Biol.* **28**, 375.
Farid, S. A. A., and Kozloff, L. M. (1968). *J. Virol.* **2**, 308.
Fitch, W. M., and Susman, M. (1965). *Virology* **26**, 754.
Forrest, G. L., and Cummings, D. J. (1969). *Bacteriol. Proc., Miami, Florida* Abstr. p. 163.
Fraenkel-Conrat, H. (1957). *Virology* **4**, 1.
Fraser, D. (1957). *J. Biol. Chem.* **227**, 711.
Fruton, J. S. (1963). *In* "The Proteins" (H. Neurath, ed.), Vol. 1, p. 189. Academic Press, New York.
Gillchriest, W. C., and Nelson, P. L. (1969). *Biophys. Soc., Los Angeles, Calif. Abstr.* No. 9.
Kanner, L. C., and Kozloff, L. M. (1964). *Biochemistry* **3**, 215.
Kellenberger, E. (1966). *In* "Phage and the Origins of Molecular Biology" (J. Cairns, G. S. Stent, and J. D. Watson, eds.), p. 116–129. Cold Spring Harbor. Lab. Quant. Biol., Cold Spring Harbor, New York.
Kellenberger, E. (1968). *Virology* **34**, 549.
Kellenberger, E., and Arber, W. (1955). *Z. Naturforsch.* **10b**, 698.
Kellenberger, E., Bolle, A., Boy de la Tour, E., Epstein, R. H., Franklin, N. C., Jerne, N. K., Reale-Scafati, A., Séchaud, J., Bendet, I., Goldstein, D., and Lauffer, M. A. (1965). *Virology* **26**, 419.
King, J. H. (1968). *J. Mol. Biol.* **32**, 231.
King, J. H., and Wood, W. B. (1969). *J. Mol. Biol.* **39**, 583.
Korn, D., Protass, J. J., and Leive, L. (1965). *Biochem. Biophys. Res. Commun.* **19**, 473.
Kozloff, L. M. (1968). *In* "Molecular Basis of Virology" (H. Fraenkel-Conrat, ed.), p. 435. Reinhold, New York.
Kozloff, L. M., and Lute, M. (1959). *J. Biol. Chem.* **234**, 539.
Larcom, L., and Bendet, I. (1968). *Biophys. Soc., Pittsburgh, Pennsylvania* Abstr. No. 8, p. 66.
Levine, L., Barlow, J. L., and Van Vunakis, H. (1958). *Virology* **6**, 702.
Levine, M. (1969). *Ann. Rev. Genet.* **3**, 323.
Levinthal, E., Hosoda, J., and Shub, D. (1967). *In* "The Molecular Biology

of Viruses" (S. J. Colter and W. Paranchych, eds.), p. 71–87. Academic Press, New York.
Luftig, R. B., and Wood, W. B. (1969). *Biophys. Soc., Los Angeles, California* Abstr. No. 9.
Luria, S. E., and Anderson, T. F. (1942). *Proc. Natl. Acd. Sci. U.S.* **28**, 127.
Maas, W. K. (1961). *Cold Spring Harbor Symp. Quant. Biol.* **26**, 183.
MacGregor, W. C. (1967). *Ann. N.Y. Acad. Sci.* **141**, 3.
Mahler, H. R., and Baylor, M. B. (1967). *Proc. Natl. Acad. Sci. U.S.* **58**, 256.
Meister, A. (1965). "Biochemistry of the Amino Acids," 2nd Ed., Vol. I. Academic Press, New York.
Minagawa, T. (1961). *Virology* **13**, 515.
Moody, M. F. (1965). *Virology* **26**, 567.
Moody, M. F. (1967a). *J. Mol. Biol.* **25**, 167.
Moody, M. F. (1967b). *J. Mol. Biol.* **25**, 201.
Mosig, G. (1966). *Proc. Natl. Acad. Sci. U.S.* **56**, 1177.
Moyed, H. S. (1961). *J. Biol. Chem.* **236**, 2261.
Peyru, G. M., and Maas, W. K. (1967). *J. Bacteriol.* **94**, 712.
Piechowski, M. M., and Susman, M. (1966). *Virology* **28**, 396.
Rammler, D. H., and Zaffaroni, A. (1967). *Ann. N.Y. Acad. Sci.* **141**, 13.
Rubenstein, I., Thomas, C. A., Jr., and Hershey, A. D. (1961). *Proc. Natl. Acad. Sci. U.S.* **47**, 1113.
Sarkar, N., Sarkar, S., and Kozloff, L. M. (1964a). *Biochemistry* **3**, 511.
Sarkar, S., Sarkar, N., and Kozloff, L. M. (1964b). *Biochemistry* **3**, 517.
Schlesinger, M. (1932). *Z. Hyg. Infektionskrankh.* **144**, 149.
Schlesinger, M. (1934). *Biochem. Z.* **273**, 306.
Schlesinger, M. (1936). *Nature* **138**, 508.
Shalitin, C., and Sarid, S. (1967). *J. Virol.* **1**, 559.
Shalitin, C., Danon, D., and Katchalski, E. (1962). *Arch. Biochem. Biophys.* **99**, 494.
Simon, L. D., and Anderson, T. F. (1967a). *Virology* **32**, 279.
Simon, L. D., and Anderson, T. F. (1967b). *Virology* **32**, 298.
Smith, K. O., and Trousdale, M. (1965). *J. Bacteriol.* **90**, 796.
Stent, G. S. (1963). "Molecular Biology of Bacterial Viruses." Freeman, San Francisco, California.
Stretton, A. O. W., and Brenner, S. (1965). *J. Mol. Biol.* **12**, 456.
Twort, F. W. (1915). *Lancet* **ii** (189), 1241.
Unger, L., and DeMoss, R. D. (1966). *J. Bacteriol.* **91**, 1556.
Van Vunakis, H., Baker, J. L., and R. K. Brown, (1958). *Virology* **5**, 327.
Williams, R. C., and Fraser, D. (1956). *Virology* **2**, 289.
Young, B. G., and Mora, P. T. (1960). *Virology* **12**, 493.

STRUCTURE AND ASSEMBLY OF SIMPLE RNA BACTERIOPHAGES

Thomas Hohn and Barbara Hohn

Departments of Biochemistry and Pathology, Stanford University School of Medicine, Stanford, California

I. Introduction

A. Structure and Assembly

Crick and Watson (1956) suggested that in all simple viruses identical protein subunits are arranged regularly to form a protective capsid for the nucleic acid. This prediction was derived from the limited size of the RNA, that could not code for a capsid without repeating units (Crick and Watson, 1957), from the striking regularity of viral X-ray diffraction

* Recent reviews of self-assembly of RNA bacteriophages: Steitz (1970); on self-assembly of simple viruses: Leberman (1968); on self-assembly: Kushner, (1969); on RNA bacteriophages: Valentine *et al.* (1969); on simple viruses: Erikson (1968), Fraenkel-Conrat (1968), Fraenkel-Conrat and Weissmann (1968), Hofschneider and Hausen (1968), Kaper (1968); J. B. Bancroft (see this volume).

patterns (Klug and Caspar, 1960), and from electron micrographs of viruses (Horne and Wildy, 1961). The teleological argument, pointing in the same direction and raised at that time, that a too high number of different components would produce too many errors during assembly is convincing today since, for instance, ribosomes are assembled successfully from about 50 different components (Nomura *et al.*, 1969). That the capsid of simple viruses consists in fact of identical subunits was shown by the homogeneity of the isolated protein by several criteria including amino acid sequence (see, e.g., Wittmann-Liebold and Wittmann, 1967).

Caspar and Klug (1962) pointed out that the assembly of viruses is related to crystallization and is governed by the law of statistical mechanics. The main difference between a virus shell and a crystal is that the one is hollow while the other is solid and that the one has a definite size while the other has not. Furthermore, helical and icosahedral symmetry are not common in crystals while they are the preferred symmetry in simple viruses. Both crystals and viruses however have a definite shape, the energy for their formation being provided by the formation of intersubunit bonds. In the final structure a maximum number of the most stable intersubunit bonds is achieved if all subunits are in equivalent position and this necessarily predicts a limited number of symmetrical structures.

Two main structural types of simple viruses exist, i.e., helical and isometric ("spherical") viruses. While in helical viruses all subunits except the ones on the ends are in equivalent position and helices of various length can be formed without changing the basic geometrical arrangement, in isometric viruses not more than 60 subunits could be arranged in strictly equivalent position. The fact that most isometric viruses, including the simple RNA bacteriophages, have more than 60 identical subunits has led to the theory on "quasiequivalent arrangement of subunits" by Caspar and Klug (1962). According to this theory the postulate of strictly mathematical equivalence of the subunits in viral shells can be dropped without violating the physical principle that in the formation of the caspid the same contacts between subunits are used over and over again. According to the theory more than 60 identical subunits can be arranged on the surface of an icosahedron in similar binding of all subunits with their neighbors if a certain variability in the angle of the bonds and/or a certain deformation of the subunits are permitted. These variations in bonding angles do not need to exceed about 5°. Subunits whose binding angles differ by this amount are considered as in quasiequivalent position. They are arranged in pentamers (pentons) on the 12 corners of the icosahedron with additional subunits arranged in hexamers (hexons) intercalated on the 20 surfaces.* The number of hexons can be varied, however, only certain numbers are permitted due to geometrical principles. The total number of subunits is quantized according to the relationship: $n = 60\ T$. T, the triangulation number, is given by the rule $T = PF^2$, where P can be any number of the series 1, 3, 7, 13, 19 . . . $(h^2 + hk + k^2)$ and f is any integer. The numbers for the RNA bacteriophages are, for instance, $P = 3$, $f = 1$, $T = 3$, $n = 180$ (Fig. 1). The theory is supported by a number of X-ray diffraction patterns of isometric viruses that show 5-3-2, i.e., icosahedral symmetry, and a number of electron micrographs that reveal a structure similar to the icosahedral models. Caspar and Klug (1962) stated also that a convincing demonstration that this principle of design is correct would be the spontaneous polymerization of subunits into icosahedral shells. This self-assembly was actually demonstrated with some icosahedral plant viruses (review by Bancroft, 1970) and with the RNA phages as described in this chapter.

B. Simple RNA Bacteriophages

The RNA bacteriophages used for self-assembly were the male specific coliphages fr, MS2, R17, f2, and Qβ. The first four of these (including M12 and others) are serologically closely related to each other (Scott, 1965; Krueger, 1969). The coat protein sequences of these phages differ only in a few amino acid exchanges and no significant differences in other respects have yet been found. Disagreements in results obtained from experiments with one or the other of these phages can not be excused by a difference in the species used. In general therefore we will abstain in this review from speaking of the different species, but instead will introduce and use the group name fII (the same name as the first isolated species but written with a Roman numeral for distinction). Qβ, though similar in size and most of the physical properties, is less closely related in many other respects (Overby *et al.*, 1966a, b) and will therefore be discussed separately. There are other phage species in these two groups and there exists a third serological group of RNA coliphages (Nishihara *et al.*, 1969) as well as the phage R23 (Watanabe *et al.*, 1968) which is similar to fII in all respects but which inhibits host protein synthesis. These phages have not yet been used in self-assembly experiments, however, and are therefore omitted from this paper.

* The terms hexamers and pentamers are used here only to facilitate the discussion of the geometrical arrangement of subunits in the icosahedron. They are not necessarily visible on phage images nor do they necessarily represent thermodynamically stable entities.

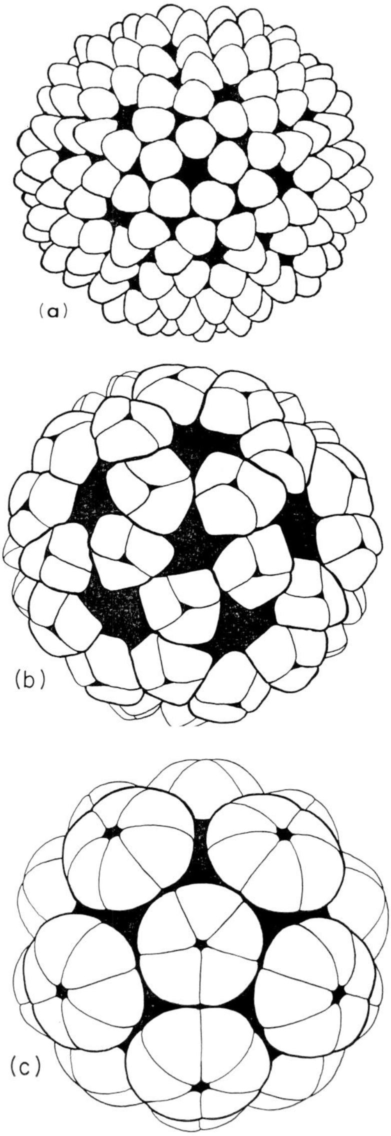

FIG. 1. Model for the icosahedral arrangement of 180 identical subunits. Triangulation number $T = 3$. (a) no clustering; (b) clustering in trimers; (c) clustering in hexamers and pentamers [(a) from Caspar, 1965).]

The RNA coliphages are of special interest because of their small size and genetic simplicity which allows a close correlation between genetic information and growth cycle, including morphopoiesis. On the single-stranded fII RNA only three genes were distinguished, i.e., RNA replicase and two structural phage components. In addition fII and Qβ RNA will probably be the first messenger RNAs of known sequence.

A further advantage of the RNA coliphage system is that much is known about the virus production *in vitro*. Bacteriophage RNA directs *in vitro* the synthesis of the two structural phage proteins and of RNA replicase. RNA replicase catalyzes the net synthesis of biologically active RNA (Spiegelman *et al.*, 1965; for reviews, see Weissmann and Ochoa, 1967; Shapiro and August, 1966). The *in vitro* reconstitution finally assembles the phage components yielding phagelike particles and phage. In principle, therefore, the way is open to produce phages in the test tube beginning with only one single copy of RNA, an *E. coli* extract, and low molecular weight precursors.

II. Structure of Phage and of Phage Capsid Derivatives other than those Obtained by *in vitro* Reconstitution

A. *Particles Containing Coat Protein, A-Protein, and RNA*

1. *Phages fII and Qβ* (see *Note added in proof*)

The normal products of a lysate of fII-infected bacteria are 10^{12}–10^{13} spherical particles/ml sedimenting at 80 S and banding in CsCl at 1.43 gm/ml (Enger *et al.*, 1963; Gesteland and Boedtker, 1964; Overby *et al.*, 1966a; Marvin and Hoffmann-Berling, 1963; Strauss and Sinsheimer, 1963; the two latter groups reported a higher CsCl density, i.e., 1.46 gm/ml). Only 1 or 2 out of 10 particles produces an infective center. This might be a consequence of heterogeneity of particles such that only 10% are perfect or of an infection process than is only 10% successful. In the electron microscope the particles appear to be spherical or hexagonal in shape with a bright periphery indicating a shell of higher electron density than the core and of roughly 40 Å thickness (Fig. 2).

In most of the fII images the coat protein subunits appear to be clustered in small units, probably trimers (Figs. 1c, 2, and 13), thereby complicating the evaluation of the capsid structure. A very small percentage of fII images did however show clustering in 32 pentamers and hexamers arranged on the surface of a regular icosahedron of the triangulation $T = 3$ (Fig. 3), the total number of subunits being 180 (Vasquez *et al.*, 1966).

The phage radius was measured from electron micrographs by several authors, yielding values ranging from 100 to 135 Å (Loeb and Zinder, 1961; Strauss and Sinsheimer, 1963; Hofschneider, 1963; Nonoyama *et al.*, 1963; Marvin and Hoffmann-Berling, 1963; Vasquez *et al.*, 1966; Franklin and Granboulan, 1966; Overby *et al.*, 1966a). More recently a

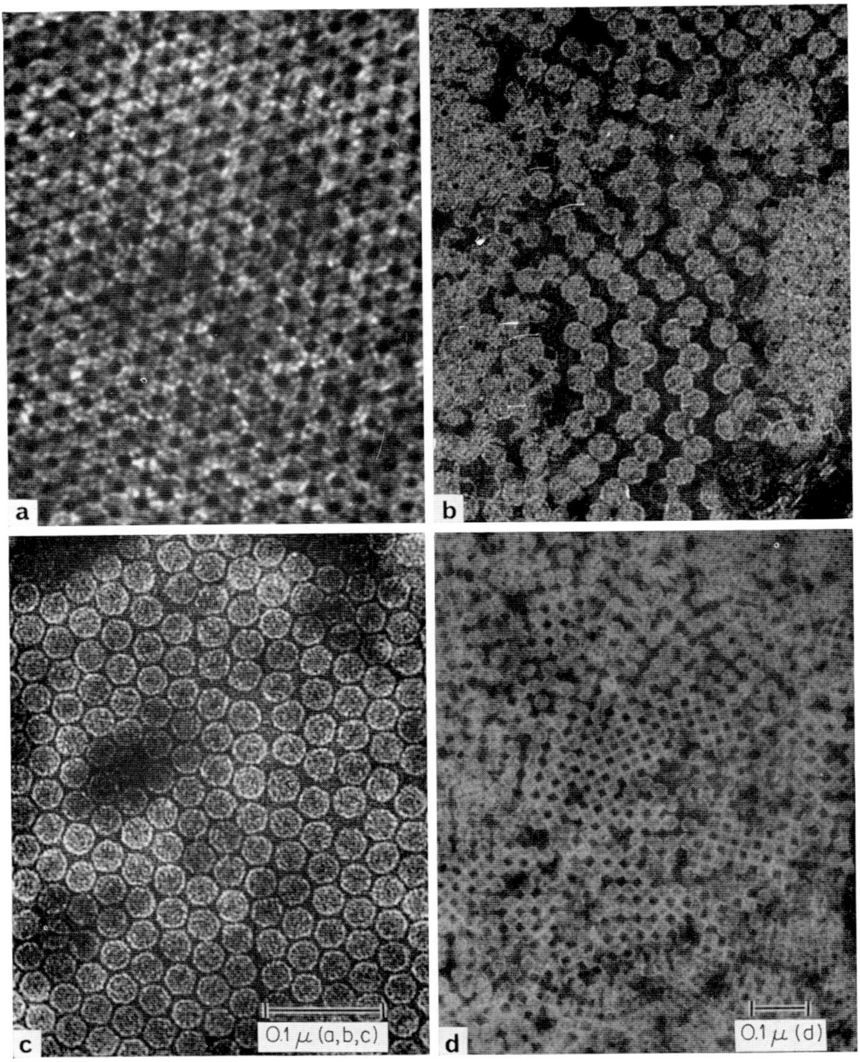

FIG. 2. fII bacteriophage arranged in paracrystalline sheets. (a–c) hexagonal, (d) tetragonal arrangement. Negative staining with uranyl acetate (a, b) and phosphotungstate (c, d).

precision measurement of the half-interparticle distance in extended paracrystalline (hexagonal and tetragonal) sheets (Fig. 2) yielded a value of 135 ± 1 Å (Franck and Hohn, unpublished observations). This value is the outermost radius (a) in Fig. 4. More information on the

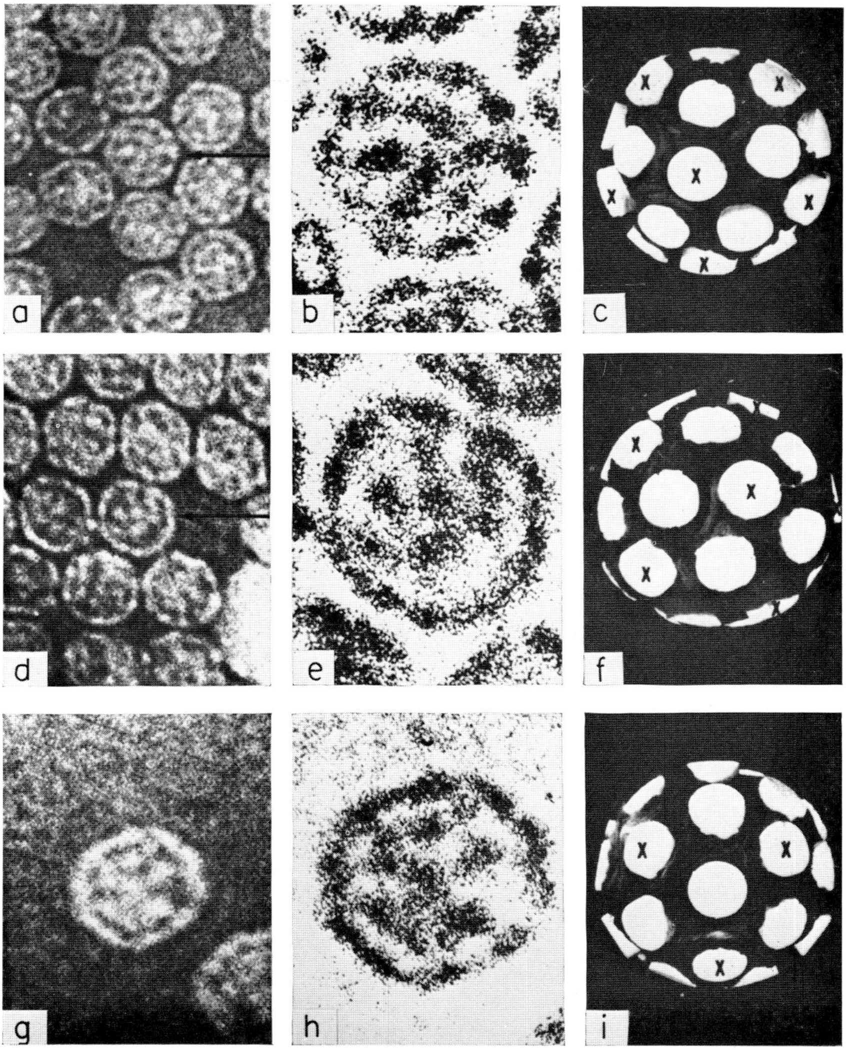

FIG. 3. Selected fII images that reveal icosahedral ($T = 3$) structure. Negative staining with phosphotungstate. First column positive prints; second column enlarged negative prints; third column a model showing the pentons (x) and hexons in approximately the same orientation as the corresponding fII images. Note the central penton surrounded by five hexons (a, b, and c), the diamond pattern (d, e, and f), and the central hexon surrounded by three hexons and three pentons (g, h, and i) (from Vasquez *et al.*, 1966).

radial phage dimensions were obtained by low-angle X-ray scattering (Fischbach *et al.*, 1965; Zipper *et al.*, 1970). The data thus obtained by the latter group are included in Fig. 4. The mean outer radius of the electron density distribution (b) is only slightly smaller than the outermost radius (a), i.e. 131.4 Å. (Fischbach *et al.*, 1965, measured b = 133 Å.) This mean outer radius is larger than what would be expected by comparison with turnip yellow mosaic virus (TYMV): At a given triangulation number the mean outer radius of a virus should be roughly

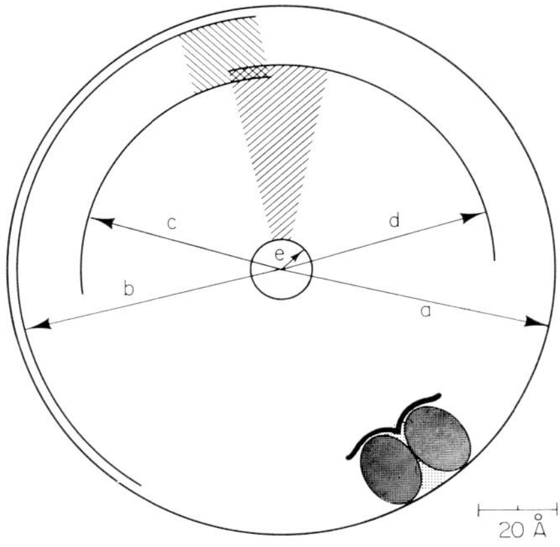

FIG. 4. Radial dimensions of fII. (see *Note added in proof,* p. 97). (a) Outermost radius as obtained from the interparticle distance in paracrystalline sheets (Fig. 2), 135 Å; (b–e) characteristic radii obtained from low-angle X-ray scattering (Zipper *et al.*, 1970); (b) mean outer radius of the shell, 131.4 Å; (c) mean inner radius of the shell = mean outer radius of the core, 100 Å; (d) mean outer radius of RNA, 105 Å; (e) mean inner radius of RNA, 15 Å. Part of the space occupied by protein is left-hatched and part of the space occupied by the RNA is right-hatched. In the lower part of the figure two hypothetical subunits are depicted as prolated ellipsoids of 40 Å length and 30 Å width, located closely to a piece of RNA.

proportional to the cubic root of the molecular weight of the coat protein subunit. Thus, since the molecular weight of the TYMV subunit is 20,000 daltons (Harris and Hindley, 1965), the molecular weight of the fII subunits is 13,750 daltons (p. 55) and the mean outer radius of TYMV is 140 Å. (Klug *et al.*, 1966), the mean outer radius of fII would be only 123 Å. This may imply that the fII subunits are either less densely packed than the TYMV subunits or that they do not reach as far into the virus core.

The radius c (Fig. 4) of 101.6 Å marks a transition of a higher electron density in the shell to a lower one in the core. The mean thickness of the shell is therefore 31.4 Å.

The mean outer and inner radii of the RNA (d, e in Fig. 4) were determined by low-angle scattering in sucrose of electron density similar to protein to be 105 and 15 Å, respectively. About 20% of the RNA penetrates into the shell.

All those radii are mean radii and the protein subunits are expected to extend beyond them, i.e., to the outermost radius and a comparable distance into the core. Similarly, the RNA will penetrate into the shell beyond the distance e (Fig. 4), possibly into the 32 spaces inside the hexons and pentons and/or into the 60 spaces between the hexons and pentons.

The volume of the protein subunit can be estimated from its molecular weight to be 19,000 ± 2000 $Å^3$ (assuming a volume/molecular weight ratio of 1.37 ± 0.12 $Å^3$/daltons, which is a mean value for proteins of known dimensions and molecular weight; for these values see for instance: Stryer, 1968; Muirhead and Perutz, 1963; Dayhoff and Eck, 1967–1968). A subunit of this volume, as a prolated ellipsoid of the length 40 Å and the radius 15 Å, is depicted in the lower part of Fig. 4. In the area of most effective packing of 180 of these hypothetical subunits about 80% of the phage surface would be covered.

The molecular weight of fII can be measured with high precision as the sum of the molecular weights of its components (180 × 13,750 daltons protein, 1.1 × 10^6 daltons RNA; see p. 55 and p. 60) as 3.62 × 10^6 daltons. This value is in good agreement with the one obtained by light scattering (3.6 × 10^6 daltons; Gesteland and Boedtker, 1964), by most of the reported hydrodynamic measurements (3.6–3.7 × 10^6 daltons; Strauss and Sinsheimer, 1963; Overby *et al.*, 1966a), and by measurement of the phages' total electron density (3.62 × 10^6 daltons; Zipper *et al.*, 1970).

The physical properties of Qβ are only slightly different from those of fII (Overby *et al.*, 1966a). Its CsCl density (1.44 gm/ml), sedimentation constant (84 S), and molecular weight (4.2 × 10^6 daltons) are slightly larger than the corresponding values of fII.

2. *Defective 5-Fluorouracil-Containing Particles*

If 5-fluorouracil (5-FU) is added to a culture of *E. coli* previously infected with fII, 5-FU-containing phage and a large number of defective particles are obtained (Shimura *et al.*, 1965, 1967). These "fluorouracil particles" have a size and general appearance similar to the phage, however, they band at a lower CsCl density, adsorb poorly to *E. coli*, are noninfectious, and serologically slightly different. These particles contain RNA of only 65% the normal length, which is not infectious for spheroblasts but which serves as a good template for protein synthesis. There is a main difference between the fluorouracil particles and the light-defective particles described on p. 53. In contrast to the defective particles, fluorouracil particles contain the intact 5′-terminus of the RNA while the original 3′-terminus is missing. This RNA fragment does still code for coat protein and does not code for RNA replicase (Shimura *et al.*, 1968).

3. *RNase-Sensitive Particles*

Different treatments of fII such as incubation at low ionic strength at 46°C (Steitz, 1968c), at high ionic strength (Kaesberg, 1966), and at normal ionic strength and high temperature (Oriel and Koenig, 1968), and freezing and thawing (Hohn, 1967) result in a loss of the RNase stability. These "RNase-sensitive particles" are different from the defective particles described on p. 53 in that they shield 0–30% of their RNA from nucleolytic cleavage, while defective particles still shield 70% of the RNA. Steitz (1968c) has shown that the particles obtained by the low ionic strength treatment are still infective although with a somewhat lower efficiency and that they sediment in 0.015 *M* NaCl between 45 and 50 S (compared with 70 S for the defective particle and 80 S for the phage). In 0.15 *M* NaCl they sediment between 60 and 65 S, while the sedimentation constant of the phage remains unchanged. In this ionic strength dependence, the sedimentation behavior mimics that of the isolated fII RNA, which sediments at 16 S in 0.01 *M* salt and at 27 S in 0.1 *M* salt (Gesteland and Boedtker, 1964). The most likely explanation for the RNase-sensitive particles is that the RNA is protruding from the capsid. This protruding is greater than in the defective particles, since more RNA is RNase sensitive and the sedimentation constant is lower. Another explanation is that the entire particle is expanded likewise exposing the RNA to the external media. It is likely that at least in the infective fraction of the particles the location of the A-protein and the 5′ terminus of the RNA is normal.

4. *"L-Particles"*

Rohrmann and Krueger (1970b) observed in normal lysates, besides normal fII, particles of slightly lower buoyant density, which they called "L-particles." L-particles are antigenically related to fII (Rohrmann and Krueger, 1970b), they contain A-protein as does the phage, and have a protein/RNA ratio similar to that of the phage. L-particles have only low infectivity, their RNA however is as infectious for protoblasts as the RNA isolated from normal fII. According to Rohrmann and

Krueger (1970b) the difference in buoyant density of fII and L-particles might indicate a difference in the capsid's surface structure.

B. Particles Lacking A-Protein (Defective Particles and Light Defective Particles)

If nonpermissive bacteria are infected with fII containing an amber mutation in the A-cistron a normal burst noninfectious phagelike particles is produced (Lodish *et al.*, 1965; Heisenberg and Blessing, 1965; Heisenberg, 1967). These have been called *defective particles.* Defective particles can not be distinguished from viable phage in the electron microscope, however, they differ in a number of other respects. Although they contain intact infectious RNA if properly shielded from RNase digestion, part of this RNA is digested when the RNA is exposed to nucleolytic attack (Heisenberg, 1966; Argetsinger and Gussin, 1966). The phage in comparison is stable to RNase. The digested defective particles (*light defective particles*) band as a broad peak in CsCl density gradients at lower density than the phage and corresponding to a mean RNA content of two-thirds of the original one. Defective particles and light defective particles both do not adsorb to the bacterial host. The sedimentation constant of defective and light defective particles was measured as 69 and 74 S, respectively, as compared with 79 S for the viable phage. The lower sedimentation constant of the defective particle can be explained by higher friction due to a protruding piece of RNA. After RNase digestion the sedimentation constant is increased because of removal of the friction of RNA, although the molecular weight is decreased (Heisenberg, 1966). Another indication that RNA protrudes from the defective particles is that they react with anti-RNA antiserum, while phages do not (Heisenberg, 1967). Steitz (1968a) found that the basic difference between phages and defective particles is that the former contain A-protein while the latter do not.

Lodish (1968a, b) has reported the isolation of a 70% fragment of phage RNA from light defective particles. He claims that this fragment contains the intact 3′-terminus of fII RNA and still codes for RNA-replicase. He concludes that it is the missing 5′-ppp terminus that protrudes from the defective particle.

An alternative method for the production of defective particles was introduced by Kaerner (1969, 1970). Knowing that the A protein contains histidine while the coat protein does not, he starved for histidine 12 minutes after infection, at which time RNA replicase has already been made and coat protein and A-protein have not. Under these conditions only very few A-protein molecules are synthesized and defective particles and light defective particles are produced instead of viable phage.

Phagelike particles, probably similar to defective particles, were also obtained in cell-free systems of *E. coli* (Knolle, 1969).

C. Particles Lacking RNA

1. "Empty Shells"

We define "empty shells" as phagelike particles that contain not more than 5% of the normal amount of RNA. Empty shells are obtained by RNase digestion of the RNase-sensitive particles already described and subsequent CsCl density centrifugation (Kaesberg, 1966; Hohn, 1967; Steitz, 1968c), or by alkali treatment of the viable phage (Samuelsen and Kaesberg, 1970). They band at 1.29 gm/ml and their sedimentation constant in 0.15 *M* buffered saline is 40–50 S. They are antigenically related to the bacteriophage (Rohrmann and Krueger, 1970c). As observed in the electron microscope, the empty shells have a similar diameter to the phage and are heavily penetrated by negative stain (Fig. 15a). The thickness of the shell is 40 ± 10 Å. At least in some cases, empty shells cannot be produced in high concentration since they have a tendency to precipitate irreversibly during the RNase treatment (own unpublished observation).

2. Subshell Protein Polymers

RNA-free protein complexes sedimenting at 11 S are obtained by treating fII with 4 *M* guanidinium-HCl at neutral pH (Zelazo and Haschemeyer, 1969). These 11 S particles remain soluble after removal of the guanidinium-HCl and can easily be purified by sucrose gradient centrifugation. Their molecular weight is 270,000 ± 6000 daltons, which is compatible with a complex of 18 protein subunits. In the electron microscope they appear ellipsoidal in shape with a clear open space in the center. Some particles are nearly spherical and some appear as two parallel bars (Fig. 15e). Zelazo and Haschemeyer suggest, reasonably, that the 11 S particles consist of 6 trimers arranged in a flattened hexagon. Possible mechanisms of the degradation process are given in Fig. 5.

At pH 4, the 11 S particles are further disintegrated yielding material sedimenting at 5.5 S. This conversion is reversible since 11S particles are regained after readjustment to pH 7 (Zelazo and Haschemeyer, 1970). The conversion of 11 S particles into empty shells is described on p. 78.

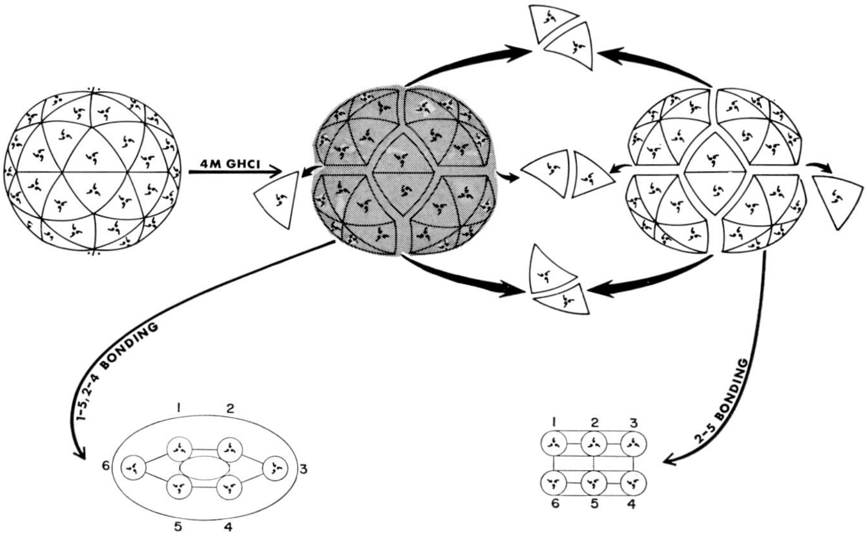

FIG. 5. Models for the degradation of fII by 4 *M* guanidinium-HCl. Left pathway, splitting into 10 identical units (11 S particles); right pathway, splitting into 11 S particles and smaller entities. The same pathways in reversal could be used for assembly. Modified from Zelazo and Haschemeyer (1969).

III. THE STRUCTURAL BACTERIOPHAGE COMPONENTS. ISOLATION AND STRUCTURE

A. Coat Protein

1. Coat Protein of fII

The main component of the fII capsid is a protein composed of 129 amino acids of known sequence (Fig. 6; Weber and Konigsberg, 1967; Weber, 1967; Wittmann-Liebold and Wittmann, 1967; Lin *et al.*, 1967). The MS2-, M12-, R17-, and f2-protein subunits have either identical sequences or differ by only one amino acid replacement. In fr, 18% of the amino acids are different and 60% of these replacements can be explained by a single base exchange in the RNA. An interesting feature of the amino acid sequence is the clustering of 7 basic amino acids between the positions 38 to 66. This might well be that site of the protein subunit that reacts with the RNA in the phage. The coat protein subunits contain no histidine, a fact useful for the specific labeling of other phage components. Its molecular weight is 13,750 daltons.

In an ideal isolation of coat protein, the subunits would separate but the monomeric unit would not be denatured. This goal has not yet been achieved, but at least methods of protein isolation are available that impose the least damage on the protein and keep the denaturation reversible. The solubility of the protein and its activity in the self-assembly system are good criteria for its quality. Phenol extraction, although optimal for RNA isolation, did not yield protein of sufficient quality (own unpublished results); alkali and high salt degradation meth-

1 5 10 15
fr Ala — Ser — Asn — Phe — **Glu** — **Glu** — Phe — Val — Leu — Val — Asn — Asp — Gly — Gly — Thr — Gly — **Asp** — Val —
f_2 Ala — Ser — Asn — Phe — **Thr** — **Gln** — Phe — Val — Leu — Val — Asn — Asp — Gly — Gly — Thr — Gly — **Asn** — Val —

20 25 30 35
fr **Lys** — Val — Ala — Pro — Ser — Asn — Phe — Ala — Asn — Gly — Val — Ala — Glu — Try — Ile — Ser — Ser — Asn —
f_2 **Thr** — Val — Ala — Pro — Ser — Asn — Phe — Ala — Asn — Gly — Val — Ala — Glu — Try — Ile — Ser — Ser — Asn —

40 45 50
fr Ser — Arg — Ser — Gln — Ala — Tyr — Lys — Val — Thr — Cys — Ser — Val — Arg — Gln — Ser — Ser — Ala — **Asn** —
f_2 Ser — Arg — Ser — Gln — Ala — Tyr — Lys — Val — Thr — Cys — Ser — Val — Arg — Gln — Ser — Ser — Ala — **Gln** —

55 60 65 70
fr Asn — Arg — Lys — Tyr — Thr — **Val** — Lys — Val — Glu — Val — Pro — Lys — Val — Ala — Thr — Gln — **Val** — **Gln** —
f_2 Asn — Arg — Lys — Tyr — Thr — **Ile** — Lys — Val — Glu — Val — Pro — Lys — Val — Ala — Thr — Gln — **Thr** — **Val** —

75 80 85 90
fr Gly — Gly — Val — Glu — Leu — Pro — Val — Ala — Ala — Try — Arg — Ser — Tyr — **Met** — Asn — **Met** — Glu — Leu —
f_2 Gly — Gly — Val — Glu — Leu — Pro — Val — Ala — Ala — Try — Arg — Ser — Tyr — **Leu** — Asn — **Leu** — Gln — Leu —

95 100 105
fr Thr — Ile — Pro — **Val** — Phe — Ala — Thr — **Asx** — **Asp** — Asp — Cys — **Ala** — Leu — Ile — Val — Lys — Ala — **Leu** —
f_2 Thr — Ile — Pro — **Ile** — Phe — Ala — Thr — **Asn** — **Ser** — Asp — Cys — **Glu** — Leu — Ile — Val — Lys — Ala — **Met** —

110 115 120 125
fr Gln — Gly — **Thr** — **Phe** — Lys — **Thr** — Gly — **Ile** — **Ala** — **Pro** — **Asn** — **Thr** — Ala — Ile — Ala — Ala — Asn — Ser —
f_2 Gln — Gly — **Leu** — **Leu** — Lys — **Asp** — Gly — **Asn** — **Pro** — **Ile** — **Pro** — **Ser** — Ala — Ile — Ala — Ala — Asn — Ser —

129
fr Gly — Ile — Tyr —
f_2 Gly — Ile — Tyr —

FIG. 6. Amino acid sequence of fII (fr and f2) coat protein. Amino acids differing in the two coat proteins are written in bold type. From article by Wittmann-Liebold and Wittmann (1967).

ods, which are very useful for plant virus isolation (Bancroft, 1970), are not applicable for fII due to its higher stability. The best results were obtained by acetic acid degradation: in 67% cold acetic acid fII is depolymerized rapidly yielding soluble protein. The insoluble RNA can be spun down easily (Hohn, 1967; Sugiyama *et al.*, 1967). The protein originally consists of monomers as can be proved by comparison of its apparent molecular weight in the ultracentrifuge with the molecular weight calculated from the amino acid composition (Herrmann *et al.*, 1968). Minor amounts of A-protein (see earlier discussion) that originally are present are lost rapidly in the course of neutralization and storage of the protein mixture (Roberts and Steitz, 1967).

The degradation in 67% acetic acid is due to a concerted action of hydrogen ions and hydrophobic acetate (Schubert, 1969). The capsid is stable in both HCl of similar pH (1.8) as 67% acetic acid and in neutral acetate buffers of high ionic strength.

Studies of the circular dichroism (CD) of this acetic acid protein have been performed (Schubert, 1969). Three typical CD spectra exist (Fig. 7) corresponding to three protein conformations, each stable at certain acetic acid molarities. Conformation I, stable in 11 *M* (67%)

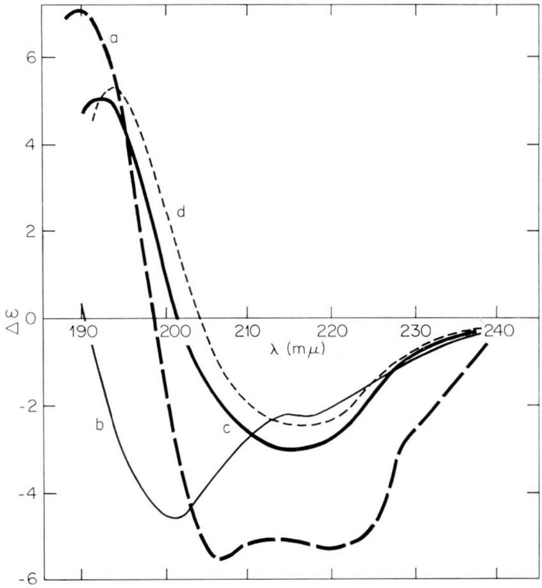

FIG. 7. Circular dichroism of fII protein. (Schubert, 1969). (a) In 11 *M* (67%) acetic acid; (b) in 3 *M* acetic acid; (c) in 0.01 *M* acetic acid; (d) in 0.02 *M* sodium phosphate buffer, pH 7.6.

acetic acid, is characterized by a high α-helix content. This conformation does not exist in hydrochloric acid of similar pH. Conformation II, stable between 3 and 0.3 *M* acetic acid (pH 2.2–2.8) and in HCl (pH 1.8–2.8), is probably a random coil. At pH 2.8 (acetic acid and hydrochloric acid) a sharp transition to conformation III exists, which has an estimated α-helix content of 25%. This conformation is not significantly changed upon further rise of pH to neutrality and by assembly of the capsid.

If acetic acid protein is neutralized, precipitation of the protein frequently occurs yielding amorphous aggregates. This might be due to false refolding of the protein. The precipitation can be avoided by very fast neutralization with a predetermined amount of 2.5 *M* tris, yielding a protein solution in tris-acetate buffer of high ionic strength (Hohn, 1967). Alternative methods are extensive dialysis of the protein against 10^{-3} *M* ice-cold acetic acid (Sugiyama *et al.*, 1967) or against quartz-distilled water prior to neutralization (Herrmann *et al.*, 1968). The two latter methods are preferable if large protein concentrations (up to 2 mg/ml) have to be handled. With the first method, precipitation still occurs frequently at protein concentrations of more than 100 μg/ml.

2. Coat Protein of Qβ (see *Note added in proof*)

The coat protein of Qβ is larger than that of fII. Its molecular weight is around 15,000 daltons (Overby *et al.*, 1966b; Garwes *et al.*, 1969). Its sequence is not yet determined, however, its amino acid composition is known (Overby *et al.*, 1966b). It is completely different from that of fII and lacks 3 amino acids, i.e., histidine, tryptophan, and methionine (Hung and Overby, 1969).

Qβ protein of good quality was prepared by degradation of Qβ in guanidinium-HCl and β-mercaptoethanol with subsequent centrifugation in a guanidinium-HCl gradient or by phenol extraction in the presence of SDS (Hung and Overby, 1969).

B. Minor Protein Components

1. Minor Protein Component of fII (A-Protein)

Studies of the defective particles synthesized by mutants in the A-cistron have revealed that the A-cistron product is in some way required for the infectivity of the phage (Lodish *et al.*, 1965; Heisenberg and Blessing, 1965). Using SDS-acrylamide gel electrophoresis of phage protein synthesized in actinomycin-treated cells and exploiting the fact that the major head protein does not contain histidine, the A-cistron product could be identified as a histidine-containing protein (Viñuela *et al.*, 1967; Nathans *et al.*, 1966) (Fig. 8). This protein is either absent or moves with altered mobility in extracts of nonpermissive cells infected with amber A-mutants. Later it was proved by gel electrophoresis of highly purified phage protein that the A-protein is part of the viable phage and absent in defective particles derived from amber A-mutants (Steitz, 1968a; Viñuela *et al.*, 1968; Herrmann, 1970). Most probably it is present only as a single copy in the bacteriophage. Its molecular weight was calculated from its amino acid composition and mobility in SDS-acrylamide electrophoresis as 37,500 ± 10% (Steitz, 1968b) and as 41,500 ± 3% (Herrmann, 1970). It is about three times as large as the coat protein.

The A-protein is highly insoluble in aqueous buffers and has, even in denaturing solvents, a high affinity to dialysis membrane and other surfaces. Due to these properties certain difficulties in the isolation and purification of A-protein arise that limit the methods and conditions

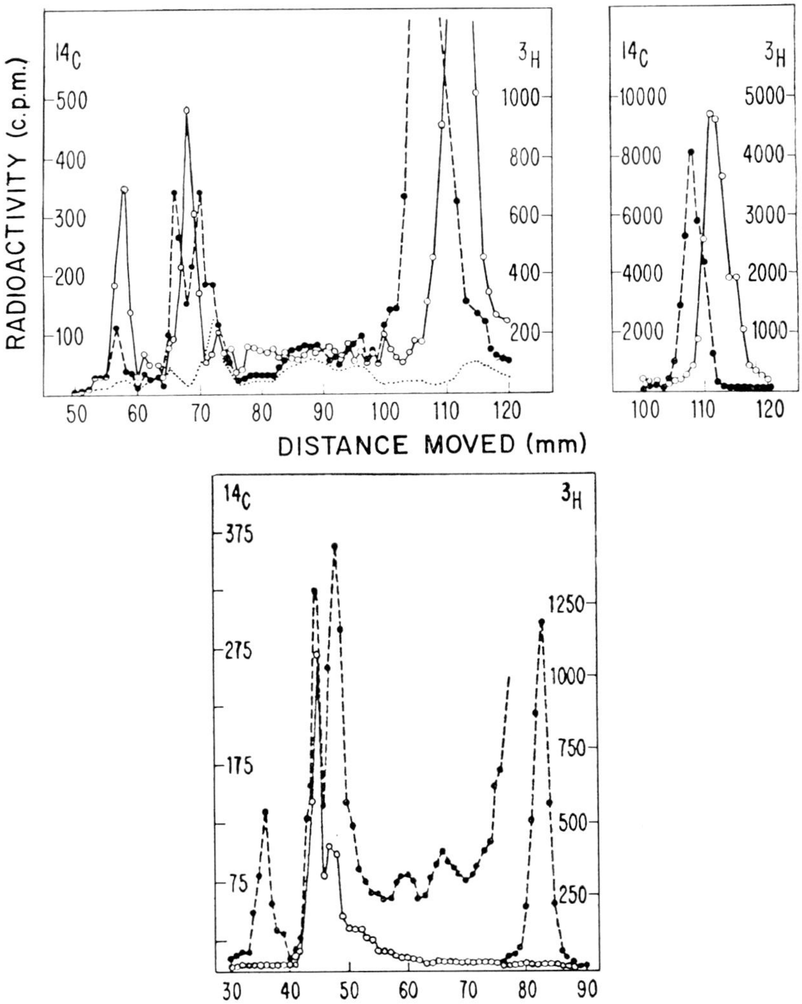

FIG. 8. Electrophoresis of fII and Qβ proteins in SDS-acrylamide gels. Top: Qβ protein (C^{14}-labeled, ●---●) co-electrophoresed with fII protein (^{3}H-labeled ○——○) as obtained from infected spheroblasts. Uninfected control (····). The peaks correspond from left to right to fII (Qβ) RNA replicase, fII A protein (Qβ minor proteins), fII (Qβ) coat protein. Bottom: Qβ virus proteins (histidine ^{3}H-labeled, ○——○) and Qβ proteins obtained from infected spheroblasts (leucine-^{14}C labeled, ●---●) coat protein peak in 20-fold reduction. (Garwes *et al.*, 1969).

of the isolation: a certain minimal amount of bacteriophage has to be used as A-protein source; certain conventional methods of protein extraction cannot be applied; denaturing solvents have to be used during all steps of the purification. Initial attempts to isolate A-protein by phenol extraction or by the acetic acid method were unsuccessful since A-protein invariably was almost totally lost during dialysis of the protein mixture against water or urea. The finally successful method for purifying A-protein consists of solubilizing 300 mg bacteriophage in 6 *M* guanidinium-HCl, dialyzing into 8 *M* urea, and chromatographing the mixture on cellulose phosphate. The A protein can be eluted from the column with a linear NaCl gradient and is dissolved in 8 *M* urea, 0.05 *M* tris-HCl, pH 8.5, and 0.2 *M* NaCl (Steitz, 1968a). Herrmann (1970) isolated A protein by preparative electrophoresis in SDS-acrylamide gels.

2. The Minor Protein Components of Qβ

Qβ has two minor phage protein components besides the main capsid protein. These were found as a double band in SDS-acrylamide gel electrophoresis of purified phage or of actinomycin-treated Qβ-infected bacterial cells in a position similar to A protein of fII (Garwes *et al.*, 1969) (Fig. 8). They contain histidine, tryptophan, and methionine, which are absent in the main coat protein. Their molecular weight, as calculated from their mobility in the electrophoretic gel, is 35,000 and 39,000 daltons. The two minor protein components contain histidine and tryptophan in different ratios, which makes it very unlikely that the one is only a slight modification of the other.

A mixture of the minor protein components was partially separated from the main capsid protein by centrifugation of the protein mixture obtained by the guanidinium-HCl method in a linear guanidinium-HCl gradient (3–20%) (Hung and Overby, 1969).

C. The RNA

1. Physical Properties

fII RNA is single stranded and has a molecular weight of $1.1 \pm 0.1 \times 10^6$ daltons (Gesteland and Boedtker, 1964; Mitra *et al.*, 1963; Strauss and Sinsheimer, 1963; Marvin and Hoffmann-Berling, 1963). Qβ-RNA has similar properties as fII RNA (Overby *et al.*, 1966b), but it may be slightly larger (Pollet *et al.*, 1967). Both RNA's have an unusual low radius of gyration and a large sedimentation constant (28 S for fII, slightly larger for Qβ), an indication of a very compact secondary structure. A helix content of about 70% was estimated for the isolated RNA and of about 80% for the RNA as packed into the capsid (Mitra *et al.*, 1963; Boedtker, 1967). In low salt (Gesteland and Boedtker, 1964) and in formaldehyde (Boedtker, 1968; Spahr *et al.*, 1969; Fenwick, 1968) the RNA extends to a more linear form and has a much lower sedimentation constant. Further indications for a highly compact structure of phage RNA came from sequence studies (see below).

2. Fragmentation

One consequence of the secondary structure of fII and Qβ RNA is that they are not degraded at random by limited nucleolytic attack (Overby *et al.*, 1966b; Fiers, 1967; Bassel and Spiegelmann, 1967; Erikson, 1968; Spahr and Gesteland, 1968; Spahr *et al.*, 1969; Hohn, 1969a,c; Adams *et al.*, 1969; Thatch and Boedtker, 1969). The first products of pancreatic RNase digestion are fragments sedimenting at 21, 15, 11, and 6 S. Similar fragments are isolated from aged bacteriophage preparations. The material in the 21 S region contains an intact 3′-terminus, the material in the 15 S region an intact 5′-terminus. Originally the 21 and 15 S material was assumed to contain one species of RNA each, two-thirds and one-third the length of the original RNA. Later Thatch and Boedtker (1969) showed that it consisted of several unique fragments that can be separated by gel electrophoresis. However, it was confirmed that the larger fragments contained the intact 3′-terminus.

The most specific fragmentation of fII RNA was achieved by digestion with RNase IV and yielded two fragments, a 60% fragment with an intact 3′-terminus and a 40% fragment with an intact 5′-terminus (Spahr and Gesteland, 1968; Spahr *et al.*, 1969). These fragments might be similar to some of the fII RNA fragments obtained by pancreatic ribonuclease. Partial Tl-RNase digestion of fII RNA also yielded a series of unique RNase fragments characterized by their electrophoretic mobility (Adams *et al.*, 1969).

3. Sequence (see *Note added in proof*)

Recently much progress was made in sequencing of phage RNA. A catalog of the fragments obtained by exhaustive digestion of fII RNA with pancreatic RNase is published (Thirion and Kaesberg, 1968, 1970; Min Jou and Fiers, 1969). Shorter and longer sequences of fII and Qβ RNA have been determined (Fig. 9 for references). A common feature of these known sequences (Fig. 9) is that simple loops can be constructed showing considerable base pairing (Fig. 10). Although some of the fragments analyzed were selected for their double strandedness, very probably further base-paired regions will be detected. They might provide

(a) 5′ p p p G G(G)U . . .

(b) 5′ p p p G G G(G)A C C C C C C U U U A G G G G G U C A C[(A C)(A C)(C U C)]A G C A G U A C U (10, 20, 30, 40)
U C A C U G A G U A U A A G A G G A C A U A U G C C U A A A U U A C C G C G U G (50, 60, 70, 80)
G U C U G C G U U U C G G A G C C G A U A A U G A A A U U C U U A A U G A U U U (90, 100, 110, 120)
U C A G G A G C U C U G G U U U C C A G A C C U(U)(U)(C)U A U C G A A U C U U C C (130, 140, 150, 160)
G A C A C G C A U C C C G U G G. . . . (170)

(c) . . . . py C C U A G G A G G U U U G A C C U A U G C G A G C U U U U A G U G. .
f Met Arg Ala Phe Ser

(d) . . py A G A G C C(C)U C A A C C G G G G U U U G A A G C A U G G C U U C U A A C U U U. . .
f Met Ala Ser Asn Phe

(e) (G)C A A A C U C C G G U A U C U A C U A A U A G A U G C C G
Ala Asn Ser Gly Ile Tyr Och Amb
(124) (129)
G C C A U U C A A A C A U G A G G A U U A C C C A U G U C G A A G A C A A C A A A G.
f Met Ser Lys Thr Thr Lys

(f) . . . py A A U U U G A U C A U G G C A A A A U U A G A G A C.. .
f Met Ala Lys Leu Glu Thr

(g) . C A U G G C G U U C G U A C U U A A A U A U G G A A U U A A C U A A U C C A A U U U U C
Ala Try Arg Ser Tyr Leu Asn Met Glu Leu Thr Ile Pro Ile Phe
(81) (90)
G C U A C G A A C U C C G. . .
Ala Thr Asn Ser Asp
(100)

(h) . . . G U U A C C A C C C A OH 3′

(i) . . . . . G C C C U C C U C U C U C C C A OH 3′

FIG. 9. Some partial sequences determined in fII- and Qβ-RNA. (a) 5′-Terminus of fII (de Wachter *et al.,* 1968; Glik, 1968); (b) 5′-terminus of Qβ (Billeter *et al.,* 1969); (c–e) ribosome attachment sites of fII (Steitz, 1969) for: coat protein (c), RNA replicase (d), A protein (e); (e) contains also the termination of the coat protein cistron (Nichols, 1970); (f) ribosome attachment site for the Qβ coat protein cistron (Hindley and Staples, 1969); (g) sequence corresponding to part of the fII coat protein (Adams *et al.,* 1969); (h) 3′-terminus of fII (Dahlberg, 1968; de Wachter and Fiers, 1967; Weith and Gilham, 1967); (i) 3′-terminus of Qβ (Dahlberg, 1968).

specific sites of recognition for enzymes, ribosomes and regulators as well as for the completed capsid. Short stretches of the 3′- and 5′-termini are complementary (Fig. 9) and might pair in the phage or at some stages of phage development (August *et al.,* 1969).

4. Phage RNA as Genome

fII-RNA codes for three known proteins, namely coat protein, A protein and RNA replicase (Horiuchi *et al.,* 1966; Gussin, 1966). These proteins have been identified by gel electrophoresis of infected *E. coli* cells (Sugiyama *et al.*, 1969) and of infected *E. Coli* cells treated with actinomycin or rifampicine (Nathans *et al.*, 1966; Viñuela *et al.*, 1968; Fromageot and Zinder, 1968). The three protein bands were coordinated with the three known genes with the help of amber mutants. The proteins were also found as products of an *in vitro* protein synthesizing system directed by fII-RNA (Capecchi, 1966; Eggen *et al.*, 1967;

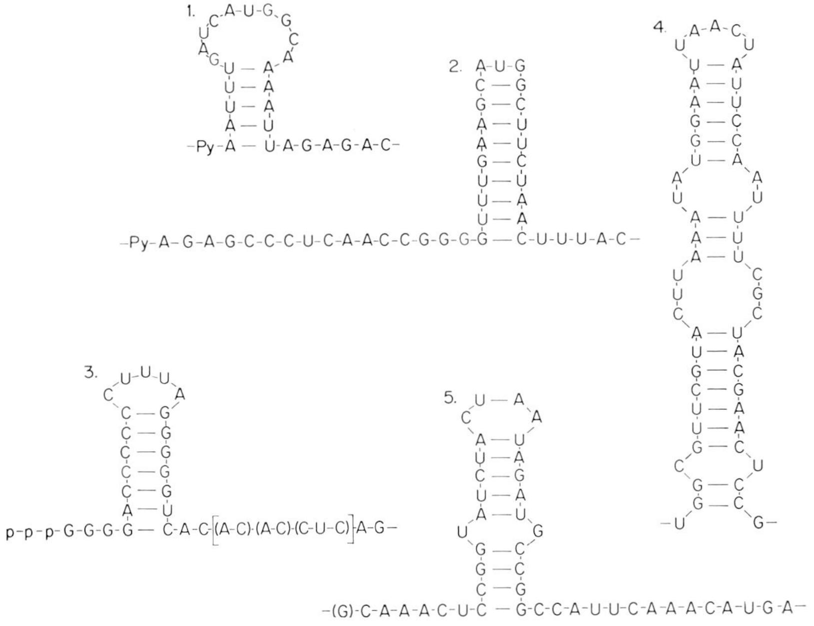

FIG. 10. Possible loop structures of some of the elucidated phage RNA sequences (Fig. 9). Ribosome attachment site for the coat protein cistron of Qβ (1) and of fII (2); 5′-terminus of Qβ (3); partial sequence of coat protein gene (4); termination of coat protein gene (5). (See Fig. 9 for references.)

Sugiyama and Nakada, 1968; Lodish and Robertson, 1969; Lodish, 1969). Qβ RNA has gene products similar to fII RNA, however one additional protein exists in the phage whose function is still unknown (Garwes *et al.*, 1969).

The order of the phage genes could not be determined genetically, since recombination between phage RNA's have not been observed and handled. Attempts to determine the gene order have therefore been made by biochemical techniques and have resulted in the order: A protein —coat protein—RNA replicase (5′ → 3′) (Jeppesen *et al.*, 1970): They located (1) specific oligonucleotides corresponding to amino acid se-

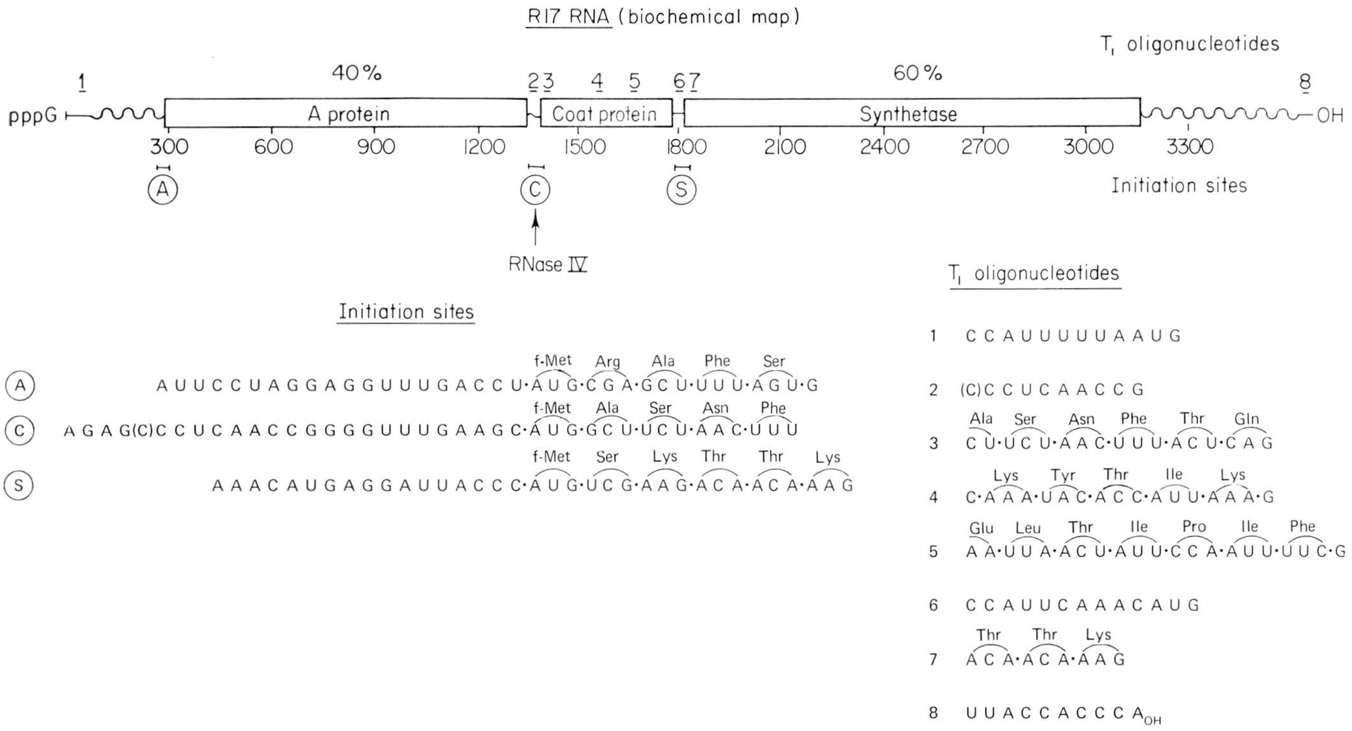

FIG. 11. Gene order of fII determined by locating 8 specific oligonucleotides (1–8) and the three ribosome iniation sites (A, C, S) on either the 40- or the 60%-fragment of fII-RNA obtained by RNase IV cleavage (from Jeppesen *et al.*, 1970).

quences in the coat protein and the RNA replicase, (2) other oligonucleotides corresponding to the 3′- and 5′-termini and initiation regions of the fII RNA, (3) the 3′ ribosome initiation sites—to either the 40%- or the 60%-fII RNA fragment obtained by RNase IV cleavage (Fig. 11). This result is supported by studies on the messenger activity of the phage RNA fragments obtained by limited nucleolytic attack (p. 61): The 60% (3′) fragment of fII RNA directs the synthesis of RNA replicase (Lodish, 1968a; Spahr and Gesteland, 1968). The 40% (5′) fragment, more active with *B. stearothermophilus* ribosomes instead of *E. coli* ribosomes (Lodish, 1969) directs the synthesis of the A protein (Lodish and Gesteland, unpublished).

Another fragment of fII-RNA derived from fluorouracil containing defective particles, having two-thirds of the size of fII RNA and containing the intact 5′ end, was found to direct coat protein synthesis and not RNA replicase synthesis.

On the other hand, Engelhardt *et al.* (1968) found that the fII replicative intermediate (R.I.) codes mainly for coat protein. Since it consists of a double strand and a single stranded "tail" which was estimated to contain 25% of the fII RNA with an intact 5′ terminus (Robertson and Zinder, 1969), it was concluded that the coat protein gene is nearest the 5′-RNA terminus. It might well be, however, that the single stranded region is longer than expected and therefore contains the A-protein as well as the coat protein cistron. The gene order of Qβ is probably similar to that of fII (except for the possible fourth gene): RNA-replicase and coat protein is coded by the 60% (3′) fragment of Qβ RNA (Bassel, 1968); the coat protein cistron is localized between the 1000th and the 1400th nucleotide of the 5′ end (Hindley, Billeter, and Weissmann, unpublished). It has been shown that the primary attachment site for ribosomes on Qβ and fII RNA is immediately to the left of the coat protein cistron (Bassel, 1968; Lodish, 1968a; Steitz, 1969). In the established gene sequence this site is in the middle of the RNA strand and a folding of the RNA has to be proposed that maintains a loop with the attachment site easily accessible.

5. *Isolation*

Phenol extraction (e.g., see Hoffmann-Berling *et al.*, 1963; Sugiyama, 1966) yields an RNA appropriate for self-assembly experiments. Alternative methods are SDS dissociation of the phage followed by sucrose gradient centrifugation (Knolle, unpublished, using a general procedure described by Noll and Stutz, 1968) and phenol extraction in the presence of SDS, followed by DEAE-cellulose chromatography (Hung, 1969). Final purification is best performed by sucrose gradient centrifugation. To obtain intact RNA in good yield a number of precautions against nucleolytic attack are advisable, i.e., the use of a bacterial host deficient in cell wall ribonuclease (Dürwald and Hoffmann-Berling, 1968), heat sterilized glassware, specially treated dialysis tubing and plasticware (Heisenberg, 1966), and RNase-free sucrose.

IV. *In Vitro* Self-Assembly

A. *Self-Assembly of Particles Lacking A-Protein (Defective Particles)*

1. *fII*

The first reconstitution of the fII capsid was performed using coat protein isolated by the acetic acid method and phage RNA isolated by phenol extraction (Hohn, 1967; Sugiyama *et al.*, 1967). The main problems were the readjustment of pH and ionic strength without losing the protein by irreversible precipitation and the timing of the RNA addition. This was overcome in two different ways. Sugiyama *et al.* (1967) dialyzed the protein against 10^{-3} M ice-cold acetic acid, then added 1 mole of RNA per 46 moles of protein subunit, adjusted to 0.15 *M* buffered saline, and incubated for several hours at 37°C. Hohn (1967) neutralized the protein solution with a predetermined amount of ice-cold tris, added 1 mole of RNA per 200 moles coat protein subunit, and dialyzed against 0.15 *M* buffered saline. Sugiyama's method is preferable because it allows the handling of larger concentrations of protein. However, it is not necessary to incubate the mixture at all.

The major products of these reconstitution experiments are particles of size and general electron microscopic appearance similar to the phage (Fig. 12a). The subunits of these particles are arranged in icosahedral ($T = 3$) symmetry (Fig. 13). If properly shielded from RNase, they band at the same CsCl density (1.43 gm/ml) as the phage and contain a normal amount of RNA. However, they do not adsorb to bacteria and only one out of 10^7 particles is infective. They sediment somewhat slower than the bacteriophage, i.e., at 70 instead of 80 S (Fig. 19). Part of the RNA is susceptible to RNase yielding particles of lower CsCl density (1.39 gm/ml). These digested particles contain only about 70% of the original RNA and sediment in a broad peak around 74 S between phage and the undigested particle. In all these properties the defective particles obtained *in vitro* very much resemble the defective particles obtained by amber A-mutants *in vivo*. It was therefore argued that the same A-protein is missing in both types of particles.

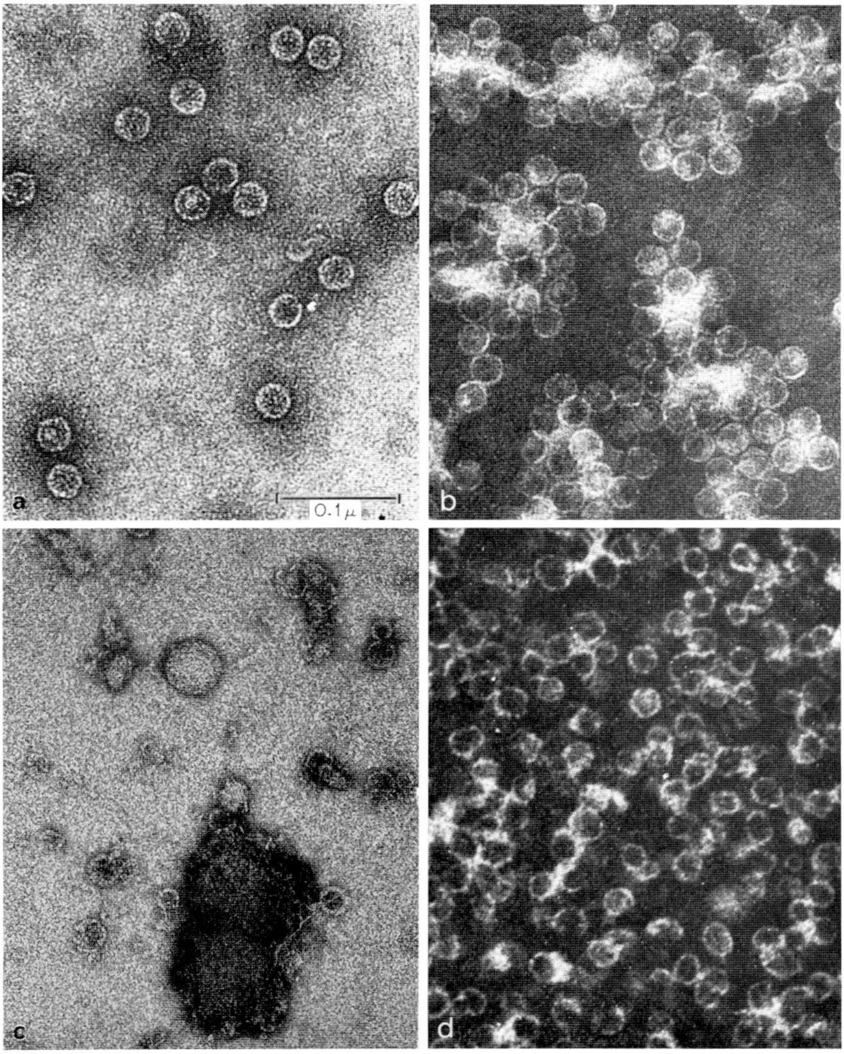

FIG. 12. Negative stainings (uranyl acetate) of phagelike particles obtained by self-assembly of fII coat protein with fII-RNA (a, b, and c) and of Qβ coat protein with Qβ RNA (d). (a) Small excess of RNA in assembly mixture; (b) excess amount of coat protein in assembly mixture; (c) particles of unusual size. Figure 12d was kindly supplied by P. P. Hung and L. R. Overby.

Besides the 70 S particles, some material sedimenting at 80 S was observed, especially if the coat protein was in excess (Hohn, 1969a). In the electron microscope this 80 S material was seen as clustered groups of particles (Fig. 12b). In some experiments particles with a

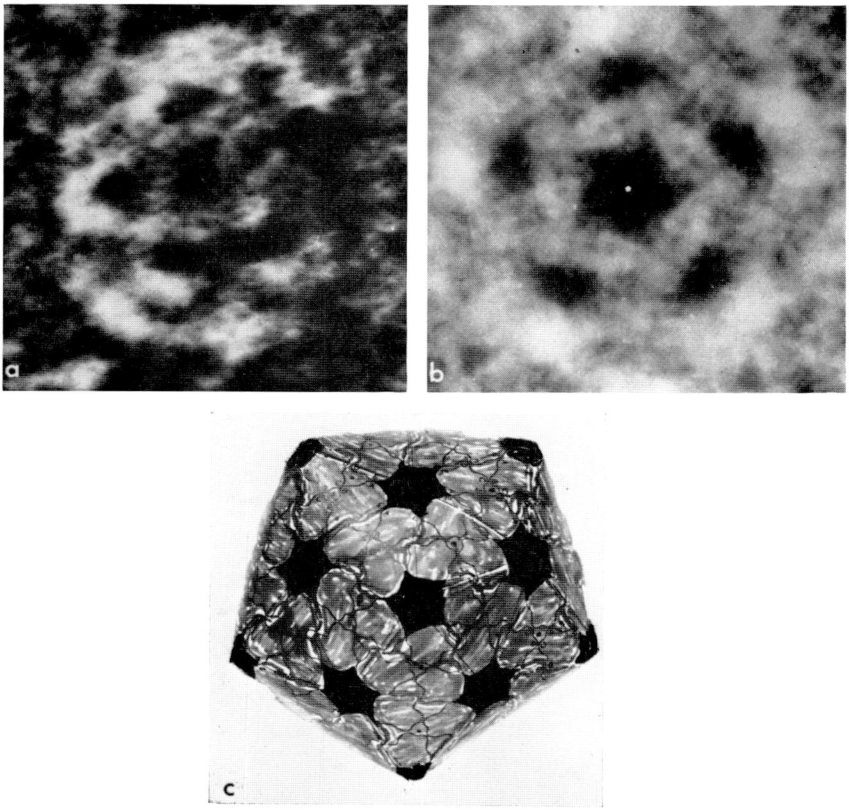

FIG. 13. Selected image of fII phagelike particle revealing icosahedral ($T = 3$) symmetry. (a) Positive print; (b) multiple exposure (Markham, 1963; Galton, 1878) of (a); (c) model showing asymmetric subunits of an $T = 3$ icosahedron that cluster in trimers.

lower sedimentation rate (50–60 S) (Fig. 19) were found besides or instead of the 70 S particles (unpublished). These particles contain RNA, appear phagelike, and do not adsorb to the host. They might be related to the RNase-sensitive particles described earlier. No further study was done on them. In addition to these particles, a few smaller and larger particles, probably of different triangulation number, and tubular structures were observed electron microscopically in crude lysates (Fig. 12c).

Mg^{2+} is not needed for the production of defective particles, in fact EDTA can be present. The ionic strength of the reaction mixture can be varied. Phagelike particles are also obtained in a buffer of one-tenth the usual ionic strength (0.015 *M* buffered saline; Hohn, 1969b), but not in a buffer of a tenfold ionic strength (1.5 *M* buffered saline). The reconstitution can be performed at 4° with the same efficiency as at 37°C. A normal yield of particles is already obtained minutes after the mixing of protein and RNA (Hohn, 1969b) (Fig. 17).

The formation of fII-defective particles was also observed in an *in vitro* protein synthesizing system of uninfected *E. coli* directed by fII RNA as well as in a similar system including an S30 extract of infected cells. In the first case particles are made *de novo,* in the second case certain precursors are completed (Knolle, 1969; see also p. 53).

2. Qβ

Qβ-defective particles were reconstituted *in vitro* using Qβ protein obtained by the guanidinium-HCl method and Qβ RNA obtained by phenol extraction. A mixture of the protein and RNA in a molar ratio of 18:1 dissolved in guanidinium-HCl was dialyzed in the cold against tris buffer containing KCl and $MgCl_2$. Defective particles similar in most of their properties to the ones in the fII system were obtained (Hung and Overby, 1969). These defective particles have dimensions similar to the viable Qβ phage, although smaller, larger, and distorted particles were observed more frequently (Fig. 12d). Qβ-defective particles sediment slower than Qβ, i.e., at 70 S compared with 84 S for the viable phage, and they band in CsCl density gradients at the same density as the phage (1.43 gm/ml). About 50% of the RNA sedimenting with the particles can be digested with nucleolytic enzymes. It was, however, not yet shown whether digested particles are approximately homogenous in RNA content or whether the RNA of some has been digested totally and of some of it not at all.

The Qβ-defective particles had antigenic determinates very similar to those of the authentic phage, although their affinity for Qβ-antiserum was about 8 times lower than the affinity of Qβ.

3. *The Role of RNA in the Reconstitution of Defective Particles*

Using the conditions described in the last sections, defective particles were only obtained in the presence of RNA. The function of RNA can be discussed in terms of "catalytic" activity (catalytic in a very broad sense of the word), enhancing the formation of a quarternary structure. The "catalyst"-product complex in this case is not dissociated, although the product is stable without RNA. The specificity of this catalytic activity was studied by testing a number of different RNA's (Hohn,

1969a; Table II). It can be seen that phagelike particles are formed with RNA of various origins and lengths. Several fII RNA fragments, plant virus RNA, Qβ RNA, and even polyuridylic acid and polyvinyl sulfate proved to be active in inducing the formation of particles in size and appearance similar to fII. RNAs smaller than 20 nucleotides were inactive, however. The varying length of RNA did not significantly influence the size of particles obtained. If shorter fragments were used, more than one RNA strand was packed into a capsid. The double-sized TMV and TYMV RNA could be shared by two growing capsids so that a high proportion of "twinned" and "tailed" particles was synthesized (Fig. 14). Occasionally somewhat larger shells corresponding to a triangulation number $T = 4$ were observed. Polyuridylic acid and some of the smaller fragments were able to escape the established capsid leaving empty shells (Fig. 15b) with a buoyant density characteristic of protein alone and a sedimentation constant characteristic for empty shells obtained by phage degradation (Table I). It is interesting that all assembled RNA-containing particles were digested by ribonuclease yielding light particles with a buoyant density of 1.38 ± 0.01 gm/ml. This corresponds to an RNA amount (70%) that might be bound to the capsid particularly efficiently. Thirty percent of phage RNA might be under a certain overpressure and can easily be released if a capsid is not perfect.

The only property in common to all the RNA's that induce formation is a certain minimal chain length and the sugar-phosphate backbone, or better, since polyvinyl sulfate is active too, a certain pattern of negative charges. It is reasonable that this repeating structure is the site for attachment to the protein rather than the base sequence which carries the genetic message and cannot have any simple repeat.

B. Self-Assembly of Infectious Particles

In the assembly systems described in the last sections, usually a very low number of infective particles (10^{-8} to 10^{-7} per input RNA) was observed. A new method of isolation of A protein by a guanidinium-HCl method (mentioned earlier) permitted its use in sufficient quantities as a third component of the assembly system. If the components were mixed together in 5.7 *M* urea and dialyzed against buffered saline, a several hundredfold increase of infectivity was observed (Roberts and Steitz, 1967).

In these experiments the bulk of particles are defective particles similar to the ones obtained in the absence of A-protein. These defective particles sediment at 70 S while the infectious particles sediment at 80 S with a shoulder at 70 S (Fig. 16). Most of the infectious particles are

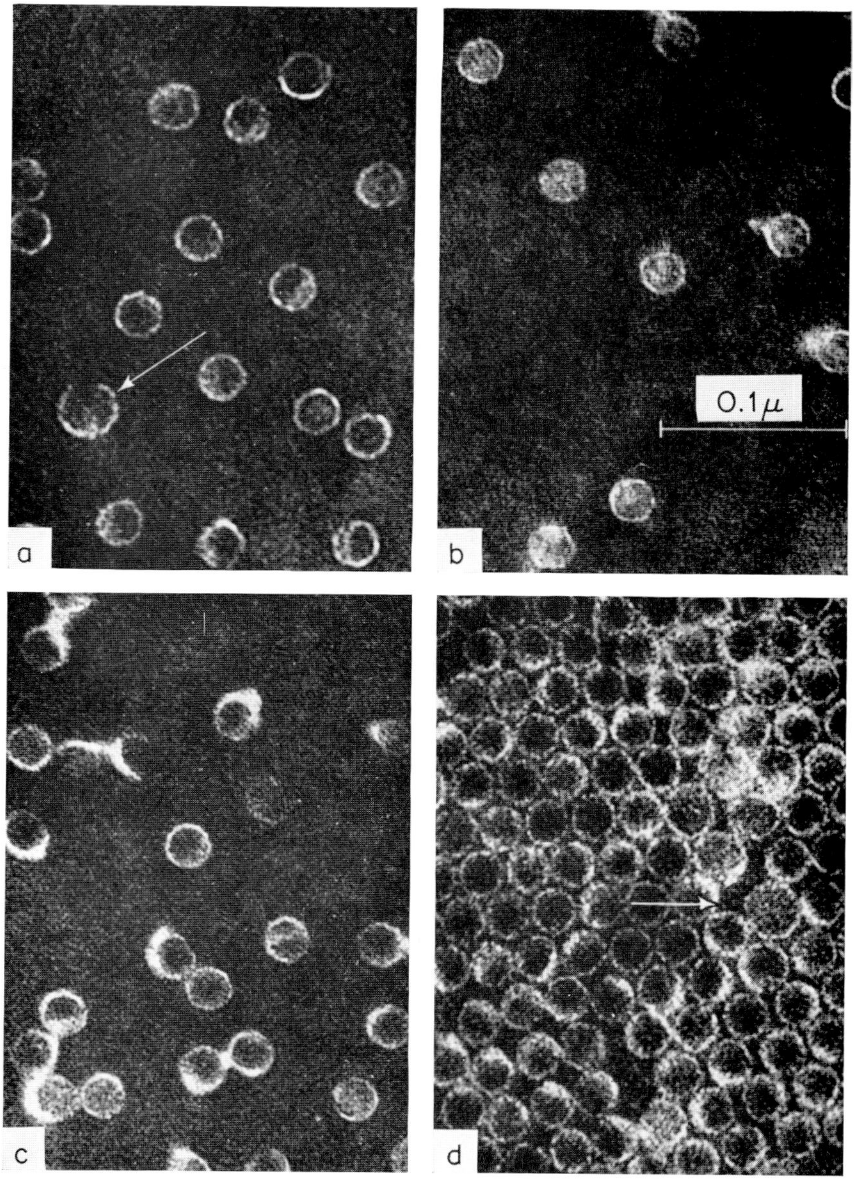

FIG. 14. Phagelike particles containing TYMV-RNA. In an assembly mixture including fII coat protein and TYMV-RNA particles banded in a wide range of CsCl density. Particles of buoyant density 1.52 (a); 1.46 (b); 1.43 (c); and 1.39 (d). Note "tailed" (b), "twinned" (c) and larger particles (arrows). Negative staining with uranyl acetate (Hohn, 1969a).

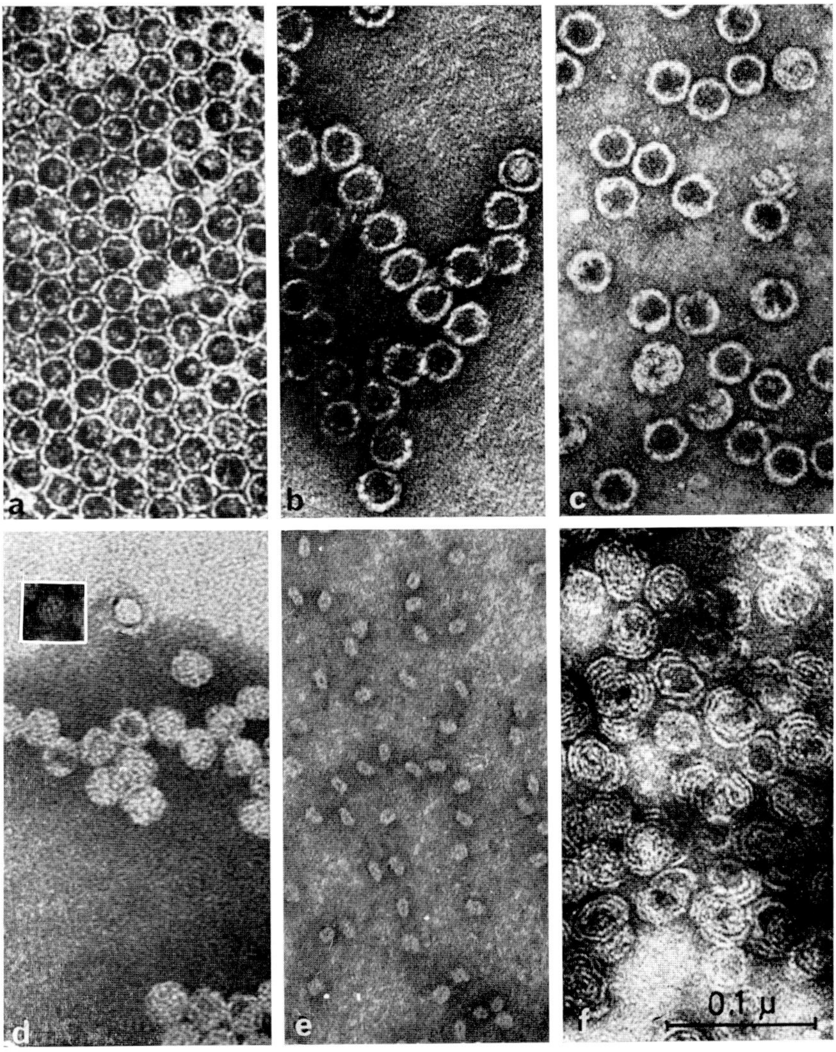

FIG. 15. Phage derivatives consisting only of protein. (a) Empty shells obtained by phage freezing and thawing followed by RNase digestion; mixed with some intact phage; (b) empty shells obtained by self-assembly in the presence of polyuridylic acid; (c) empty shells obtained from 11 S particles in the absence of RNA; (d) protein particles (double shells?) obtained by self-assembly in the absence of RNA; in the left upper corner two smaller particles, probably $T = 1$ (e) 11 S particles; (f) multishells obtained by self-assembly in the absence of RNA and at low pH. [(c) and (e) from Zelazo and Haschemeyer (1969, 1970); (f) from Schubert and Franck (1970a, b).]

TABLE I
fII PHAGE DERIVATIVES

	s_{20}[b]	ρ_{CsCl}[b]	RNA content % of normal	A protein	RNase stable	Infective	Adsorb to bacteria	Source
Particles obtained *in vivo*								
Bacteriophage	80	1.43	100	+	+	+	+	
RNase-sensitive particle	45–65[a]	1.43	100	+	−	(+)	+	Various
5-FU particle	Similar to phage	1.39	65	+		−	(+)	Phage growth in 5-FU
L particles		c	100	+	+	(+)		
Defective particle	68	1.43	100	−	−	−	−	Mutants in A gene
Light-defective particle	74	1.39	70	−	+	−	−	RNase treatment of defective particle
Empty shell	50 (41–43)	1.29	<5	−?	+	−	−	RNase treatment of RNase-sensitive particle; Alkali treatment of phage
Nearly empty shell			20	−?	+	−	−	RNase treatment of RNase-sensitive particle
Particles obtained *in vitro*								
Infectious particles	80	1.43	100	+	+	+	+	Self-assembly in presence of A protein
	80	1.43	100	+	−	+	+	
	70	1.43	100	+	−	+	+	
Defective particles	70	1.43	100	−	−	−	−	Self-assembly in absence of A protein
	80			−	−	−	−	
	50	1.43	100	−	−	−	−	
Light-defective particles		1.39	70	−	+	−	−	RNase treatment of above.
Abnormal particles				−		−	−	Self-assembly
Heterogeneous particles	See Table II							
Empty shells	50 (38)	1.29	0	−	+	−	−	Assembly with polyuridylic acid or in absence of RNA at pH 4
Protein particles	68 (55)	1.29	0	−	+	−	−	Assembly in absence of RNA at pH 7
Multishells			0	−	+	−	−	Assembly in absence of RNA at low pH
11 S Particles	11		0	−	−	−	−	Phage degradation
5.5 S Particles	5.5		0	−	+	−	−	

[a] Low values in 0.015 M NaCl; high values in 0.15 M NaCl.

[b] s_{20} and ρ_{CsCl} values, as published by different authors, vary for some types of particles. They were chosen to provide the best comparison between the types of particles. In most cases s_{20} values were derived from sucrose gradient centrifugation using phage as a standard. This might give too high a value for particles consisting only of protein. s_{20} values of those particles obtained by direct measurement in the analytical centrifuge are given in parentheses.

[c] ρ_{CsCl} 1.44 as compared with ρ_{CsCl} = 1.46 for the phage.

sensitive to RNase, especially the ones sedimenting with the 70 S shoulder. This indicates that they have some imperfections in comparison with the phage obtained *in vivo*.

Herrmann (1970) synthesized infectious particles by a similar self-assembly process using "A protein" obtained by preparative SDS-acrylamide electrophoresis. The yield of infectious particles was low, however, probably due to some residual SDS that could not be removed. Herrmann (1970) also studied the effect of sequence of component addition on the yield of infectious particles. Infectivity was obtained if A protein was added to RNA prior to coat protein and simultaneously with coat protein and if A protein was added to complex I

TABLE II

ABILITY OF RNA'S AND RNA ANALOGS TO FORM PARTICLES AND COMPLEX I WITH fII COAT PROTEIN

Input RNA		Particle formation					Complex I or Ia formation
Type	Approx. chain length	±	ρCsCl	ρCsCl after RNase digestion	s_{20}	EM	
fII 28 S	3000	+	1.43	1.39	70	Phagelike	+
fII 18 S	2000	+	1.39	1.39	72	Phagelike	+
fII 11 S	1000	+	1.37	1.37	72	Phagelike	+
fII 6 S	300–500	+	1.37	1.37	72	Phagelike	+
fII RNase digest	Mainly 1, 2, 3	−					
fII RNase core	10	−					
Qβ	3300	+	1.44	1.39	70	Phagelike	−
TMV	6000	+	1.39–1.52	1.38	70–100	Many "twins" and	−
TYMV	6000	+	1.38–1.52	1.38	70–100	"tailed" particles	−
tRNA	100						−
rRNA							−
Poly U	300	+	1.29	1.29	40–50	Empty shell	−
Oligo U	20	−					
Poly A							−
Heparin	150	−					
Polyvinyl sulfate	500	+			70	Phagelike	
fII R.I.	3000 (Partially double strand)	+		1.29	50–70	Phagelike, some connected	+
fII Double strand	3000 (Double strand)	−					

(p. 79) prior to coat protein. No infectivity could be obtained by adding A protein to preformed defective particles.

Infectious particles of Qβ could be obtained by self-assembly of Qβ RNA, Qβ coat protein, and a concentrate of minor Qβ protein (Hung and Overby, 1969). In that case,a linear response of PFU as a function of added A protein was observed. All infectious Qβ particles sedimented at the position of viable phage. Most of the infectivity was lost upon RNase digestion.

The reconstitution of infectious fII particles as well as of infectious Qβ particles was enhanced by the presence of divalent cations. The addition of 1% β-mercaptoethanol enlarged the yield of infectivity in the fII system and deteriorated the yield in the $Q\beta$ system (Roberts and Steitz, 1967; Hung and Overby, 1969). The overall yield in infectivity is still low in both the fII and $Q\beta$ systems: 2×10^{-6} RNA molecules per input RNA or less are converted into infectious particles. There might be several reasons for the low yield: (*1*) The components of the assembly system may be partially inactive due to the harsh treatment they had suffered during their isolation. The participation of slightly damaged components could account for the RNase sensitivity of some of the infectious particles. The A protein especially seems

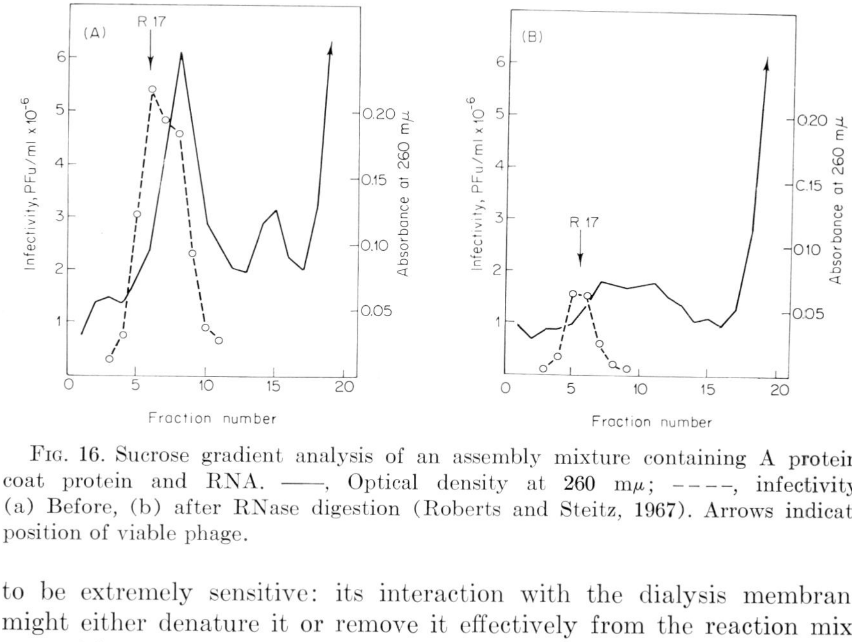

FIG. 16. Sucrose gradient analysis of an assembly mixture containing A protein, coat protein and RNA. ——, Optical density at 260 mμ; ----, infectivity. (a) Before, (b) after RNase digestion (Roberts and Steitz, 1967). Arrows indicate position of viable phage.

to be extremely sensitive: its interaction with the dialysis membrane might either denature it or remove it effectively from the reaction mixture. (*2*) Part of the RNA might have been damaged by nucleolytic attack by contaminating enzymes. In fact, Hung and Overby (1969) observed a 1000-fold decrease of infectivity in a spheroblast system of the RNA that has gone through an assembly experiment. (*3*) Low molecular cofactors of the system might be missing. (*4*) A correct folding of either RNA or protein might be performed with higher efficiency in the viable cell than *in vitro*. (*5*) It is entirely possible that *in vivo* the synthesis of RNA and protein and their combination are simultaneous processes that guarantee the correct RNA folding and packaging. As a matter of fairness, one has to point out that 90% of the particles produced *in vivo* are noninfectious.

Both in TMV and in the small icosahedral plant viruses described in the accompanying review (Bancroft, 1970), the infectivity restored in *in vitro* reconstitution experiments is of the same order of magnitude as the infectivity of the *in vivo* produced phage. Small icosahedral plant viruses, however, consist only of two components (RNA and coat protein) and a sophisticated infection process is unlikely. The penetration of a thick plant cell wall is much more difficult than the penetration of a bacterial cell wall, and it is likely that plant viruses enter only damaged cells. Therefore unshielded icosahedral plant virus RNA is nearly as successful in plant infection as the virus itself and it is conceivable that a minor incorrectness in the virus capsid that would prevent the infection process of fII or Qβ does not impair the infection process of the plant viruses.

C. Self-Assembly of Particles Lacking RNA (See *Note added in Proof*)

Although the assembly of phagelike particles as discussed in the last sections depends strictly on the presence of RNA, conditions were found which in the absence of RNA premitted the assembly of protein particles (Herrmann *et al.*, 1968; Hohn, 1969b; Rohrmann and Krueger, 1970a) and of empty shells (Zelazo and Haschemeyer, 1970). The "protein particles" are spherical in shape, have a size similar to the one of the phage, and sediment at 68 S. They co-electrophorese with viable phage, indicating a similar surface charge, and have similar antigenic properties (Herrmann, 1970).

"Protein particles" are obtained at a lower rate than RNA-containing defective particles (Fig. 17), within a smaller range of ionic strength (i.e., at low ionic strength; Fig. 18), and at higher (but not too high) protein concentrations (Herrmann, 1970). The "protein particles" are considerably different from the "empty shells" obtained by phage degradation (p. 54) or self-assembly in the presence of polyuridylic acid (p. 70). Their sedimentation constant is high (68 as compared with 50 S of the empty shell) and they are not penetrated by negative stain (Fig. 15d), to an even lesser extent than the phage. Most of the "protein particles" have a diameter of 260 $\pm$ 10 Å, however 2% of the particles have a diameter of 160 $\pm$ 10 Å (Fig. 15d) which would fit into a $T = 1$ icosahedral surface lattice. It might well be that these *small particles*, although not very stable, serve as a mold for the formation of the $T = 3$ icosahedral shell, resulting in particles in which the small icosahedral shell is surrounded by the large one. For such a structure, the low penetration with negative stain would become explainable. It would have a total of 240 protein subunits and a molecular weight of 3.3 $\times 10^6$ daltons. The theoretical sedimentaion constant calculated for

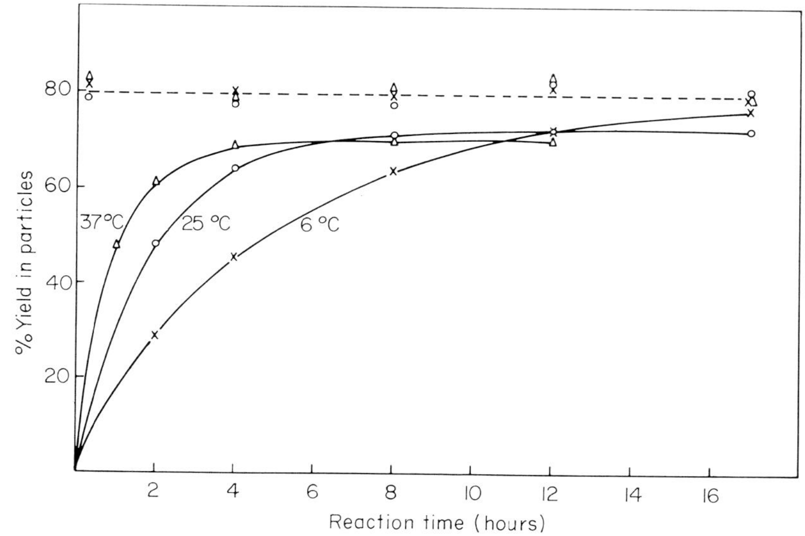

FIG. 17. Kinetics of the self assembly of fII defective particles and fII protein particles. ----, Defective particles in the presence of RNA; ——, protein particles in the absence of RNA; × at 4°, ○ at 25°, △ at 37°C. Yield is defined as the percentage of protein in sucrose gradients sedimenting between 50 and 80 S (Hohn, 1969b).

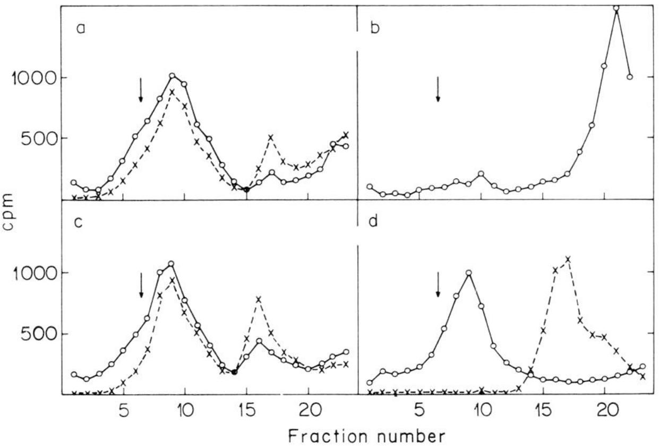

FIG. 18. Sucrose gradient analysis of assembly mixtures with (a, c) and without (b, d) RNA. Assembly was performed in 0.15 *M* buffered saline (a, b) and in 0.015 *M* buffered saline (c, d). Protein as radioactivity of ^{35}S (○——○), RNA as radioactivity of ^{32}P (×---×). Arrows indicate position of viable phage (Hohn, 1969b).

this structure by the Svedberg equation is in good agreement with the high sedimentation constant of 68 S actually found (Hohn, 1969b).

There is, however, also another explanation possible for the particle's high sedimentation constant and low stain penetration in comparison with the empty shell. The empty shell might be incomplete due to removal of some of the coat protein subunits, thus having a lower molecular weight and hence a lower sedimentation constant. The "protein particle," on the other hand, might be so densely packed that the negative stain is excluded (Herrmann, 1970).

Protein particles are formed at a pH range from less than 4.5 to 10.5. At a lower pH "multishells" are observed (Fig. 15f) (Herrmann, 1970; Schubert and Franck, 1970a,b).

The 11 S particles mentioned in Section II, C which are assumed to consist of 6 × 3 protein subunits can be used for the reconstitution of empty shells. If they are dialyzed at 4°C against pH 4 buffer they are further degraded to 5.5 S material. Upon dialysis at 24–34°C against the same buffer, however, empty shells are formed (Zelazo and Haschemeyer, 1970). At higher pH, protein particles similar to those mentioned in the previous section are assembled.

The empty shells sediment sharply at 37 S and are stable in neutral buffers. They are indistinguishable from the empty shells obtained by phage degradation with respect to electrophoretic mobility and electron microscopic appearance. It is not yet clear whether in this assembly system the 18 S particles are used directly or whether first 5.5 S subunits are formed. In any case, this system confirms clearly that the information required for the capsid's quaternary structure resides ultimately in the structure of the subunit.

V. Precursors in Phage Assembly

A. Models of Assembly Pathways

The RNA bacteriophage as a complex of 180 components obviously cannot be formed in one single step. Intermediates in the phage assembly and a pathway connecting them must exist. Since they are less stable than the complicated phage particles, they are difficult to detect. Three pathways of assembly could be imagined:

(*1*) The protein molecules first react with each other forming originally loosely bound protein aggregates that end up in an empty shell, which in a final step is filled with RNA (empty shell model).

(*2*) Free RNA has roughly the size and shape of the RNA as it exists inside the capsid. Around this mold the protein subunits assemble and form the capsid (mold model).

(3) The RNA reacts with a few protein subunits and forms an initiation complex. RNA condensation occurs either during this step or in the subsequent aggregation of additional subunits that yields the capsid (initiation complex model).

The correct model also has to be specific about the form of RNA used (free single-stranded RNA or RNA in the process of its synthesis), the possibility of subassembly of protein subunits, and the role of the A-protein in the assembly process. The A-protein could either act early in phage assembly participating in the condensation of RNA or late in phage assembly reacting with the finished capsid.

The empty shell model was suggested by Herrmann *et al.* (1968) following the successful reconstitution of phagelike particles in the absence of RNA (see Section IV,C). However, even in conditions favorable for protein particle formation the assembly process is drastically accelerated by the presence of RNA (leading to RNA-containing defective particles). The protein particles, once formed, cannot be chased into RNA-containing defective particles since they probably contain additional coat protein subunits as core (Hohn, 1969b; Herrmann, 1970). *In vitro* formation of empty shells has also been shown but at lower than physiological pH (Zelazo and Haschemeyer, 1970). It has not yet been studied whether these empty shells can incorporate RNA.

The catalytic activity of RNA in particle formation at neutral pH makes the empty shell model unlikely. The lack of specificity of the catalytic activity of RNA for particle formation with regard to the size and base composition of the RNA (see Section IV,A,3) rules out the mold model since equal molds of the different RNA species used are unlikely. Consistent with the initiation model would be the existence of complexes consisting of a few protein subunits and one RNA strand. Complexes of this type have indeed been observed and are described in the following section.

B. Complex I and Initiation Complexes

A complex of a few protein subunits per fII RNA was first observed by Capecchi and Gussin (1965) as newly *in vitro* synthesized protein subunits cosedimenting with RNA. Sugiyama *et al.* (1967) found a similar complex (named complex I) in their assembly system at low protein/RNA ratios and suggested its function as a modulated messenger (see below). Hohn (1969a) studied the products of self-assembly as a function of the molar protein/RNA input ratio. At high ratios (e.g., 200:1) predominantly defective particles are formed; at low ratios (e.g., 6:1) predominantly complex I is formed. At intermediate ratios a mixture of particles and complex I is obtained rather than new complexes of intermediate protein content (Fig. 19). Similarly Kaerner (1970) could observe complex I and particles *in vivo*, however, no complexes of an intermediate protein content. A saturation curve (Fig. 20) revealed that a maximum of 6 protein subunits can be bound to RNA in complex I (Eggen and Nathans, 1969). Spahr *et al.* (1969) found binding of 6 protein subunits in buffers containing Na^+ and the binding of only one coat

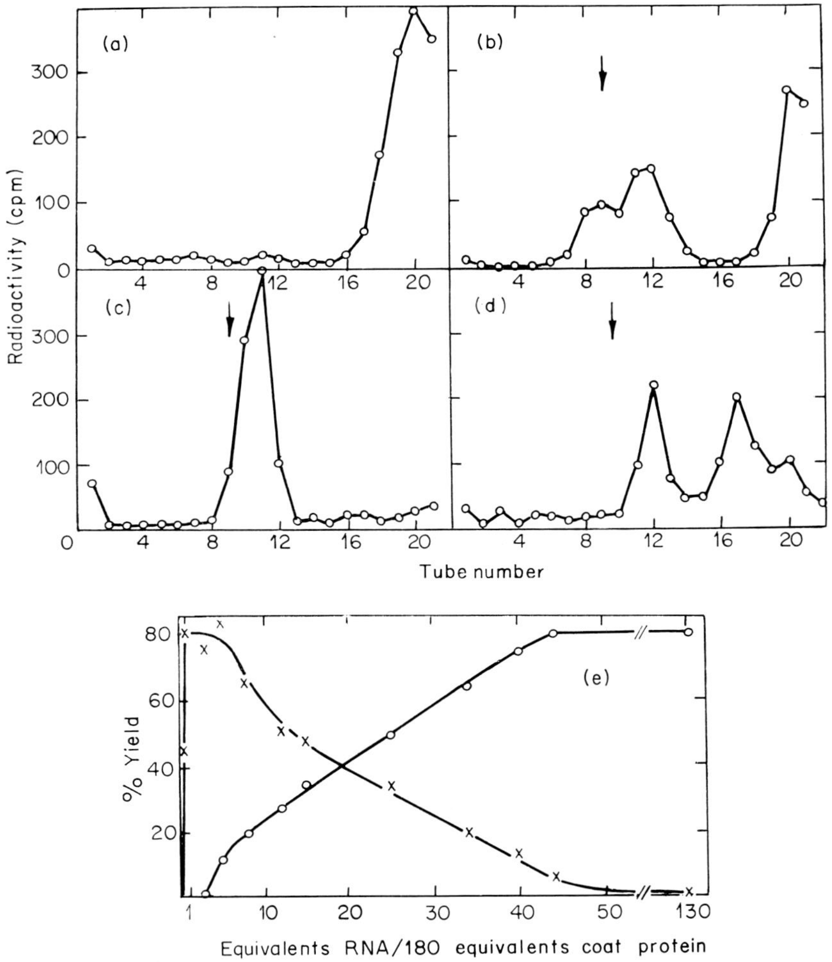

FIG. 19. Sucrose gradient analysis of assembly mixtures containing different molar RNA/protein input ratios (a = 0/180; b = 0.5/180; c = 2/180; d = 20/180). In Fig. 18d a considerable amount of complex I is formed (fraction 17). Data from these and other sucrose gradients are summarized in e. ×---×, defective particles; ○---○, complex I. Radioactivity as ^{35}S (Hohn, 1969c).

protein subunit per RNA strand in the presence of K^+ and Mg^{2+}. This protein molecule binds to the 3′ proximal 60% of fII RNA. Complex Ia, as we like to name the resulting complex for comparison has a very low dissociation constant; a maximal value can be estimated from the proportion of unbound to bound coat protein in a reaction mixture as 1.4 $\times 10^{-10}$ *M*/liter (Fig. 21).

The morphology of complex I is not yet known. Ward *et al.* (1968), considering the function of the complex I as modulated messenger (see p. 84) suggested that the 6 protein subunits are bound as one hexameric unit to the RNA and predicted that this hexameric unit together with

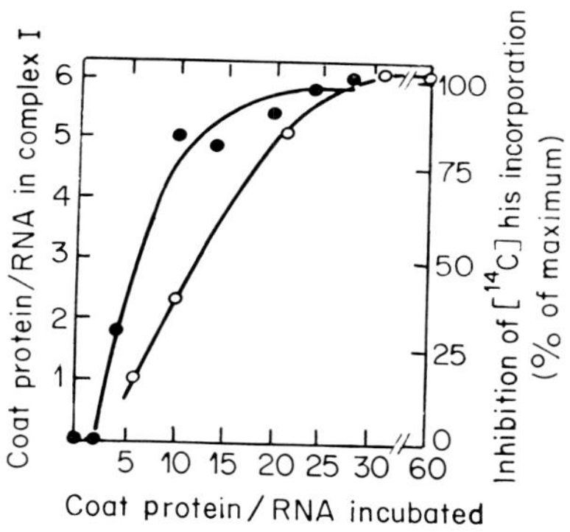

FIG. 20. Comparison of complex I formation and inhibition of histidine incorporation by fII coat protein. ○——○, number of coat proteins bound per RNA strand; ●——● = inhibition of histidine-^{14}C incorporation in an *in vitro* protein synthesizing system, both as a function of the coat protein/RNA input ratio (from Eggen and Nathans, 1969).

a piece of RNA containing the attachment site could be isolated by RNase digestion. Hohn (1969c) however found that mild RNase digestion of complex I yields several specific RNA fragments [of a size similar to the fragments obtained from unbound RNA (p. 61)] which all contained one or a few protein subunits. More extensive RNase treatment yields smaller RNA fragments and free coat protein subunits. Hexameric units could not be isolated at any stage of RNase digestion (Fig. 22).

In agreement with these findings and the existence of complex Ia, we would favor a model according to which in complex I six coat protein subunits are bound to different specific sites as monomers, dimers and/or trimers at the most.

One can conceive the RNA recognition site for the protein subunits consisting of one of the double-stranded loops whose existence has been suggested based on RNA sequence data (p. 61). The site on the pro-

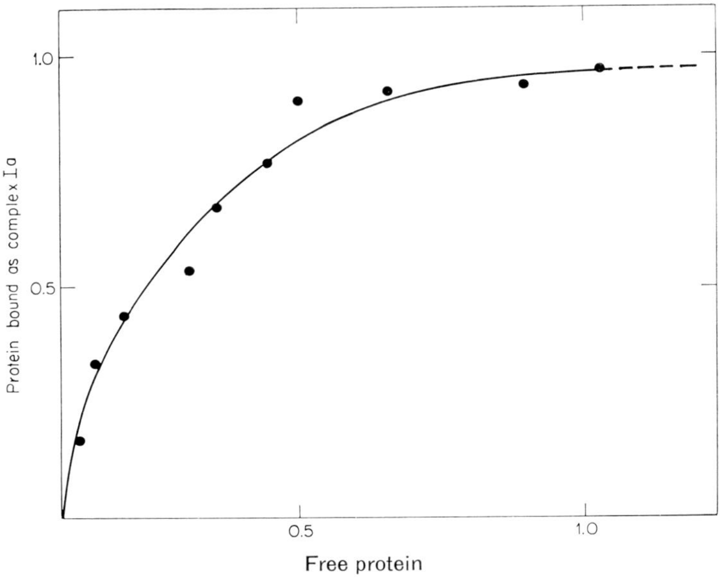

FIG. 21. fII coat protein bound as complex Ia to RNA as a function of the coat protein/RNA input ratio. The data of Spahr *et al.* (1969) were used. From this curve it can be calculated that the dissociation constant of complex Ia is around 1.4×10^{-10} moles/liter or smaller.

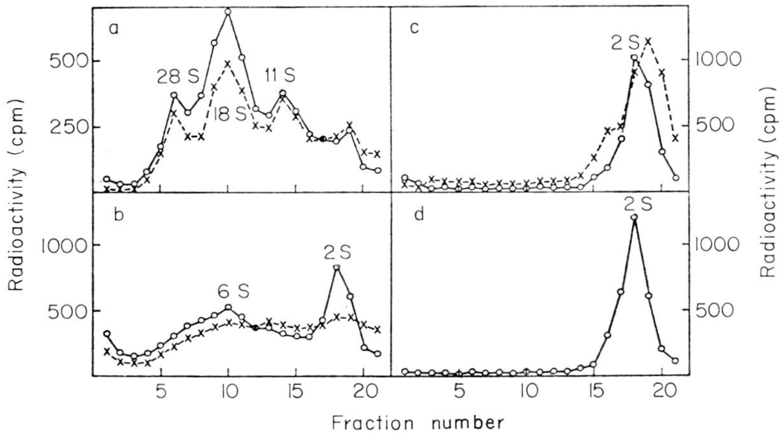

FIG. 22. Sucrose gradient analysis of 45 μg of complex I partially digested with RNase (a, 20 pg; b, 200 pg; c, 2 μg) for 5 minutes at 37°C in 200 ml of buffered saline. (d) Free coat protein. ○——○, coat protein as radioactivity of ^{35}S; ×- - -×, RNA as radioactivity of ^{32}P (Hohn, 1969c).

tein subunit responsible for recognition of the RNA might be the stretch of amino acids rich in the positively charged lysine and arginine (Fig. 6). The interactions between the polyanionic phosphate-sugar backbone of RNA and the polycationic stretches of protein are likely to provide the binding energy, while tertiary structure of protein and RNA provide the specificity.

Complex I formation of fII protein is very specific with regard to the RNA partner: a number of unrelated RNA's as well as Qβ RNA do not form complexes with low protein content stable enough to be detected in sucrose gradient analysis (Table II) (Sugiyama *et al.*, 1967; Robertson *et al.*, 1968; Eggen and Nathans, 1969; Hohn, 1969c; for Qβ RNA, however, different results were obtained by Ling *et al.*, 1969). Since these heterologous RNA species readily induce particle formation using fII protein, one might conclude that complex I is not a typical precursor. It is possible, however, that heterologous RNA forms complexes with fII protein also but with a higher dissociation constant. Similarly, one can assume that fII RNA possesses additional sites for protein interactions used to form intermediates of higher protein content and lower stability.

In the Qβ system these additional interactions are strong enough to be detected as intermediate complexes (Hung *et al.*, 1969). Qβ protein seems to have a higher affinity for homologous and heterologous RNA than has fII coat protein. A spectrum of protein-RNA complexes in protein content and sedimentation constant ranging between complex I and defective particles was obtained by assembling Qβ protein with Qβ RNA or fII RNA and named *initiation complexes.*

The observation that bacterial cells mixedly infected with Qβ and fII produced only homologous phage progeny (Ling *et al.*, 1970) has led to experiments aimed at imitating the preferential formation of homologous particles *in vitro* to obtain more information on the role of complex I and initiation complexes as intermediates in self-assembly. The following could be observed:

(*a*) *In vitro,* as *in vivo,* no mixed fII/Qβ capsids are formed (Ling *et al.*, 1970).

(*b*) Complex I, once formed, can only be chased into phagelike particles by an excess of the coat protein that is already the complex's partner (Hung *et al.*, 1969). Similar observations were made in an *in vitro* protein synthesizing system using an S-30 extract of fII-infected cells that contain undefined fII capsid precursors. Only fII RNA and not Qβ RNA could direct the synthesis of protein able to complete particle formation (Knolle, 1969). These results can be interpreted in terms of specificity of protein-protein interaction.

(*c*) Controversial results were obtained in competition experiments involving limited amounts of one type of coat protein and two types of RNA (one of which is homologous to the coat protein and therefore able to form complex I with it). Using acetic acid fII protein and Qβ and fII RNA, Hohn (1969b) observed that the complexable and non-complexable RNA had an equal chance to become encapsulated. Likewise, complex Ia (see p. 81) does not exhibit any preference over uncomplexed RNA in the competition for particle formation (Spahr *et al.*, 1969). On the other hand, using guanidinium-HCl, fII or Qβ protein and fII and Qβ RNA in three-component systems, Ling *et al.* (1969) obtained under favorable conditions some specificity in particle formation. Necessary for this specificity might be a special state of the coat protein enabling formation of initiation complexes or the absence or presence, respectively, of a minor component. Since the ability of a protein preparation to form particles only with its homologous RNA coincides with the ability of the preparation to form infective particles, the infectivity of which is A-protein dependent, the A-protein seems to be a likely candidate for the suggested minor component.

Sidetrack: Complex I and Regulated Messenger

In vivo viral coat protein has to be synthesized in large amounts whereas RNA replicase, whose gene is located distal to the coat protein gene, is needed in only minor quantities. The phage uses various ways to repress the translation of the replicase gene:

(*a*) The coat protein molecules themselves prevent synthesis of replicase: amber mutants late in the coat protein gene overproduce replicase (Lodish and Zinder, 1966a); complex I of fII directs the *in vitro* synthesis of coat protein and not that of RNA replicase (Sugiyama *et al.*, 1967; Sugiyama and Nakada, 1967, 1968; Ward *et al.*, 1967, 1968; Robertson *et al.*, 1968; Lodish, 1968a; Eggen and Nathans, 1969).

(*b*) Initiation of replicase translation occurs only if the ribosome attachment site of the gene is brought into a very accessible condition by translation of the coat protein gene (amber mutants early in the coat protein gene are polar for replicase; Lodish and Zinder, 1966a).

(*c*) Further regulation of the RNA replicase might be caused by the use of the replicative intermediate as messenger (Engelhardt *et al.*, 1968).

Synthesis of A-protein is not affected by coat protein (Lodish, 1968a). Its low level may be explained by assuming a masking of the initiation site of A-protein translation by an RNA secondary structure (Lodish, 1968a,b).

C. A-Protein in the Assembly Process and Its Final Location in the Phage

It is not yet clear at which stage the A-protein enters the assembly process. The phagelike particles which are formed in the absence of A-protein might be precursors of infectious phage or, alternatively, the A-protein might be needed early in the assembly process for proper RNA folding and packaging.

Experiments by Kaerner (1970) provide evidence for the second possibility. If infected *E. coli* cells are deprived of histidine 12 minutes after infection, i.e., at a time at which a small amount of RNA replicase had been formed, phage RNA and coat protein (which does not contain histidine) but no A-protein (which contains histidine) is synthesized and defective particles are assembled.*

When histidine was added back to the culture, A-protein was synthesized as measured by the appearance of biologically active phage. These particles were *newly* synthesized, however, the A-protein could not "rescue" preformed defective particles and complex I, i.e., they could not be chased into viable phage particles. This implies a reaction of A-protein with RNA prior to the reaction of coat protein with RNA. Some affinity between RNA and A-protein might in fact exist: complexes of RNA with all three phage-specific proteins have been detected in an actinomycin-treated host (Richelson and Nathans, 1967), but not characterized further.

The relative time at which the A-protein enters the assembly process does not allow any prediction about its final location in the phage. The different functions of the phage attributed to the presence of the A-protein, namely protection of the RNA in the absence of the host, adsorption to the bacterial pili, and release of the RNA during the infection process allow different models for the location. According to the "core" model the A-protein is located in the phage core with the primary function of RNA coiling. According to the "tail" model it is located on the phage surface with the primary function of host adsorption and triggering of RNA release (Argetsinger and Gussin, 1966). The core model would have to explain the failure of the defective particles to adsorb to the host with a conformational shift in the capsid structure caused by the core or by some interference of the protruding RNA with the adsorption process.

The location of the A-protein is also of geometrical interest. Steitz

* The experiment is more complicated insofar as the host bacteria exert stringent control over the viral RNA in the absence of histidine. This was overcome by addition of CM until enough RNA was formed and removal of CM for protein formation.

(1968b) has shown that the phage contains only one molecule of A-protein. A location of this molecule in the core would not result in a disturbance of the capsid's symmetry. If it is situated on the surface, it would have to select only 1 out of at least 12 geometrically identical locations (i.e., the corners of the icosahedron). However, this one location might be unique with respect to its relation to the phage RNA, preferentially its 5′-terminus which is proposed to extrude from the capsid in the defective particles, is proposed to be injected first (Lodish, 1968a) and contains a large, nontranslatable region (Billeter *et al.*, 1969). A site at or near the 5′-terminus rather than a site on the capsid might be the primary recognition site for the A-protein molecule and thus early interaction of RNA and A-protein would be necessary (Kaerner, 1970).

Silverman and Valentine (1969) and Silverman and Norton (described in Valentine *et al.*, 1969) give some evidence that the A-protein reacts directly with the bacterial pili and therefore must be located on the phage surface. After adsorption of fII to the host pili, RNA is injected into the bacterium while empty shell and free A protein is released into the medium. When fII adsorbs to a host mutant that cannot be infected, particles containing some RNA and free A-protein are released. Similar results are obtained by reaction of fII with wild-type host in the absence of divalent cations. These results can best be explained by a model in which the A-protein is an adsorption organelle on the phage surface triggering the RNA release.

D. Subshell Protein Polymers, Possible Precursors?

The clusters of either 3 or 5 and 6 subunits as seen on some of the electron microscopic phage images (Figs. 1, 3, and 13) do not necessarily represent real and stable entities; nevertheless they could be precursors in phage assembly. Until now the existence of free hexamers and pentamers or trimers of fII and Qβ have not been established, although the 5.5 S material of fII (p. 54) observed by Zelazo and Haschemeyer (1970) might be such entities. Rohrmann and Krueger (1970a,c) observed a protein aggregate in 0.01 *M* acetic acid that might be a dimer or larger entity and a precursor in capsid assembly. Hexamers and pentamers bound to RNA have been proposed to form complex I (p. 84). Such a structure, however, could not be verified yet. The 11 S subshell particles, which consist probably of 3 $\times$ 6 subunits, are good candidates for precursors also. These particles and/or somewhat smaller entities were actually used as precursors in the reconstitution of empty shells (Zelazo and Haschemeyer, 1970). In this manner in reversal of the degradation mechanisms proposed in Fig. 5 the capsid assembly could proceed via 10 identical 11 S particles or via some 11 S particles and some smaller entities.

Another interesting possibility for a virus capsid precursor was suggested by Mayor (1963). He postulated that viral capsids in general are formed by a winding process of linearly arranged subunits. Such a winding can, of course, be easily imagined for helical capsids. It is, however, also possible for polyhedra; accurate models of polyhedra, in

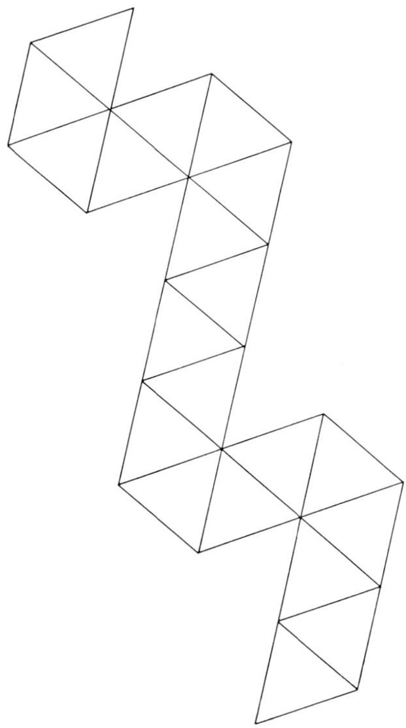

FIG. 23. Strip of paper that can easily be folded into an icosahedron.

general (Gorham, 1888), and of icosahedra, in particular (Pargeter, 1959) can be formed by braiding a long flat strip in a certain manner (Fig. 23). Mayor's theory as applied to the icosahedral reovirus was supported by fluorescence photographs and electron micrographs of viral antigen, which early after infection appears as long threads.

Some observations on fII coat protein are compatible with Mayor's theory: long threads of fII protein have been observed in the electron microscope after staining of originally low molecular weight protein with uranyl acetate at pH 5 (Fig. 24; unpublished). Similarly, coils,

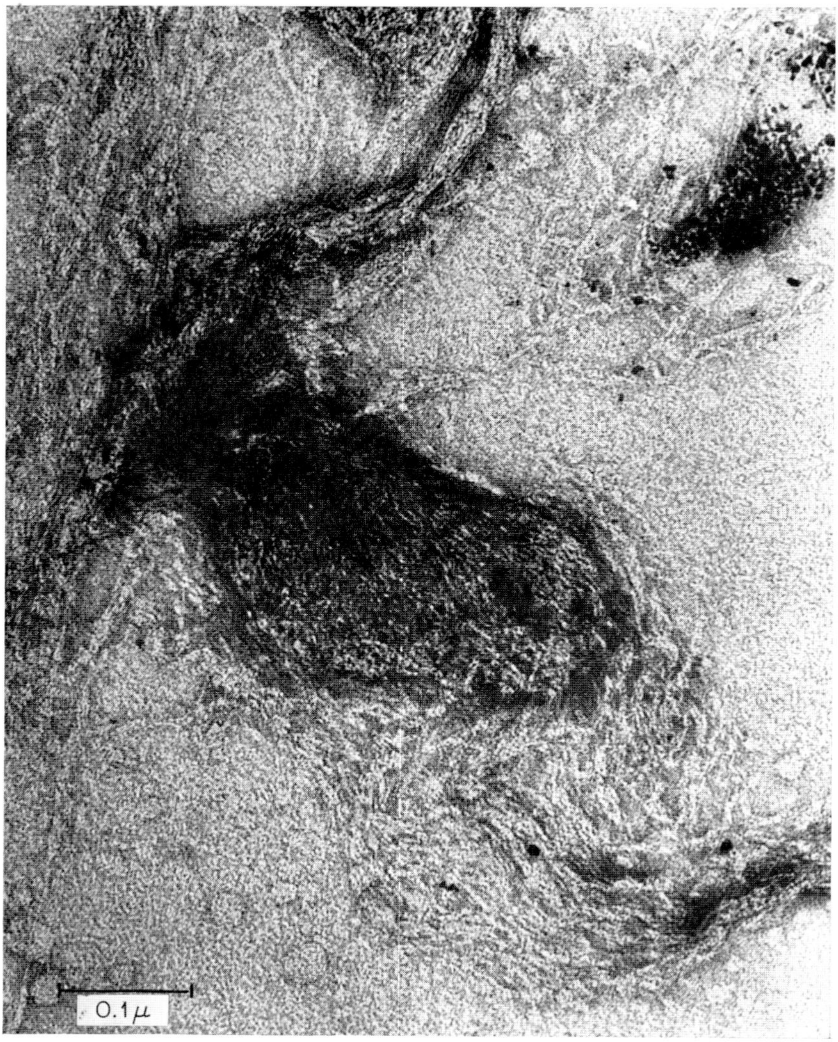

FIG. 24. fII protein stained with uranyl acetate, pH 5.

spirals, and linearly shaped material of fII protein has been observed by Zelazo and Haschemeyer (personal communication).

The idea of linearly arranged protein precursors becomes intriguing if they are arranged along RNA since it offers plausible explanation for an economic and correct pairing of RNA during the assembly process.

The formation of the "tailed" and "twinned" particles obtained with fII protein and TMV or TYMV RNA (p. 70 and Fig. 14) might be explained by such a mechanism. Portein arranged linearly along the RNA strand braids until a complete capsid is formed; since the RNA is twice as long as fII RNA, a stretch of RNA remains forming the "tail." Often capsid formation proceeds from both sides of the RNA and again a stretch of protein-RNA remains which forms the bridges connecting the "twins."

VI. A Model for Phage Assembly *in Vivo*

The phage assembly *in vivo* is probably different in some respects from the one *in vitro,* especially with regard to local concentrations of the components, their nascent state, and the availability of bacterial structures. For instance, single-stranded RNA is used in the *in vitro* reconstitution experiments while *in vivo* a pool of single-stranded RNA

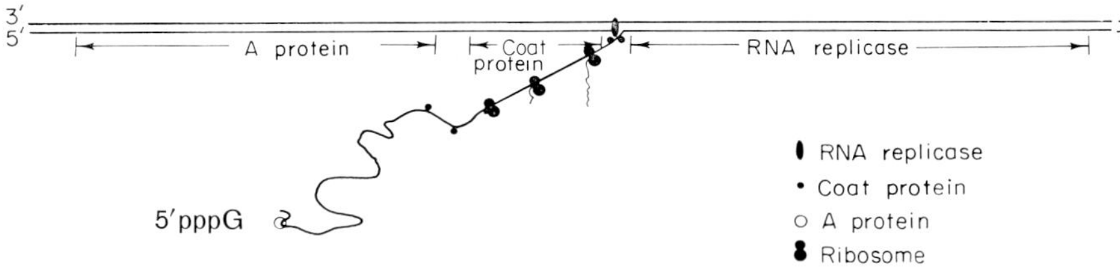

Fig. 25. Model of fII RNA at a certain stage of transcription coupled with translation, regulation, and phage assembly.

either is very small or does not exist at all (Godson, 1968). It is very likely that assembly starts on RNA molecules that are just being synthesized and still being translated. Thus transcription, translation, and self-assembly might be coupled and regulate each other. A model of such a complex in the initiation phase of assembly is shown in Fig. 25. At the stage shown, the RNA replicase has replicated the single-stranded tail to the extent that the A protein cistron as well as the coat protein cistron are available for translation. One molecule of A-protein and a few molecules of coat protein have already been synthesized and are bound to the RNA. The ribosomes continue to translate. The coat protein molecules situated close to the RNA replication fork and RNA replicase delay further RNA synthesis. RNA replicase production is thus repressed at the level of RNA transcription [Robertson *et al.,* 1968; August, Rensing, and Valentine (Discussion to Sinsheimer, 1969), however, report that $Q\beta$ coat protein does not inhibit $Q\beta$ RNA transcription]. More coat protein is synthesized that binds to the RNA on different sites except for the coat protein cistron that is occupied by ribosomes. Then the RNA replicase resumes its activity and releases the completed RNA (+) strand that, however, remains repressed for RNA replicase synthesis, this time at the level of translation (Lodish and Zinder, 1966b). Finally, the ribosomes fall off and the capsid is completed.

Although a structure as shown in Fig. 25 has not been isolated yet (and might be difficult to isolate), different complexes each containing several of the model's components have been isolated or constructed *in vitro*:

(*1*) The existence of partially double-stranded RNA as intermediate in the synthesis of single-stranded phage RNA is well established (Erikson *et al.*, 1964; Weissmann and Feix, 1966; Franklin, 1967; Billeter and Weissmann, 1966; Pace *et al.*, 1968). Replicative intermediate consists of a complete double-stranded RNA and a single-stranded tail that contains the 5′-terminus of the (+) strand and that can direct the synthesis of only the coat protein (Robertson and Zinder, 1969). It was discussed as a regulated messenger (Engelhardt *et al.*, 1968).

(*2*) Gentle artificial lysis of infected bacteria yields replicative intermediate connected to one or several ribosomes (Godson and Sinsheimer, 1967; Hotham-Iglewsky *et al.*, 1968; Godson, 1968).

(*3*) The affinity of coat protein for single-stranded RNA to form complex I and the morphology of this complex were discussed in previous sections. Complex I was shown to act as modulated messenger directing the synthesis of coat protein and not that of RNA replicase.

(*4*) Coat protein also binds to replicative intermediate, but there is disagreement on the binding site on the RNA. Knolle and Hohn (1968, 1970) found coat protein bound to single-stranded tails but not the double-stranded region: coat protein does not bind to double-stranded RNA obtained by mild RNase digestion of the replicative intermediate. Robertson *et al.* (1968) however detected binding even after shearing the replicative intermediate, a treatment supposed to remove single-stranded RNA. They concluded that the binding site is on the double-stranded region of replicative intermediate.

(*5*) Knolle and Hohn (1968, 1970) also observed that phagelike particles linked to double-stranded RNA can be formed by *in vitro* reaction of replicative intermediate and coat protein. The link consists of single-stranded RNA since RNase digestion of this complex yields defective particles and double-stranded RNA.

(*6*) RNA replicase and A-protein synthesized in an actinomycin-treated host can be complexed to single-stranded RNA as well (Richelson and Nathans, 1967).

(*7*) Haywood *et al.* (1969) observed that newly synthesized fII RNA is bound to membrane, and that, under certain conditions, it organizes on the membrane into yet undefined particles which might be phage precursors.

Further notions are consistent with the model: The A-protein is needed early in the assembly of infective phage particles (Kaerner, 1970) and is synthesized as the first structural protein after infection (Viñuela *et al.*, 1967) (Fig. 26). The gene order (p. 63) is suggested to be A-protein-coat protein-RNA replicase. Finally, a rapid complexing

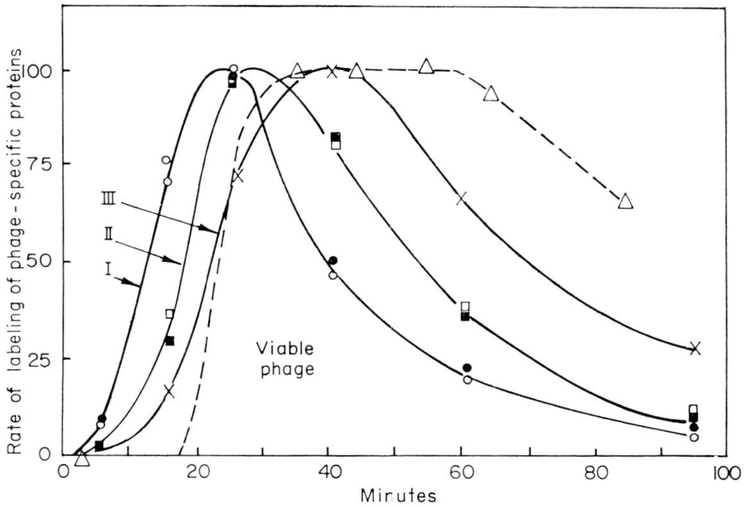

FIG. 26. Relative rate synthesis of phage specific protein as a function of time after infection of actinomycin-treated spheroblasts. Values are calculated from electrophoretic analysis of radioactive labeled protein (○, □, ×, leucine-^{14}C; ●, ■ histidine-^{14}C) as in Fig. 8. The rate is expressed in percentage of the maximal value. I, RNA replicase; II, A protein; III, coat protein.

of the RNA that is being translated might serve as an escape of the viral mRNA from degradation of the 5′-terminus which cellular RNA's are subjected to during translation (Morse *et al.*, 1969).

A complex as proposed could be visualized directly in the electron microscope using a shock-sensitive host (Schlessinger, 1969; Mangiarotti *et al.*, 1966) and the electron microscope technique developed by Miller and Beatty (1969).

The regulating role of fII coat protein on transcription and translation and the coupling of nucleic acid synthesis and phage maturation seems to be a feature common to many bacteriophages: single-stranded ϕXDNA is only synthesized if three of its four coat proteins are present and in active form (Sinsheimer, 1969); no mature λ-DNA is formed if one of the λ head genes *A*, *B*, *C*, *D*, or *E* is defective (Mackinley and Kaiser, 1969); maturation of T4 DNA and production of filled T4 heads are both affected by the mutations in the genes 16, 17, and 49 (King, 1968).

VII. Conclusion

All we have really achieved in the knowledge of phage assembly is the general realization that the components of the system possess the intrinsic ability of forming a specific quaternary structure, namely the phage. In principle the phage assembly occurs according to the general theories of Crick and Watson (1956) and Caspar and Klug (1962). Not surprisingly another little morsel is seized from the threshhold of vitalism (Crick, 1966).

Concerning the details of phage assembly we are just at the beginning of exploration. Practically nothing is yet revealed about the driving energy, kinetics, the intermediates of phage assembly or about its coupling to transcription and translation of the genome. Concerning these questions we tried to present some possible solutions. Our subjective inclination toward some of the alternatives should be a challenge to prove or disprove.

The variety of phage related structures that exist (Table I) is remarkable. They reflect a variety of protein-protein and protein-RNA interactions which will be revealed once these structures are examined and compared in detail.

Our attention was called to the versatility of the phage RNA. Its 3000 nucleotides provide specific attachment sites for RNA replicase, ribosomes, coat protein, and A-protein thus enabling transcription, translation, regulation, and initiation of assembly. Besides the specific interactions with these proteins the RNA acts "catalytically" in the capsid formation by a more unspecific mechanism.

Of what kind are these interactions? Are they due to a specific recognition of certain RNA secondary and tertiary structures? Interesting aspects of this question arise from the sequence analysis of phage RNA: A special feature of phage RNA is the existence of nucleotide stretches that can (at least on paper) be arranged in base paired loops. These could be imagined as providing sites for RNA-protein interactions. One of these loops, for instance, is located at one of the ribosome attachment sites; another one near the 5′-terminus is a candidate for interaction with A-protein or RNA replicase.

Thus, phage assembly is and will be a promising tool for the study of biological questions of general interest, especially on the nature of protein-protein and protein-nucleic acid interactions.

Phage assembly might open an interesting possibility for biotechnology. It is possible to pack heterologous RNA into the phage capsid. Once the techniques for producing infective particles are better controlled this might become an interesting tool for providing a cell with mRNA at the experimentators' will. Even more interesting in that respect would of course be a self-assembly system in animal viruses.

ACKNOWLEDGMENTS

We acknowledge the providing of preliminary information, the personal discussions of the manuscript, and other forms of cooperation of many persons, especially D. L. D. Caspar, H. Fraenkel-Conrat, R. H. Haschemeyer, R. Herrmann, P. P. Hung, A. D. Kaiser, H. C. Kaerner, R. G. Krueger, H. Lodish, G. F. Rohrmann, D. Schubert, J. A. Steitz, T. Sugiyama, R. Valentine, and P. O. Zelazo.

REFERENCES

Adams, J. M., Jeppesen, P. G. N., Sanger, F., and Barrell, B. G. (1969). *Nature (London)* **223,** 1009.

Argetsinger, J. E., and Gussin G. N. (1966). *J. Mol. Biol.* **21,** 421.

August, J. T., Eoyang, L., Franze de Fernandez, M. T., Hasegawa, S., Kuo, C. H., Rensing, U., and Shapiro, L. (1969). *J. Cell. Physiol.* **74,** Suppl. 1, 187.

Bancroft, J. B. (1970). *Advan. Virus Res.* **16,** 99.

Bassel, B. A. (1968). *Proc. Nat. Acad. Sci. U. S.* **60,** 321.

Bassel, B. A., and Spiegelman, S. (1967). *Proc. Nat. Acad. Sci. U. S.* **58,** 1155.

Billeter, M. A., and Weissmann, C. (1966). *In* "Procedures in Nucleic Acid Research" (G. L. Cantoni and D. R. Davis, eds.), p. 498. Harper & Row, New York.

Billeter, M. A., Weissmann, C., Dahlberg, J. E., Goodmann, H. M., and Hindley, J. (1969). *Nature (London)* **224,** 1083.

Boedtker, H. (1967). *Biochemistry* **6,** 2718.

Boedtker, H. (1968). *J. Mol. Biol.* **35,** 61.

Capecchi, M. R. (1966). *J. Mol. Biol.* **21,** 173.

Capecchi, M. R., and Gussin, G. (1965). *Science* **149,** 417.

Caspar, D. L D. (1965). *In* "Viral Rickettsial Infections in Man" (Horsfall and Tamm, eds.), p. 51. Lippincott, Philadelphia, Pennsylvania.

Caspar, D. L. D., and Klug, A. (1962). *Cold Spring Harbor Symp. Quant. Biol.* **27,** 1.

Crick, F. H. C. (1966). "Of Molecules and Men." Univ. of Washington Press, Seattle and London.

Crick, F. H. C., and Watson, J. D. (1956). *Nature (London)* **177,** 473.

Crick, F. H. C., and Watson, J. D. (1957). *Nature of Viruses, Ciba Found. Symp., 1956,* p. 5.

Dahlberg, J. E. (1968). *Nature (London)* **220,** 548.

Dayhoff, M. O., and Eck, R. V. (1967–1968). "Atlas of Protein Sequence and Structure." Biomed. Res. Found., Silver Springs, Maryland.

de Wachter, R., and Fiers, W. (1967). *J. Mol. Biol.* **30,** 507.

de Wachter, R., Verhassel, J. P., and Fiers, W. (1968). *Fed. Eur. Biochem. Soc. Lett.* **1,** 93.

Dürwald, H., and Hoffmann-Berling, H. (1968). *J. Mol. Biol.* **34,** 331.

Eggen, K., and Nathans, D. (1969). *J. Mol. Biol.* **39,** 293.

Eggen, K., Oeschger, M. P., and Nathans, D. (1967). *Biochem. Biophys. Res. Commun.* **28,** 587.

Engelhardt, D. L., Robertson, H. D., and Zinder, N. D. (1968). *Proc. Nat. Acad. Sci. U.S.* **59,** 972.

Enger, M. D., Stubbs, E. A., Mitra, S., and Kaesberg, P. (1963). *Proc. Nat. Acad. Sci. U.S.* **49,** 857.
Erikson, R. L. (1968). *Annu. Rev. Microbiol.* **22,** 305.
Erikson, R. L., Fenwick, M., and Franklin, R. M. (1964). *J. Mol. Biol.* **10,** 519.
Erikson, R. L., and Franklin, R. M. (1966). *Bacteriol. Rev.* **30,** 267.
Fenwick, M. L. (1968). *Biochem. J.* **107,** 851.
Fiers, W. (1967). *Virology* **33,** 413.
Fischbach, F. A., Harrison, P. M., and Anderegg, J. W. (1965). *J. Mol. Biol.* **13,** 638.
Fraenkel-Conrat, H. (1968). "Molecular Basis of Virology" (H. Fraenkel-Conrat, ed.), p. 134. Reinhold, New York.
Fraenkel-Conrat, H., and Weissmann, C. (1968). In "Molecular Basis of Virology" (H. Fraenkel-Conrat, ed.), p. 209. Reinhold, New York.
Franklin, R. M. (1967). *J. Virol.* **1,** 64.
Franklin, R. M., and Granboulan, N. (1966). *J. Bacteriol.* **91,** 834.
Fromageot, H. P. M., and Zinder, N. D. (1968). *Proc. Nat. Acad. Sci. U.S.* **61,** 184.
Galton, F, (1878). *Nature (London)* **18,** 97.
Garwes, D., Sillero, A., and Ochoa, S. (1969). *Biochim. Biophys. Acta* **186,** 166.
Gesteland, R. F., and Boedtker, H. (1964). *J. Mol. Biol.* **8,** 496.
Glik, D. (1968). *Biochemistry* **7,** 927.
Godson, G. N. (1968). *J. Mol. Biol.* **34,** 149.
Godson, G. N., and Sinsheimer, R. L. (1967). *J. Med. Biol.* **23,** 495.
Gorham, J. (1888). "A System for the Construction of Plaited Crystal Models on the Type of an ordinary plait; Exemplified by the Forms Belonging to the Six Axial Systems in Crystallography." Spon, London.
Gussin, G. N. (1966). *J. Mol. Biol.* **21,** 435.
Harris. J. I., and Hindley, J. (1965). *J. Mol. Biol.* **13,** 894.
Haywood, A. M., Harris-Cramer, J. and Lancaster-Shoemaker, N. (1969). *J. Virol.* **4,** 364.
Heisenberg, M. (1966) *J. Mol. Biol.* **17,** 136.
Heisenberg, M. (1967). *Biochem. Biophys. Res. Commun.* **27,** 131.
Heisenberg, M., and Blessing, J. (1965). *Z. Naturforsch.* **20***B*, 859.
Herrmann, R. (1970). Thesis, Univ. of Tübingen, Tübingen, Germany.
Herrmann, R., Schubert, D., and Rudolph, U. (1968). *Biochem. Biophys. Res. Commun.* **5,** 576.
Hindley, J., and Staples, D. H. (1969). *Nature (London)* **224,** 964.
Hoffmann-Berling, H., Marvin, D. A., and Dürwald, H. (1963). *Z. Naturforsch.* **18***B*, 876.
Hofschneider, P. H. (1963). *Z. Naturforsch.* **18***B*, 203.
Hofschneider, P. H., and Hausen, P. (1968). In "Molecular Basis of Virology" (H. Fraenkel-Conrat, ed.), p. 169. Reinhold, New York.
Hohn, T. (1967). *Eur. J. Biochem.* **2,** 152.
Hohn, T. (1969a). *J. Mol. Biol.* **43,** 191.
Hohn, T. (1969b). *Biochem. Biophys. Res. Commun.* **36,** 7.
Hohn, T. (1969c). *Eur. J. Biochem.* **8,** 552.
Horiuchi, K., Lodish, H. F., and Zinder, N. D. (1966). *Virology* **28,** 438.
Horne. R. W., and Wildy, P. (1961). *Virology* **15,** 348.
Hotham-Iglewsky, B., Phillips, L., and Franklin, R. M. (1968). *Nature (London)* **219,** 700.
Hung, P. P. (1969). *Biochim. Biophys. Acta* **186,** 220.
Hung, P. P., and Overby, L. R. (1969). *Biochemistry* **8,** 820.
Hung, P. P., Ling, C. M., and Overby, L. R. (1969). *Science* **166,** 1638.

Jeppesen, P. G. N., Steitz, J. A., Gesteland, R. F., and Spahr, P. F. (1970). *Nature (London)* **226,** 230.

Kaerner, H. C. (1969). *J. Mol. Biol.* **42,** 259.

Kaerner, H. C. (1970). *J. Med. Biol.* (in press).

Kaesberg, P., (1966). *Proc. Edmonton Virus Symp.* p. 241.

Kaper, J. M. (1968). *In* "Molecular Basis of Virology" (H. Fraenkel-Conrat, ed.), p. 1. Reinhold, New York.

King, J. (1968). *J. Mol. Biol.* **32,** 231.

Klug, A., and Caspar, D. L. D. (1960). *Advan. Virus Res.* **7,** 225.

Klug, A., Longley, W., and Leberman, R. (1966). *J. Mol. Biol.* **15,** 315.

Knolle, P. (1969). *Biochim. Biophys. Acta* **190,** 496.

Knolle, P., and Hohn, T. (1968). *Proc. 12th Int. Congr. Genet.,Tokyo* **1,** 39.

Knolle, P., and Hohn, T. (1970). *Eur. J. Biochem.,* (in press).

Krueger, R. G. (1969). *J. Virol.* **4,** 567.

Kushner, D. J. (1969). *Bacteriol. Rev.* **33**(2), 302.

Leberman, R. (1968). *Symp. Soc. Gen. Microbiol.* **18,** 183.

Lin, J. Y., Tsung, C. M., and Fraenkel-Conrat, H. (1967). *J. Mol. Biol.* **24,** 1.

Ling, C. M., Hung, P. P., and Overby, L. R. (1969). *Biochemistry* **8,** 4464.

Ling, C. M., Hung, P. P., and Overby, L. R. (1970). *Virology* **40,** 920.

Lodish, H. F. (1968a). *Nature (London)* **220,** 345.

Lodish, H. F. (1968b). *J. Mol. Biol.* **32,** 681.

Lodish, H. F. (1969). *Nature (London)* **224,** 867.

Lodish, H. F., and Robertson, H. D. (1969). *J. Mol. Biol.* **45,** 9.

Lodish, H. F., and Zinder, N. D. (1966a). *J. Mol. Biol.* **19,** 333.

Lodish, H. F., and Zinder, N. D. (1966b). *Science* **152,** 372.

Lodish, H. F., Horiuchi, K., and Zinder, N. D. (1965). *Virology* **27,** 139.

Loeb, T., and Zinder N. D. (1961). *Proc. Nat. Acad. Sci. U.S.* **47,** 282.

Mackinley, A. G., and Kaiser, A. D. (1969). *J. Mol. Biol.* **39,** 679.

Mangiarotti, G., Apirion, D., and Schlessinger, D. (1966). *Science* **152,** 892.

Markham, R. (1963). *In* "Viruses, Nucleic Acids and Cancer," Symposium. p. 180. Williams & Wilkins, Baltimore, Maryland.

Marvin, D. A., and Hoffmann-Berling, H. (1963). *Z. Naturforsch* **18***B*, 884.

Mayor, H. D. (1963). *In* "Viruses, Nucleic Acids and Cancer," Symposium, p. 63. Williams & Wilkins, Baltimore, Maryland.

Miller, O. L., and Beatty, B. R. (1969). *Science* **164,** 955.

Min Jou, W., and Fiers, W. (1969). *J. Bol. Biol.* **40,** 187.

Mitra, S. Enger, M. D., and Kaesberg, P. (1963). *Proc. Nat. Acad. Sci. U.S.* **50,** 68.

Morse, D. E., Mosteller, R., and Yanofsky, C. (1969). *Cold Spring Harbor Symp. Quant. Biol.* **34,** 725.

Muirhead, H., and Perutz, M. F. (1963). *Nature (London)* **199,** 633.

Nathans, D., Oeschger, M. P., Eggen, K., and Shimura, Y. (1966). *Proc. Nat. Acad. Sci. U.S.* **56,** 1844.

Nichols, J. L. (1970). *Nature (London)* **225,** 147.

Nishihara, T., Haruna, I., Watanabe, I., Nozu, Y., and Okada, Y. (1969). *Virology* **37,** 153.

Noll, H., and Stutz, E. (1968). *Methods Enzymol.* **12B,** 129.

Nomura, N., Mizushima, S., Ozaki, M., Traub, P., and Lowry, C. V. (1969). Cold *Spring Harbor Symp. Quant. Biol.* **34,** 49.

Nonoyama, M., Yuki, A., and Ikeda, Y. (1963). *J. Gen. Appl. Microbiol.* **9,** 299.

Oriel, P. J., and Koenig, J. A. (1968). *Arch. Biochem. Biophys.* **127,** 274.

Overby, L. R., Barlow, G. H., Doi, R. H., Jacob, M., and Speigelman, S. (1966a). *J. Bacteriol.* **91,** 442.
Overby, L. R., Barlow, G. H., Doi, R. H., Jacob, M., and Spiegelman, S. (1966b). *J. Bacteriol.* **92,** 739.
Pace, N. R., Haruna, I., and Spiegelman, S. (1968). *Methods Enzymol.* **12*B*,** 540.
Pargeter, A. R. (1959). *Math. Gaz.* **43,** 88.
Pollet, R., Knolle, P., and Weissmann, C. (1967). *Proc. Nat. Acad. Sci. U.S.* **58,** 766.
Richelson, F., and Nathans, D. (1967). *Biochem. Biophys. Res. Commun.* **29,** 842.
Roberts, J. W., and Steitz, J. A. (1967). *Proc. Nat. Acad. Sci. U.S.* **58,** 1416.
Robertson, H. D., and Zinder, N. D. (1969). *J. Biol. Chem.* **244,** 5790.
Robertson, H. D., Webster, R. E., and Zinder, N. D. (1968). *Nature* (*London*) **218,** 533.
Rohrmann, G. F., and Krueger, R. G. (1970a). *Biochem. Biophys. Res. Commun.* **38,** 406.
Rohrmann, G. F., and Krueger, R. G. (1970b). *J. Virol.,* (in press).
Samuelsen, G., and Kaesberg, P. (1970). *J. Mol. Biol.* **47,** 87.
Schlessinger, D. (1969). *Bacteriol. Rev.* **33,** 445.
Schubert, D. (1969). *Biochim. Biophys. Acta* **188,** 147.
Schubert, D., and Franck, H. (1970a). *Hoppe-Seylers Z. Physiol. Chem.* **351,** 130.
Schubert, D., and Franck, H. (1970b). In preparation.
Scott, D. W. (1965). *Virology* **26,** 85.
Shapiro, L., and August, J. T. (1966). Symposium on Replication of Viral Nucleic Acids. *Bacteriol. Rev.* **30,** 279.
Shimura, Y., Moses, R. E., and Nathans, D. (1965). *J. Mol. Biol.* **12,** 266.
Shimura, Y., Moses, R. E., and Nathans, D. (1967). *J. Mol. Biol.* **28,** 95.
Shimura, Y., Kaizer, H., and Nathans, D. (1968). *J. Mol. Biol.* **38,** 453.
Silverman, P. M., and Valentine, R. C. (1969). *J. Gen. Virol.* **4,** 111.
Sinsheimer, R. L. (1969). *J. Cell. Physiol.* **74,** Suppl. 1, 21.
Spahr, P. F., and Gesteland, R. F. (1968). *Proc. Nat. Acad. Sci. U.S.* **59,** 876.
Spahr, P. F., Farber, M., and Gesteland, R. F. (1969). *Nature* (*London*) **222,** 455.
Spiegelman, S., Haruna, I., Holland, I. B., Beaudreau, G., and Mills, D. (1965). *Proc. Nat. Acad. Sci. U.S.* **54,** 919.
Steitz, J. A. (1968a). *J. Mol. Biol.* **33,** 923.
Steitz, J. A. (1968b). *J. Mol. Biol.* **33,** 937.
Steitz, J. A. (1968c). *J. Mol. Biol.* **33,** 947.
Steitz, J. A. (1969). *Nature* (*London*) **224,** 957.
Steitz, J. A. (1970). *FEBS Symp.,* **1970,** 21.
Strauss, J. H., and Sinsheimer, R. L. (1963). *J. Mol. Biol.* **7,** 43.
Stryer, L. (1968). *Ann. Rev. Biochem.* **37,** 25.
Sugiyama, T. (1966). *Virology* **28,** 488.
Sugiyama, T. and Nakada, D. (1967). *Proc. Nat. Acad. Sci. U.S.* **57,** 1744.
Sugiyama, T., and Nakada, D. (1968). *J. Mol. Biol.* **31,** 431.
Sugiyama, T., Hebert, R. R., and Hartman, K. A. (1967). *J. Mol. Biol.* **25,** 455.
Sugiyama, T., Stone, H. O., and Nakada, D. (1969). *J. Mol. Biol.* **42,** 97.
Thatch, S., and Boedtker, H. (1969). *J. Mol. Biol.* **45,** 451.
Thirion, J. P., and Kaesberg, P. (1968). *J. Mol. Biol.* **33,** 379.
Thirion, J. P., and Kaesberg, P. (1970). *J. Mol. Biol.* **47,** 193.
Valentine, R. C., Ward, R., and Strand, M. (1969). *Advan. Virus Res.* **15,** 2.
Vasquez, C., Granboulan, N., and Franklin, R. M. (1966). *J. Bacteriol.* **92,** 1779.
Viñuela, E., Algranati, I., and Ochoa, S. (1967). *Eur. J. Biochem.* **1,** 3.
Viñuela, E., Algranati, I. D., Feix, G., Garwes, D., Weissmann, C., and Ochoa, S. (1968). *Biochim. Biophys. Acta* **155,** 558.

Ward, R., Shive, K., and Valentine, R. C. (1967). *Biochem. Biophys. Res. Commun.* **29,** 8.
Ward, R., Strand, M., and Valentine, R. C. (1968). *Biochem. Biophys. Res. Commun.* **30,** 310.
Watanabe, M., Watanabe, H., and August, J. T. (1968). *J. Mol. Biol.* **33,** 1.
Weber, K. (1967). *Biochemistry* **6,** 3144.
Weber, K., and Konigsberg, W. (1967). *J. Biol. Chem.* **242,** 3563.
Weissmann, C., and Ochoa, S. (1967). *Progr. Nucl. Acid Res. Mol. Biol.* **6,** 353.
Weissmann, C., and Feix, G. (1966). *Proc. Nat. Acad. Sci. U.S.* **55,** 1264.
Weith, H. L., and Gilham, P. T. (1967). *J. Amer. Chem. Soc.* **89,** 5473.
Wittmann-Liebold, B., and Wittmann, H. G. (1967). *Mol. Gen. Genet.* **100,** 358.
Zelazo, P. O., and Haschemeyer, R. H. (1969). *Biochemistry,* **8,** 3587.
Zelazo, P. O., and Haschemeyer, R. H. (1970). *Science,* **168,** 1461.
Zipper, P., Kratky, O., Herrmann, R., and Hohn, T. (1970). *Eur. J. Biochem.,* (in press).

Notes added in proof

Section II,A,1: The data on the fII dimensions in this review represent original values which have been slightly modified since then (main reference list, Zipper *et al.,* 1970).

Section III,A: The sequence of the Qβ coat protein has been analyzed by Konigsberg *et al.* (1970). It has 131 amino acids (two more than the fII coat protein) and is lacking the three amino acids methionine, tryptophane, and histidine. It is distantly related to the fII coat protein: if aligned in a way that allows insertions and deletions (Fig. 27), 30 residues occupy identical positions, and 62 residues can be accounted for by single base changes.

Section III,C,3: Additional fII RNA fragments were analyzed by the following authors: Robinson *et al.* (1969) (the 18 first nucleotides of the coat protein cistron); Gupta *et al.* (1970) (a large fragment containing the coat protein initiation site); Adams and Cori (1970) (74 nucleotides of the 5′-terminus), Jeppesen *et al.* (1970) (two additional fragments of the coat protein cistron). Weissmann *et al.* (1970) analyzed about 50 nucleotides of the 5′-terminus of the Qβ RNA minus strand. All structures analyzed can partially be arranged in base paired hairpins. The possible hairpins of the coat protein cistron so far analyzed show an interesting regularity (Fig. 28) (Jeppesen *et al.,* 1970).

Section IV,C: Matthews (1970) found conditions for the assembly of fII protein monomers to empty shells. As far as tested these shells are similar to the ones described on p. 54 and p. 78, which were obtained from larger precursors. The reaction is much slower than the one in presence of RNA and the optimal conditions for empty shell formation are considerably different than the ones for protein particle formation. Protein particles as described on p. 76 are obtained at low ionic strength (0.015 *M* NaCl) and the type of anion is not critical; empty shells are obtained at high ionic strength (1 *M* ammonium acetate) and the type of anion is critical. Acetate works well; chloride inhibits the reaction. Protein particles and empty shells are probably formed by different reaction mechanisms involving nucleation by additional coat protein in the one case and neutralization of the coat protein charge by counterions in the other.

References

Adams, J. M., and Cory, S. (1970). *Nature (London)* **227,** 570.
Gupta, S. L., Chen, J., Schaefer, L., Lengyel, P., and Weissman, S. M. (1970). *Biochem Biophys. Res. Commun.* **39,** 883.

Jeppesen, P. G. N., Nichols, J. L., Sanger, F., and Barrell, B. G. (1970). *Cold Spring Harbor Symp. Quant. Biol.* **35,** in press.
Konigsberg, W., Maita, T., Katze, J., Weber, K. (1970). *Nature (London)* **227,** 271.
Matthews, K. S. (1970). Thesis, University of Berkeley, California.
Robinson, W. E., Frist, R. H., and Kaesberg, P. (1969). *Science* **166,** 1291.
Weissmann, C., *et al.* (1970). In preparation.

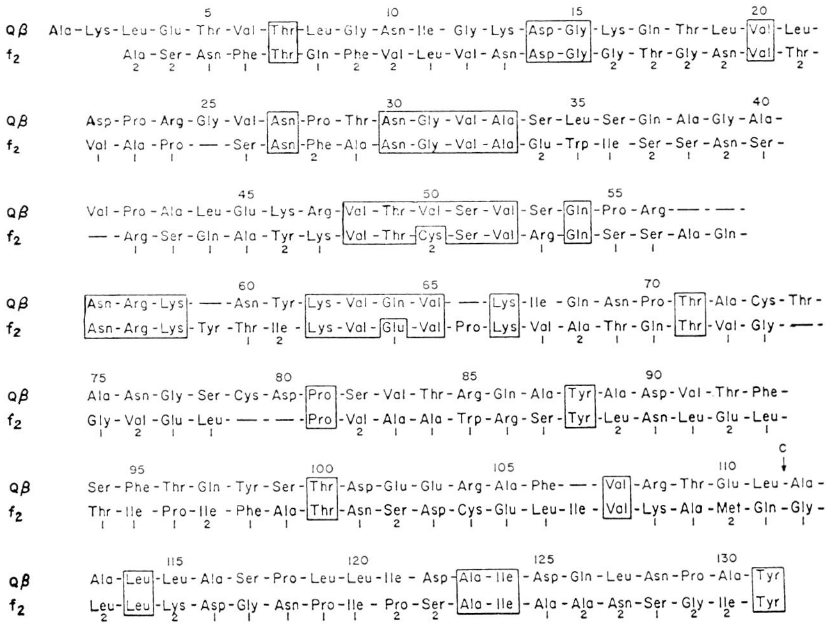

FIG. 27. Amino acid sequence of Qβ protein. The sequence of fII coat protein has been provisionally aligned to maximize the number of identical residues. The number under each residue represent the minimum number of base changes per codon necessary to account for the amino acid interchanges at each position in the fII and Qβ coat proteins. (From Konigsberg *et al.*, 1970).

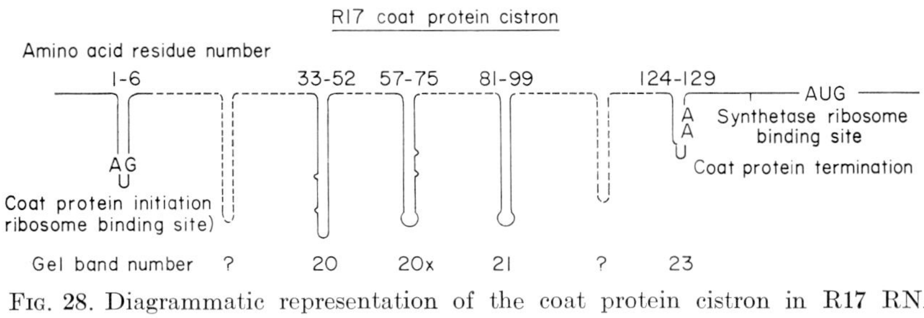

FIG. 28. Diagrammatic representation of the coat protein cistron in R17 RNA. Continuous lines represent portions whose sequences are known. The two loops in the unknown regions are purely speculative. (From Jeppesen *et al.*, 1970).

THE SELF-ASSEMBLY OF SPHERICAL PLANT VIRUSES

J. B. Bancroft

Department of Botany and Plant Pathology, Purdue University, Lafayette, Indiana

I. Introduction

The experimental work of Takahashi and Ishii (1952) and Fraenkel-Conrat and Williams (1955) along with the theoretical considerations of Horne and Wildy (1961) and Caspar and Klug (1962) were of great importance in focusing attention on the promise of experimental approaches to the problems of virus assembly. The former authors showed that self-assembly could actually occur, at least with tobacco mosaic virus (TMV) protein, and the latter formulated general principles, since amplified (Caspar and Klug, 1963; Caspar, 1964, 1966; Klug *et al.*, 1966a; Klug, 1967), for the design and assembly of viruses within a general geometric and thermodynamic framework. They argued that the directions for self-assembly in all simple viruses resided in their protein structure units, which were equated with single equivalent protein molecules, which aggregated to form minimum-energy structures. Icosahedral as well as tubular viruses were predicted to self-assemble on this basis. However, it was over 10 years after the initial studies of TMV assembly (see Lauffer and Stevens, 1968, for a recent review) before it became evident how to conduct the analogous experiments on simple icosahedral viruses that were needed to either confirm or reject expectation. The question was not one of not knowing generally what to do, but rather one of explicit choice as to virus and procedure. The early significant experiments were made with certain icosahedral bacterial viruses (Takai, 1966; Sugiyama *et al.*, 1967; Hohn, 1967; Roberts and Steitz, 1967) and plant viruses (Bancroft *et al.*, 1967; Bancroft and Hiebert, 1967), quite different approaches necessarily being used in the critical disassembly step by the bacterial and plant virus workers as reviewed by Leberman (1968). Recent experimental advances with the bacterial viruses are detailed elsewhere in this volume (Hohn and Hohn, 1970). Those confined to icosahedral viruses and a near relative attacking higher plants will be reviewed here.

II. Cowpea Chlorotic Mottle, Brome Mosaic, and Broad Bean Mottle Viruses

A. General Properties

Cowpea chlorotic mottle virus (CCMV), brome mosaic virus (BMV), and broad bean mottle virus (BBMV) comprise a group of mutually distinct, high-yielding, icosahedral plant viruses which are easily purified and sediment as single components. All happen to respond in a useful way to high NaCl concentrations near neutrality as will be discussed. They are small plant viruses with molecular weights of about 4.6×10^6 for CCMV (Bancroft *et al.*, 1968a) and BMV (Bockstahler and Kaesberg, 1962) to 4.8×10^6 for BBMV (Finch *et al.*, 1967). Each contains about 1 to 1.1×10^6 molecular weight units of RNA and each belongs to the same general hexamer-pentamer $T = 3$ surface lattice class (Bancroft *et al.*, 1967; Finch and Klug, 1967). That is, each virus contains 180 structure units clustered in 32 groups, 12 around five-fold axes and 20 around three-fold axes (Fig. 1). One chemical unit equals a structure unit and the chemical units of the three viruses differ in their amino acid compositions, residue numbers, and mass. CCMV subunits each contain 183 residues with a molecular weight of 19,600 (Bancroft *et al.*, 1968a); BMV subunits contain 189 residues with a molecular weight of 20,300 (Stubbs and Kaesberg, 1964) and BBMV subunits are composed of 194 amino acids with a molecular weight of 20,900 (Miki and Knight, 1965). There is no evidence at present to suggest that more than one protein type is involved with each virus although a minor protein component could be overlooked by the analytical methods used. In other words, there is no reason to believe that a "maturation factor," such as found for the RNA bacteriophage R17 (Roberts and Steitz, 1967), is associated with the plant viruses to be discussed.

The nucleic acids of the viruses occur in discrete size classes, those from populations of CCMV or BMV being isolated in three sizes with molecular weights of about 0.3, 0.7, and 1.0×10^6. The smaller pieces, as judged by their size and labeling characteristics (Bockstahler and Kaesberg, 1965a; Bancroft *et al.*, 1968a) are perhaps derived *in vivo* from the largest which alone seem infective (Bockstahler and Kaesberg, 1965b; Bancroft *et al.*, 1968a). Ribonucleic acid (RNA) from BBMV is usually isolated as a whole infective piece and as approximately ⅓-sized molecules which are *in vivo* degradative products of the infectious RNA (Kodama and Bancroft, 1964).

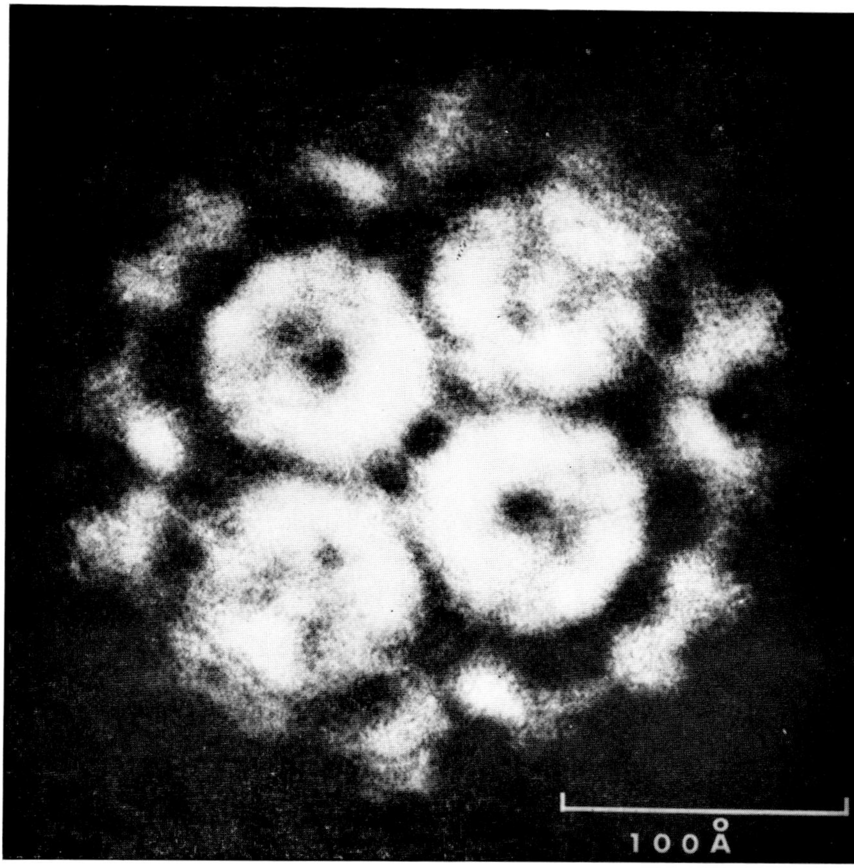

FIG. 1. An "average" picture of CCMV, oriented precisely in the two-fold position. The picture was obtained by superimposing four views of the particle rotated 180 Å with the negative unreversed and reversed. There are 32 morphological units, 12 composed of 5 structure units each (pentamers) clustered about five-fold axes and 20 composed of 6 structure units each (hexamers) clustered about three-fold axes. The strain is 1%, uranyl acetate, pH 4.7.

B. Disassembly

The critical step in assembly is really disassembly. Virus must be disassembled in such a way that released protein subunits retain their ability to reassemble in a specific manner relating to their origin. Proper assembly constitutes the test for proper disassembly. Clues as to how to disassemble viruses come from studying their properties in a systematic fashion. CCMV sediments at 88 S at pH 5.0 and 78 S at pH 7.0 (Bancroft *et al.*, 1967). The molecular weights of the two sedimenting forms are about the same (Bancroft *et al.*, 1968a) indicating a pH-induced conformational change, as was also suggested for BMV (Incardona and Kaesberg, 1964) which behaves like CCMV. BBMV sediments about 6 S slower at pH 6 than it does at pH 7 (unpublished). The normal or fast or 88 S form of CCMV is infective but the 78 S or slow or "swollen" form is not, probably due to scission of RNA during swelling of the virus (Bancroft *et al.*, 1968a). Presumably the same breakage occurs with BMV, but not with BBMV which retains its infectivity at neutrality (unpublished) perhaps because it does not swell to the same extent as the other viruses. The swelling effect is easily reversed in gross physical terms as measured hydrodynamically for CCMV, BBMV, and BMV and also by titrations for the latter virus (Incardona and Kaesberg, 1964), but the nucleic acid is not, of course, repaired by a reversal in pH and infectivity is not regained. If CCMV is dialyzed to near neutrality with Mg^{2+}, it sediments at close to the rate of the fast form (about 3 S slower) and remains infective (Bancroft *et al.*, 1968a; Hiebert and Bancroft, 1969). BMV responds in the same way as CCMV to Mg^{2+} (unpublished), but Mg^{2+} does not have a clear effect on the sedimentation rate of BBMV. An effect could be hard to observe because the S value of the swollen form is not as distinct from the normal as it is with CCMV and BMV. Actually, a number of polycations can be used in place of Mg^{2+} including polyamines (Hiebert and Bancroft, 1969) in which case, with CCMV at least, infectivity is retained; however, the $s_{20,w}$ is about 6 S below that of the normal fast form. This may reflect the volume taken up by the polyamines between the structure units, but may also indicate a minor structural alteration.

The swelling response of CCMV may mean that paired hydrogen bonds exist between critical carboxyl groups on adjacent subunits near pH 6.0 and below, but that near neutrality, the carboxyl groups ionize and repel each other (Bancroft *et al.*, 1967). This situation, which has been considered for TMV (Caspar, 1963), can be described by the series

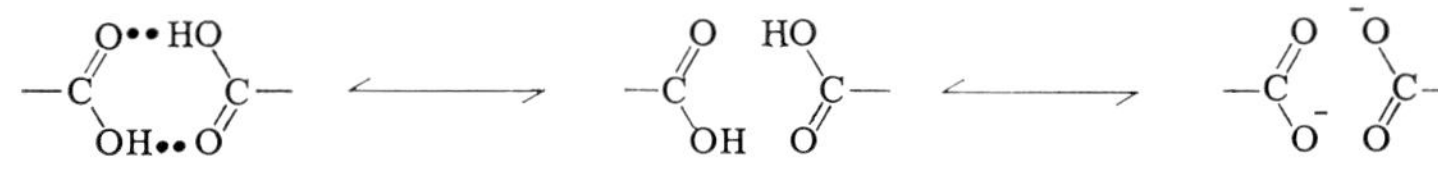

from pH 6.0 to 7.0. The middle state perhaps corresponds to the transition form described by Incardona and Kaesberg (1964) for BMV. The carboxylate ions on adjacent subunits would repel each other, the subunits would tend to separate and the virus would become swollen. Specific bonding identity in a complex molecule is very difficult to prove, but the idea is not unreasonable since the pK's of hydrogen-bonded carboxyl groups would be anomalous and the pH range in which swelling occurred is about what would be expected from Scheraga's (1963) estimates of the behavior of carboxyl—carboxyl hydrogen bonds. Further, the titration curve of BMV showed an abnormal loss of protons near neutrality (Incardona and Kaesberg, 1964) which approximates in terms of the simplest scheme (Fig. 2) to two protons

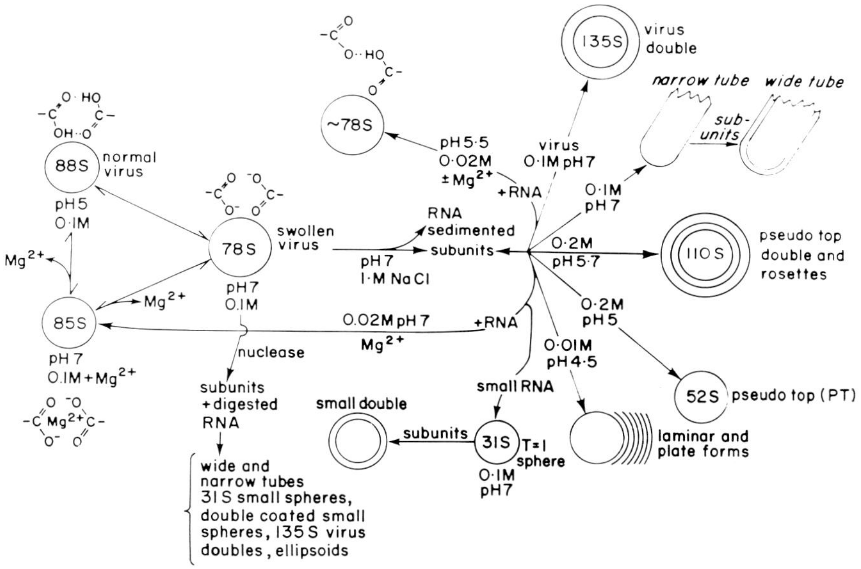

FIG. 2. The relationships among the principal forms of CCMV and CCMV protein as related to disassembly and reassembly. The carboxyl groups and carboxylate ions that may be critical in swelling are notated above the appropriate forms of the virus. The positioning of the carboxyl groups for the defective 78 S form assembled at pH 5.5 is particularly diagrammatic. The size of the "small" RNA is not known, but is probably less than about 20 nucleotides for CCMV. The critical role, if any, of takadiastase T_1 in the production of small doubles and wide tubes, as mentioned in the text, is not known.

per structure unit. Even if the outlined scheme does not represent the precise picture, the swelling of virus can be easily rationalized as an accumulation of net negative charge. Thus, swelling is also observed when carboxyl-containing resins are titrated to a neutral pH. Incardona and Kaesberg (1964) did not consider the carboxyl interactions but instead suggested the amino groups of adenine and cytosine as possibilities. In order to check possible amino group involvement, it would be interesting to examine poly

U-BMV or -CCMV protein hybrids by titration and to determine their sedimentation constants at pH 6 and 7.

The sedimentation rate of the normal or fast form of CCMV at pH 5 or 6 is not affected by Mg^{2+} whereas that of the swollen pH 7 form is increased by the presence of Mg^{2+}. A possible reason for this difference in effect is that Mg^{2+} may form ionic bridges between carboxylate ions on adjacent subunits, and thereby prevent swelling (Bancroft *et al.*, 1967). The virus is less electronegative in the presence of Mg^{2+} near neutrality than it is in its absence (Bancroft *et al.*, 1968a) and this result is consistent with such a suggestion. The Mg^{2+} effect is reversible, which is also reasonable. The other metals and polyamines tested (Hiebert and Bancroft. 1969) probably function in a similar manner and both the di- and polyvalent cations have a critical role in assembly (Hiebert and Bancroft, 1969). Monovalent ions do not substitute for the divalent ones even if the former are used at relatively high concentrations.

Although CCMV becomes swollen at pH 7, it does not fall apart at moderate ionic strengths if RNA is present, indicating that nucleic acid has a structural role in icosahedral viruses, a possibility also suggested by X-ray analyses of turnip yellow mosaic virus which showed RNA projecting up between the structure units of the virus (Klug *et al.*, 1966b). Further, pancreatic ribonuclease does not cause CCMV to fall apart at pH 5 to 6, but it does so degrade the swollen form of the virus (Bancroft *et al.*, 1967), as is also the case with BMV (Incardona and Kaesberg, 1964) and BBMV (unpublished). This degradation is as expected if RNA actually fulfills its assigned structural role. From the diffusion coefficient of pancreatic ribonuclease, it might be expected that openings approximating to 30 Å diameter exist on the surfaces of the swollen spheres. Takadiastase T_1 has also been used for degradation. The nuclease type of degradation gave protein capable of reassembly into various tubular and icosahedral forms (Bancroft *et al.*, 1967) which is not surprising considering the mild conditions involved. However, such a procedure results in a mixture of reactants not the least troublesome of which is ribonuclease.

Charge-charge interactions probably constitute important links between protein and nucleic acid in a virus, and such attractions should be responsive to counterions. Thus, CCMV, BMV, or BBMV come apart if dialyzed overnight in 1 *M* NaCl at pH 7 to yield protein and RNA (Bancroft *et al.*, 1967; Hiebert *et al.*, 1968). This result is consistent with the carboxylate model. In 1 *M* NaCl at pH 6, the subunits would interact favorably and, in fact, the viruses remain intact in such an environment. The protein and nucleic acid from the pH 7 treatment can be separated by overnight ultracentrifugation (Bancroft and Hiebert, 1967); the protein remains in the supernatant. The yield of protein is usually about 50% for CCMV, BMV, and BBMV and the level of RNA contamination about 0.5%. This level can be reduced by $(NH_4)_2SO_4$ precipitation or by the use of various columns (Hermann *et al.*, 1968; Leberman, 1968), but this is not usually done. A reducing agent such as dithiothreitol (Cleland, 1964) is best used in the disassembly procedure and it is wisest to use freshly prepared CCMV and BBMV protein. BMV protein is rather more stable than the other proteins. Virus grown for no longer than 10 days or so is the best protein source. Protein in 1 *M* NaCl at neutrality can be added directly to RNA for subsequent successful reassembly. Virus can also be disassembled in 1 *M* $CaCl_2$ (Yamazaki and Kaesberg, 1963b) or 1 *M* $MgCl_2$, but these salts must be replaced by 1 *M* NaCl prior to addition to RNA which precipitates in 1 *M* Mg or $CaCl_2$ (Hiebert and Bancroft, 1969). Interestingly, with CCMV at least, 3 *M* NaCl does not effectively disassemble the virus. The reason for this is not known, although the high salt could stabilize hydrophobic interactions.

The isolated protein subunits of BMV seem to exist predominately as dimers of the chemical units, as indicated by hydrodynamic studies. This has been interpreted as being the result of hydrophobic association (Stubbs and Kaesberg, 1964). Isolated CCMV subunits seem to exist as trimers (Frist, 1968) but the S value increased with increasing concentrations indicating concentration-dependent association (Frist, personal communication).

The preparation of nucleic acids from these viruses has been accomplished by the phenol method at 22°C (Hiebert *et al.*, 1968). It is unwise to use detergents such as dodecylsulfate during the preparation of RNA for assembly experiments. The effects of chance contamination on added protein are easily evident. Bentonite (Fraenkel-Conrat *et al.*, 1961) is often used in the first phenol extraction and is not usually troublesome, but can cause protein precipitation if used without discrimination. The RNA to be used in assembly experiments is usually dialyzed against either water or 0.01 *M* Tris, pH 7.4, 0.01 *M* KCl, 5×10^{-4} *M* $MgCl_2$, depending on experimental requirements, prior to mixing with protein.

C. Assembly in the Presence of Nucleic Acid

The formation, in a stoichiometric mixture of initially separated RNA and protein, of a nucleoprotein that has the properties of the virus from which the constituents were derived affords proof of reconstitution. If CCMV protein in 1 *M* NaCl near neutrality is mixed with RNA so that the final salt concentration is about 0.5 *M* or higher and the mixture is dialyzed against 0.01 *M* KCl, 0.01 *M* Tris, pH 7.4, 5×10^{-3} *M* $MgCl_2$ at 4°C, nucleoprotein is quantitatively formed which usually consists, depending on the polycation, of two sedimenting species (Fig. 3). The major species sediments at the rate of the virus and is about as infectious as the virus (Bancroft and Hiebert, 1967). However, the infectivity of the naked nucleic acid is also approximately that of the virus, so infectivity in the absence of snake venom phosphodiesterase is not necessarily a measure of proper reassembly. The critical observation is that the infectivity of only the encapsulated RNA is unaffected by the diesterase. Pancreatic ribonuclease is not used in these experiments because native CCMV, as well as BMV and BBMV, is inactivated by the enzyme at pH 5.0, but without appar-

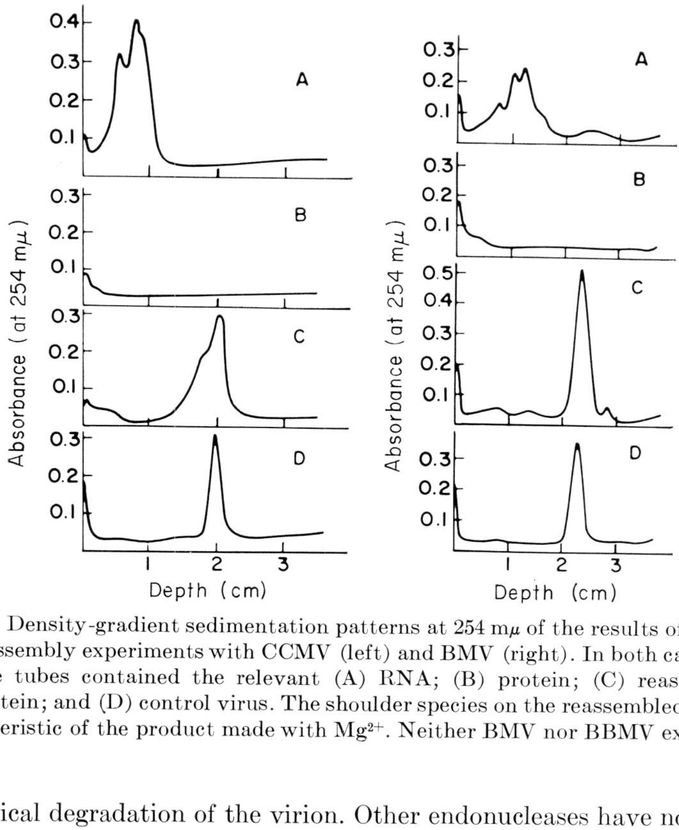

FIG. 3. Density-gradient sedimentation patterns at 254 mμ of the results of homologous reassembly experiments with CCMV (left) and BMV (right). In both cases, the centrifuge tubes contained the relevant (A) RNA; (B) protein; (C) reassembled nucleoprotein; and (D) control virus. The shoulder species on the reassembled CCMV is characteristic of the product made with Mg^{2+}. Neither BMV nor BBMV exhibits a shoulder.

ent physical degradation of the virion. Other endonucleases have not been investigated. The minor or shoulder species, which sediments about 10 S slower than the infective nucleoprotein, is not infective. Both species look like CCMV in the electron microscope, and have about the same electrophoretic mobility, spectral characteristics, and density as the virus (Hiebert *et al.*, 1968). Further, once the reassembled product is formed under the above conditions, it behaves like CCMV at pH 5, and can be converted to the swollen form with the usual loss of infectivity (Hiebert and Bancroft, 1969). The shoulder species is degraded under swelling conditions. Thus, there is fairly good evidence that the major product of CCMV reassembly is very similar and perhaps identical to native CCMV, but that the minor shoulder species is not.

BMV has been subjected to the same conditions for reassembly as has CCMV. Reassembled BMV is about as infectious as native BMV in the presence or absence of diesterase. It looks like the virus in the electron microscope and sediments as one species at the rate of native BMV (Hiebert *et al.*, 1968); the minor slowly sedimenting species found with CCMV is not formed by BMV protein (Fig. 3). Considering the already described heterogeneity of the starting RNA, it is clear that BMV protein is able (as is that of CCMV and BBMV) to encapsulate more than one piece of RNA, but that the molecular weight of the encapsulated RNA does not exceed that of the normal complement (unless it is one large piece; see below). Reassembled BMV does not exhibit all the characteristics of native BMV, however, since only the latter is soluble at pH 5 and is electrophoretically homogeneous (Wagner and Bancroft, 1968). The isolation or assembly conditions required to overcome this difference are not known.

The properties of BBMV, assembled as for CCMV and BMV, are similar to those of the virus. Although limited infectivity assays with reassembled virus suggested susceptibility to diesterase, it has been concluded that BBMV protein can encapsulate RNA properly *in vitro* because BBMV protein:CCMV or BMV-RNA "hybrids," which are easier to assay than BBMV, are resistant to the enzyme (Hiebert *et al.*, 1968).

The responses of self-assembly systems to various systematic alterations of environment not only tell how best to proceed, but give a general indication of the interactions involved. Thus, it is likely that ionic interactions have a critical function in the assembly of CCMV, BMV, and BBMV proteins around nucleic acid since low temperatures, ionic strengths, and divalent cations are required (Hiebert and Bancroft, 1969). These conditions are quite distinct from those used for TMV assembly in which hydrophobic associations seem to predominate (Lauffer and Stevens, 1968).

The effects of divalent cations and pH on the reassembly of the icosahedral viruses are of particular interest and have been investigated in most detail with CCMV. If Mg^{2+} is omitted in the neutral reassembly solution, a slowly sedimenting heterogeneous aggregate is formed which is only slightly infective and which is susceptible to diesterase. If 5×10^{-4} rather than 5×10^{-3} M $MgCl_2$ is used, the product is still defective, although not to the same extent as when Mg^{2+} is absent. Actually, 5×10^{-4} M Mg^{2+} is enough for roughly 1/20 of all the negatively charged viral-associated ions in a typical reassembly experiment and much more than would be expected to be required on the simplest basis and in terms of titration experiments with BMV (Incardona and Kaesberg, 1964). In place of Mg^{2+}, Ca^{2+} may be used and theoretically an isotope such as ^{45}Ca might be useful as a tool. Both Mg^{2+} and Ca^{2+} are more effective in terms of specific infectivity of the product than Sr^{2+}, Co^{2+}, Ni^{2+}, Mn^{2+}, and Fe^{2+}, respectively (Hiebert and Bancroft, 1969). The polyamines 3,3′-diaminodipropylamine, spermidine, and spermine generally function as well as Mg^{2+} in satisfying the polyvalent cation requirement. Interestingly, the slowly sedimenting shoulder associated with CCMV reassembled with Mg^{2+} is largely absent when polyamines are used.

The effect of pH on the assembly process is critical. Although once assembled, CCMV behaves normally at pH 5 to 6, a normal product is not formed if assembly itself is conducted at such pH levels. Thus, if assembly is at pH 5.5, nucleoprotein is made which sediments about 10 S slower than the virus, is not very infective, and is susceptible to diesterase. The acidic product is not greatly affected by Mg^{2+}. CCMV, BMV, and BBMV behave in the same general way but to different degrees to divalent cation and pH changes (Hiebert and Bancroft, 1969).

The conditions used to assemble CCMV can affect both protein and RNA and it is difficult to prove that the effect of Mg^{2+} is more critical in regard to the behavior of the protein than it is to the behavior of the RNA. It is probable, however, that the effect of Mg^{2+} on the nucleic acid is merely incidental because a variety of nucleating agents (see below) with presumably different conformations can be used with CCMV protein to form spheres. Further, the effect of Mg^{2+} on assembly is quite different at pH 5.5 and 7.0 where the conformation of the RNA would not be greatly different at the same temperature and KCl and $MgCl_2$ concentrations. Also, Mg^{2+} affects swollen virus in which the conformation of the RNA is already dictated to a large extent by the protein. Last, Mg^{2+} is apparently unessential to the assembly of the icosahedral cucumber mosaic virus (see below).

A hypothesis for assembly should not disregard the conditions required for disassembly since the two processes may represent different aspects of the same thing. An outline of CCMV assembly in terms of the behavior of the virus (Hiebert and Bancroft, 1969) is presented in Fig. 2. It is probable that when subunits are released from the virus at neutrality, their acidic and basic groups are ionized. When RNA is added and the ionic strength decreased during dialysis against reassembly solution, the basic groups may form ionic linkages with the nucleic acid and the protein subunits are cooperatively stabilized with critical carboxylate ions forming the termini for specific intersubunit Mg^{2+} bridges necessary for correct positioning. As the pH is subsequently lowered, carboxylate ions become protonated, Mg^{2+} is lost, and hydrogen bonds form to stabilize the particle in the normal or fast form. Virus assembled at pH levels where the carboxyl groups might not be ionized, after the subunits come together on the nucleic acid, would be improperly assembled perhaps because the protein conformation could be changed and because carboxyl groups not normally associated might become hydrogen bonded since Mg^{2+} would not function as a positioner at that pH. This being the case, the effect of Mg^{2+} on assembly at about pH 6 and below should be less than near neutrality and this is found experimentally. Such a simple scheme ignores most of the subunit amino acids and possible hydrophobic contributions and has no direct proof to support it, but it does have internal consistency in terms of present data and of factors affecting the virus and its assembly and incorporates events that could occur *in vivo*.

D. Foreign Nucleating Agents

There is no present evidence to suggest that specificity exists between particular nucleic acids and proteins in capsid formation with spherical plant viruses. CCMV, BMV, and BBMV offer, when disassembled, nine protein-RNA reassembly possibilities and all have been accomplished physically. CCMV protein formed the slowly sedimenting shoulder regardless of which RNA was used and had the same electrophoretic mobility with BMV-RNA, for example, as with its own RNA. In other words, the sedimentation and electrophoretic properties were those of the protein donors. Infectivity assays were conducted with the six nucleoproteins containing either CCMV or BMV-RNA. All were infective and all resisted diesterase treatment (Hiebert *et al.*, 1968). Such results have been considered in terms of possible phenotypic mixing, a phenomenon that probably has been established for plant viruses with barley yellow dwarf virus (Rochow, 1969) and which seems to be operative in a special case involving normal and temperature-sensitive strains of TMV (Sakar, 1969), and which may be important in "helper" systems (Smith, 1946; Hull and Adams, 1968). CCMV protein, if freshly made and used, resulted in the most infective particles with both CCMV and BMV-RNA, regardless of the assay host. Changes in protein coat neither extended nor restricted the host range of a particular nucleic acid insofar as tested.

The RNA's of CCMV, BMV, and BBMV have about the same molecular weight and somewhat similar base ratios and all come from $T = 3$ particles. TMV-RNA has a molecular weight of 2×10^6 and quite a distinct base ratio. Initial observations (Hiebert *et al.*, 1968) showed that CCMV-protein encapsulated TMV-RNA (protein:RNA = 4:1) to form a product sedimenting at the rate expected of a particle containing twice as much RNA as usual and having the diffusion coefficient of a CCMV protein $T = 3$ sphere, which was reasonable from electron microscope observations. The infectivity of such particles was about 9% of the TMV used as the RNA source. Particles with CCMV, BMV, and BBMV proteins were subsequently assembled with diesterase-resistant infectivities about equal to that of TMV. The CCMV protein coated particles, at least, are photoreactivable (Gordon, personal communication) whereas TMV is not. Highly infective particles were made if protein was added to RNA in such amounts (10:1) that particles sedimenting at about 150 S were formed (Verduin and Bancroft, 1969). This type of result presents interpretative problems not encountered with tubular viruses and it was suggested on a basis of mainly hydrodynamic considerations that such particles were probably $T = 7$. That is, the proteins of these spherical viruses, at least, responded optimally in terms of infectivity by changing lattice number. That lattice numbers can change with proteins from spherical viruses was first noted in self-assembly experiments with CCMV and BMV which formed $T = 1$ particles in ribonuclease-treated swollen virus preparations (Bancroft *et al.*, 1967). The $T = 1$ particles did not form in the absence of ribonuclease-digested RNA and probably resulted from combination with oligonucleotides (Bancroft *et al.*, 1969a). The ability of these protein subunits to assemble in different icosahedral shells may signify different bonding regions at different radii on the sides of the structure units. Studies on the stabilities of particles other than those of the $T = 3$ class have not been made.

A variety of other naturally occurring nucleic acids in addition to TMV-RNA has been used with CCMV-protein at a protein:nucleic acid ratio of 3:1 (Hiebert *et al.*, 1968). Thus, spherical particles have been made with RNA from bacteriophage f_2, soybean ribosomal RNA, and yeast sRNA. With the latter, it was estimated on a basis of the sedimentation rate of the nucleoprotein that about 25 molecules were encapsulated in each shell. Single-stranded DNA from bacteriophage S-13 has also been successfully used as a nucleating agent suggesting that circular as well as noncircular nucleic acids can be encapsulated. The use of double-stranded calf-thymus DNA of a molecular weight of about 1.5×10^6 has resulted, with BMV protein, but not with those from CCMV or BBMV, in the production of so far unique linear forms (Fig. 4) (Bancroft *et al.*, 1969b). It would be of interest to use DNA from cauliflower mosaic virus (Shepherd *et al.*, 1968) since biological as well as structural observations could be made.

A series of homo- and heteropolyribonucleotides have also been used with CCMV, BMV, and BBMV proteins (Bancroft *et al.*, 1969b). All have resulted in the production of spherical particles, those made from polyinosinic acid or polyinosinic-guanylic acid, which would be expected to have a good deal of self structure, being insoluble. In addition, oligouridylic acid, containing an average of 23 nucleotides, served as nucleating agent. The product with BMV protein, at least, contained mainly what were probably $T = 1$ particles (Bancroft *et al.*, 1969b). This suggests that this oligonucleotide size was close to that utilized in the RNase-treated RNA preparations used previously in the preparation of $T = 1$ particles (Bancroft *et al.*, 1969a).

Uridylic acid, for example, does not act as a nucleating agent. Moreover, if mononucleotide is mixed with a CCMV protein preparation before CCMV-RNA is added prior to dialysis against reassembly solution, nor-

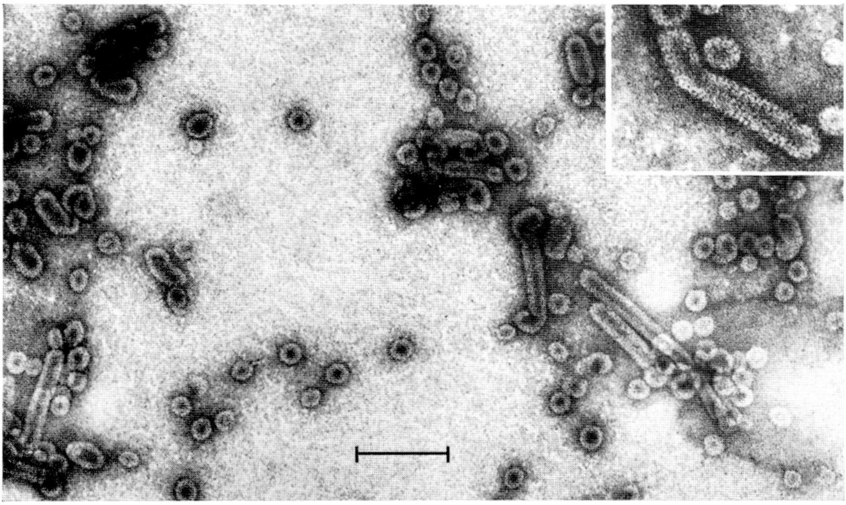

FIG. 4. Electron micrographs of bacilliform particles from preparations containing BMV protein and calf-thymus DNA. Scale line = 0.1 μ. The inset (*top right*) is of a particle at higher magnification showing 37 Å striations. Stained in uranyl acetate.

mal spheres form. This suggests that uridylic acid does not compete efficiently against CCMV-RNA in the assembly process (Bancroft *et al.*, 1969a). Nor does arginine compete against protein subunits for nucleic acid.

In addition to nucleic acids, polyvinyl sulfate, sodium dextran sulfate, and polygalacturonic acid (Frist, 1968) have been used successfully as nucleating agents with CCMV protein. The critical property shared by all nucleating agents is that they are polyanions.

The lack of specificity in capsid formation in the above *in vitro* reactions presents certain problems if taken at face value. It is not known if structure units are initially laid down in any particular order at any particular place on a given nucleating agent when capsids are to be formed. There is a specific aggregate, called "complex I," in which five or so bacteriophage coat protein subunits become attached *in vivo* and probably *in vitro* only to homologous RNA (Sugiyama *et al.*, 1967) to act as a repressor of phage noncoat protein synthesis (Eggen and Nathans, 1969). This regulatory complex apparently need not be connected with capsid formation *in vitro*, at least, since the latter is nonspecific with simple RNA phages (Hohn, 1969) just as it is with plant viruses. However, specific complex I-type aggregates apparently are not formed with at least some plant virus proteins since ^{14}C-labeled BMV protein binds equally well with high multiplicities of either BMV- or CCMV-RNA under a number of conditions (unpublished). Even if the specific aggregates were found to occur, the possibility that in a population of spherical virus particles there is diversity in the detailed arrangement of nucleotide sequences vis-a-vis protein subunits in terms of symmetry axes would not necessarily be eliminated. This might be minimized *in vivo* if RNA were coated as it was synthesized. Host polyanions are probably not found coated with viral proteins because the host products themselves would usually be complexed and, even if they were not, have locations distinct from that of the viral proteins. Exceptions may occur, however, since the pseudovirions of polyoma virus contain mouse DNA (Winocour, 1969). A prerequisite for the coating of host polyanions would be the existence of a viral subunit pool. There is evidence for such pools with TMV. Further, phenotypic mixing would require their presence. The nucleic acid-free top components found associated with many spherical plant viruses may represent a special type of pool. The idea that RNA may go into or onto preformed shells as suggested for polio virus procapsids (Jacobson and Baltimore, 1968) is not supported by the best *in vitro* experiments with simple plant and bacterial viruses although there is evidence that some nucleic acid may enter or go onto preformed 52 S CCMV protein capsids (see below).

E. Mixed Coats

The distinct electrophoretic and serological properties of CCMV, BMV, and BBMV, the proteins of which have different amino acid compositions and molecular weights (Bancroft *et al.*, 1968a; Miki and Knight, 1965; Stubbs and Kaesberg, 1964; Yamazaki and Kaesberg, 1963a), have been exploited in immunoelectrophoretic experiments designed to determine if structure units from more than one virus may occur in a single particle. If mixed coat particles did not form, then two populations of nucleoproteins with the electrophoretic and serological characteristics of the protein donors would result upon the addition of a mixture of proteins to nucleic acid. Alternatively, if more than one structure type could occur in an individual particle, then a heterogeneous population of particles with an average electrophoretic rate, depending on the ratio of proteins, intermediate between those of the parents would be formed which would react with antisera to either of the parents. The latter possibility has been shown to be correct with various mixtures principally between CCMV, and BMV, and CCMV and BBMV proteins (Wagner and Bancroft, 1968). The particles that were formed had a normal appearance and were not of the double-

TABLE I

EFFECT OF pH AND NaCl CONCENTRATION ON CCMV PROTEIN ASSEMBLED AT 6°C

Buffer, 0.01 *M*	pH	NaCl concentration								
		0			0.1 *M*			0.2 *M*		
		$s_{20,w}$		Predominant EM form	$s_{20,w}$		Predominant EM form	$s_{20,w}$		Predominant EM form
		Major	Minor		Major	Minor		Major	Minor	
Glycine	3	2.7	—	Disorganized	10	—	Disorganized	52	18	Sphere and disorganized
Acetate	3.5	2.7	52	Sphere and laminar	52	45(10)[c]	Sphere	52	—	Sphere
Acetate	4.0	2.7	80–100[a]	Laminar	52	45(10)	Sphere	52	—	Sphere
Acetate	4.5	2.7	80–100[a]	Laminar and plate	52[b]	45(10)	Sphere			
Acetate	5.0	Precipitate	—	Few laminar and sphere	52[b]	—	Sphere	52	—	Sphere
Acetate	5.3	NT[d]	NT	NT	NT	NT	NT	52	110	Sphere with shell
Acetate	5.7	NT	NT	NT	NT	NT	NT	2.7	110	Sphere and rosette
Cacodylate phosphate	6.0	2.7	—[a]	Disorganized	2.7[a]	—	Tube[e]	2.7[a]	110	Tube
Cacodylate phosphate	7.0	2.7	—[a]	Disorganized	2.7[a]	—	Tube	NT	NT	NT
Tris	8.0	NT	NT	NT	NT	NT	Tube	NT	NT	NT
Tris	9.5	NT	NT	NT	NT	NT	Disorganized	NT	NT	NT

[a] Partial precipitate.
[b] Some protein preparations precipitated completely; others remained soluble.
[c] In some preparations, the 10 S rather than the 45 S component formed.
[d] NT designates not tested.
[e] All tubes were of the narrow type (Bancroft *et al.*, 1967).

shelled type (see below). The infectivities of the various mixtures were usually high enough to suggest that some mixed coat particles themselves were infectious. All particles that were infective remained so after diesterase treatments.

The responses of the mixed-capsid particles to pH have not been tested and the bonding associations between different proteins as compared to those between like proteins are not known. A nucleating agent is not always required for the formation of mixed capsids since mixtures of BMV and CCMV proteins, if dialzyed against 0.2 *M* NaCl, pH 5, form mixed pseudo-top component capsids (see below).

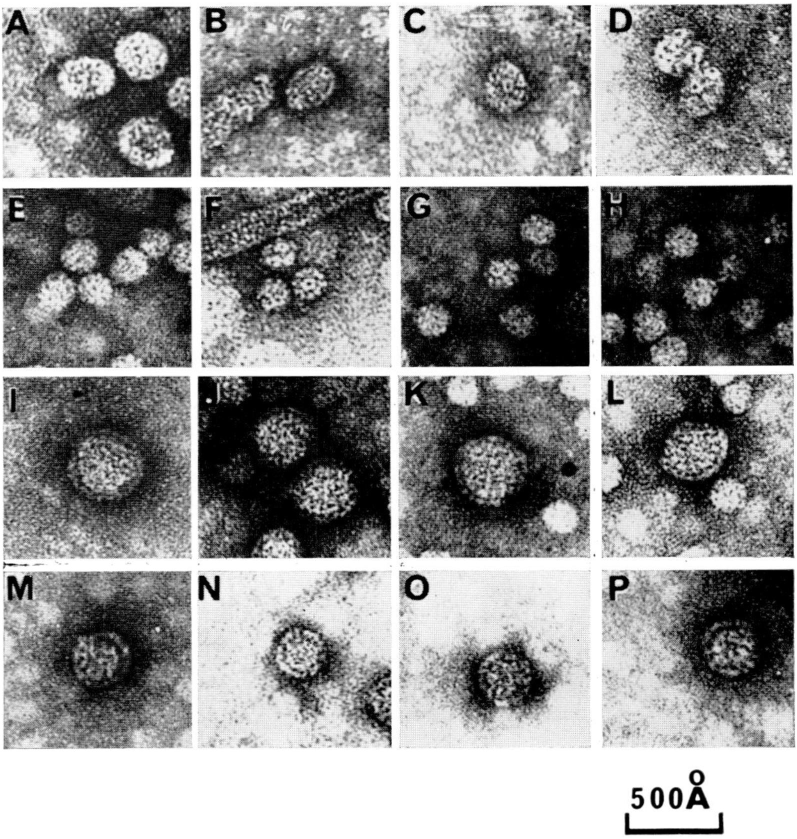

FIG. 5. Electron micrographs of different particle types after treatment of "swollen" CCMV with pancreatic ribonuclease or takadiastase T_1 enzyme. (A–D) 210 × 280 Å, 45 S ellipsoidal particles; (E–H) 160 Å, 31 S small spheres; (I–L) 340 Å, 135 S viruslike particles with a double outer shell; (M–P) 250 Å small spheres with a double outer shell. Stained in uranyl acetate.

F. Assembly in the Absence of Nucleic Acid

CCMV protein, particularly, may aggregate in a number of ways depending upon conditions (Figs 5–12; Table I). The initial description (Bancroft *et al.*, 1967) of some of the structures formed by CCMV protein were of products generated in a mixture of RNase-digested RNA plus protein. This situation arose because the disassembly experiments at the time were performed by RNase digestion of the RNA inside swollen virus. It is now known that the only particles directly requiring RNA for their formation were the 31 S 160 Å $T = 1$ (Fig. 5) and 250 Å $T = 3$ spheres found in these preparations. These particles themselves served as nucleating agents for CCMV protein, so that the 250 Å "small-doubles" (Fig. 5) or $T = 1$ particles surrounded by an extra protein coat and the 340 Å "virus-doubles" (Fig. 5) or $T = 3$ particles also surrounded by an extra coat, were formed; RNA was thus only indirectly involved in the formation of these particles. The 45 Å radial increase would suggest that the ends of the subunits might be buried in the surface of the underlying particles. The formation of the "small-doubles" has not since been systematically reinvestigated and the part played by takadiastase T_1 as originally described is worth further study. "Virus-doubles" can easily be made if CCMV protein is added in excess to either reassembled or native CCMV. The electrophoretic mobility of such particles is less than that of the virus and the subunits can be removed by trypsin (unpublished). If RNA is added to the "virus-doubles," the outer protein coat is removed and assembles around the added RNA (unpublished). The "virus-doubles" are infective and have a sedimentation rate of about 135 S. This rate is not necessarily consistent with the idea that the extra coat around the $T = 3$ particles is a $T = 7$ shell, as suggested as perhaps being the case (Bancroft *et al.*, 1967). CCMV protein can go around viruses other than CCMV, the most interesting case being that of the formation on TMV of an extra coat the geometry of which is related to that of the underlying TMV particle (Frist, personal communication). A 45 S 210 × 280 Å ellipsoidal particle type (Fig. 5) has also been noted. It was originally considered that this particle type may have arisen from reorganization rather than assembly, but this currently seems questionable.

In addition to the various spherical self-assembled forms just mentioned, single- and double-walled tubular aggregates with rounded ends and with diameters of 160 and 250 Å, respectively, were found (Fig. 6). The production of the latter form was usually, but not always, mediated by takadiastase T_1 for as yet unknown reasons. These aggregates, usually of the 160 Å or narrow tube variety, can easily be made in 0.1 *M* or 0.2 *M* NaCl (but not 0.01 *M* NaCl) near neutrality in the absence of RNA (Bancroft *et al.*, 1969a) and show that the preferred bonding pattern for the isolated CCMV protein near pH 7.0 is distinct from that found in the presence of RNA. That is, the minimum free energy form for the protein itself near neutrality may be a tubular structure whereas that for protein in the presence of RNA is an icosahedron.

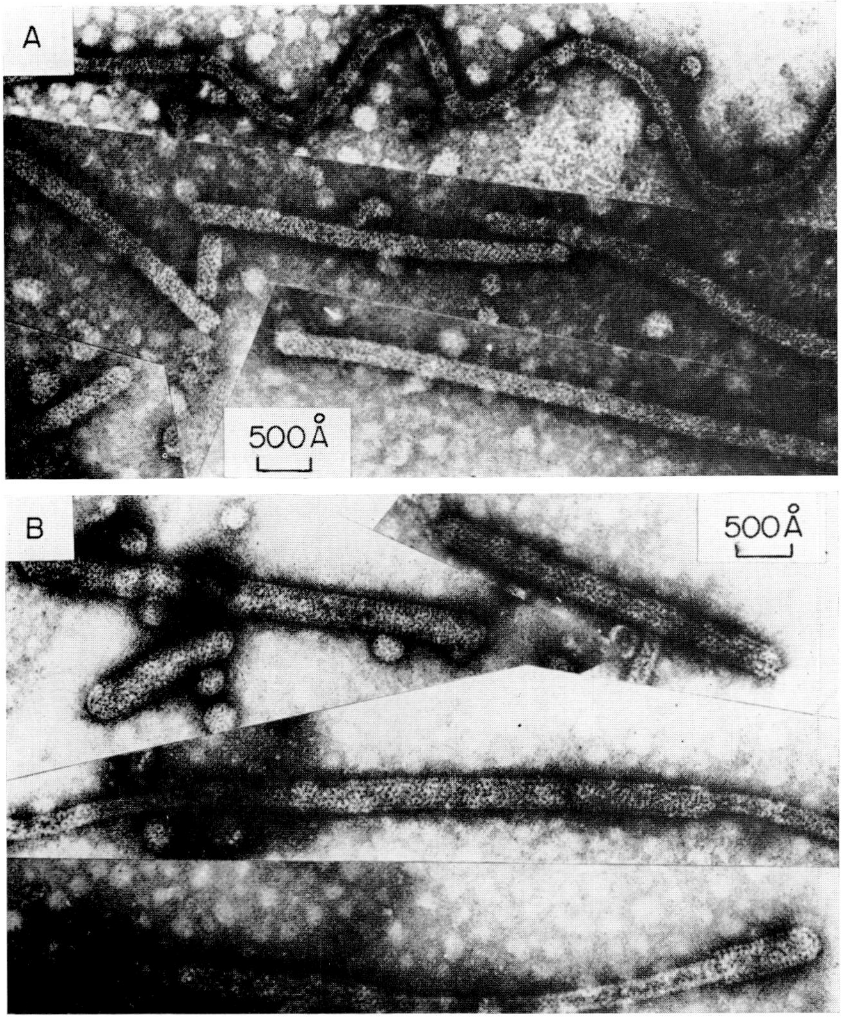

FIG. 6. Electron micrographs of (A) 160 Å narrow tubes and (B) 250 Å wide tubes. These tubes in these particular preparations were prepared by treating "swollen" CCMV with pancreatic ribonuclease for (A) and takadiastase T_1 for (B). Stained in uranyl acetate.

The structure of the tubular forms has been analyzed by obtaining optical diffraction patterns by the passage of coherent light through suitable electron micrographs of negatively stained tubes (Bancroft *et al.*, 1967). The patterns showed the same features and orientation for both the narrow and wide tubes, indicating similarity of structure. Analysis was based on the reasonable premise that the optical transforms represented areas of stain deposition in the centers of hexamers and where any three hexamers met, so that the measured pitch of 42 Å, which can be seen directly in micrographs, was actually ½ of the minor dimension of a hexamer. The

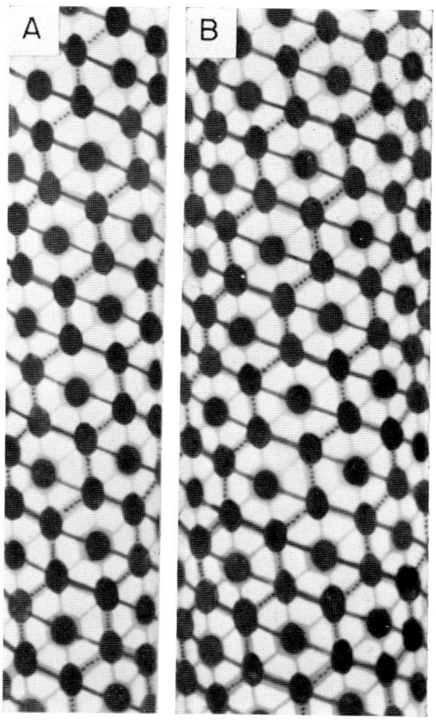

FIG. 7. (A) An idealized drawing of the surface of a narrow tube, showing the way hexamers may be packed to form a helix having 5.6 hexamers per turn when superimposed over the double helix, shown as continuous liners, derived by locating stain absorbing areas in the centers of the hexamers and at places where 3 hexamers meet. Note that the pitch of the double helix is steeper and reversed in sense to that of the hexamer helix and that the spacing of the double helix is half that of the width of a hexamer. (B) A diagram of a wide tube composed of coaxial pairs of helices, each with 28 hexamers in 3 turns of the helix, derived from stain accumulation centers as in A.

positions of stain accumulation were reconcilable with hexamer packing (Fig. 7). The narrow tubes are composed of hexamers so arranged that 5.6 occurred in each turn of a single helix with a pitch of 84 Å, the pitch angle being about 9° to the short axis. The tubes were rounded off at the ends presumably by pentamers. The wide tubes are constructed in a similar fashion except that they are composed of coaxial pairs of helices, each with 28 hexamers in three turns of the helix (Fig. 7). Further indications of the general validity (certain variations in detail are possible) of

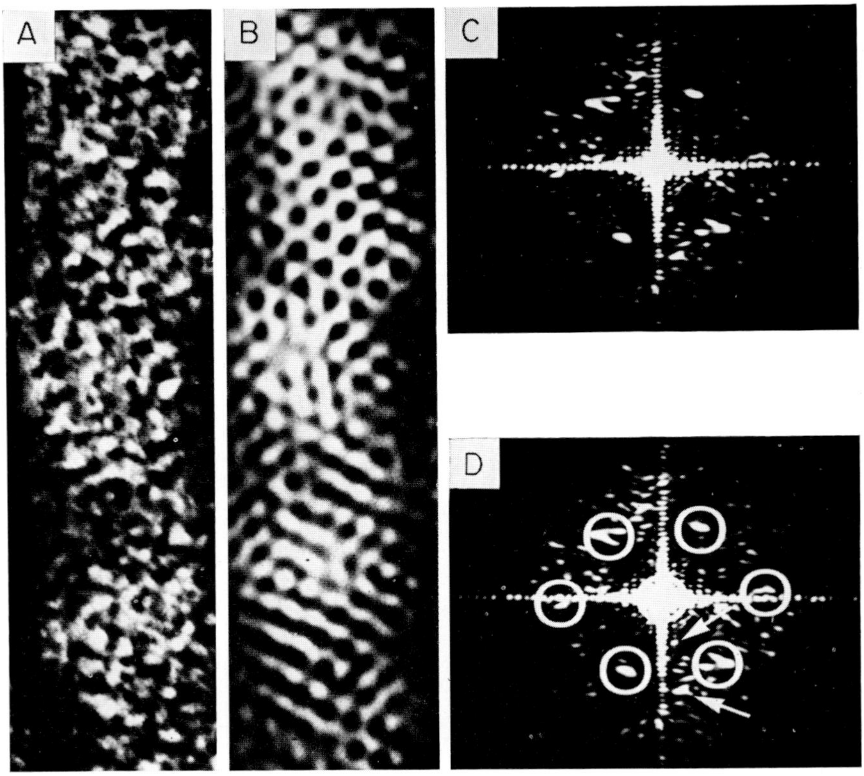

FIG. 8. Image reconstruction of a wide tube. (A) Original electron micrograph of wide tube used for the image reconstruction; (B) reconstructed image with "noise" removed by mask, containing information only from the six major diffracted rays and the undeviated ray, and showing the hexagonal distribution of stain which is particularly good in the top third; (C) optical transform from the area of A corresponding to the best region of B; (D) optical transform identical with C, but showing the areas of the diffraction pattern used for the image reconstruction inside the seven white circles.

the proposed structures were obtained by taking transforms of photographs of drawings of the structures and also by reconstituting the general structure of a tube optically, from its transform, after filtering out "noise" from the original micrograph by means of a suitably drilled diaphragm placed in the position of the diffraction pattern, as it occurred in the diffractometer (Fig. 8). Models of the various spherical and tubular forms are shown in Fig. 9. The tubes formed *in vivo* by many, but not all, oncogenic viruses are constructed in the same pattern as CCMV tubes, but with different dimensions (Bancroft *et al.*, 1967). Neither BMV nor BBMV proteins form tubes under any conditions yet tested.

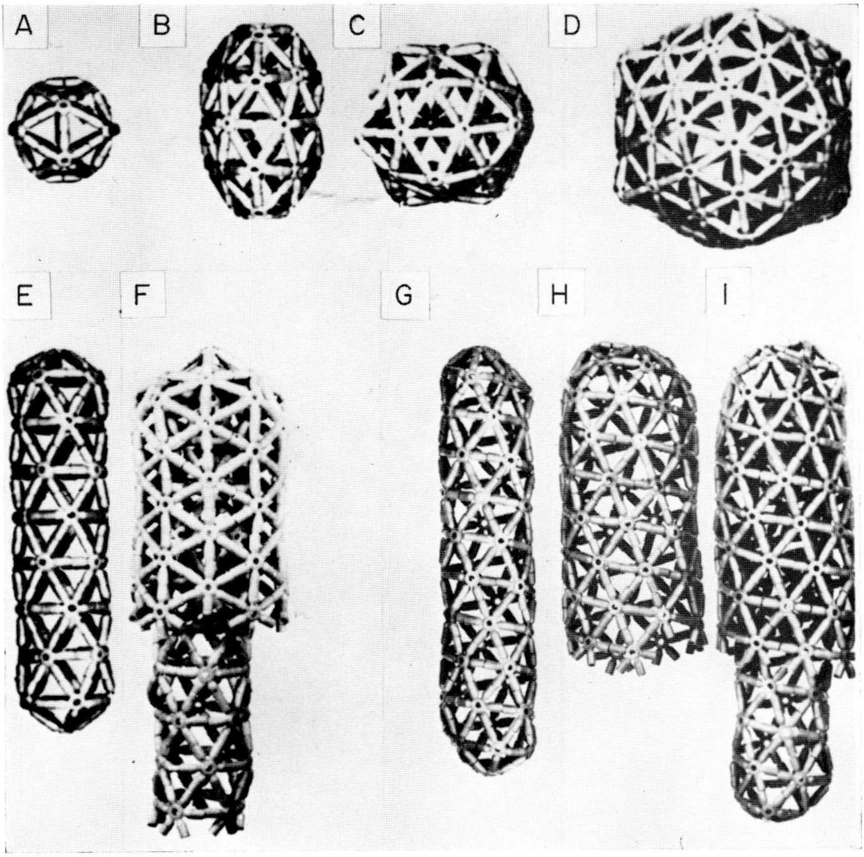

FIG. 9. Models constructed from Geodestix pentamer and hexamer connectors of (A) small icosahedral "sphere;" (B) ellipsoid; (C) CCMV; (D) outer shell of viruslike particle with a double shell; (E) narrow tube constructed by interpolating hexamer subunits along five-fold axes of an icosahedron; (F) wide tube constructed by interpolating hexamer subunits along five-fold axes of a rhombic triacontrahedron enclosing a narrow tube. Models E and F do not represent the actual structure of the tubes; (G) narrow tube; (H) wide tube; both G and H are models of structures deduced from the optical transforms seen in Fig. 8A and C; (I) wide tube enclosing narrow tube.

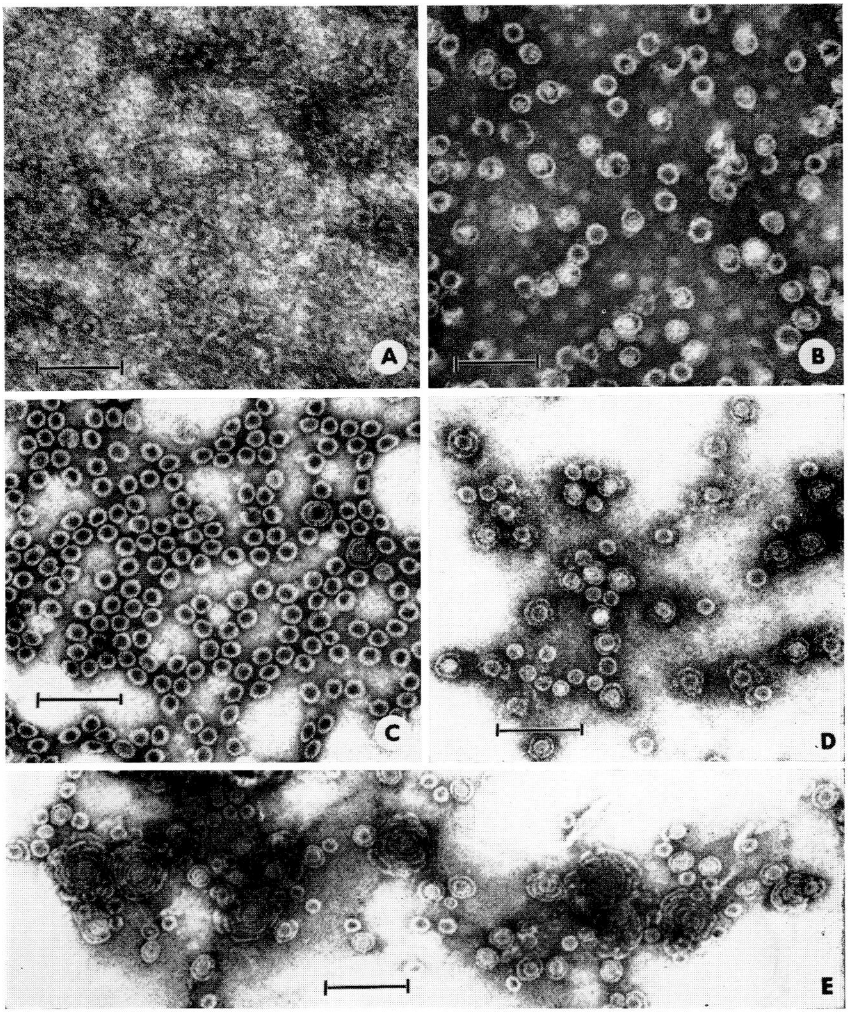

FIG. 10. Forms assumed by CCMV protein after dialysis against 0.1 *M* or 0.2 *M* NaCl at pH levels from 3 to 5.7 (A) 0.1 *M* NaCl, pH 3.0, showing 10 S protein product; (B) 0.1 *M* NaCl, pH 3.5, showing 4 S and 52 S particles; (C) 0.1 *M* NaCl, pH 5.0, showing largely 250 Å 52 S PT particles; (D) 0.2 *M* NaCl, pH 5.7, showing 410 Å 110 S double-shelled PT particles; (E) 0.2 *M* NaCl, pH 5.7, showing rosettes. D was fixed in 0.5% glutaraldehyde, pH 4.6, and stained in 1% PTA, pH 6.0; A–C and E were directly stained in uranyl acetate. Scale line = 0.1 μ.

CCMV protein is capable of forming aggregates other than tubes with a slight change in pH (Fig. 10, Table I). Thus, in 0.1 *M* NaCl at pH 6.0, tubes are found, whereas, at pH 5.7 complicated "rosettes" (Fig. 10) are common. These appear to be composed of capsids, surrounded by ribbons of protein (Bancroft *et al.*, 1969a). Another form found with CCMV is the "pseudo-top (PT) doubles" as opposed to the "virus-doubles" formed at pH 6.0 and above. The "PT-doubles" are presumably (sequential additions have not been done) made from the addition of an extra protein coat to the outside of nucleic acid-free spheres so that the final diameter of the particles, which sediment at about 110 S, is approximately 410 Å. This is about the size that would be expected if the outside protein subunits did not enter into the surface of the central particle. Apparently similar forms have been described for wild cucumber mosaic virus *in vivo* (Hitchborn and Hills, 1965).

Spherical particles (Fig. 10) with a sedimentation rate slightly less than that predicted for a nucleic acid-free CCMV sphere and with the surface structure of CCMV can be made quantitatively if CCMV protein is dialyzed to pH 5.0 in 0.2 *M* NaCl (Bancroft *et al.*, 1968b; Finch and Bancroft, 1968). These particles, which are called 52 S or "pseudo-top" (PT) because their charge differs from that of the virus, form only at pH 5.0 or below, depending on salt concentration. Their electrophoretic mobility is -4.3×10^{-5} cm^2 volt^{-1} sec^{-1} as opposed to one of -5.2×10^{-5} cm^2 volt^{-1} sec^{-1} for the virus under the same conditions. If RNA is added to CCMV, nothing obvious happens, but if it is added to PT, precipitation occurs. This suggests that PT has basic groups not exposed on CCMV. Interestingly, if the precipitate is treated with pancreatic ribonuclease, the solubilized product sediments at 70 S suggesting that about 0.5×10^6 molecular weight units of RNA have become associated in some way with the PT particles (unpublished). In spite of the possibility of exposed basic groups on CCMV-PT, the particles are not susceptible to trypsin under conditions in which trypsin will digest CCMV protein (unpublished). Regardless of the charge differences, serological tests using antisera to both CCMV-PT and CCMV show no differences between the particles.

Protein isolated from BMV will also form PT particles in 0.2 *M* NaCl, pH 5.0 acetate buffer. These have about the same relationship to BMV as does CCMV-PT to CCMV. CCMV and BMV protein will coaggregate, as noted, to form mixed-capsid PT particles (unpublished). BBMV will not form PT particles. The largest aggregates found with BBMV protein comprise a heterogeneous 25 S population found in 0.2 *M* NaCl, pH 5.0. The aggregates do not look organized in the electron microscope.

The stability of CCMV-PT has been compared with that of the virus. If it is assumed that the protein subunits of CCMV and CCMV-PT are, notwithstanding the differences in surface charge, held together the same way, then PT should dissociate at neutrality, under which conditions the virus would be swollen, and at a low ionic strength, since RNA is not present. PT does indeed dissociate at pH 7.0 in 0.1 *M* NaCl. If Mg^{2+} is directly added to PT and the protein is dialyzed to pH 7 with Mg^{2+}, it still falls apart indicating that even if Mg^{2+} bridges are formed between subunits, they are not of sufficient strength to hold the particle together in the absence of RNA under conditions in which the subunits themselves presumably are able to form the maximum number of bonds as tubular structures. A number of compounds such as EDTA, glutaric acid, and lysine have also been tested as stabilizers under various conditions but with no effect; however, the RNA-treated PT mentioned previously may have some distinctive properties.

The aggregation form of CCMV protein depends on its history. If protein in 0.5 *M* NaCl is dialyzed to pH 6 in 0.5 *M* NaCl, it remains largely dissociated, but if it is first dialyzed directly to pH 5 in 0.5 NaCl before back dialysis to pH 6, it remains as PT (unpublished). Thus, the protein can exist in two distinct and kinetically stable states under the same conditions depending on its previous treatment.

If CCMV protein is dialyzed to pH 3.5 to 4.0 rather than pH 5 in 0.1 *M* NaCl, either 45 S (Fig. 10) or 10 S aggregates are found in addition to the 52 S form, depending on the preparation (Bancroft *et al.*, 1969a). The 45 S particles are somewhat disorganized spheres. No organized structures are seen at pH 3.0, 0.1 *M* NaCl (Fig. 10). The structure of the 10 S form is not obvious in the electron microscope, but may be composed of aggregates of six structure units since its molecular weight, as determined by sedimentation-equilibrium, is about 123,000 (unpublished). The latter form is not apparent at pH 3.5 if assembly occurs at 37°C in 0.2 *M* NaCl—only PT being observed, conceivably as a consequence of hydrophobic association.

It should be remembered that the formation of PT is due to a self-assembly process and is distinct from the production of artificial top component (ATC) particles made by the evacuation of RNA from normal nucleocapsids. The production of an ATC was first described by Kaper (1960) from turnip yellow mosaic virus. Subsequently, Incardona (1968) titrated BMV to pH 12 in 1 *M* KCl, the method being similar to that described in detail by Kaper (1964) for turnip yellow mosaic virus, to obtain a product sedimenting at about 50 *S*. Essentially the same experiments have been done with CCMV which yields an ATC product sedimenting at about 54 *S* and with BBMV which does not form an ATC (unpublished). The CCMV-ATC particles are considerably more angular than are PT particles in the electron microscope. The isolated ATC, which has a protein spectrum, is stable in 1 *M* KCl at pH 5 but not at 0.2 *M* KCl at the same pH and so has a stability different from that of PT. If the evacuated RNA is not removed from ATC and the solution is dialyzed to 0.2 *M* NaCl or KCl pH 5, the ATC is stable and sediments at about 70 S. This suggests that ATC is able to accept RNA as can PT. CCMV protein will not assemble to form capsids in 1 *M* KCl at pH 12, but rather forms a product sedimenting at about 7 S. The basis of the stability of CCMV-ATC is not known and its occurrence is inconsistent with the ideas used to explain the behavior of CCMV.

Protein from CCMV, but not from BMV or BBMV, forms a distinct series of aggregates, called the laminar and plate forms, in about 0.01 *M* solutions at pH levels (4.0 to 4.5 being best) where PT forms in 0.1 or higher salt molarities. The laminar forms (Fig. 11) appear to be composed of series of arcs of protein, each arc being formed upon a preceding one which acts as a nucleating agent, the structure apparently being usually initiated at the surface of a PT particle. Helices and knocked-over stacked discs were considered and rejected as possibilities. Occasionally, two or more series of arcs can be seen issuing from the surface of a single PT and sometimes single large arcs form on more than a single PT particle. The plate form sometimes occurs in the same low salt preparations as the arc form. The plates (Figs. 11 and 12) are composed of hexamers, as would be expected and as evidenced by optical transforms (Fig. 12), and occur singly or in stacks. Neither the laminar nor plate structures form in the presence of RNA.

G. Serology

The serological characteristics of the proteins in various states of assembly as related to each other and to disassembled protein are worth attention. With CCMV, we have routinely checked with various precipitin tests that the various forms which have been described at least react against antisera made to the virus. All do, but only CCMV-PT and CCMV have been examined by reciprocal cross-absorption experiments. These showed CCMV and CCMV-PT to be indistinguishable, but this does not mean that all forms representing different quaternary associations will behave in the same way. We have not been able to make antisera to disassembled CCMV protein that would react either homologously or with CCMV nor have we been able to observe a reaction between disassembled protein and antiserum to the virus.

Antiserum has, however, been made to BMV protein prepared in $CaCl_2$, formalinized antigens best being used, by von Wechmar and van Regenmortel (1968) who showed that antigenic groups which are probably buried in the intact particle, existed specific for the dissociated protein. They further demonstrated that groups specific for the capsid surface existed and sug-

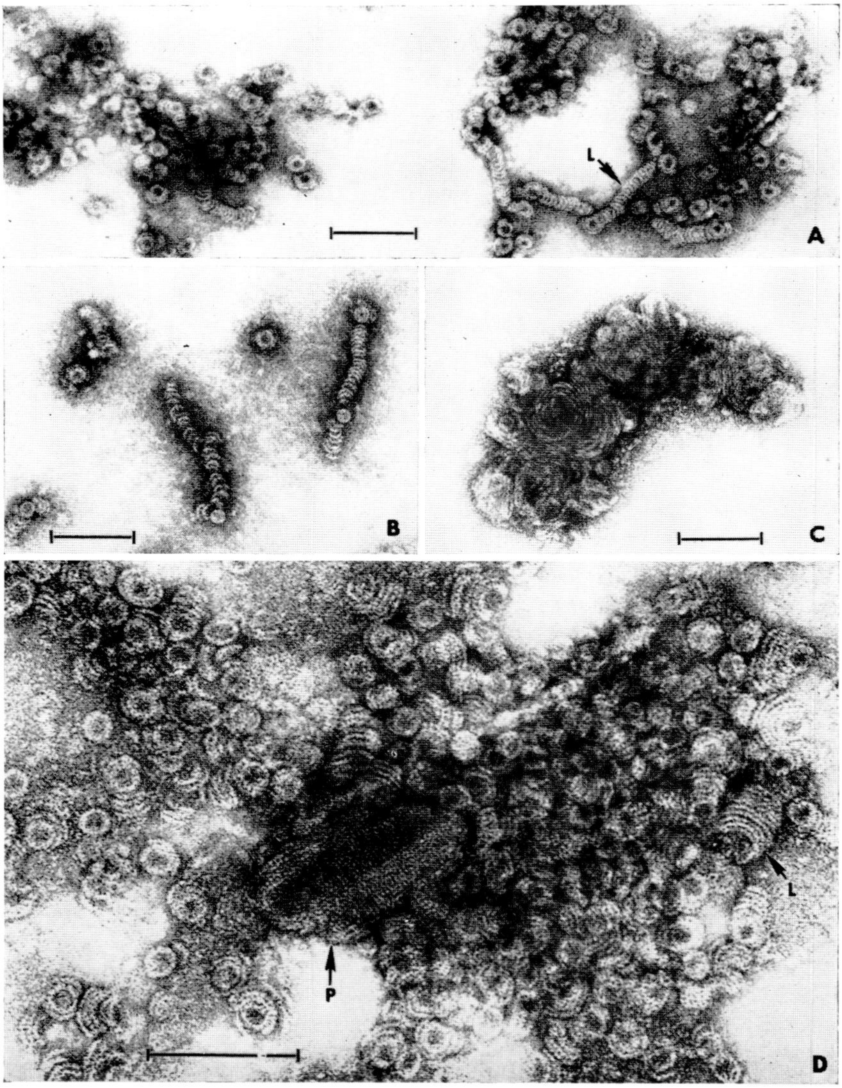

FIG. 11. Laminar (L) and plate (P) forms assumed by CCMV protein after dialysis of different preparations against 0.01 *M* acetate, pH 4.5, buffer. (A) Laminar forms fixed in glutaraldehyde and stained with uranyl acetate; (B) laminar forms fixed in glutaraldehyde and stained in PTA; (C) complicated laminar form; and (D) mixture of laminar and plate forms in the same preparation stained in uranyl acetate. Scale lines = 0.1 μ.

gested that these groups were perhaps generated by the favorable positioning of residues on neighboring structure units, although other possibilities were considered. This observation confirmed, in principle, a similar one made by Rappaport *et al.* (1965) for phenol-dissociated turnip yellow mosiac virus.

III. Cucumber Mosaic Virus

Cucumber mosaic virus (CMV) is a single-component icosahedral virus which exists naturally as a number of strains of different stabilities. Several

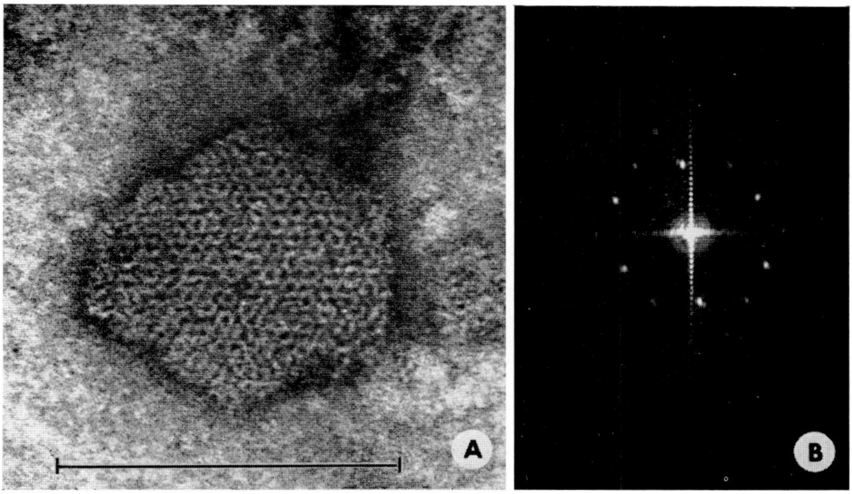

Fig. 12. (A) Plate form of CCMV protein found after dialysis against 0.01 *M* acetate buffer, pH 4.5. Stained in uranyl acetate. Scale line = 0.1 μ. (B) Optical transform of (A).

different molecular weights have been published for the virus, the currently most internally consistent being those of van Regenmortel (1967) for the stable S strain. Thus, sedimentation-diffusion measurements gave a molecular weight of 6.3×10^6 and sedimentation-equilibrium determinations one of 6.7×10^6 avograms. The hydrodynamic molecular weight of the protein subunits initially isolated in 1 *M* $CaCl_2$ was 32,200. The subunits apparently existed as monomers since a molecular weight of 32,000 was found by addition of the weights of the 287 amino acid residues found in the chemical unit. Finch *et al.* (1967) determined that CMV was of the $T = 3$ class, and in view of its extraordinarily large structure units, regarded it as a "scaled-up" version of BBMV. The RNA of the virus has a molecular weight approximating to 1.0×10^6 and exists as three classes with sedimentation coefficients of 13.3, 19.6, and 22.9 S (Kaper *et al.*, 1965) only the largest class being infective (Diener *et al.*, 1964). Most strains of the virus are stable at pH levels around 9, aggregate very easily with low concentrations of Ca^{2+} (Francki *et al.*, 1966) and Mg^{2+}, and dissociate in either 1.5 *M* KCl (Kaper *et al.*, 1965), 2.0 *M* LiCl (Francki *et al.*, 1966), or 1 *M* $CaCl_2$ as mentioned, depending to a certain extent on the strain. The sedimentation rate and infectivity of CMV strain S remained unchanged between at least pH 4 to 8.5 (Kaper, personal communication). The virus is also susceptible to pancreatic ribonuclease near neutrality (Francki, 1968) and down to pH 4 (Kaper, personal communication). The protein obtained from virus disassembled in the various ways apparently precipitates at low salt levels, near neutrality, to form as yet undescribed aggregates.

The similarity of CMV to CCMV, BMV, and BBMV is evident. Kaper (1969) dissociated strain S of the virus in 2 *M* LiCl containing 2.5×10^{-3} *M* Cleland's reagent and caused the RNA and protein mixture to reaggregate in 0.02 *M* Tris, 0.08 *M* KCl, 1×10^{-3} *M* Cleland's reagent to form a product which usually had 10–25% of the infectivity of the source virus. Infectivities of up to 50 % or more of the starting material have since been obtained (Kaper, personal communication). The yield of nucleoprotein sedimenting at about the rate of the virus was approximately 40%. Reassembly was also achieved, although with less efficiency, if separated RNA and protein were mixed stoichiometrically in the low molarity buffer. The addition of Mg^{2+} which is essential for CCMV, BMV, and BBMV was deleterious for CMV, causing aggregation of the product. In other words, best results were obtained without a divalent cation suggesting that folding of RNA by such elements is not necessary for the assembly of a spherical virus thus supporting the idea that the prime importance of such additives in CCMV assembly is to the protein, *per se*.

The CMV observations open the way not only to many experiments of the type already described for CCMV and associated viruses, but also for important biological experiments. CMV is aphid transmitted in a nonpersistent fashion and the way is now clear to determine what the coat of a virus has to do with aphid transmissibility. The central experiment would be a comparison of the transmission of virus "hybrids" composed of CMV-coat with CCMV-RNA and CCMV-coat with CMV-RNA.

IV. Turnip Crinkle Virus

Turnip crinkle virus (TCV) has a hydrodynamic molecular weight of about 9×10^6 and contains 15 to 20% RNA. The surface structure of the icosahedral particle is different from those so far considered in that it appears that instead of hexamer-pentamer clustering, the structure units of TCV exhibit dimer clustering on a $T = 3$ surface lattice (Klug *et al.*, 1966a). This structure is probably most easily realized by visualizing the 90 dimer morphological units on the edges of a truncated icosahedron, the three- and five-fold axes remaining uncovered. The size of the structure unit is in question, hydrodynamic measurements giving a value of about 50,000 (Klug *et al.*, 1966a) perhaps representing a dimer or trimer, and amino acid analyses one of 17,800 (Symons *et al.*, 1963). The question of the mass of the structure unit in regard to that of the particle related to its structure is particularly important because there are indications, first noted by Haselkorn *et al.* (1961), and subsequently by Klug *et al.* (1966a), that TCV, which has a diameter of about 300 Å, may contain a 180 Å $T = 1$ protein core. Thus 180 + 60 structure units would have to be accounted for in the particle molecular weight if a core exists, and neither the 50,000 nor 17,800 subunit molecular weight values make reasonable sums, a value of about 30,000 seeming more likely if the particle molecular weight is correct. The virus needs further investigation. TCV, although serologically unrelated to tomato bushy stunt virus, nevertheless appears to be structurally similar to that virus, and radial density distribution analyses of tomato bushy stunt virus are suggestive of an internal protein core (Harrison, 1969). The molecular weight of the structure unit of tomato bushy stunt virus, which like TCV has a molecular weight of about 9×10^6, seems also currently questionable.

Degradation studies of TCV have been described by Leberman (1968) who found that if TCV solutions were adjusted to pH 9, 0.1 *M* Tris, 0.5 *M* KCl and left for an hour at 0° before adjustment to neutrality, a 4 S protein fraction (50,000 mol. wt.) and a 30 S RNA species were observed in the analytical centrifuge. If such a solution was dialyzed overnight against 0.1 *M* NaCl at 4°C it became opalescent and contained 45 S "cores" as well as faster sedimenting species some of which were susceptible to RNase. The 45 S particles were shown to occur in concentrations in excess of what would be possible if they were released cores, so some sort of reassociation had occurred. The reassociation of TCV subunits into "cores" show that the subunits are capable of forming structures other than the virus capsid, as is also the case for CCMV protein (Bancroft *et al.*, 1967), but does not prove that cores exist in TCV, although they may well do so.

Reconstitution studies in which separated protein and RNA were mixed in 4:1 ratio presumably in 0.5 *M* KCl at neutrality and dialyzed to practically zero ionic strength have been summarized (Leberman, 1968). The product was heterogeneous, but some of the particles sedimented at about the rate of the virus (126 S), but showed no clear surface structure. Although no biological tests of the nucleoproteins have been reported and it is doubtful if true reconstitution was achieved, the stage is now set for a detailed search for the conditions leading to successful reconstitution.

V. Alfalfa Mosaic Virus

A. *General Properties*

Alfalfa mosaic virus (AMV), the properties of which have recently been reviewed (Hull, 1969), is a virus which behaves like some of the spherical viruses discussed but which is composed of 4 to 5 differently sedimenting nucleoprotein species of various shapes and sizes all having a width of about 18 mμ and containing about 18% RNA. The largest nucleoprotein, called the 99 S or bottom component, is a rodlet or bacilliform particle of about 57×18 mμ which is constructed of a hexamer tube probably terminated by icosahedra halved through three-fold axes (Hull *et al.*,1969*a*). This anisometric particle is composed of about 186 subunits, and has a molecular weight of 7.3×10^6, the molecular weight of the RNA being 1.3×10^6. The smallest commonly observed nucleoprotein, named the 68 S or top component is 18×28 mμ, contains about 96 subunits and has a molecular weight of 3.8×10^6, the RNA accounting for 0.7×10^6 molecular weight units (Hull *et al.*, 1969*a*). All components are made of the same structure units which have a molecular weight of 32,600 (Hull *et al.*, 1969*b*). Kruseman (1969) has recently questioned this value, reporting a subunit molecular weight of about 24,000. No components are infectious by themselves, mixtures being required to initiate infection (van Vloten-Doting and Jaspars, 1967).

B. *Dissociation and Reassociation*

The first indication that AMV could be easily dissociated was provided by Kelley and Kaesberg (1962) who found that the virus came apart in 1 *M* NaCl at neutrality at 45°C, the protein precipitating. Subsequently, Bol and Kruseman (1969) dissociated the virus in 0.5 *M* $MgCl_2$. The advantage of their procedure was that the protein remained soluble, most of the RNA sedimenting upon low-speed centrifugation. The soluble protein dialyzed against 0.05 *M* acetate buffer, pH 5.5, containing 2-mercaptoethanol, sedimented at 2.9 S and no viruslike particles were visible in the electron microscope. However, upon dialysis to 0.1 *M* phosphate buffer, pH 7, such dissociated protein formed spherical particles of about 19 mμ. The same type of result for the behavior of protein was reported by Lebeurier *et al.* (1969b) who prepared protein from AMV by a 1 *M* NaCl, pH 7.4, method similar to that used for CCMV (Bancroft and Hiebert, 1967). In this regard, AMV is not known to "swell" as CCMV does and there may be no significant intersubunit links (Hull *et al.*, 1969*a*), as is also probably the situation with CMV, so that a high salt concentration at any pH where the protein is not denatured and where it remains soluble should be effective, as seems to be the case. The protein isolated in 1 *M* NaCl sedimented at 2.3 S but upon dialysis to 0.01 *M* Tris, 0.01 *M* KCl, 5×10^{-3} *M* $MgCl_2$, 1×10^{-3} *M* Cleland's reagent at pH 7.4 for 6–12 hours at 20°C, a homogeneous population of spherical particles sedimenting at 35 S formed which were not present in the original preparations. These particles are presumably of the same class as observed by Bol and Kruseman (1969). It would seem from the foregoing that the most stable form of the protein in low salt near neutrality in the presumed absence of RNA might be a spherical aggregate. However, Hull (1970), after obtaining protein relatively free of RNA by combining ultracentrifugation and dialysis with a pH 5, 0.5 *M* $MgCl_2$ method concluded that protein alone would not form spheres or other aggregation products when dialyzed against 0.02 *M* Tris, 0.08 *M* KCl, 10^{-3} *M* glutathione (TKG) or 0.1 *M* phosphate at pH 7.3. However, if small amounts of RNA were present, spheres of about 22 mμ diameter and sedimenting at 33 S were obtained in low yields. These correspond to the products of Lebeurier *et al.* (1969*b*) and Bol and Kruseman (1969). Protein prepared by 1.5 *M* NaCl or LiCl and which had an $A_{260/280}$ ratio of greater than 1, yielded small quantities of 40 and 48 S components. It is not really clear how the formation of the spherical products relates to that of the, at least superficially, similar spherical particles observed by Bol and Veldstra (1969) after extensive degradation of virus in 0.1 *M* phosphate buffer by pancreatic ribonuclease. Presumably the virus dissociated in the presence of the nuclease and the protein reformed into spherical aggregates around bits of RNA. In any event, it currently seems likely that AMV protein, unlike that from CCMV or BMV, is unable to form organized products in the absence of a nucleating agent with the strains and under the conditions so far tested.

If RNA is not removed after dissociation of AMV, products resembling the original nucleoproteins in some ways may result upon reassociation. Bol and Kruseman (1969) dissociated AMV in 1.5 *M* NaCl (so that the RNA would not precipitate rapidly) in the presence of reducing agent and 4×10^{-3} *M* $MgSO_4$ at pH 5.5 and caused the RNA-protein mixture to reassociate at 4°C in 0.1 *M* phosphate buffer, pH 7, containing 2×10^{-3} *M* $MgSO_4$. The sedimentation pattern of the reassociated material approximated that of the original virus. Infectivity experiments were apparently not conclusive. Lebeurier *et al.* (1969a), using the methods mentioned for the isolated proteins except that the RNA was not removed, ran similar experiments and obtained preparations about one-tenth as infective as the controls. Further, previously isolated top and bottom components have been dissociated and reassociated (Bol and Kruseman, 1969). Although the reassociated populations were more heterogeneous in the analytical centrifuge than the starting materials, over 50% of the reformed particles had the dimensions and sedimentation rates of the parental forms suggesting that the size and shape of the particles were determined by the size of the RNA encapsulated.

The dissociation-reassociation process is not as straightforward as it might seem. Hull (1970) dissociated AMV in 1.5 *M* NaCl, pH 5 for 15 minutes and then reassociated it in TKG, which does not contain Mg^{2+}, obtaining results similar to those described by Bol and Kruseman (1969). However, if the RNA was allowed to precipitate (as it will do if the dissociation mixture is kept at 4°C for an hour or if it is frozen) and then was mixed with the protein supernatant, reassociation of at least the larger AMV components did not occur. Hull interpreted these results as meaning that dissociated virus preparations while still at the first or soluble stage were actually composed of "opened-out" particles with protein subunits still attached to the RNA which thereby retained some critical conformation. Such preparations could be reassociated into the larger AMV components. If the second stage of dissociation in which the protein had separated from the still intact precipitated RNA was reached, rodlets did not form upon dialysis against TKG. On this basis, reconstitution as opposed to reassociation should prove to be difficult to achieve, as will be discussed. These experiments provide a clear example of why the precaution of using pure and separate RNA and protein moieties for a demonstration of reconstitution is so necessary.

C. Assembly

True reconstitution of AMV by the addition of previously separated RNA and protein has been attempted. Lebeurier *et al.* (1969b), using methods already described, obtained a heterogeneous product composed of species sedimenting from 35 to 66 S, containing few if any long particles and having negligible infectivity. Similar results were found even if TMV-RNA (2×10^6) was used in place of AMV-RNA. No long rodlets were evident. The most successful assembly experiments were with BMV-RNA which gave upon mixing with AMV protein highly infective preparations with four components sedimenting between 40 and 85 S. Presumably, the 85 S species contained the 1×10^6 RNA of BMV and those sedimenting at roughly 55 and 70 S (as estimated from a single published picture) the 0.3 and 0.7×10^6 RNA species. Electron micrographs showed few tubular particles of the axial ratios approximating what one would expect to constitute at least the 85 S species. Reconstitution experiments have also been described by Hull (1970) who added stoichiometric amounts of AMV protein, prepared by the aforementioned $MgCl_2$ method before dialysis against 0.1 *M* acetate buffer, pH 5, to RNA in the same buffer. Such mixtures precipitated but became soluble during dialysis against TKG and contained species sedimenting at 70, 60, 48, and 40 S which collectively were about one-quarter as infective as the starting virus. Few particles resembled the major AMV bacilliform components in appearance. The same products were obtained at 4° and 20°C with or without treatment with EDTA. In an attempt to relate RNA size with particle type, AMV-RNA was fractionated into 24 + 20 S, 13 S, and 5 S species before protein was added separately to each. Unfortunately, no particles characteristic of the bacilliform AMV particles were seen, although some ellipsoidal forms were associated with the larger RNA species. Heterologous reconstitution experiments were made with RNA from BBMV, turnip yellow mosaic virus and yeast, as well as polyadenylic acid and sodium dextran sulfate. Only the preparations containing sodium dextran sulfate had a significant proportion of long particles, these having preferred lengths of 35, 43, and 50 mμ and a lattice spacing similar to that of native AMV. Apparently the dextran salt had a configuration suitable for the formation of bacilliform particles under the conditions used whereas the other nucleating agents did not. Further, tubular forms can be made with nucleating agents such as long-chain phospholipids (Hull, personal communication) and double-stranded DNA (Hirth, personal communication). The problem of AMV reconstitution thus resolves to the question of finding the conditions consistent with protein aggregation under which RNA would have a configuration suitable for the formation of the bacilliform particles associated with natural AMV.

VI. Conclusions

The realization that treatment of certain spherical viruses with 1 *M* NaCl or other salts at suitable pH levels provided a method for preparing protein subunits appropriate for reconstitution studies has probably assured that a considerable number of viruses will be so treated in the future. Some of the viruses will respond to the method and others will not. Those that will respond will probably lack a true nucleic acid-free top component, but may have more than one component, such as pea enation mosaic virus or Tulare apple mosaic virus. Members of the turnip yellow mosaic virus family or the squash mosaic virus family, for example, have proved to be more recalcitrant and it is from the latter groups that the next methodological insight will arrive.

It is now clearly established that spherical viruses will self-assemble, as will a variety of other biologically significant structures (see Kushner, 1969, for a general review), and it is becoming apparent that the detailed conditions required will, not unexpectedly, differ among the viruses. Thus, although ionic interactions seem to predominate in all the reconstitutable systems with spherical viruses so far examined, CCMV, for example, requires a divalent cation whereas CMV does not. The assembly of the PT form of CCMV, which has a structure similar to that of the virus, occurs under conditions distinct from those best for virus assembly, low pH, and relatively high salt levels being required along, under some conditions, with elevated temperatures suggesting that in the absence of nucleating agent, hydrophobic associations may predominate in the formation of a capsid. Analyses of the conditions required to make viruses or other forms give first approximations as to what kind of interactions may be involved in polymerization. But more than approximations are required to understand the self-assembly process. All that has been done so far is to present a hypothesis for the behavior of CCMV consistent with its assembly in terms of the ionic conditions required and to establish the ground rules necessary to produce various structures, some of which have been described in some detail. It is important that some high-yielding, easily manipulated, and measured viruses be examined intensively and either CCMV or BMV are currently favorable candidates on these grounds. The types of experiments that will have to be done are already clear in principle. Physicochemical approaches should be more extensively utilized and hopefully be eventually considered in terms of X-ray analyses. The latter will require that crystallization procedures for the virus and its protein be worked out. It will be necessary to know what particular amino acids are critically involved in the various reactions and this will necessitate exploiting the power of amino acid replacement data in terms of protein sequences related to quaternary associations. CCMV mutants which will not swell, or which will not form tubes, or which will not copolymerize with RNA, for example, are well worth obtaining. The extent of the endeavor that will be required is formidable.

Implicit in the evaluation of results gained from the study of *in vitro* assembly processes is the possibility that the events in such processes may turn out to resemble those that occur *in vivo*. The conditions required to keep CCMV, BMV, or BBMV protein soluble and the virus intact, at least when pure preparations are considered, are now apparent. Thus, if subunits occur in reasonable quantities *in vivo*, it is not improbable that rational approaches leading to procedures for their isolation will be forthcoming. Such isolation procedures would open the way to comparative reconstitution studies and would also make kinetic studies on the production and utilization of subunits possible so that some understanding of the sequence of events leading to virus production might be gained and integrated with what is already known.

ACKNOWLEDGMENTS

I wish to thank Drs. Gordon, Frist, Kaper, Hull, and Hirth for sending me manuscripts prior to publication or for permitting me to refer to unpublished data, and

Dr. Roy Markham for his active interest. Much of the work concerned with CCMV, BMV, and BBMV was supported by the National Science Foundation.

References

Bancroft, J. B., and Hiebert, E. (1967). *Virology* **32**, 354.
Bancroft, J. B., Hills, G. J., and Markham, R. (1967). *Virology* **31**, 354.
Bancroft, J. B., Hiebert, E., Rees, M. W., and Markham, R. (1968a). *Virology* **34**, 224.
Bancroft, J. B., Wagner, G. W., and Bracker, C. E. (1968b). *Virology* **36**, 146.
Bancroft, J. B., Bracker, C. E., and Wagner, G. W. (1969a). *Virology* **38**, 324.
Bancroft, J. B., Hiebert, E., and Bracker, C. E. (1969b). *Virology* **39**, 924.
Bockstahler, L. E., and Kaesberg, P. (1962). *Biophys. J.* **2**, 1.
Bockstahler, L. E., and Kaesberg, P. (1965a). *J. Mol. Biol.* **13**, 127.
Bockstahler, L. E., and Kaesberg, P. (1965b). *Virology* **27**, 418.
Bol, J. F., and Kruseman, J. (1969). *Virology* **37**, 489.
Bol, J. F., and Veldstra, H. (1969). *Virology* **37**, 74.
Caspar, D. L. D. (1963). *Advan. Protein Chem.* **18**, 37.
Caspar, D. L. D. (1964). *In* "Molecular Architecture in Cell Physiology" (T. Hayashi and A. G. Szent-Györgyi, eds.), p. 191. Prentice-Hall, Englewood Cliffs, New Jersey.
Caspar, D. L. D. (1966). *Principles of Biomol. Organ. Ciba Found. Symp., 1965*, p. 7.
Caspar, D. L. D., and Klug, A. (1962). *Cold Spring Harbor Symp. Quant. Biol.* **27**, 1.
Caspar, D. L. D., and Klug, A. (1963). *M. D. Anderson Symp.* **17**, 27.
Cleland, W. W. (1964). *Biochemistry* **3**, 480.
Diener, T. O., Scott, H. A., and Kaper, J. M. (1964). *Virology* **22**, 131.
Eggen, K., and Nathans, D. (1969). *J. Mol. Biol.* **39**, 293.
Finch, J. T., and Bancroft, J. B. (1968). *Nature* **220**, 815.
Finch, J. T., and Klug, A. (1967). *J. Mol. Biol.* **24**, 289.
Finch, J. T., Klug, A., and van Regenmortel, M. H. V. (1967). *J. Mol. Biol.* **24**, 303.
Fraenkel-Conrat, H., and Williams, R. C. (1955). *Proc. Nat. Acad. Sci. U.S.* **41**, 690.
Fraenkel-Conrat, H., Singer, B., and Tsugita, A. (1961). *Virology* **14**, 54.
Francki, R. I. B. (1968). *Virology* **34**, 694.
Francki, R. I. B., Randles, J. W., Chambers, T. C., and Wilson, S. B. (1966). *Virology* **28**, 729.
Frist, R. H. (1968). *Biophys. J.* **8**, A-69.
Harrison, S. C. (1969). *J. Mol. Biol.* **42**, 457.
Haselkorn, R., Hills, G. J., Markham, R., and Rees, M. W. (1961). *1st Int. Congr. Biophys., Stockholm* p. 293 (Abstr.).
Hermann, R., Schubert, D., and Rudolph, V. (1968). *Biochem. Biophys. Res. Commun.* **30**, 576.
Hiebert, E., and Bancroft, J. B. (1969). *Virology* **39**, 296.
Hiebert, E., Bancroft, J. B., and Bracker, C. E. (1968). *Virology* **34**, 492.
Hitchborn, J. H., and Hills, G. J. (1965). *Virology* **26**, 756.
Hohn, T. (1967). *Eur. J. Biochem.* **2**, 152.
Hohn, T. (1969). *J. Mol. Biol.* **43**, 191.
Hohn, T., and Hohn, B. (1970). This volume, p 43.
Horne, R. W., and Wildy, P. (1961). *Virology* **15**, 348.
Hull, R. (1969). *Advan. Virus Res.* **15**, 365.
Hull, R. (1970). *Virology* **40**, 34.
Hull, R., and Adams, A. N. (1968). *Ann. Appl. Biol.* **62**, 139.

Hull, R., Hills, G. J., and Markham, R. (1969a). *Virology* **37**, 416.
Hull, R., Rees, M. W., and Short, M. N. (1969b). *Virology* **37**, 404.
Incardona, N. L. (1968). *Biophys. J.* **8**, A-69.
Incardona, N. L., and Kaesberg, P. (1964). *Biophys. J.* **4**, 11.
Jacobson, M. F., and Baltimore, D. (1968). *J. Mol. Biol.* **33**, 369.
Kaper, J. M. (1960). *Nature* **186**, 219.
Kaper, J. M. (1964). *Biochemistry* **3**, 486.
Kaper, J. M. (1969). *Virology* **37**, 134.
Kaper, J. M., Diener, T. O., and Scott, N. A. (1965). *Virology* **27**, 54.
Kelley, J. J., and Kaesberg, P. (1962). *Biochim. Biophys. Acta* **55**, 236.
Klug, A. (1967). *Symp. Int. Soc. Cell Biol.* **6**, 1.
Klug, A., Finch, J. T., Leberman, R., and Longley, W. (1966a). *Principles Biomol. Organ. Ciba Found. Symp., 1965.* p. 158.
Klug, A., Longley, W., and Leberman, R. (1966b). *J. Mol. Biol.* **15**, 315.
Kodama, T., and Bancroft, J. B. (1964). *Virology* **22**, 23.
Kruseman, J. (1969). Ph.D. Dissertation, University of Leiden, Leiden, Netherlands.
Kushner, D. J. (1969). *Bacteriol. Rev.* **33**, 302.
Lauffer, M. A., and Stevens, C. L. (1968). *Advan. Virus Res.* **13**, 1.
Leberman, R. (1968). *Symp. Soc. Gen. Microbiol.* **18**, 183.
Lebeurier, G., Wurtz, M., and Hirth, L. (1969a). *C. R. Acad. Sci. Ser. D* **268**, 1897.
Lebeurier, G., Wurtz, M., and Hirth, L. (1969b). *C. R. Acad. Sci. Ser. D* **268**, 2002.
Miki, T., and Knight, C. A. (1965). *Virology* **25**, 478.
Rappaport, I., Siegel, A., and Haselkorn, R. (1965). *Virology* **25**, 325.
Roberts, J. W., and Steitz, J. E. A. (1967). *Proc. Nat. Acad. Sci. U.S.* **58**, 1416.
Rochow, W. F. (1969). *Phytopathology* **59**, 1046.
Sakar, S. (1969). *Mol. Gen. Gen.* **105**, 87.
Scheraga, N. A. (1963). *In* "The Proteins" (H. Neurath, ed.), Vol. 1, p. 477. Academic Press, New York.
Shepherd, R. J., Wakeman, R. J., and Romanko, R. R. (1968). *Virology* **36**, 150.
Smith. K. M. (1946). *Parasitology* **37**, 126.
Stubbs, J. D., and Kaesberg, P. (1964). *J. Mol. Biol.* **8**, 314.
Sugiyama, T., Hebert, R. R., and Hartman, K. A. (1967). *J. Mol. Biol.* **25**, 455.
Symons, R. H., Rees, M. W., Short, M. N., and Markham, R. (1963). *J. Mol. Biol.* **6**, 1.
Takahashi, W. N., and Ishii, M. (1952). *Phytopathology* **42**, 690.
Takai, M. (1966). *Biochem. Biophys. Acta* **119**, 20.
van Regenmortel, M. H. V. (1967). *Virology* **31**, 391.
van Vloten-Doting, L., and Jaspars, E. M. J. (1967). *Virology* **33**, 684.
Verduin, B. J. M., and Bancroft, J. B. (1969). *Virology* **37**, 501.
von Wechmar, M. B., and van Regenmortel, M. H. V. (1968). *Virology* **34**, 36.
Wagner, G. W., and Bancroft, J. B. (1968). *Virology* **34**, 748.
Winocour, E. (1969). *Advan. Virus Res.* **14**, 153.
Yamazaki, H., and Kaesberg, P. (1963a). *J. Mol. Biol.* **6**, 465.
Yamazaki, H., and Kaesberg, P. (1963b). *J. Mol. Biol.* **7**, 760.

MYCOPLASMA DISEASES OF PLANTS AND INSECTS

Karl Maramorosch, Robert R. Granados, and Hiroyuki Hirumi

Boyce Thompson Institute for Plant Research, Yonkers, New York

I. Introduction

In the preparation of a review on mycoplasma etiology of plant diseases for Advances in Virus Research, several aspects had to be considered. Until 1967 the diseases in question were considered, without exception, to be virus diseases. This, in itself, seems to justify the reviewing of the subject in the present volume. Since the review will be primarily of interest to workers dealing with plant diseases and with invertebrate vectors of the disease agents, it seemed appropriate to include an introduction on the biology, morphology, and serology of mycoplasmas, as these subjects are fairly new to plant pathologists and entomologists. Animal virologists, who have been familiar with mycoplasmas as contaminants of cell cultures for several years, will be less interested in this introduction to the review.

Plant pathologists did not consider or even suspect mycoplasmas as causal agents of plant diseases before 1967. This statement refers, of course, to the present-day use of the term, and not to the "mycoplasm" term, originally used by Eriksson (1897) and considered by him as a stage in the development of rust fungi (Eriksson, 1910). The confusion caused by the use of the same term has been pointed out by a "Letter to Plant Pathologists" by Heimbeck (1966), and recently clarified by Brčák *et al.* (1969).

Agents of plant diseases were listed as viruses whenever these agents were graft-transmissible and no bacteria, fungi, or protozoa could be implicated as etiologic agents in the diseased plants or in vectors. Furthermore, in some cases strain interference, similar to virus interference (called by plant virologists "cross-immunity"), was demonstrated in infected plants and in insect vectors. In several instances, dodder transmission was successful, and at least one of the disease agents was reported filterable. Experimental evidence was provided for the multiplication of a few of these disease agents in leafhopper vectors and in vector tissues *in vitro,* and certain species of leafhoppers were shown to act as alternate hosts and reservoirs of the disease agents. These aspects were paralleling phenomena in well-established plant-pathogenic viruses and virus diseases (Maramorosch, 1963; Whitcomb and Davis, 1970; Casper, 1969).

Although many disease symptoms were similar to those in virus-caused diseases, all attempts to purify the causative agents by virological methods, and to characterize them morphologically and chemically as viruses remained unsuccessful. Current work indicates that many diseases of this type are caused not by viruses, but by mycoplasmas. As an introduction to the present state of our knowledge of plant mycoplasma diseases, a brief resume of important events dealing with animal diseases caused by representatives of this group will be presented.

Although the total number of plant diseases in which mycoplasma etiology has been reported on the basis of electron microscopy was not more than 40 at the time the review of the literature for this chapter was concluded (March 1, 1970), and an effort was made to include all references, it might well be that some publications escaped the scrutiny of the reviewers. Some of the diseases may have been listed under different names, as distinct diseases, and eventually they may prove to be identical. It is not possible, at present, to ascertain whether the etiologic agents of big-bud disease of tomato in Australia, stolbur in Europe, and certain big-bud disease of North America are related. Virescence and dwarf diseases of clover, tomato ("mal azul" disease), and other yellows diseases may be identical or closely related insofar as their causal agents are concerned, or they may be completely different. Eventually, these relationships will be determined by serological methods, hopefully with cultured mycoplasma agents. Until now, only one economically important disease agent in this group, the mycoplasma causing white leaf of sugarcane in Taiwan, has been reported as being cultured on solid mycoplasma media and proved to be the causative agent of the disease (Lin and Lee, 1969). Indirect evidence for mycoplasma agents was provided for aster yellows (Hirumi and Maramorosch, 1969b; Davis *et al.*, 1970) and corn stunt (Chen and Granados, 1970), by injecting leafhopper vectors with the respective disease agents, maintained in cell-free media. In all other instances mycoplasma etiology has been implied indirectly from electron microscopic observations, from the remission of diseases following tetracycline treatment, and, in a few instances, from the results of heat treatments of diseased plants.

II. Historical Background

The mycoplasma microorganisms have a somewhat unusual history. In 1898 they were first isolated by Nocard and Roux in Pasteur's laboratory and proved to be the causal agent of infectious bovine pleuropneumonia, an economically important and world-wide epidemic disease of cattle. Nocard and Roux (1898) cultured the microorganisms in media containing serum, and demonstrated that the pleomorphic microbes could produce the disease in inoculated, healthy cattle. A quarter of a century later, Bridré and Donatien (1923) found that another species of mycoplasma caused an udder disease in goats and sheep. Eleven years later, parasitic strains of mycoplasma were isolated from dogs (Shoetensack, 1934), and later from poultry (Nelson, 1935) and from rodents (Sabin, 1938) with respiratory diseases. Saprophytic strains have been found in sewage (Laidlaw and Elford, 1936), and in soil (Seiffert, 1937).

Since mycoplasmas were found to pass through filters capable of retaining bacteria, and since some species could be grown on artificial media, numerous workers became interested in the study of these microorganisms during the last decade, and their findings have enriched our knowledge and opened new pathways for exploration.

III. Biology of Mycoplasmas

The mycoplasmas are now considered to be members of a distinct class of microorganisms, containing DNA and RNA, lacking a cell wall, but surrounded by a highly elastic membrane, which accounts for their pleomorphism (Thomas, 1969). Several species have been grown on solid agar media, where they usually form characteristic "fried egg" colonies. The mycoplasmas differ from L-forms of bacteria, as was demonstrated by immunological and nucleic acid homology tests. Certain mycoplasma species require sterols for their growth and multiplication, while others, such as *M. laidlawii,* are not dependent on sterol. Mycoplasmas are heat-susceptible and can be destroyed usually by treatment at 50°C for 6 hours. They are highly susceptible to osmotic shock, inhibited by their specific antibodies, and—being devoid of cell walls—are resistant to penicillin. In some instances, tetracycline antibiotics have been found to be mycoplasmastatic, but in no instance mycoplasmacidal. In tissue cultures, in which electron microscopy observations have often revealed the presence of mycoplasma contamination, the microorganisms were usually found to be tetracycline resistant. Only a few of the tissue culture contaminants observed by electron microscopy have yielded to cultivation on cell-free culture media.

Dienes and Edsall (1937) isolated the first mycoplasma from female urogenital tracts. Today, there are at least five species, isolated from man, and regarded as nonpathogenic: *M. salivarum, M. hominis, M. orale* types 1 and 2, and *M. fermentans,* all considered part of the normal microflora of the human oral cavity. The only proved pathologic mycoplasma from man is *M. pneumoniae*, the causal agent of primary atypical pneumonia, known until recently as "Eaton's agent" (Eaton *et al.*, 1944). The Eaton agent was considered a virus until 1962, when it was finally cultivated on a cell-free agar medium (Chanock *et al.*, 1962; Hayflick, 1965; Hayflick and Chanock, 1965; Razin, 1969).

The three major animal diseases caused by mycoplasmas—bovine pleuropneumonia, enzootic pneumonia of swine, and primary atypical pneumonia in man—were first thought to be caused by viruses. Similarly, the entire group of yellows diseases of plants was regarded until recently as caused by viruses. The implication of mycoplasmas as agents of many economically important diseases of cultivated plants now opens a new area for investigation.

IV. Nomenclature and Classification of the Order *Mycoplasmatales*

For plant pathologists, the problem of classification and nomenclature of the various disease agents in this group will soon become of importance. The agents, erroneously classified as viruses, will be given new names in accordance with the rules of the International Subcommittee on Mycoplasma Nomenclature. At the IX International Congress of Microbiology in 1966, the recommendations on the taxonomy of the *Mycoplasmatales* were approved and subsequently published (Edward *et al.*, 1967). According to the International Code of Nomenclature of Bacteria, which applies to mycoplasmas, the order *Mycoplasmatales* belongs to the class Mollicutes parallel to, but distinct from the class Schizomycetes. The Subcommittee has urged microbiologists in the mycoplasma field to provide, whenever publishing a new specific name, an adequate description that will allow laboratory identification of the new species, and its differentiation from other *Mycoplasma* species. Such a description should include serological and biological characters as defined by available, standard methods. It would be most desirable to provide a direct serological comparison with previously established *Mycoplasma* species. "A new specific name should not be published unless it is accompanied or preceded by an adequate description as defined here, and the designation of the type of the taxon. It must be emphasized that no priority or legal recognition can be given to specific names under the International Code of Nomenclature of Bacteria unless these are accompanied by adequate description" (Edward *et al.*, 1967). A representative prototype strain is to be supplied immediately to a National Type Culture Collection, and the new name published in a journal of a known wide circulation among microbiologists in general. "Primary publication in journals devoted to highly specialized fields and of limited availability or in books, though formally accepted as effective publication, is to be deprecated" (Edward *et al.*, 1967). If a name is published in a journal other than the International Journal of Systematic Bacteriology (IJSB), a note drawing attention to the publication should be forwarded to the Editor of IJSB.

V. Serology

Serological techniques, devised for the study of viruses (Casals, 1967; Matthews, 1967), have been adapted to the study of mycoplasmas. Purcell *et al.* (1969) recently reviewed the different serological techniques applied to mycoplasmas and pointed out that they differ greatly in sensitivity and specificity. For instance, agglutination and complement fixation are not sensitive for mycoplasma identification, and antisera and antigens from human mycoplasma species, although entirely distinct serologically when tested by growth inhibition, metabolic inhibition, or immunofluorescence, will cross-react to a significant degree when compared by complement fixation. Gel diffusion, inhibition of hemagglutination, hemadsorption, and spermadsorption have been used, as has indirect hemagglutination. The latter has not been widely accepted because of difficulties encountered in maintaining reproducibility. Latex agglutination, neutralization in animals, serological tests in tissue culture, fluorescent focus inhibition, cytopathic effect inhibition, and colony formation have been compared and found less specific than the following four methods. Immunofluorescence, growth inhibition on agar medium or in liquid medium, and metabolic inhibition have been found most sensitive, along with cytopathic effect inhibition. These four techniques are not only sensitive but also so specific that different *Mycoplasma* species appear almost entirely unrelated by these techniques. The most specific technique is the metabolic inhibition, which can detect serological differences within a *Mycoplasma* species. The least specific are hemagglutination, agglutination inhibition, indirect hemagglutination, and gel diffusion. Thus many serological tests, applied by earlier workers, are now considered inadequate because of low sensitivity. Tube agglutination (Klieneberger, 1938), commonly used with animal-pathogenic mycoplasmas, is less specific than other tests, according to Hayflick (1969). Complement fixation (Campbell and Turner, 1936) does not produce a satisfactory nonanticomplementary antigen and this test also suffers from a relatively high degree of cross-reactivity with heterologous antisera (Hayflick, 1969). Gel diffusion, although widely used, has some of the shortcomings of complement fixation tests because of growth-medium components that evoke common antibody responses.

There are only two plant diseases of presumptive mycoplasma etiology in which serological identification of the disease agents has been reported. The first is stolbur of potatoes. Pozděna (1954), Pozděna and Čěch (1958), and more recently, Gáborjányi and Bencsics (1968) obtained antisera from partially purified plant material. Gáborjányi and Bencsics (1968) showed that antisera to the stolbur agent can be prepared for diagnostic purposes, using fairly crude extracts from diseased tomato plants. The precipitin reaction, used by the authors, was reportedly obtained with dilutions of the antiserum up to 1/32. The authors worked under the assumption that the disease agent was a virus. The results, if confirmed, would indicate that certain yellows-type diseases might be diagnosed eventually by simple serological tests.

The second attempt was reported in 1969 (Hampton *et al.*, 1969a,b) and it is controversial for a number of reasons that will be dealt with at the end of this review. The serological tests were of the agglutination type, which are now generally considered insufficient for the distinction of mycoplasmas.

VI. Electron Microscopy

Mycoplasmas have no cell walls and their membranes account for their plasticity and fragility. Fixation and staining for electron microscopy may disrupt or disturb them, and it is difficult to estimate the degree of distortion because no comparison can be made with the living organisms, since they are too small in size for such observations.

The methods used for plant mycoplasmas are essentially those used for the electron microscopy of virus-infected plants (Shikata and Maramorosch, 1969b) and, to a certain degree, those used in the study of mycoplasmas infecting higher animals (Maniloff, 1969). Usually small pieces of plant material are fixed immediately after removal from a living plant, using 6% glutaraldehyde in 0.1 *M* phosphate buffer at pH 7.2 for 2 hours at room temperature. Afterward the pieces are rinsed in phosphate buffer for 2 hours, and postfixed in 2% osmium tetroxide in 0.1 *M* phosphate buffer at pH 7.2 for an additional 2 hours at room temperature. The fixed material is then dehydrated in a graded series of acetone and embedded in an epoxy resin. Ultrathin sections are stained with 6% uranyl acetate aqueous solution for 5 minutes, washed in absolute ethanol and with distilled water in indirect light, followed by staining with lead citrate for 3 minutes in a carbon dioxide-free chamber. Dehydration is sometimes carried out in graded series of ethanol instead of in acetone.

The preparation of insect tissues for electron microscopy has been described by Hirumi and Maramorosch (1969a) as follows: insects are killed in cold 3% glutaraldehyde in 0.14 *M* sodium cacodylate buffer and then dissected. Excised organs are placed in fresh fixative for 2 hours, then rinsed with the sodium cacodylate buffer at 4°C for 2 hours. Postfixation in 1% osmium tetroxide in 0.1 *M* Veronal-acetate buffer with 5% sucrose is carried out for 2 hours at 4°C. Fixed specimens are dehydrated in graded ethyl alcohol and embedded in an epoxy resin. Ultrathin sections are stained with uranyl magnesium acetate and lead citrate. Granados (1969b) used phosphate buffer instead of cacodylate buffer.

Negative staining has been carried out by Belli (1969) with crude extracts following the virological methods of Brandes (1957) and Kitajima (1965), and the electron microscopy of murine strains of mycoplasma (Nelson and Lyons, 1965). Clarified extracts have also been prepared by Belli (1969), who used 1 gm of infected leaves, ground in 2.5 ml of 0.02 *M* phosphate buffer at pH 7.0. After filtration the leaf extract was centrifuged at 6000 *g* for 15 minutes. Drops of the supernatant were mixed 1:1 with the staining solution and after 2 minutes were sprayed on collodion-coated grids covered with carbon. Granados (1969b) used 50 gm of stem tissue from corn plants, cut them into small pieces with razor blades, placed them in 200 ml of a buffer solution consisting of 0.1 *M* glycine and 0.01 *M* MgCl at pH 7.0 (Brakke, 1956), and ground them in a blender for 2 minutes. The extract, after being squeezed through cheesecloth, was clarified by centrifuging at 5000 *g* for 10 minutes, centrifuged at 48,000 *g* for 20 minutes, the pellets resuspended in 0.01 *M* K_2HPO_4, pH 7.0, at a temperature between 0° and 4°C. Samples of the resuspended pellets and the supernatants from the high-speed centrifugation were placed on Formvar-coated grids, and stained with 2% phosphotungstic acid (PTA). This method, similar to Belli's method for the examination of purified and concentrated extracts, was also used by Giannotti *et al.* (1969a) for grapevine tissues infected with "flavescence dorée." The electron microscopy of mycoplasma reproduction is, at best, a reconstruction of the process from photographs of killed organisms, and it is, therefore, subject to error.

It is generally believed that there are morphological differences between *Mycoplasma* species. Recently Knudson and MacLeod (1970) used electron microscopy to compare two animal *Mycoplasma* species grown on agar and concluded that their technique might provide a useful tool to aid in the morphological identification of mycoplasmas. Boatman and Kenny (1970) found considerable differences between the fine structure of *M. felis* and *M. gallisepticum*. Earlier electron microscopy observations have usually stressed the features in common to all mycoplasmas, and not the distinctions that may differentiate them. This is also true in the case of observations on plant mycoplasmas, where, until now, most observations stressed the similarity between the plant-infecting and the animal-infecting or saprophytic forms. The only exception was the comparison of various mycoplasmas in *Vinca* plants, as illustrated by Ploaie and Maramorosch (1969).

The morphology of mycoplasmas varies according to the physical nature of the surrounding medium, whether they are inside of cells, in broth, in agar, or in phloem sap of plants. It also differs according to the chemical and physical factors, particularly osmotic pressure.

Most of the morphological characteristics of plant-pathogenic mycoplasmas have been obtained from studies of various species in thin sections of plant and invertebrate animal tissues. Some information has also been provided by negative staining of mycoplasmas in crude sap or in clarified or purified preparations, and, to a limited degree, as dispersed in liquid media. In thin sections, mycoplasmas are seen bounded by a unit membrane, which in high magnification micrographs is presented as two black lines separated by a clear space. In the cytoplasm of a mycoplasma there are typical ribosomes, containing RNA, as has been shown by Maniloff *et al.* (1965) who used histochemical and electron microscopic techniques. Similar techniques have also been used by Giannotti *et al.* (1968a) for plant mycoplasmas. The nuclear material occupies a region free of ribosomes, and in thin sections appears as fine filaments within the cytoplasm. The strands are more or less clumped, depending on the fixation procedure. Sometimes the nuclear region has a homogeneous appearance which probably reflects the biochemical state of the nuclear material (Anderson, 1969). If fixation is poor, a vacuolar area can be seen near, or at, the nuclear region.

Dense spherules, about 60–100 nm in diameter, are seen in many electron micrographs. These spherules are generally assumed to be elementary bodies. Usually no details can be seen in them. Sometimes, in addition to the "free" elementary bodies, they are found in the peripheral cytoplasms of large mycoplasma bodies, or are observed budding from the surface of larger bodies. The spherules described by Hirumi and Maramorosch (1969a) inside mycoplasma cells observed in the salivary gland of aster leafhoppers were surrounded by a membrane. It is unlikely that they could be released from the larger bodies by budding, since this would result in the formation of two overlying unit membranes and none has ever been observed. In the mentioned study of salivary gland cells infected by aster yellows mycoplasma (Hirumi and Maramorosch, 1969a) several intermediate forms were described, ranging from 80–100 nm to the large 800 nm in diameter bodies (Fig. 3, top).

Blebs have been described in cultivated *M. gallisepticum* (Maniloff *et al.,* 1965). At first it was believed that blebs were elementary bodies in the process of being released, but it was shown that the blebs are devoid of nucleic acid and, apparently, are related to the process of binary fission (Maniloff and Morowitz, 1967).

Filamentous forms of two types have been described in animal-pathogenic mycoplasmas (Anderson and Barile, 1965). In one there is a very dense center, like that in the elementary body. A string of beads, or cocci forms, has also been observed in animal-parasitic forms. The second type has in cross section the same internal structure as spherical, larger bodies, with ribosomes at the periphery and DNA filaments in the center.

Mycoplasmas observed in the phloem elements of plants are often less pleomorphic than animal-infecting forms described from artificial media. However, budding, chains of spherules, and long filamentous forms have been observed (Worley, 1969, 1970; Hirumi and Maramorosch, 1969b; Granados, 1969a) (Figs. 3, bottom right, 4B).

VII. Reproduction

A. *Binary Fission*

According to Anderson (1969) mycoplasmas can reproduce by binary fission, by the formation of granula, and by filamentous growth. Binary fission has been suspected from titrations of cultured species, where the number of bodies in broth cultures increased logarithmically. As pointed out by Anderson (1969) this logarithmic increase by itself, although consistent with binary fission, does not prove that this process has occurred. Some electron micrographs of mycoplasmas seem to have dumbbell-shaped forms that could represent simple division. Figure 3 (bottom, left) shows such forms from plant cells. Definitive proof of binary fission has been obtained only for two species, *M. gallisepticum* (Morowitz and Maniloff, 1966) and *M. orale* (Furness, 1968), and no conclusive data are available on other animal- or plant-infecting mycoplasmas. Binary fission is certainly a plausible way of multiplication of mycoplasmas (Maniloff and Morowitz, 1967).

B. *Elementary Bodies*

In thin sections, electron-dense spherules, 100 nm in diameter, have been noted in broth, in tissue culture, and in agar cultures of animal-infecting species, as well as inside of cells of infected plants and insect vectors.

The morphology of elementary bodies does not prove their establishment (existence) as viable stages in the life cycle of mycoplasmas. In thin sections all stages of transition are found between elementary bodies and the typical large cells—transitional not only in size but also in structural detail. They could, of course, be degenerative products, or cross sections through filaments. On the other hand, they could represent spores, formed in certain conditions and serving as means of survival in adverse conditions.

According to Morowitz (1969), *M. hominis* H 39 encodes 637 cistrons, with 800,000 daltons of DNA constituting an average cistron. Morowitz (1967, 1968) expressed doubt that this amount of DNA in the mycoplasma genome could fit into the 80–100 nm elementary body. If this assumption and calculation are correct, the elementary bodies cannot constitute a viable stage of the mycoplasma reproductive cycle, as they would not be able to carry the complete genome. The assembly of several hundred amino acids in the same sequence seems to require a minimal weight of the DNA strand. *Mycoplasma* species seem to be equipped with the information, contained in the DNA strand, which enables them to synthesize the essential components from a cell-free medium. Subdivision, most likely by binary fission, has to be delayed, therefore, until the organism is large enough for its two new pieces to encompass a fully representative group of the organism's components.

This hypothesis is further strengthened by the recent finding that strains that do not require sterols and can live as saprophytes, such as *M. laidlawii* and *M. granularum*, have 1.0×10^9 daltons, that is, twice that of all other mycoplasmas (Bak *et al.*, 1969). Probably several mycoplasmas have a common phylogenetic origin, which is reflected in their present-day genome weight. Further support of this idea is found in the fact that elementary bodies seem to be absent from the logarithmic growth phase of young cultures and they seem to appear only in older cultures. More data may be needed before it can be decided whether dense spherules are viable or not.

C. Filamentous Growth

In broth cultures, certain species of mycoplasmas form mycelia or filaments. Constrictions may form a chain of elementary bodies that looks like a string of beads. There is no general agreement concerning the breaking apart of such beads and their role in a new cycle. Filamentous cells have been observed in certain species of *Mycoplasma* (Knudson and MacLeod, 1970). In others, they might be artifacts, as pointed out by Reuss (1967) who showed that spherical bodies assume irregular shapes if not fixed properly. In properly fixed and sectioned plant cells, both regular round bodies and filamentous, beaded forms have been observed (Worley, 1969; Granados, 1969b; Hirumi, unpublished data) (Figs. 3, bottom right, 4A, B). In cultured forms, rich media favor filament formation (Razin *et al.*, 1966). Probably the presence of filaments depends on the growth conditions as well as on the species.

D. Budding

Evidence for reproduction by budding is not conclusive. Budlike structures seen in electron micrographs in thin sections might represent initial stages of the formation of filaments (Anderson and Manaker, 1966). Work with animal-infecting and free-living forms suggests that true budding does not occur in this group of microorganisms (Freundt, 1969).

VIII. Mycoplasma Diseases of Plants

The demonstration of leafhopper-borne, well-characterized plant-pathogenic viruses *in situ* in cells of diseased plants and in insect vectors (Fukushi *et al.*, 1960; Shikata *et al.*, 1964) led several workers to study yellows-type diseases by the same techniques. The first reports on identifying mycoplasmalike microorganisms in plants by electron microscopy of thin sections came from Japan (Doi *et al.*, 1967), and the interpretation of the findings was further strengthened by the remission of one of the diseases following tetracycline treatment (Ishiie *et al.*, 1967). The same year, Nasu *et al.* (1967) reported mycoplasma microorganisms in plants infected with rice yellow dwarf as well as in leafhopper vectors transmitting the disease agent to rice plants.

Since the most important Japanese references have been available only in Japanese (Nasu *et al.*, 1967) or in the form of Japanese papers with short English abstracts (Doi *et al.*, 1967; Ishiie *et al.*, 1967), they will be discussed here in some detail, particularly because they have opened this important new area of investigation to plant pathologists. Extensive and definitive tetracycline chemotherapy tests have been carried out in 1967–1969 in Japan, but again the complete reports have been available only in Japanese (without English titles or abstracts) (Tetracycline Research Group, 1968, 1969).

A. Aster Yellows

Aster yellows disease has been considered as a classic representative of a yellows-type plant virus disease since its first detailed description by Smith (1902). The disease has been described from North America, Europe, and Asia (Smith, 1902; Kunkel, 1926; Richter, 1936; Heinze and Kunze, 1955; Valenta *et al.*, 1961; Sukhov and Vovk, 1945; Rischkov, 1943; Fukushi, 1930). The pioneering work of L. O. Kunkel at the Boyce Thompson Institute in the 1920's established that the agent of aster yellows can infect mono- and dicotyledonous plants, belonging to some 40 families (Kunkel, 1926), in which it induces chlorosis, malformation, phyllody of flower, sterility, adventitious shoots, and stunting. Among economically important plants affected by aster yellows in nature are potato, onion, celery, carrot, lettuce, and spinach. The principal vector in North America is the six-spotted aster leafhopper, *Macrosteles fascifrons* (Stål) (Kunkel, 1926).

The agent of aster yellows requires a long incubation in insect vectors and in plants. It can be inactivated in the body of the living vector and in certain living plants by heat treatments (Kunkel, 1937b, 1938, 1941). Approximately 32°C was found to be the critical temperature above which transmission by insects ceased. *Vinca rosea* plants with aster yellows, maintained for several days in a moist atmosphere at 44°C, became permanently cured while infective aster leafhoppers, subjected for eight days to 36°C, lost infectivity permanently. Such cured insects could be reinfected by repeated confinement to diseased plants.

Various naturally occurring strains of the aster yellows agent have been recognized and their heat lability was found to differ (Granados and Chapman, 1968). An attenuated strain has been obtained by heat treatment (Kunkel, 1937a). Strains of the aster yellows agent can interfere in inoculated plants and in vectors (Kunkel, 1955, 1957; Freitag, 1964, 1967; Valenta, 1959a,b). The agent has been filtered through Berkefeld N and V filters (Black, 1943) but only with difficulty, and whenever the filtrate possessed infectivity the preparation was contaminated with a small bacterium, indicating that the agent was larger than known viruses. The agent has been transmitted to insects mechanically by needle inoculation (Black, 1940) but it has not been transmitted mechanically to plants. The intrinsic incubation of the agent in mechanically inoculated insects varies with the dosage of the inoculum (Maramorosch, 1950). Serial passage from insect to insect provided direct evidence for its multiplication (Maramorosch, 1952a). Interference between two strains of the aster yellows agent has been described by Kunkel (1955) and interpreted as virus interference, or cross-immunity. Cytopathic changes have been described in leafhoppers carrying the aster yellows agent (Littau and Maramorosch, 1956, 1960). Various organs of vectors are systemically invaded by the agent, as has been established by infectivity tests (Hirumi and Maramorosch, 1963; Sinha and Chiykowski, 1967). The agent was maintained for 2 weeks in vector tissues *in vitro* (Maramorosch, 1956), for more than 6 hours in a medium containing fetal bovine serum

(Hirumi and Maramorosch, 1969b), and for 24 hours in a medium containing horse serum (Davis *et al.*, 1970). Attempts to find virus particles in aster yellows-infected plants and insects were unsuccessful. The agent was not purified by standard virus purification methods, including agar gel filtration (Steere, 1967) and differential centrifugation (Lee and Chiykowski, 1963). The riddle of its nature was finally understood in 1967, when Doi *et al.* (1967), Nasu *et al.* (1967), and Ishiie *et al.* (1967) suggested that aster yellows and similar yellows-type diseases are caused by mycoplasmas.

Among the characteristic features that distinguish the aster yellows agent from viruses are: morphology *in situ* in plant and in insect vector cells; susceptibility to certain tetracycline antibiotics in plants and in insect vectors *in vivo;* effect of comparatively low temperature (below 47°C) on the agent in plants and in insect vectors *in vivo.* There are additional, indirect indications of pleomorphism of the agent, obtained by agar-gel filtration (Steere, 1967; Whitcomb and Davis, 1969) where infectivity was distributed in the column, whereas for a uniform particle of a virus a narrow, concentrated zone would be expected. The induction of sterility in plants might also be a characteristic feature.

Many other aspects are common to both viruses and mycoplasma agents of plant diseases, which account for the difficulties in the identification of mycoplasma agents. The same species of insect vector may be able to transmit a virus and a mycoplasma. For instance, *M. fascifrons* can carry the oat blue dwarf virus (Zeyen and Banttari, 1969) as well as the aster yellows mycoplasma agent. *Nephotettix* sp. can carry the rice dwarf virus as well as the mycoplasma agent of rice yellow dwarf. Deleterious effects in insect vectors may be caused by viruses, as well as by mycoplasmas, as in Western X mycoplasma (Jensen, 1959, 1968; Maramorosch and Jensen, 1963; Jensen and Nasu, 1970), rice dwarf virus (Shinkai, 1960), or corn stunt mycoplasma (Granados, unpublished data).

1. Electron Microscopy

Pleomorphic bodies, with characteristic unit membranes of mycoplasmas, were observed by Shikata in China aster plants (*Callistephus chinensis* Nees), and in *Nicotiana rustica* plants, as well as in the salivary glands and fat-body tissues of the leafhopper vector, *M. fascifrons,* working at the Boyce Thompson Institute in 1963–1965, but the publication of these findings was delayed because the interpretation of the electron micrographs could not be reconciled with the then prevailing and accepted belief that the disease was of viral etiology.

After the publication of the findings in Japan by Nasu *et al.* (1967) on mycoplasmas in rice yellow dwarf-infected plants and insect vectors, and by Doi *et al.* (1967) and Ishiie *et al.* (1967) on four diseases, including aster yellows, several of the earlier observations at Boyce Thompson Institute were published and further work was intensified (Maramorosch *et al.*, 1968a,b; Granados *et al.*, 1968a; Ploaie, 1968a,b; Ploaie and Ionică, 1968; Ploaie *et al.*, 1968; Staron *et al.*, 1968; Shikata *et al.*, 1968; Tetracycline Research Group, 1968; Lin and Lee, 1968; Maillet *et al.*, 1968; Giannotti *et al.*, 1968a,b,c,d; Davis *et al.*, 1968a,b; Cousin *et al.*, 1968; Borges and David-Ferreira, 1968; Bowyer *et al.*, 1969; Maillet and Folliot, 1968).

Thin sections of flower stalks from experimentally infected *C. chinensis* revealed the presence of large accumulations of polymorphic bodies, ranging in size from 80–800 nm (Fig. 1, top). These bodies were bounded by unit membranes, approximately 8 nm thick. Their ribosomes, of about 12 nm in diameter, were smaller than the ribosomes of the plant cells. Thin connections between some of the bodies suggested that they may arise from binary fission (as indicated in Fig. 1, top, by arrows). In a central, nuclear area of the larger bodies, strands, presumably of DNA, were observed. Often one phloem cell was observed completely filled with mycoplasmas, while an adjoining cell appeared normal and free from the pleomorphic bodies (Fig. 1, top; Fig. 2, top). In aster yellows-infected plants, mycoplasmas were found in veins of chlorotic leaves, in distorted flowers, and in stems of plants (Shikata *et al.*, 1969a). In all instances, the mycoplasmas were bounded by unit membranes, and their ribosomes were always smaller than those of the cells of the host plants. No mycoplasmas were found in healthy plants.

The movement of mycoplasmas from cell to cell and the invasion of adjacent cells apparently occurs through sieve pores in the sieve plates, as indicated in Figs. 1, bottom, 2 bottom. Ultrathin sections from salivary glands (Hirumi and Maramorosch, 1969a) and from adipose tissue (Shikata *et al.*, 1969a) of infective *M. fascifrons* (previously verified as having transmitted the aster yellows agent) revealed mycoplasmas in the cell cytoplasm (Fig. 3, top). The mycoplasmas closely resemble those found in cells of diseased plants. Neither mycoplasmas nor virus particles were found in control insects and no virus particles were found in aster yellows-diseased plants.

To obtain further information on the aster yellows mycoplasmas, an attempt was made to correlate infectivity of inocula from plant and insect vector material with the presence or absence of the pleomorphic bodies. Inocula were prepared from healthy controls, as well as from infective *M. fascifrons* (Hirumi and Maramorosch, 1969b). Aliquots

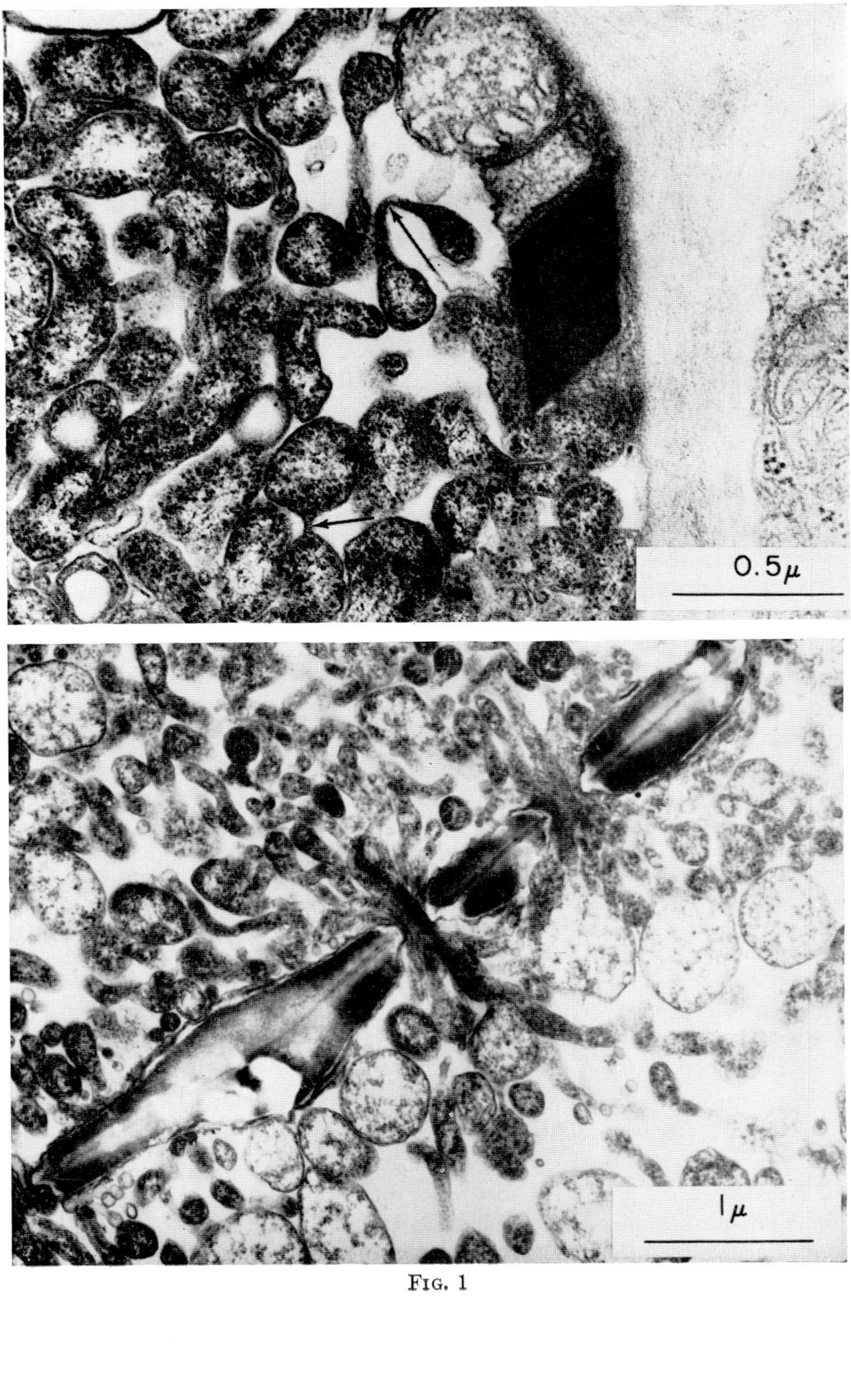

FIG. 1

of the extracts were negatively stained with 2% phosphotungstic acid and examined by electron microscopy. Mycoplasmas were found in extracts from diseased plants and infective insects, but not in controls. The mycoplasmas were irregularly shaped, with filaments, swellings, and blebs. Sometimes very long filaments were found to connect irregularly shaped bodies. The morphology of the aster yellows mycoplasmas from plant and insect material, as observed in negatively stained preparations, was believed to be similar to that of mycoplasmas infecting higher animals (Chu and Horne, 1967). Similar forms were recently described from plants with "flavescence dorée" (Giannotti *et al.,* 1969a), tomato plants with stolbur, clover phyllody sap, and *Euscelis plebejus* vector hemolymph (Giannotti *et al.,* 1968d), from rice plants with "Giallume" disease (Belli, 1969), and corn stunt (Granados, 1969b). Injected adult *M. fascifrons* were tested on *C. chinensis* seedlings and infectivity of the inoculum was correlated with the presence of mycoplasmas (Hirumi and Maramorosch, 1969b). Infectivity was retained at least 6 hours at room temperature and under liquid nitrogen for 48 hours (Davis *et al.,* 1970). The demonstration of mycoplasmas in infective, but not in noninfective material, provided support for the mycoplasma etiology of the aster yellows disease.

A brief note published in the 1968 Canada Department of Agriculture, Vancouver, B. C. Research Station report (1969) stated that a mycoplasmalike organism was isolated from aster plants with aster yellows, grown in a liquid culture at 25°C, and subcultured onto agar. The medium required plant extract instead of the usual serum fraction. Thymidine-^{3}H was incorporated in the mycoplasma DNA proving its viability. The microorganism was resistant to penicillin, but sensitive to tetracycline. This work was in progress in 1968, but no further reports have appeared. As far as could be ascertained, the aster yellows disease was not reproduced by the cultured microorganism.

Further observations of mycoplasmas in aster yellows-infected plants came from an electron microscopy study by Worley (1969, 1970), who confirmed the presence of typical mycoplasma microorganisms in aster yellows-diseased *N. rustica* and *C. chinensis.* Of particular interest were

FIG. 1. *Top:* Mycoplasma of aster yellows in a phloem cell from a flower stalk of a China aster plant (*Callistephus chinensis*) infected with aster yellows. Noninvaded cell at right has retained its normal appearance. Note apparent binary fission (arrows) of several mycoplasmas inside the plant cell. The microorganisms are bounded by unit membranes, with DNA strands in the nuclear regions, and with RNA-containing ribosome granules at the periphery. From Shikata *et al.* (1969a). With the permission of FAO Plant Prot. Bull., Rome. *Bottom:* Elongated mycoplasmas passing through sieve pores of a sieve plate of a corn plant (*Zea mays*) infected with corn stunt. Note pleomorphism of the bodies. From Shikata *et al.* (1969a). With the permission of FAO Plant Prot. Bull., Rome.

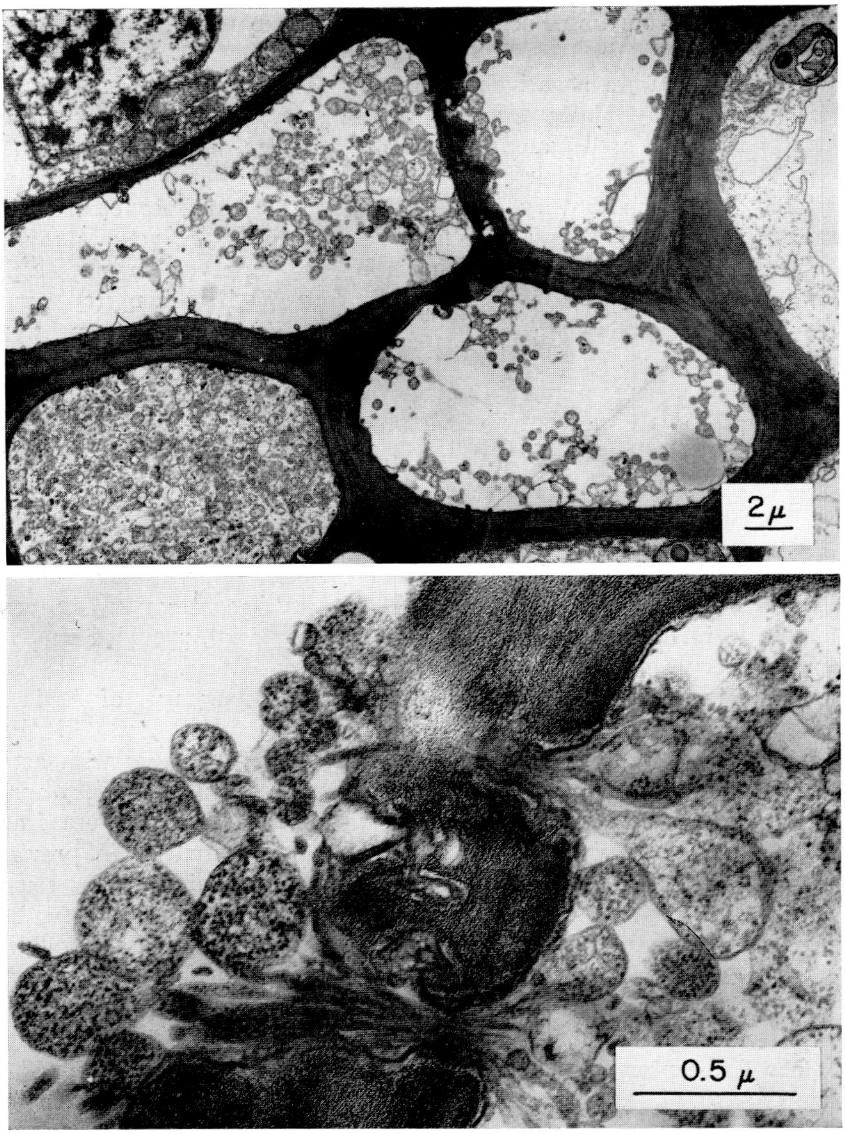

FIG. 2. *Top:* Low magnification electron micrograph of a thin section through phloem cells of a tobacco plant (*Nicotiana rustica*) severely infected with aster yellows. Note cell at lower left corner, filled with mycoplasmalike bodies. Adjacent cells contain fewer bodies, and the cell in upper left corner and in the extreme right seem free from infection. Original electron micrograph by H. Hirumi. *Bottom:* Passage of aster yellows mycoplasma through sieve pores in the sieve plate of a *N. rustica* plant infected with aster yellows. The cell at right is heavily infected, indicating that the direction of passage was from that cell to the one at left. Original electron micrograph by H. Hirumi.

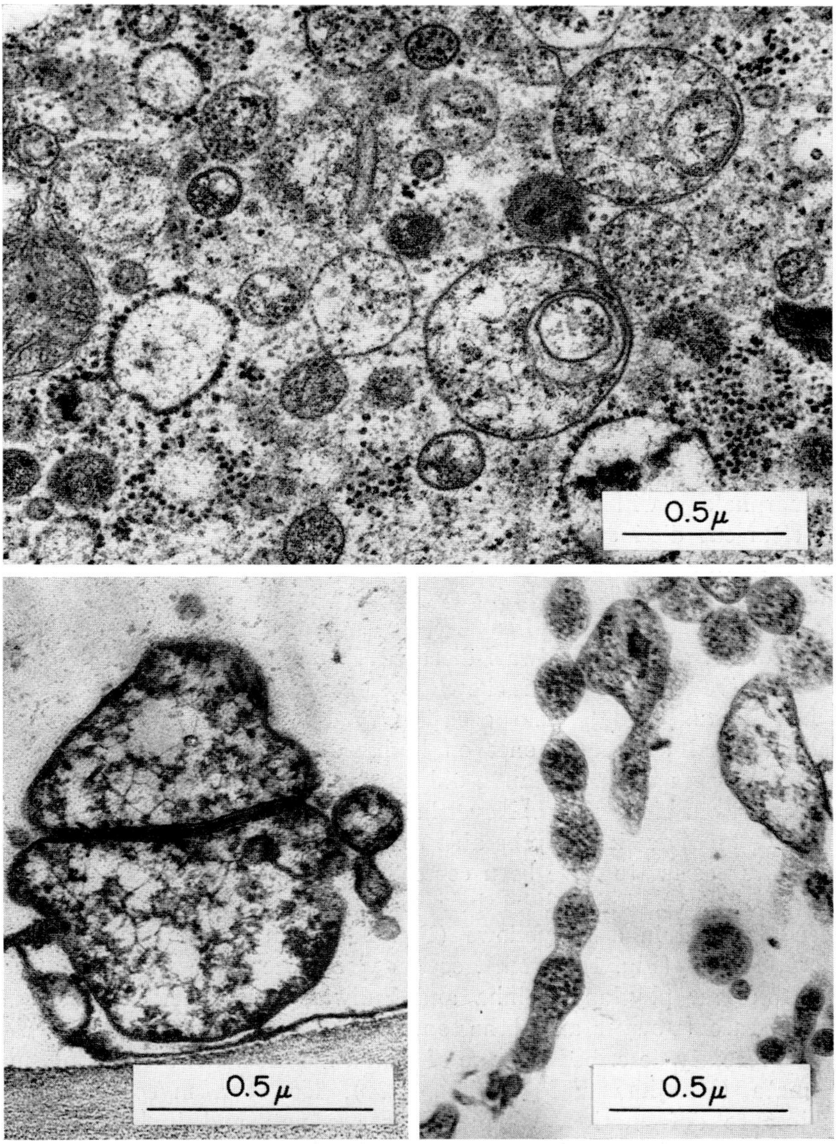

FIG. 3. *Top:* Mycoplasmalike bodies of aster yellows in the cytoplasm of a salivary gland cell of an infective leafhopper vector, *Macrosteles fascifrons,* 1 month after acquisition of the aster yellows agent. Note the pleomorphic bodies, ranging in diameter from 80–800 nm. At upper right, note large body with inclusion; both the large and the small inclusion body are bounded by unit membranes, and both seem to contain DNAlike strands and small ribosomes. Original electron micrograph by H. Hirumi. *Bottom, left:* Two mycoplasmalike bodies, in a phloem cell of *N. rustica* infected with aster yellows. The electron micrograph strongly suggests that the bodies were fixed just after they underwent binary fission. Original electron micrograph by K. Maramorosch. *Bottom, right:* Beaded string of mycoplasmalike bodies in a phloem cell of *N. rustica* with aster yellows. These chainlike configurations are reminiscent of structures reported for *Mycoplasma mycoides* var. *mycoides* (Freundt, 1969). Original electron micrographs by H. Hirumi.

filamentous forms, beaded chains, and bodies that showed budding protrusions. These were similar to the mycoplasmas illustrated in 1967 in sieve tubes of paulownia affected by witches'-broom (Doi *et al.*, 1967), but not reported previously for aster yellows-diseased plants (Fig. 3, bottom left).

It has been suggested that various mycoplasmas, causing different diseases of plants, may differ morphologically when observed in the same plant species (Ploaie and Maramorosch, 1969). However, the observed differences in the morphology of five mycoplasmas of European diseases, in experimentally infected *Vinca rosea* phloem cells, could also be interpreted as due to differences in the severity stage of the disease (Fig. 4A,B). It is generally admitted that eventually differences in morphology will be detected by electron microscopy, but until now no clear-cut distinctions have been made in forms that were studied by examination of thin sections. The possibility of mycoplasma multiplication by binary fission has also been indicated by Ploaie (1968a,b) from interpretations of his electron micrographs of aster yellows, parastolbur, and clover dwarf-diseased *V. rosea.* An illustration of the presumptive binary fission is shown in Fig. 3, bottom, right.

Doi *et al.* (1967), who occasionally observed small mycoplasma bodies mixed with large ones on both sides of sieve plates in potato witches'-broom-infected plants, did not report the presence of elongated bodies within sieve pores. Nevertheless, they suggested that bodies of small or medium size may be able to pass through the sieve pores. This suggestion seems to have been correct. Actual presence of mycoplasmas in sieve pores, indicating their passage through such pores, has been observed in aster yellows (Fig. 2 bottom), corn stunt (Shikata *et al.*, 1969a) (Fig. 1 bottom), cotton virescence (Gourret and Maillet, 1969), clover phyllody (Sinha and Paliwal, 1969), and legume little leaf disease (Bowyer and Atherton, 1970). This passage is reminiscent of the recently described passage of dahlia mosaic virus through plasmodesmata (Kitajima and Lauritis, 1969). However, mycoplasmas are subject to deformation, while virions are not, and it has therefore been assumed by Kitajima and Lauritis that plasmodesmal openings are probably susceptible to enlargement and reversible transformation, thus avoiding possible "plugging" by elements of the endoplasmic reticulum.

The observed passage of mycoplasmas through sieve pores of sieve plates explains not only the passage of these disease agents within plants, but also their ability to slip through pores of filters that retain small bacteria.

The observation that dodder (*Cuscuta* sp.) is often affected by

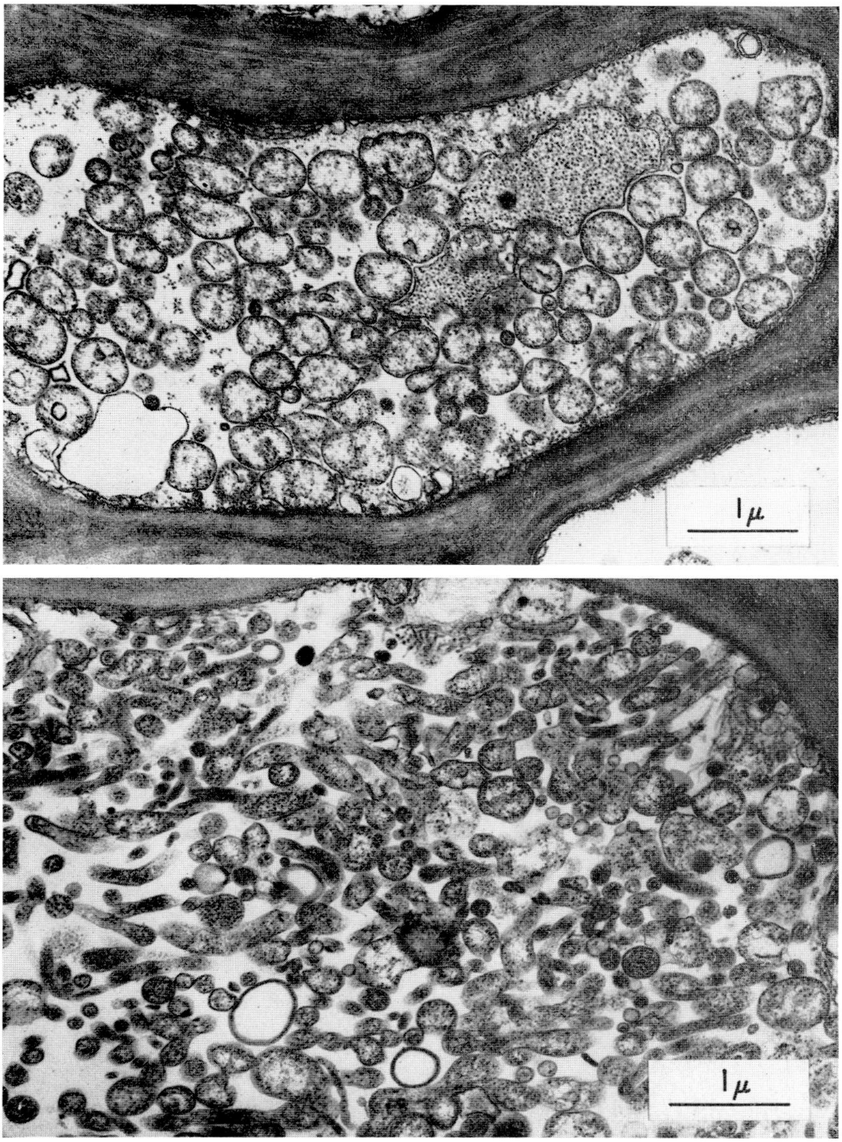

FIG. 4. Mycoplasmalike bodies of aster yellows in the phloem cells of an infected *N. rustica* plant. Note the predominance of rounded bodies in the upper electron micrograph (A), and the large number of filamentous, elongated bodies in the lower (B). These morphological differences are apparently due to stages in the development of the microorganisms, since the infectious agent, as well as the host plant, is the same in both instances. Original electron micrograph by H. Hirumi.

yellows-type diseases when it acts as a bridge between diseased plants has resulted in several electron microscopy studies of dodder during the past year. The first observation of mycoplasmas in dodder, parasitizing aster yellows-infected plants, was made by Dale and Kim (1969). The authors found an abundance of mycoplasmas in dodder cells, which they interpreted as suggesting the multiplication of the microorganisms within the parasitic plant. They concluded that dodder is not a passive participant in the transmission of mycoplasmas, but that it plays the role of an alternate host. Earlier observations of yellows symptoms in different species of *Cuscuta* used in transmission studies had led to the same conclusions. It is interesting to note that similar electron microscopic observations, and similar conclusions, have been made independently by examination of dodder, transmitting the agent of stolbur (Giannotti *et al.,* 1969d).

2. Chemotherapy

The extensive work on aster yellows chemotherapy carried out in Japan in 1967–1969 (Tetracycline Research Group, 1968, 1969; Ishiie *et al.,* 1967) as well as in the United States (Davis *et al.,* 1968a,b; Davis and Whitcomb, 1969; Whitcomb and Davis, 1970; Freitag and Smith, 1969), and in France (Cousin and Staron, 1969; Cousin *et al.,* 1968; Staron *et al.,* 1968, 1969) provided additional support for the mycoplasma etiology of the disease. The Japanese tests, reported in April 1968 and in March 1969, were coordinated through the Tetracycline Research Group in Tokyo, and carried out by teams of scientists from the Plant Pathology Department, Faculty of Agriculture, Tokyo University; The Division of Pesticides, Agricultural Research Institute, Nishigahara, Tokyo; the Division of Plant Pathology, Agricultural Research Institute, Nishigahara, Tokyo; the Second Research Division of the Plant Virus Research Institute in Chiba; the Department of Pathology, Silkworm Research Institute, Tokyo; the Faculty of Agriculture, Hokkaido University; the Institute of Agricultural Biology, Okayama University; the Chugoku Agricultural Experiment Station; the Silkworm Research Institute, Kyushu; the Kumamoto Silkworm Research Institute; and the Nihon Noyaku Company of Japan. These groups of scientists used aster yellows-diseased tomato, carrot, and cosmos plants. Besides, six other diseases of the yellows group were included in the tests: mulberry dwarf, potato witches'-broom, rice yellow dwarf, rice stripe, pea and green pea yellow dwarf, and sugarcane white leaf. The tests were carried out at thirteen experiment stations. In addition to the treatment of yellows-diseased plants, the insect vector of rice yellow dwarf, *Nephotettix* sp., was treated by feeding on filter paper disks soaked with tetracycline antibiotics, or by feeding on plants that acquired antibiotics through root dipping, as well as by abdominal injection with measured amounts of antibiotics. Four major groups of tetracycline antibiotics were tested: tetracyclines, chlortetracyclines, dimethylchlortetracyclines, and oxytetracyclines. In addition, various salts and chelates of the above four groups were also specially prepared by chemists from the Nihon Noyaku Company and used at all of the thirteen experiment stations. Plants were treated by dipping their roots and by spraying their leaves. Tests also involved temperature variations, tests of the solubility and uptake of the various antibiotics, heat stability, light stability, and the effect of rain.

The final results of these elaborate tests have been summarized in the eighty page report published in March 1969 by the Tetracycline Research Group. Tetracyclines had only a temporary effect, causing remission, but not permanent cure, of the seven mycoplasma diseases tested. Stabilizing chemicals, salts, or chelates increased the effectiveness of the treatment. Negative results have also been listed in detail, so as to provide complete data to all those who are interested in the applied aspects of yellows disease chemotherapy. Antibiotics other than tetracyclines were tested, but were found ineffective. Only tetracycline antibiotics caused temporary remission of the seven diseases. The dimethylchlortetracyclines (such as dediomycin) were found most effective. The Japanese workers found no correlation between the stage of disease, the time of treatment, and the resulting remission. Attempts to control the spread of yellows diseases by means of treating insect vectors with tetracycline antibiotics gave no practical results and it was concluded that vector treatment with antibiotics is not a feasible approach to plant protection. By maintaining plants in hydroponic cultures, constant concentrations of tetracycline antibiotics could be maintained during an application. The report concluded the chemotherapy with tetracyclines might eventually lead to practical results, provided that the mode of application could be improved.

Suppression of aster yellows disease was also reported by others during the past 2 years. In annual chrysanthemum (*Chrysanthemum carinatum* Schousb.), application of chlortetracycline, tetracycline, or chloramphenicol suppressed the development of symptoms (Davis *et al.*, 1968a,b). Foliar sprays were found much less effective in remission of symptoms than the administration of antibiotics through the roots, which confirmed the work of the Japanese investigators. Plants severely affected before treatment and maintained in hydroponic culture with 10 ppm chlortetracycline produced new, symptomless axillary growth, and even symptomless flowers. Control plants developed no new growth and remained yellowed and stunted. In further tests (Davis and Whitcomb, 1969) additional antibiotics were tested. Remission of aster yellows disease occurred after treatments with chlortetracycline, oxytetracycline, tetracycline, and methacycline, but not spectinomycin, oleandomycin, or kanamycin. The results were interpreted as indicating an antibiotic spectrum for the aster yellows agent that was different from the spectrum of known avian and human species of mycoplasmas. However, their tests did not indicate whether the antibiotics that did not cause remission, were actually taken up by the plants, retained by them, and remained in a stable, active form within plant tissues. A spectrum of the aster yellows mycoplasma could only be properly ascertained by application of the antibiotics to the cultured microorganisms, which has not yet been achieved.

The remission of aster yellows, caused by different strains, has been compared by Freitag and Smith (1969). These authors found that achromycin and aureomycin treatment of aster, plantain, and celery plants infected with strains of aster yellows resulted in remission of symptoms in some plants. Fewer *M. fascifrons* leafhoppers, fed on such treated plants, acquired the infecting agent than did controls feeding on untreated diseased plants. No differences were found in the tetracycline susceptibility of various strains of aster yellows, whether treated in plants or in insect vectors.

A study of the uptake and retention of tetracycline antibiotics in diseased plants was reported by Staron *et al.* (1968). Although in several instances the treatment with tetracyclines, followed by remission of symptoms, was also accompanied by the disappearance of mycoplasmas from phloem cells, this has not always been the case. Symptomless plants may still contain some mycoplasmas, which will multiply when the treatment is stopped, and which thus account for the relapse of the disease. The presence of mycoplasmas in symptomless plants merely indicates that these microorganisms cannot be eliminated by tetracyclines. Since studies with cultured mycoplasmas that infect higher animals have shown that tetracyclines are only mycoplasmastatic, and never mycoplasmacidal, the finding is in line with the observations of veterinary and human disease researchers. A different conclusion was reached by Staron *et al.* (1969), who interpreted the finding of mycoplasmas in symptomless-treated plants as an indication of a different antibiotic spectrum from that of animal-infecting species. On the other hand, they recognized that tetracycline treatment and subsequent remission of symptoms could be used as a diagnostic tool for some of the yellows-type diseases.

Tetracyclines, even in low concentration, may have an inhibitory effect on plants (Cousin *et al.*, 1968; Brčák *et al.*, 1969; Klein, 1970). Growth inhibition, yellowing, necrosis, and even death may occur in some plant species. Therefore, delay in the appearance of symptoms is not a good criterion in evaluating the efficacy of tetracycline treatment. It seems worthwhile to point out some of the limitations in diagnosing the nature of plant diseases through the application of tetracycline chemotherapy. Factors such as light, moisture, temperature, pH, tannins, and many others, may interfere with the activity of the compounds. The solubility of the drugs, as well as their uptake, or lack of uptake, and their stability may prevent the achievement of clear-cut or even of reproducible results. Nonspecific compounds as well as synergistic effects could obscure the interpretation. For instance, careful testing of various compounds on aster yellows-diseased plants (Klein and Maramorosch, 1970) showed that sulfadiazine enhances the action of tetracyclines, although sulfadiazine does not act on mycoplasmas *in vitro* (Newnham and Chu, 1965). Even more important, tetracyclines can cause the remission of diseases caused by known bacteria and even by fungi (Müller, 1969).

The mycoplasma etiology of aster yellows has been questioned recently on the basis of observations made by electron microscopy of leafhopper saliva by Raine and Forbes (1969). These authors describe bodies which they consider to be mycoplasmalike found in salivary excretions of both infective and noninfective (healthy stock) *M. fascifrons*. They concluded that the finding casts doubt on the suspected etiologic role of mycoplasmas as the sole or primary agent of aster yellows. They stated that "perhaps these microorganisms occur in nontransmitting vectors and require a complementary component to make them infectious." This speculation was based on earlier reports by Maillet *et al.* (1968) and Maillet and Folliot (1968) who believed that mycoplasma and "Phi particles" are associated in the germinal cells of female *Typhlocyba douglasi* Edv. It might be worthwhile to examine critically the evidence that is given in support of the claim that mycoplasmas occur in the saliva of vectors as well as nonvectors. There is no real indication from the presented electron micrographs that the structures photographed in the saliva are mycoplasmas. Raine and Forbes (1969) did not find bodies in the range of 500–800 nm and rationalized this by assuming that the large bodies probably remain in the salivary glands where they produce small and intermediate bodies that are released into the saliva. No unit membranes can be recognized in the electron micrographs, and the structures do not correspond morphologically to the Mycoplasmatales. It should also be pointed out that others, who carefully examined stock *M. fascifrons*, found that healthy insects were devoid of mycoplasmas (Shikata *et al.,* 1969a; Shikata and Maramorosch, 1969a).

There has also been speculation that mycoplasmas are not the actual etiologic agents, but that they act as vectors of viruses (Atanasoff, 1969; Peary, 1969). There is no evidence to support this speculation, and electron microscopy of mycoplasmas infecting insects or plants has not indicated the presence of viruses or viruslike particles inside the mycoplasma microorganisms.

B. Mulberry Dwarf

This disease, of considerable economic importance in Japan, where the mulberry tree serves as a source of food for the silkworm, has been studied for many years in the Orient. Several findings reported from Japan can now be reinterpreted as clues leading to the identification of the mycoplasma etiology of the disease agent. Tahama found that the disease agent may be affected by frost (Tahama, 1961), which would not indicate a viral agent, but could be explained on the basis of a highly labile, unit membrane-bound mycoplasma. The same author reported that the disease agent of mulberry dwarf was inactivated experimentally in living plants by 37°C (Tahama, 1963). Complete cure was also achieved by the application of heat (Tahama, 1964). Strains were also recognized in mulberry dwarf (Tahama, 1967). In 1967, Doi *et al.* reported that in ultrathin sections of phloem-parenchyma cells they found spherical or asymmetrical ellipsoidal bodies of various sizes, 80–800 nm in diameter. These bodies were not found in healthy mulberry tissues, but were always observed in the sieve tubes of diseased trees, and sometimes also in the phloem-parenchyma cells adjacent to the sieve tubes. Young shoots of naturally infected mulberry trees and trees infected artificially by grafting or by the insect vector *Hishimonus sellatus,* at an early stage of infection, had numerous bodies in phloem tissues. The mycoplasmas were bounded by unit membranes about 8 nm in thickness. The smallest bodies were 100–250 nm in diameter, nearly spherical, and usually filled with ribosomelike granules about 13 nm in diameter. Sometimes netlike strands, similar to those found in the nuclear regions of certain animal-pathogenic mycoplasmas, were inside the bodies. Larger bodies, over 300 nm in diameter, were usually asymmetrical ellipsoid and possessed a large central vacuole surrounded by ribosomelike granules at the periphery. Frequently structures similar to nuclear net-strands were observed inside the vacuolated areas. Both large and small bodies were frequently present in the same sieve tubes. The suggestion was made that small bodies might perhaps arise from large ones by constriction of the middle portion, or that small bodies were produced within large ones by breakdown. No similar bodies were observed in healthy controls. The mycoplasmalike bodies were considered as parasitic microorganisms. They were confined to the phloem elements, and were not observed in the xylem, intracellular spaces, or other tissues. Ishiie *et al.* (1967) applied tetracyclines to diseased mulberry plants and observed a remission of the disease. When such recovered plants were used for electron microscopy observations, phloem tissues of the stems and leaves were devoid of mycoplasmas.

Doi *et al.* (1967) suggested that sieve tubes of the phloem tissues of higher plants may perhaps provide the most favorable environment for mycoplasmas because their fluid contents have a high osmotic pressure and are slightly alkaline. The authors noted that mycoplasmas sometimes completely occluded the sieve tubes. This could account, in part, for the observed impairment of growth. Since tetracycline antibiotics caused remission of the disease, and since no mycoplasmas were found in the phloem tissue of plants that recovered from mulberry dwarf disease following tetracycline treatment, this was considered as indirect evidence that the mycoplasmalike bodies found in the phloem tissue were the etiologic agent of the disease. These authors also pointed out that heat therapy of mulberry dwarf and similar diseases supports the mycoplasma etiology. Finally, they stressed the ability of the etiologic agents to multiply, in some instances, in diseased plants, as well as in insect vectors. In this respect, the plant pathogenic mycoplasmas seem to be less specific than the species infecting higher animals that seem to be highly species-specific.

C. White Leaf Disease of Sugarcane

This disease is perhaps the most important for the present review, because it is the only one for which a mycoplasma has been cultured on solid agar media and, upon direct mechanical reinoculation into plants, reproduced the original disease.

The disease, first reported in Taiwan in 1968 (Lin and Lee, 1968), has since been spread by cuttings and insect vectors. The leafhopper *Epitettix hiroglyphicus* Matsumoto has been reported to carry the disease agent from plant to plant (Matsumoto *et al.*, 1969). In 1967, E. Shikata suggested a study, by electron microscopy, of healthy and diseased sugarcane, to establish the suspected virus etiology of the disease (Shikata *et al.*, 1969b). Two reports resulted. One, by Shikata *et al.* (1968), described mycoplasmalike microorganisms found in sieve tubes of diseased sugarcane; healthy sugarcane was devoid of such bodies. The mycoplasmalike structures were compared with similar ones found in American aster yellows and corn stunt, as well as in rice yellow dwarf in the Philippines. In all instances, typical morphology of mycoplasmas indicated that the diseases might be caused by mycoplasma agents. Incidentally, in all these instances, the disease agents are known to be leafhopper-borne. In addition, suppression of the disease was observed following tetracycline treatment. After the retirement of Prof. Matsumoto as consultant to the Taiwan Sugarcane Experiment Station, Shu-Chen Lin was employed there to continue the investigations on the disease. A report was published together with Ching-Shiou Lee (Lin and Lee, 1968), giving further details of the findings. The authors used the highly susceptible sugarcane variety 56-2080, inoculated by means of the leafhopper vector. In addition, leaves from naturally infected plants were also included in the material that was fixed, embedded, and sectioned for electron microscopy. The sectioning and electron microscopy observations were made by Y. Doi and K. Yora. The findings confirmed the presence of mycoplasmalike bodies in diseased tissues, and their absence in healthy material.

Further work with sugarcane white leaf disease (Lin and Lee, 1969) was reported in September 1969. Tetracycline treatment alone, by immersion of cuttings for 24, 48, and 72 hours in solutions containing 200 ppm of tetracycline, or of oxytetracycline, caused a remission of the disease for a period of 1 to 2 months. The additional heat treatment, combined with tetracycline treatment, resulted in a prolonged remission (at least 11 months) and perhaps complete cure. The latter is strongly suspected since at the time of the report the symptomless plants had been under observation for approximately 1 year. Further observations were contemplated.

The most important part of the report concerns the successful cultivation of the mycoplasma isolated from diseased sugarcane cuttings. Buds from a severely diseased stalk were first washed in 5% calcium hypochloride for 5 minutes, then placed in Bacto-PPLO enrichment broth and incubated at 37°–38°C for 36–72 hours. An aliquot from the liquid culture was transferred to Bacto-PPLO agar plates containing 1% Bacto-PPLO serum fraction and incubated again at 37°–38°C. After 36–48 hours, fried egg-like colonies, typical for agar-grown mycoplasmas, developed on the plate.

Attempts were then made to inoculate the mycoplasmas into healthy sugarcane mechanically. These attempts were successful. Buds and root-bands of healthy one-bud cuttings were immersed in a suspension of cultured mycoplasmas and pierced by needles. The cuttings were kept in the suspension for 18 hours at 37°–38°C, then planted in pots in a greenhouse. Of seventy-two cuttings inoculated mechanically in three separate tests, five developed typical disease symptoms. Controls remained healthy. If confirmed, this constitutes the first successful cultivation of a mycoplasma known to cause a plant disease. The sugarcane white leaf mycoplasma has also been cultivated successfully by others, according to Shikata (1969). Dr. Han, presently at Hokkaido University, appears to have obtained cultures, as has Dr. R. Y. Wu (1969) of the Institute of Botany, Academia Sinica, Nankang, Taipei, Taiwan. However, these investigators, who kindly wrote us about their tests, had not yet succeeded in inoculating the mycoplasma into plants so had not reproduced the sugarcane white leaf disease with the cultured microorganisms.

The results would indicate that some plant-parasitic species of mycoplasmas can be grown on commercial mycoplasma media in the same manner as some animal-infecting species. Other species may yield to similar attempts, but it is likely that certain species will prove more fastidious than others, just as has been the case in species infecting animal cell cultures, where very few have yielded to cultivation attempts. Several commercial media for mycoplasma cultivation, have been tested with the aster yellows mycoplasma in at least four laboratories without success (at Boyce Thompson Institute, at Wistar Institute, at Sloan Kettering Institute, and at Stanford University). The maintenance of corn stunt mycoplasma in liquid media, reported in the next section of this review, is a step in the direction of cultivation and promises to yield results.

D. Corn Stunt

The corn stunt disease (maize stunt, achaparramiento) causes considerable losses in Latin America and also, in certain years, in several southern states of the United States (Stoner, 1965). Kunkel, who in 1946 discovered the first leafhopper vector of the corn stunt agent, *Dalbulus maidis* DeL & W. reported (Kunkel, 1948) that the disease agent could not be transmitted to plants by grafting, and that it required a comparatively long extrinsic incubation period in its vector and in plants. Kunkel (1948) hypothesized that the agent of corn stunt multiplied in insect vectors as well as in plants. Maramorosch (1951) transmitted the infectious agent to leafhoppers by needle inoculation and subsequently demonstrated that it multiplied in its leafhopper vector (Maramorosch, 1952b). On the basis of symptomatology and mode of transmission, Kunkel (1946) and all later investigators until 1967 considered the agent to be a virus. The finding of "cross-protection", that is, of interference between two strains of corn stunt in plants and in insect vectors (Maramorosch, 1958) also supported the virus hypothesis.

Corn stunt is transmitted by at least five leafhopper species, of which *Dalbulus elimatus* (Ball) (Niederhauser and Cervantes, 1950) and *D. maidis* are the most efficient vectors (Granados *et al.*, 1968b). Of several strains of corn stunt, the Mesa Central, Rio Grande, and Louisiana strains have been studied in more detail (Maramorosch, 1955; Granados *et al.*, 1966).

1. Electron Microscopy

Structures morphologically similar to mycoplasmas were observed in the salivary glands, malpighian tubules, intestinal tract, brain and ventral ganglia of *D. elimatus* (Granados *et al.*, 1968a; Maramorosch *et al.*, 1968a,b; Shikata *et al.*, 1969a) and *D. maidis* (Granados, 1969b) infected with corn stunt. Shikata and Maramorosch (1969a) also reported the occurrence of mycoplasmalike bodies in fat-body cells of *D. maidis* infected with corn stunt. No similar bodies were observed in healthy control insects (Shikata and Maramorosch, 1969a; Shikata *et al.*, 1969a; Granados, 1969b). The bodies were very pleomorphic and ranged from spherical- to filamentous-shaped structures. Most spherical-shaped bodies measured approximately 400 to 1000 nm in diameter, and filamentous forms as long as 2000 nm were often observed. The diameter of filamentous forms ranged from 80 to 300 nm. Small electron-dense bodies, 60 to 100 nm in diameter, similar to the "elementary bodies" described from mycoplasmas infecting man and other higher animals were observed. Each body was surrounded by a single unit membrane about 9 nm thick with an intermediate light line of the same thickness. The bodies possessed two main types of internal structures (Granados, 1969b). One type had zones of netlike strands thought to be nuclear areas. These areas were centrally located and were surrounded by a peripheral cytoplasmic area which contained ribosomelike granules approximately 15 nm in size. The second type contained ribosomelike granules in a pale to dark ground substance, but no areas of netlike strands.

Forms of various shapes observed by electron microscopy were interpreted as representing three probable modes of replication in infective leafhoppers and in diseased plants. These presumptive developmental stages could account for budding, beading, and binary fission (Granados, 1969b). Similar structures have been reported in plants infected with several yellows-type diseases (Doi *et al.*, 1967; Sinha and Paliwal, 1969; Brčák *et al.*, 1969; Worley, 1970), where they have been considered as representing possible developmental stages of the causal agents.

In diseased corn (*Zea mays* L.) plants, mycoplasmalike bodies were observed in phloem sieve elements of infected plants (Granados *et al.*, 1968a; Granados, 1969b; Maramorosch *et al.*, 1968a,b; Shikata *et al.*, 1968, 1969a; Shikata and Maramorosch, 1969a). These bodies were initially observed 24–48 hours prior to the appearance of the disease symptoms (Granados, 1969b). Only a few bodies were observed at this time and all were confined to one or two sieve tube cells. One week after symptom development, the bodies were found in larger concentrations and several sieve tube cells were affected. In late stages of infection, the bodies were found in very high concentrations. The morphology of the bodies found in plant cells appeared to be similar to those found in infected insect cells. Sometimes a cell contained almost nothing other than mycoplasmalike bodies (Shikata *et al.*, 1969a). Some cells filled with bodies of high electron density, perhaps elementary-type bodies, seemed to degenerate. Such degenerating cells were also commonly observed in diseased plants with aster yellows, sugarcane white leaf, and rice grassy stunt (Shikata *et al.*, 1969a). The elongated bodies were frequently observed within sieve pores, which might explain the route of mycoplasmas within infected plants that results in systemic infection (Fig. 1, bottom). It should be stressed that in diseased corn plants, mycoplasmalike bodies were found free in the infected plant cell cytoplasm, or within cytoplasmic vacuoles, and, in addition to this intracellular occurrence, they were also observed extracellularly. Similar findings, concerning mycoplasmalike bodies in vectors and in stunted corn plants, were recently made by Kitajima (1969) in Brazil.

Granados (1969b) reported that electron microscope grids prepared by the dip method of Brandes (1957) revealed the presence of mycoplasmalike bodies in plant sap from infected plants but not from healthy ones. The negatively stained preparations showed filamentous and irregularly shaped bodies in high concentrations. Branched filamentous forms up to 6000 nm in length were the most conspicuous found in plant sap. These forms usually had a main body approximately 0.3 to 0.5 μ in diameter.

The retention of infectivity in plant extracts prepared from corn stunt-infected plants can be tested by injection into healthy corn leafhoppers (Maramorosch, 1951). Infective extracts from plants with the Louisiana strain were negatively stained and examined by electron microscopy (Granados, 1969b). Bodies similar to those observed in plant sap from diseased plants were reported present in the infective extracts. Similar negatively stained bodies have been reported by others from plants infected with "flavescence dorée" (Giannotti *et al.*, 1969a), rice yellows (Belli, 1969), and aster yellows (Hirumi and Maramorosch, 1969b).

2. Chemotherapy

Preliminary tests carried out in 1967 and 1968 indicated that corn stunt disease can be arrested by tetracycline treatment (Maramorosch *et al.*, 1968a). Further tests showed that symptom development was suppressed or completely blocked in corn plants treated immediately after inoculation by immersing the roots in 1000 ppm of either tetracycline hydrochloride or chlortetracycline hydrochloride for 15 to 30 minutes (Granados, 1969a). At concentrations of 100 ppm, these antibiotics delayed symptom development for 2 to 3 weeks but did not block infection of the corn plant. Kanamycin sulfate or penicillin G did not suppress corn stunt symptom development in inoculated plants. Symptom development was delayed up to 5 weeks or completely blocked in plants grown in hydroponic solution with 10 ppm of tetracycline hydrochloride for 2 or 4 days after exposure to infective vectors. Tetracycline hydrochloride at 1000 ppm severely reduced the ability of infective *D. elimatus* leafhoppers to transmit corn stunt; the antibiotic was administered by placing the insects on a healthy plant grown in a solution of tetracycline.

Retention of infectivity of the corn stunt agent was reported in a cell-free medium (Chen and Granados, 1970). Plant sap from small cubes of diseased stem tissue, or pieces of atactosteles were transferred into a culture medium consisting of undetermined amounts and kinds of organic acids, purines, pyrimidines, vitamins, amino acids, steroids, coenzymes, ATP, sugars, inorganic salts, and supplemental nutrients. In dilutions of the original medium, infectivity was detected up to 50 days at 25°C. All infective preparations contained only pleomorphic, mycoplasmalike bodies, which possessed an irregular shape with several filaments emerging from their surfaces. Since extracts from diseased corn plants in buffer solution at room temperature are noninfective after 4 hours, this undefined medium was apparently successful in maintaining the infectivity of the corn stunt agent. The authors stated that their experiments satisfied Koch's postulates and proved the mycoplasma etiology of the corn stunt disease.

E. Stolbur

Stolbur, a yellows-type disease affecting various plants in the Solanaceae family, is perhaps the most important yellows-type disease of potatoes and tomatoes in southern and eastern Europe ("Stolbur," 1958; Valenta *et al.*, 1961). During 1968 and 1969, not less than 18 references pertaining to the mycoplasma etiology of this disease have appeared (Cousin *et al.*, 1968, 1969a,b; Cousin and Staron, 1969; Giannotti *et al.*, 1968c,d,e; Giannotti *et al.*, 1969b,c,d; Maillet *et al.*, 1968; Ploaie, 1968a,b, 1970; Ploaie and Ionică, 1968; Ploaie and Maramorosch, 1969;

Ploaie *et al.,* 1968; Staron *et al.,* 1968). Until now, stolbur is the only disease of presumptive mycoplasma etiology in which serological tests have been reported as successful diagnostic tools (Pozděna, 1954; Pozděna and Čech, 1958; Gáborjányi and Bencsics, 1968).

The electron microscopy of diseased plants revealed the presence of numerous pleomorphic bodies in the sieve tube cells. No such bodies were detected in the epidermis or parenchyma. Ploaie and Maramorosch (1969) grouped the bodies into three categories on the basis of their size and morphology. The very small ones were 50–80 nm in diameter, and were characterized by high electron opacity. The intermediate ones were from 80 to 110 nm in diameter, ovoid to spherical, and the third were from 110 to 960 nm, bound by a unit membrane, as visualized clearly by two electron-dense layers with an inner transparent layer. The larger bodies had nuclear strands in the nuclear area, and ribosomelike particles at their periphery. The stolbur agent was also detected by electron microscopy in the insect vector *Hyalestes obsoletus* (Ploaie, 1968b) in several lobes of the salivary gland. Giannotti *et al.* (1968d) observed the stolbur mycoplasma agent in vector hemolymph preparations, negatively stained with phosphotungstic acid, as well as in phloem cells of potato plants (Giannotti *et al.,* 1968c). Cousin *et al.* (1968) also detected the mycoplasma bodies in *Vinca rosea, Solanum lycopersicum* (tomato), and *Nicotiana tabacum* plants infected with stolbur, and succeeded in getting a remission of the disease by applying tetracycline antibiotics. Cousin and Staron (1969) made a careful comparison of the action of several tetracycline antibiotics on stolbur-diseased plants. The uptake and persistence of the antibiotics were also tested in the treated plants (Staron *et al.,* 1968). Maillet *et al.* (1968) also described mycoplasmas from stolbur-infected plants. These authors did not report similar observations in the vector, but compared the mycoplasmas with symbiontlike structures which they observed in certain homoptera insects. Other investigators distinguished the rickettsialike symbionts that possess a rippled wall from the membrane-bound mycoplasmas (Maramorosch *et al.,* 1968a). A partial review of the stolbur mycoplasma work has appeared (Giannotti *et al.,* 1969d).

The rapid method for the preparation of an antiserum to stolbur from partially purified plant extracts may need confirmation. It indicates that reliable, simple serological methods can be developed for detecting and comparing the agents of yellows-type diseases, even if their cultivation in cell-free media may not succeed soon.

F. Clover Phyllody

Under the name of "clover phyllody," diseases of clover have been described from North America and Europe, and it is not possible at this moment to determine whether these are caused by related or unrelated agents. For the purpose of this review, the findings on "clover phyllody" will be discussed as if the diseases were the same. The reader is referred to the description of symptoms and comparison with other yellows-type diseases to the papers by Albouy *et al.* (1967) and Valenta (1959a,b).

The electron microscopy studies of plants infected with the agent of clover phyllody (Giannotti *et al.*, 1968a; Maillet *et al.*, 1968; Ploaie, 1968b; Ploaie *et al.*, 1968; Ploaie and Maramorosch, 1969; Sinha and Paliwal, 1969; Cousin *et al.*, 1968) carried out in different laboratories, demonstrated the presence of mycoplasmas in the phloem cells of infected plants. The smallest bodies were described as having a diameter of 75–80 nm, and the largest ranged from 800 to 1100 nm in diameter or maximum length. The sieve elements of vascular tissues of stems, leaves, roots, and flowers contained these pleomorphic bodies in systemically infected plants. An earlier study by Sinha and Chiykowski (1968), in which the agent of the disease was still considered as a virus, showed that it is present in the hemolymph, alimentary canal, and salivary glands of leafhopper vectors, *M. fascifrons*. Giannotti and Devauchelle studied the cytology of *Euscelis plebejus* carrying the clover phyllody agent, and observed by light microscopy cytoplasmic lesions in various tissues. The electron microscopic examination revealed the presence of mycoplasmas in the midgut and salivary glands (Giannotti and Devauchelle, 1969). In two other vectors of the clover phyllody agent, *Euscelis variegatus* KBM and *Aphrodes bicinctus* Schrank, cellular lesions were observed in the midgut, salivary glands, aorta, and epithelial cells (Giannotti, 1969).

The study of Maillet *et al.* (1968) presented evidence for the presence of clover phyllody mycoplasmas in adjacent cells of sieve elements accumulated particularly near the sieve pores of sieve plates. These observations were similar to those made earlier with paulownia witches'-broom by Doi *et al.* (1967) and by Shikata *et al.* (1969a) and Shikata and Maramorosch (1969a) who suggested that the bodies probably pass through the sieve pores. The same suggestion has recently been made by Sinha and Paliwal (1969) who confirmed the earlier observations. It is now apparent that in systemically infected plants, mycoplasmas pass through sieve pores, probably as fairly large and elongated bodies, and not as "elementary" bodies, as evidenced by the elongated structures observed within the pores (Shikata and Maramorosch, 1969a; Shikata *et al.*, 1969a).

A hypothetical and highly speculative growth cycle was proposed for the clover phyllody mycoplasma agent (Sinha and Paliwal, 1969). The speculation considered among others the propagative function of elementary bodies. The shortcomings of such a scheme have been discussed in the introduction. It might be worthwhile to point out that all so-called "stages of development," described for mycoplasmas on the basis of observations of thin sections from various yellows-type diseases, have been observed and illustrated in the first paper on this subject by Doi *et al.* in 1967. These authors described the structure and size of large and intermediary bodies, the budding and beading (Fig. 23, Doi *et al.*, 1967), and the electron dense "elementary bodies," but they refrained from speculating on possible sequential stages of development, realizing that such assumptions could not be made on the basis of the material under study.

In their study of the clover phyllody mycoplasma, Giannotti *et al.* (1968a) used cytochemical staining which provided evidence of DNA and RNA in the salivary gland cells and filter chamber of *E. plebejus* vectors. Similar results were obtained by staining phloem cells of clover with clover phyllody disease. Since mycoplasmas contain both DNA and RNA, this observation of the presence of both substances in areas of mycoplasma accumulation (evidenced in parallel electron micrographs) confirmed the microorganismal nature of the disease agents.

Giannotti *et al.* (1968e) recorded the presence of abnormal-appearing mycoplasma bodies devoid of the usual content. Such bodies were interpreted as degenerating mycoplasmas, and their presence was established in old *E. plebejus* vectors as well as in plants with prolonged clover phyllody infection. According to Giannotti *et al.* (1968e), Cousin (1968) and Giannotti *et al.* (1970), the partial recovery which sometimes occurs in infected clover plants might be explained by the degeneration of the infectious agent in the phloem cells. Giannotti *et al.* (1968e) also observed that the vectors carrying the mycoplasma agent of clover phyllody are deleteriously affected and this was interpreted as a pathogenic action, particularly since the same increased mortality of vectors was noted when clarified and filtered extracts were inoculated into healthy *E. plebejus*.

G. Rice Yellow Dwarf

This disease was listed until recently as one of the important virus diseases affecting rice in the Orient ("The Virus Diseases of the Rice Plant," 1969; Ou *et al.*, 1969). In 1967, Nasu *et al.* reported the absence of virus particles in diseased plants and vectors, and the presence of mycoplasmalike bodies in infected plants and leafhopper vectors. This finding was the first published demonstration of mycoplasmas in the midgut and salivary glands of a leafhopper vector. The species studied by the Japanese authors were *Nephotettix apicalis* and *N. cincticeps*.

The rice yellow dwarf disease was included among the diseases studied by the Tetracycline Research Group in Japan (1968, 1969) and the leafhopper vectors were also treated. The extensive tests resulted in remission, but not in cure of diseased rice plants. Transmission by insects was hampered, but not eliminated entirely. In 1968, Shikata *et al.* (1968) found mycoplasma bodies in rice yellow dwarf-infected plants in the Philippines. The bodies were somewhat less abundant in rice plants with yellow dwarf than in aster yellows-, sugarcane white leaf-, or corn stunt-diseased plants (Shikata *et al.*, 1969a). Shikata (1970) pointed out that rice virus diseases seem more limited in their geographic distribution than rice mycoplasma diseases. It would be of interest to gather more data on this subject to see whether or not this hypothesis is correct and, if so, what the reasons for such a difference might be, since the distribution of the leafhopper vectors, often the same species as for rice viruses, is much wider than that of the diseases.

The recent finding of mycoplasmas in rice yellow dwarf-infected plants in East Pakistan by Galvez and Shikata (1969) provided further evidence for the mycoplasma etiology of this disease. The authors carried out an electron microscopic study which revealed the systemic distribution of mycoplasmas in diseased rice plants. They also treated diseased plants with 100 ppm of aureomycin and observed remission of the disease.

The economic importance of the yellow dwarf disease of rice becomes apparent when one considers the role of rice as a staple food for all of Southeast Asia and the Orient. If the rice plants become infected while very young, they often die, while those that survive produce defective heads or remain without heads (Shikata *et al.*, 1969a).

H. Giallume-Yellows of Rice Plants

In 1967, Corbetta described a yellows-type disease of rice plants occurring in Northern Italy, in the provinces of Pavia and Novara. The affected plants were stunted and the leaves became yellow (Corbetta, 1967). No virus particles have been found in diseased plants, but recently mycoplasmas have been suspected as disease agents. An electron microscopy study of ultrathin sections prepared from diseased plants (Belli, 1969; Pellegrini *et al.*, 1969) revealed the presence of mycoplasmalike bodies in stunted plants. Electron micrographs of negatively stained plant extracts illustrated the presence of particles that resembled those found by Giannotti *et al.* (1969a) in purified preparations from grapevine tissues with "flavescence dorée," and recently by Granados (1969b) from plants with corn stunt, and interpreted as mycoplasmas. The negatively stained particles from rice plants ranged in size from 60 to 800 nm, and their shape was highly pleomorphic. The detailed report of Belli (1969) can be considered as the first report concerning clarified plant extracts containing mycoplasmas. It remains to be shown whether the negatively stained bodies are in reality the same as the mycoplasma bodies observed in thin sections. If this could be proved, the method would provide a convenient test for plant mycoplasmas.

I. Rice Stripe

This rice disease was studied in Japan along with several other diseases of mycoplasma etiology, in the extensive tests with tetracyclines (Tetracycline Research Group, 1968, 1969). The remission of the disease, following tetracycline treatment, indicated that it might belong to the same group of diseases as the yellows-type mycoplasma diseases. No electron microscopy study has been reported.

J. Grassy Stunt of Rice

This disease of rice plants in the Philippines, until 1967 considered a leafhopper-borne virus disease, has been studied recently by Shikata *et al.* (1969a). Preliminary results indicate that no virus particles occur in either the diseased plants or the leafhopper vectors. Mycoplasmalike bodies were observed in the phloem cells of grassy stunt-diseased rice plants. Vectors carrying the disease agent have not yet been studied.

K. Potato Witches'-Broom

The mycoplasma etiology of this disease was first suggested in 1967 by Doi *et al.* (1967), who reported the finding of mycoplasmalike bodies in the sieve tubes and phloem parenchyma of stems and leaves of potato plants, propagated from diseased potato tubers. The fine structure of the mycoplasmalike bodies was similar to that found in mulberry dwarf, but the larger, ellipsoidal bodies were more numerous in diseased potato plants. The mycoplasmas were observed in the cytoplasm of phloem parenchyma cells, often on both sides of the sieve pores. The authors suggested, therefore, that the middle- and smaller-sized bodies could perhaps pass through sieve pores. This suggestion was later found to be correct (Shikata *et al.*, 1969a; Gourret and Maillet, 1969; see also Fig. 2 bottom, for aster yellows mycoplasmas passing through sieve pores).

The size of the pleomorphic bodies was in the same range as that of other mycoplasmas; Doi *et al.* (1967) found that the large bodies were from 400–800 nm in diameter. Recently Brčák *et al.* (1969) confirmed these findings, and described "elementary bodies" and filaments of 50–60 nm in diameter, and the largest bodies of up to 1000 nm. These authors speculated on the possible mode of reproduction of the microorganisms, implying that elementary bodies, as well as binary fission might play a role in mycoplasma proliferation. The mycelial growth and the formation of filaments were considered to result in the subsequent release of free elementary bodies.

The extensive Japanese tests mentioned earlier (Tetracycline Research Group, 1968, 1969) included plants infected experimentally with potato witches'-broom. It was concluded from the results that the disease symptoms could only be suppressed or the disease appearance delayed, but that infected plants cannot be cured by the application of tetracyclines. This conclusion was also confirmed by Brčák *et al.* (1969). These authors applied tetracycline antibiotics to diseased plants by spraying, watering, by a wick, or by means of capillaries. The appearance of disease symptoms could be suppressed temporarily, but no permanent cure was achieved. The authors confirmed the earlier observation by Cousin *et al.* (1968) that tetracyclines cause phytotoxicity. Following antibiotic treatment, veins of healthy as well as of diseased plants were turning yellow within 3 to 5 days. This was followed by the appearance of necrotic spots on the leaves. As many as half of the treated plants died in some tests. Watering with tetracycline solutions retarded the growth of potato plants. Because of this phytotoxicity, the antibiotic treatments were considered to be of limited practical value.

The occurrence of mycoplasmalike bodies in European potato witches'-broom disease has also been confirmed by Harrison and Roberts (1969). Oval-shaped bodies, 200–800 nm in diameter, as well as some that had lobes or slender protrusions, were described. Strands in the nuclear region were not apparent, probably because of inadequate preparation of the material.

L. Vinca rosea Yellows in Rumania

A disease of *Vinca rosea,* similar to aster yellows, was observed for the first time in 1963 in Rumania among plants grown outdoors at an experiment station for the cultivation of medicinal plants. The disease agent was apparently transmitted by *Macrosteles quadripunctulatus* Kbm. (Ploaie, 1970). Electron micrographs revealed the presence of mycoplasmalike bodies in phloem cells of diseased plants (Ploaie and Maramorosch, 1969), and it was concluded that the agent is very similar to the agent of American aster yellows. It remains to be shown whether the disease, found in Rumania, is identical to any of the yellows diseases of Europe or America, or a different yellows-type disease.

M. Papaya Bunchy Top

The bunchy top disease of papaya (*Carica papaya*) was reported to be of mycoplasma etiology (Story, 1969; Story and Halliwell, 1969). Electron micrographs of phloem sieve tubes and adjacent parenchyma cells contained mycoplasmalike bodies that were absent from healthy plants. No virus particles were found in the diseased plants. Seedlings infected with bunchy top responded to tetracycline treatments and the remission of the disease provided further evidence for mycoplasma etiology. No electron microscopy observations have been reported with the leafhopper vector, *Empoasca papaye*.

It is hoped that studies of this disease will be continued in the Caribbean Islands. The disease agent is known to move very slowly in affected plants, and the removal of diseased tops often provides a cure. "Decapitation," in combination with tetracycline application, might become a practical means of treatment in papaya plantings affected by bunchy top disease.

N. Eggplant Little Leaf

The etiologic agent of this disease is reportedly transmitted by the leafhopper vectors *Hishimonus phycitis* and *Empoasca devastans* (Raychaudhuri *et al.*, 1970). The disease causes the production of enlarged calyxes of flowers, and is, therefore, similar to other big-bud diseases (Anjaneyulu and Ramakrishnan, 1968). Recently mycoplasmas were reported as the presumptive etiologic agents of little leaf disease of eggplant, *Solanum melongena* L. A study in India where the plant is widely used and known under the name of brinjal, typical mycoplasma bodies were observed in diseased phloem cells. Similar bodies were also reported to have been found in leaf parenchyma cells (Raychaudhuri *et al.*, 1970). The published electron micrographs (Varma *et al.*, 1969) show bodies ranging in size from 40 to 460 nm, but their fine structure and unit membranes are not discernible. Tetracycline hydrochloride, chlortetracycline hydrochloride, and dimethylchlortetracycline were applied to diseased *S. melongena* plants by means of cotton wicks (Anjaneyulu and Ramakrishnan, 1969). A significant delay in the appearance of disease symptoms was reported in treated plants. Controls, fed distilled water through cotton wicks, came down with little leaf after 22–29 days; while tetracycline-treated plants showed disease symptoms after 40–51 days. These results support the mycoplasma etiology of little leaf disease. Similar results were obtained in experimentally infected *Vinca rosea*, where newly developed shoots appeared healthy and bore normal-sized flowers following repeated treatment with chlortetracycline hydrochloride at 500 ppm (Anjaneyulu and Ramakrishnan, 1969).

Although eggplant little leaf has been considered identical with tomato big-bud (Anjaneyulu and Ramakrishnan, 1968), no serological studies are available to support this assertion. Therefore, in this review, the big-bud of tomato in Australia and in Brazil is discussed separately.

O. Sandal Spike

This disease is of considerable economic importance, because of the high value of the wood of sandal. In 1941, it was reported that the leafhopper *Jassus indicus* Walk. was the vector of the disease agent. No further confirmation of the leafhopper vector has been made. Recently, electron microscopy observations resulted in the finding of mycoplasma-like bodies in diseased sandal plants (Varma *et al.*, 1969). The reported diameter, 40–460 nm, of the bodies appears smaller than that observed for mycoplasmas in most yellows diseases. The discrepancy may have been caused by shrinkage of the material, since embedding was in methacrylate, and not in epoxy resin. Dijkstra and Ie (1969) also found mycoplasma-like bodies in sandal spike.

P. Cotton Virescence

This disease was described in 1965 from Upper Volta and the border area of Mali, Africa (Delattre, 1965). Although its known area is now limited to approximately 25,000 hectares of cotton plantings, it may well be more widely spread and eventually be identified in other parts of Africa. The vector of the disease agent is not known at present. The economic importance of the disease is considerable because of the losses incurred. Erroneously, this disease has been listed in a recent review as occurring in Europe (Whitcomb and Davis, 1970).

The yellows-type symptoms of the disease induced Cousin *et al.* (1969b) to study ultrathin sections by electron microscopy techniques. Typical mycoplasma bodies, with unit membranes, nuclear strands, and ribosomes at the periphery were observed in phloem cells of diseased plants. The necrotic degeneration of some phloem cells filled with electron-dense material was also noted.

In a recent report (Gourret and Maillet, 1969), the ultrastructure of the mycoplasmas was presented in great detail. Elongated, filamentous forms as well as mycoplasmas passing through sieve pores have been illustrated. The latter are reminiscent of the aster yellows and corn stunt mycoplasmas discussed earlier (Figs. 1 bottom, 2 bottom). Gourret and Maillet (1969) speculated that the vector of the agent would be found to belong to a leafhopper family. While this assumption may prove correct, there is no *a priori* reason to believe that all mycoplasmas causing plant diseases are carried by leafhoppers. In fact, some are already known to be transmitted by other vectors (Hibino and Schneider, 1970).

Q. Western X Disease

Although the evidence for a mycoplasma etiology of Western X disease is excellent, very little has been published to date on this sub-

found in young sieve tube elements, companion cells, or parenchyma cells. Control trees were free from such bodies. The electron micrographs showed typical unit membranes, ribosome granules, and strands in the nuclear region. Some of the bodies appeared to be dividing by binary fission. This report is particularly important since it describes the first well-authenticated instance of a psyllid-borne agent believed to be a plant-pathogenic mycoplasma. The same type of mycoplasmalike bodies as found in pears infected with pear decline was also found in other hosts, described recently as susceptible to the disease agent (Schneider, 1970).

BB. Sweet Potato Little Leaf (Witches'-Broom) Disease

In an introduction of sweet potato [*Ipomoea batatas* (L.) Lam.] from Tonga, received by the Glenn Dale, Md., U. S. Plant Quarantine via New Zealand, proliferation, yellowing, dwarfing, and little leaf symptoms were observed (Kahn and Monroe, 1969). The disease was similar to the sweet potato dwarf (witches'-broom) on Ryukyu Islands (Summers, 1951; Murayama, 1966), and the little leaf disease of Papua and New Guinea (Van Velsen, 1967).

Electron microscopy of diseased plants revealed the presence of typical mycoplasmalike bodies in the phloem cells (Smith, 1970; Lawson *et al.*, 1970). Diseased plants were treated with heat, and remission of the disease was achieved. Tetracycline treatment, by dipping the whole plants in an achromycin solution, resulted in complete disappearance of disease symptoms, which was interpreted as indicating cure of the disease (Lawson *et al.*, 1970).

CC. Oat Sterile Dwarf Disease

This disease, reported from Europe, was earlier considered to be a virus disease. The disease agent is transmitted by the leafhopper *Javesella pellucida* (F.). A recent communication (Brčák and Králík, 1969) indicated that the agent of oat sterile dwarf disease might belong to the mycoplasma group. Thin sections of vectors were studied by electron microscopy. Although the electron micrographs were interpreted as showing mycoplasmalike bodies, this interpretation is open to criticism. Neither the unit membranes, nor the ribosomes or nuclear strands were illustrated. No report of the occurrence of mycoplasmalike bodies in diseased plants with oat sterile dwarf is available. While it is possible that this disease belongs to the group of yellows diseases, the brief communication (Brčák and Králík, 1969) does not provide the basis for concluding the presence of mycoplasmalike bodies.

DD. Phloem Necrosis of Elm

The disease agent of phloem necrosis is leafhopper-borne. *Scaphoideus luteolus* Van Duzee has been reported by Baker (1948) as the vector. A related species, *S. littoralis* Ball, carries the agent of the European grape disease "flavescence dorée." Phloem cells in affected trees collapse, the roots die, and the crowns wilt. The coloration of the inner bark becomes butterscotch. The disease, originally considered a virus disease, has recently been studied by Charles L. Wilson, formerly at the University of Arkansas, and now at the Ohio Shade Tree & Ornamental Plants Laboratory in Delaware, Ohio. Although the results of this work have not yet been published, Wilson (1969) consented to their inclusion in this review.

Electron micrographs of diseased phloem cells revealed the presence of typical mycoplasmalike bodies. Some of these appeared to divide by binary fission. Ribosomelike particles were clearly seen in the bodies. No similar structures were found in healthy elm phloem cells. The electron micrographs, which were also examined by us, leave little doubt but that the phloem necrosis-diseased elms contain mycoplasmalike microorganisms. The reported association of "flavescence dorée" with mycoplasma (Giannotti *et al.*, 1969a) has been reviewed elsewhere.

EE. Witches'-Broom of Opuntia tuna

Cactus collectors and growers are familiar with the so-called "variety" *Opuntia tuna monstrosa,* widely propagated because of its anomalous growth characteristics. The plant was considered an ornamental species until Uschdraweit (1961) demonstrated that the factor responsible for the witches'-broom appearance can be transmitted by grafting to *Opuntia tuna.* Uschdraweit (1962) also found similar witches'-broom cacti on Luzon Island in the Philippines, which indicated that the disease is spread by a vector in nature.

Recently Lesemann and Casper (1970) found mycoplasmalike bodies in the phloem of *O. tuna monstrosa,* but not in *O. tuna.* No viruslike particles were associated with the witches'-broom disease. The authors also observed the occurrence of mycoplasmalike bodies within the sieve pores of sieve plates, and concluded that the disease is caused by mycoplasma agents.

FF. Safflower Phyllody

A yellows-type disease of safflower (*Carthamus tinctorius* L.) is currently under investigation in Israel (Klein, 1970). The infectious agent was found to be transmitted by the leafhopper *Circulifer fenestratus.* The disease causes phyllody, axillary branching, chlorosis, sterility, and a witches'-broom appearance of plants. *Circulifer fenestratus* transmitted the disease agent to several plant species belonging to the Compositae, as well as to *V. rosea*. Electron microscopy of phloem cells from experimentally infected *V. rosea* plants revealed the presence of numerous, characteristic mycoplasmalike bodies, primarily near sieve plates.

GG. Phormium Yellow Leaf

This disease of *Phormium tenax* has been studied in New Zealand by R. Ushiyama and R. E. F. Matthews, according to Matthews (1969, 1970). Electron micrographs of mycoplasmalike bodies showed the characteristic features associated with mycoplasmas.

HH. Purple Top of Potato

In Mexico, this disease has been of economic importance in certain regions. It was suspected as one of the yellows diseases to be of mycoplasma etiology. Sections of potato leaves from diseased plants were studied by electron microscopy in a joint study undertaken by Dr. Sanchez Delgado in Mexico and Dr. Hirumi at Boyce Thompson Institute. Preliminary results indicated that mycoplasma bodies were present in the phloem tissues of purple top-diseased plants.

II. Cassawa Witches'-Broom

According to Kitajima (1969), mycoplasmalike bodies occur in cassawa phloem cells with witches'-broom disease. Healthy plants are devoid of such bodies. The disease, prevalent in Brazil, is now under study at Campinas.

JJ. Yellow Wilt of Sugar Beets

The etiology of this disease, reported from Chile, is not well established. Although no electron microscopy has been carried out, there are indications from chemotherapy experiments in Chile (Bennett, 1969; Ehrenfeld, 1970) that yellow wilt ("marchitez virosa") may belong to the group of mycoplasma diseases. The infectious agent was transmitted by the leafhopper *Patanus exitiosus* Beamer to sugar beet seedlings. The diseased plants were treated with chlortetracycline hydrochloride at 100 ppm. Marked suppression of symptoms was observed, especially following root dipping. Recovery was almost complete in a number of plants. When a relapse occurred in treated plants after several days or weeks, typical disease symptoms appeared in the new foliage (Ehrenfeld, 1970).

KK. Currant Reversion

Black currant reversion is one of the most important diseases affecting currants in several European countries. The black currant gall mite,

Cecidophyopsis ribis (West.) = *Phytoptus ribis* Nal., has been considered as the vector of the disease agent, which was reported as a virus. Two recent reports question the virus etiology as well as the vector identity (Silvere and Tiits, 1969; Silvere, 1970). An electron microscopy study of diseased plants seemed to indicate that mycoplasma-like bodies were associated with diseased, but not with healthy currant plants. Since no viruslike particles were found in the infected plants, the virus etiology has been questioned. Thin sections were also prepared from mites reared on reverted currant plants. It was found earlier that the mites were feeding only on the surface layer of leaves. The electron micrographs of thin sections from gall mites were interpreted as showing deteriorating mycoplasmas. Another insect frequently found associated with diseased currant plants, *Thrips fuscipennis,* also contained similar bodies, and the possible role of this insect in the transmission of the agent has been considered.

Although the above reports (Silvere and Tiits, 1969; Silvere, 1970) are preliminary, they raise the possibility that mites or thrips may act as vectors of plant-pathogenic mycoplasmas. The demonstration, that nonleafhopper vectors such as psyllids carry mycoplasma disease agents to plants (Hibino and Schneider, 1970), may now widen the search for these disease agents to several other groups of vectors. Caution is indicated, however, since the retention of mycoplasma in various invertebrates does not necessarily mean that the invertebrates are acting as vectors. This is well illustrated by the survival of *Mycoplasma gallisepticum* after ingestion by saprozoic nematodes (Jensen and Stevens, 1969).

LL. Wallflower Virescence

A phyllody disease has been studied in a horticultural variety of wallflower, *Cheiranthus allioni* Hort. by Le Normand and Gourret (1969). Although it seems likely that this disease belongs to the yellows-type group, the electron micrograph presented in support of mycoplasma etiology is not convincing.

MM. Alfalfa Mosaic

A report claiming isolation of mycoplasma from pea plants infected with alfalfa mosaic was published in July 1969 in the Plant Disease Reporter (Hampton *et al.,* 1969b). The case was presented through a variety of other channels, including a talk at the American Phytopathological Society's Annual Meeting at Spokane in August 1969, followed by an abstract in *Phytopathology* (Hampton *et al.,* 1969a), a U. S. Department of Agriculture press release dated July 15, 1969, an editorial in Agricultural Research of November 1969, and a popular account in *Dateline in Science* on September 19, 1969. The authors concluded that they had found mycoplasmalike bodies in the parenchyma cells of pea plants infected with alfalfa mosaic virus, and that these bodies were pleomorphic, ranging in size from 15–250 nm. They named the presumptive mycoplasma "618M," and stated that they were able to transmit the agent mechanically to healthy plants. Furthermore, they reported that they isolated and purified the mycoplasma 618M, and grew it in a serum-rich medium, the composition of which was not published. Purified 618M was reportedly "reestablished in pea plants," in which it did not reproduce the original disease, but caused a faint chlorotic mottle. It was again reisolated, and "serological tests indicated a close antigenic relationship between 618M and *Mycoplasma meleagridis* and *M. gallisepticum* (avian) and *M. salivarum* (human)." The original disease was reportedly reproduced through a combined action of 618M and alfalfa mosaic virus.

An analysis of the work of Hampton *et al.* (1969b) reveals that most of the assumptions can be neither proved nor disproved, but the consensus of their peers, and also of their colleagues in the Department of Agriculture (Whitcomb and Davis, 1970), is that at least some of the assumptions are wrong.

In view of the fact that the claims are so sensational, and that, if correct, they would have a bearing on public health matters and on basic concepts of bacteriology, it seems worthwhile to analyze the work insofar as the published accounts permit. The size of the bodies, 15–250 nm, places most of them outside the known mycoplasma microorganisms. The so-called bodies appeared to be poorly fixed, deteriorating plant mesophyll, and they did not resemble mycoplasma. The serological affinity seems most unusual, and, if true, would constitute a very important new finding. However, the tests used were plate agglutination, a rapid but nonspecific test for mycoplasma. If it were assumed that a plant-pathogenic species of mycoplasma has in fact been isolated and cultured, the plate agglutination has failed to show any specificity. Highly specific or highly sensitive tests should be applied to test serologic relationships of various mycoplasmas, irrespective of whether they are isolated from plants, or from other sources.

NN. Paulownia Witches'-Broom

Paulownia witches'-broom is one of the four diseases originally studied in Japan by Doi *et al.* (1967). The abundance of mycoplasmalike bodies in sieve tubes was correlated with the severity of the disease. No bodies were detected in new, apparently healthy twigs that grew on branches infected by witches'-broom the previous year.

IX. Male Sterility in *Drosophila paulistorum*

Since many of the mycoplasma agents of plant diseases also infect arthropod vectors in which they multiply, and which, in certain instances, are deleteriously affected by the microorganisms, it seems appropriate to call attention to a newly recognized mycoplasma infection of an arthropod, not linked with any plant disease.

Infectious hybrid sterility was reported to occur in crosses between Santa Marta and Mesitas strains of the superspecies *Drosophila paulistorum* (Ehrman, 1962, 1963; Williamson and Ehrman, 1967, 1968). Back-crosses provided evidence that a cytoplasmic factor was responsible for inducing the sterility. This factor is transmitted via the maternal line only, presumably in the egg cytoplasm, and it can sometimes be transferred by injection of homogenates to other *D. paulistorum* (Ehrman and Williamson, 1965). Heat shocks administered to flies carrying the sterility factor interfered with it temporarily, but did not provide a permanent cure (Ehrman, 1967). Different semispecies of the *D. paulistorum* complex seem to be carriers of different strains of the sterility factor (Ehrman and Williamson, 1969). An electron microscopy study also revealed the presence of mycoplasmalike bodies in the testes of sterile males and intracellularly in ovarian follicles (Kernaghan and Ehrman, 1970). Certain antibiotics were found to suppress the sterility factor, but none eliminated it entirely (Ehrman, 1968).

The morphology of the bodies reveals their similarity with bodies described from thin sections of yellows-diseased plants (Kernaghan and Ehrman, 1969). The bodies are bounded by unit membranes in both instances, contain a nuclear region with strands, presumably DNA, and have ribosomelike granules (Kernaghan and Ehrman, 1970). The resemblance is further seen in the mechanical transmissibility of the disease agents by abdominal injection of cell-free extracts, antibiotic sensitivity, and heat sensitivity. The sterility, which is the only disease manifestation described in *D. paulistorum,* is reminiscent of the sterility caused in plants by yellows agents. So far, attempts to culture the male sterility factor on cell-free media have yielded no results.

X. Fate of Mycoplasmalike Agents in Insect Vectors

This subject has received considerable attention, although it was not realized at the time that the agents differ from viruses. It has been shown that the mycoplasmalike agents of aster yellows can multiply in their insect vectors (Maramorosch, 1963), in which they attain a fairly high concentration, probably dependent on the vector species (Chiykowski and Sinha, 1969). The evidence for multiplication was obtained on the basis of infectivity tests. The presence of the aster yellows agent was ascertained by the same means of infectivity tests in various organs of vectors (Hirumi and Maramorosch, 1963; Sinha and Chiykowski, 1967). No electron microscopy study has been made to date to follow up the earlier findings.

The harmful effect of mycoplasmalike agents on vectors has been reported in several instances (Maramorosch and Jensen, 1963; Jensen *et al.*, 1967; Maramorosch, 1969). The ability to maintain the agents *in vitro* in tissues of plants and of insect vectors has also been demonstrated (Maramorosch, 1965). It can be expected that the awareness of the nature of the yellows-type agents, and of other similar disease agents, will focus attention on the invasion of vectors and the direct or indirect effects on vectors. Some of the classic examples of "virus multiplication in vectors" have already been placed in the mycoplasmalike category, and others, such as the multiplication of clover club leaf virus, may soon follow suit. The agent of clover club leaf has never been purified or characterized morphologically. It is heat labile, which may well be an indication that it belongs to the same group as the yellows-type agents. Nevertheless, several viruses of well-defined morphology and chemistry are known to be carried by vectors that also carry mycoplasmalike agents. To these belong rice dwarf and wound tumor viruses, carried by vectors that also carry the presumptive plant-pathogenic mycoplasmas. It will be interesting to study the interaction of both types of agents in the same invertebrate host.

XI. Conclusions

The nonviral nature of numerous graft-transmissible, arthropod-borne disease agents of plants has now been established. Electron microscopy revealed the characteristic morphology of the presumptive microorganisms observed in diseased phloem cells and in various vectors, but absent from healthy phloem or from noninfected vectors. These observations support the assumption that the etiologic agents of many important plant diseases belong to the Mycoplasmatales.

Caution is indicated in concluding that these agents are actually mycoplasmas (Hirumi, 1970). Chemotherapy of the diseased plants and of certain leafhopper vectors, while in line with the mycoplasma hypothesis, provides no proof of the actual nature of the agent, although the results strongly indicate that the agents are not among viruses. No spectrum can be ascertained for antibiotic sensitivity from *in vivo* treatments of diseased plants. It is known that tetracyclines can inhibit various fungi, such as rusts and others (Müller, 1969). Plants can recover from yellows-type diseases when treated with sulfa drugs that definitely do not affect mycoplasmas, and they sometimes recover when treated solely with fertilizers (Klein, 1970). Only specific criteria, accepted by microbiologists, should be used in the determination of the actual etiology of the presumptive mycoplasma diseases. These criteria require the cultivation of the isolated agents on solid media with the production of mycoplasma colonies, the reinoculation of susceptible healthy plants with the cultured mycoplasmas, and the subsequent reproduction of the original disease. The matter of criteria applied to the decision that a particular disease is caused by mycoplasmas ought to be particularly rigorous in view of the long history of erroneous classification of so many diseases as virus or mycoplasma diseases on the basis of partial or circumstantial evidence (Dmochowski *et al.*, 1967). The mycoplasma or, better still, the mycoplasmalike agents, observed in plants, seem not to be limited to leafhopper vectors or leafhopper-borne cases. Observations of mycoplasmalike bodies have recently been made in third instar larvae of *Melolontha melolontha* L. (Devauchelle *et al.*, 1969). The authors reported the occurrence of characteristic mycoplasma bodies in the fatbody and cardiac cells. No implication with an insect disease has been noted and it is not known whether the bodies represent pathogenic or saprophytic forms. The fact that other groups of invertebrates can be infected with such agents, including nonvector species such as *Drosophila,* should be kept in mind when diseases of uncertain etiology of plants, as well as of insects, are being studied. The practical implications of the findings, particularly the possible chemical treatment and cure by using various chemicals as well as physical agents such as heat, open new possibilities in plant protection. Some earlier work, received with skepticism by those who thought that chemotherapy of "virus diseases" is not feasible, can now be viewed in a different light. This applies especially to the work of Stoddard (1947).

Finally, it can be forecast that research concerning diseases listed in the review, as well as many others that soon will be added to the list, will no longer be described in journals dealing with virology. Instead, they will form a new group, most likely added to the diseases caused by bacteria.

Some of the classic chapters in plant pathology will also need revision. One of the widely quoted instances of multiplication of a plant-pathogenic virus in leafhopper vectors concerns clover club leaf virus (Black, 1950). It now seems likely that the agent of club leaf is a mycoplasma, rather than a virus. This is not based on evidence as yet, except for the heat lability of the agent. However, our suspicions concerning the etiology of this disease are shared by Black (1969) who now considers that the agent of club leaf belongs most likely to the same group as the agent of aster yellows. It certainly comes as a surprise to many that there are numerous instances of economically important diseases of presumptive mycoplasma etiology, while there are very few such diseases affecting higher animals and man. Perhaps, as in the case of fungus diseases, plants have been the main hosts for these pathogens.

Acknowledgments

Mycoplasma investigations at the Boyce Thompson Institute were supported in part by grants from the National Science Foundation (No. GB-11861), the U. S. Public Health Service (No. AI-04290 and AI-07687), the U. S. Department of Agriculture (No. 12-140100-9202), and the Foreign Scientists Exchange Program of the National Academy of Sciences, Washington, D. C.

Several Japanese papers, some of which are without English abstracts, have been translated by Dr. H. Hirumi, and by Dr. Shiji Tsuyumi, to whom we are indebted for this unselfish task.

Thanks are due to Dr. Lee Ehrman for supplying the references on *Drosophila* male sterility and for checking the text pertaining to this subject.

References

Albouy, J., Cousin, M.-T., and Grison, C. (1967). *Ann. Epiphyt.* **18,** No. Hors Serie, 157.

Anderson, D. R. (1969). *In* "The Mycoplasmatales and the L-phase of Bacteria" (L. Hayflick, ed.), p. 365. Appleton-Century-Crofts, New York.

Anderson, D. R., and Barile, M. F. (1965). *J. Bacteriol.* **90,** 180.

Anderson, D. R., and Manaker, R. A. (1966). *J. Nat. Cancer Inst.* **36,** 139.

Anjaneyulu, A., and Ramakrishnan, K. (1968). *Curr. Sci.* **37,** 673.

Anjaneyulu, A., and Ramakrishnan, K. (1969). *Curr. Sci.* **11,** 271.

Atanasoff, D. (1969). *Biol. Zentralbl.* **88,** 571.

Bak, A. L., Black, F. T., Christiansen, C., and Freundt, E. A. (1969). *Nature (London)* **224,** 1209.

Baker, W. L. (1948). *Science* **108,** 307.

Belli, G. (1969). *Riv. Patol. Veg.* **5,** 3.

Bennett, C. W. (1969). Personal communication.

Black, L. M. (1940). *Phytopathology* **30,** 2.

Black, L. M. (1943). *Phytopathology* **33,** 2.

Black, L. M. (1950). *Nature (London)* **166,** 852.

Black, L. M. (1969). Personal communication.

Boatman, E. S., and Kenny, G. E. (1970). *J. Bacteriol.* **101,** 262.

Borges, M. V. de L. (1969). *Ann. Phytopathol. (Paris)* No. Hors Serie, 443.

Borges, M. V. de L., and David-Ferreira, J. F. (1968). *Bol. Soc. Broteriana* **42,** 321.

Bowyer, J. W., and Atherton, J. G. (1970). *Aust. J. Biol. Sci.* **23,** 115.

Bowyer, J. W., Atherton, J. G., Teakle, D. S., and Ahern, G. A. (1969). *Aust. J. Biol. Sci.* **22,** 271.

Brakke, M. K. (1956). *Virology* **2,** 463.

Brandes, J. (1957). *Nachbrichtenbl. Deut. Pflanzenschutzdienstes* **9,** 151.

Brčák, J., and Králík, O. (1969). *Biol. Plant.* **11,** 95.

Brčák, J., Králík, O., Limberk, J., and Ulrychová, M. (1969). *Biol. Plant.* **11,** 470.

Bridré, J., and Donatien, A. (1923). *C. R. Acad. Sci.* **177,** 841.

Campbell, A. D., and Turner, A. W. (1936). *Bull. Counc. Sci. Ind. Res. Aust.* **97,** 11.

Canada Department of Agriculture (1969). Research Branch, Research Report 1968, p. 351. Vancouver, B. C.

Casals, J. (1967). *In* "Methods in Virology" (K. Maramorosch and H. Koprowski, eds.), Vol. 3, p. 113. Academic Press, New York.
Casper, R. (1969). *Nachrichtenbl. Deut. Pflanzenschutzdienst* (*Braunschweig*) **21,** 177–82.
Chanock, R. M., Hayflick, L., and Barile, M. F. (1962). *Proc. Nat. Acad. Sci. U. S.* **48,** 41.
Chen, T. A., and Granados, R. R. (1970). *Phytopathology* **60,** 573.
Chiykowski, L. N., and Sinha, R. C. (1969). *J. Econ. Entomol.* **62,** 883.
Chu, H. P., and Horne, R. W. (1967). *Ann. N.Y. Acad. Sci.* **143,** 190.
Corbetta, G. (1967). Il Risicoltore. August.
Cousin, M.-T. (1968). Personal communication.
Cousin, M.-T., and Staron, T. (1969). *Ann. Phytopathol.* (*Paris*) **1,** 267.
Cousin, M.-T., Maillet, P.-L., Gourret, J.-P., Grison, C., and Staron, T. (1968). *C. R. Acad. Agr. Fr.* p. 887.
Cousin, M.-T., Gourret, J.-P., Lacote, J.-P., and Leclant, F. (1969a). *Ann. Phytopathol.* (*Paris*) **1,** 297.
Cousin, M.-T., Maillet, P.-L., and Gourret, J.-P. (1969). *C. R. Acad. Sci., Ser. D* **268,** 2382.
Dale, J. L., and Kim, K. S. (1969). *Phytopathology* **59,** 1765.
Davis, R. E., and Whitcomb, R. F. (1969). *Phytopathology* **59,** 1556.
Davis, R. E., Whitcomb, R. F., and Steere, R. L. (1968a). *Phytopathology* **58,** 884.
Davis, R. E., Whitcomb, R. F., and Steere, R. L. (1968b). *Science* **161,** 793.
Davis, R. E., Whitcomb, R. F., and Purcell, R. H. (1970). *Phytopathology* **60,** 573.
Delattre, R. (1965). *Coton Fibres Trop.* **20,** 289.
Devauchelle, G., Vago, C., Giannotti, J., and Quiot, J. M. (1969). *Entomophaga* **14,** 457.
Dienes, L., and Edsall, G. (1937). *Proc. Soc. Exp. Biol. Med.* **36,** 740.
Dijkstra, J., and Ie, T. S. (1969). *Neth. J. Plant Pathol.* **75,** 374.
Dmochowski, L., Dreyer, D. A., Grey, C. E., Hales, R., Langford, P. L., Pipes, F., Recher, L., Seman, G., Shively, J. A., Shullenberger, C. C., Sinkovics, J. G., Taylor, H. G., Tessmer, C. F., and Yumoto, T. (1967). *Ann. N.Y. Acad. Sci.* **143,** 578.
Doi, Y., Terenaka, M., Yora, K., and Asuyama, H. (1967). *Nippon Shokubutsu Byori Gakkaiho* **33,** 259.
Eaton, M. D., Meiklejohn, G., and van Herick, W. (1944). *J. Exp. Med.* **79,** 649.
Edward, D. G. ff., Freundt, E. A., Chanock, R. M., Fabricant, J., Hayflick, L., Lemcke, R. M., Razin, S., Somerson, N. L., and Wittler, R. G. (1967). *Science* **155,** 1694.
Ehrenfeld, K. R. (1970). *Agr. Tec.* (*Santiago de Chile*) **30,** 43.
Ehrman, L. (1962). *Nature* (*London*) **193,** 1208.
Ehrman, L. (1963). *Proc. Nat. Acad. Sci. U.S.* **49,** 155.
Ehrman, L. (1967). *Proc. Nat. Acad. Sci. U.S.* **58,** 195.
Ehrman, L. (1968). *Mol. Gen. Genet.* **103,** 218.
Ehrman, L., and Williamson, D. L. (1965). *Proc. Nat. Acad. Sci. U.S.* **54,** 481.
Ehrman, L., and Williamson, D. L. (1969). *Genetics* **62,** 193.
Eriksson, J. (1897). *C. R. Acad. Sci.* **124,** 475.
Eriksson, J. (1910). *Biol. Centralbl.* **30,** 618.
Freitag, J. H. (1964). *Virology* **24,** 401.
Freitag, J. H. (1967). *Phytopathology* **57,** 1016.
Freitag, J. H., and Smith, S. H. (1969). *Phytopathology* **59,** 1820.

Freundt, E. A. (1969). *In* "The Mycoplasmatales and the L-phase of Bacteria" (L. Hayflick, ed.), p. 281. Appleton-Century-Crofts, New York.
Fukushi, T. (1930). *Agr. Gardening* **5,** 557.
Fukushi, T., Shikata, E., Kimura, I., and Nemoto, M. (1960). *Proc. Jap. Acad.* **36,** 352.
Furness, G. (1968). *J. Infec. Dis.* **118,** 436.
Gáborjányi, R., and Bencsics, M. S. (1968). *Acta Phytopathol.* **3,** 31.
Galvez, E. G. E., and Shikata, E. (1969). *Agr. Trop.* (*Paris*) **24,** 109.
Giannotti, J. (1969). *Ann. Soc. Entomol. Fr.* **5,** 155.
Giannotti, J., and Devauchelle, G. (1969). *Ann. Zool. Ecol. Anim.* **1,** 31.
Giannotti, J., Devauchelle, G., and Vago, C. (1968a). *C. R. Acad. Sci., Ser. D.* **266,** 2168.
Giannotti, J., Morvan, G., and Vago, C. (1968b). *C. R. Acad. Sci., Ser. D.* **267,** 76.
Giannotti, J., Marchoux, G., Vago, C., and Duthoit, J.-L. (1968c). *C. R. Acad. Sci., Ser. D* **267,** 454.
Giannotti, J., Vago, C., and Duthoit, J.-L. (1968d). *Rev. Zool. Agr. Appl.* **67,** 69.
Giannotti, J., Vago, C., Devauchelle, G., and Marchoux, G. (1968e). *Entomol. Exp. Appl.* **11,** 470.
Giannotti, J., Caudwell, A., Vago, C., and Duthoit, J.-L. (1969a). *C. R. Acad. Sci., Ser. D* **268,** 845.
Giannotti, J., Devauchelle, G., Marchoux, G., and Vago, C. (1969b). *C. R. Acad. Sci., Ser. D* **268,** 1354.
Giannotti, J., Marchoux, G., and Devauchelle, G. (1969c). *Ann. Phytopathol.* (*Paris*) **1,** No. Hors Serie, 419.
Giannotti, J., Marchoux, G., and Devauchelle, G. (1969d). *Ann. Phytopathol.* (*Paris*) **1,** No. Hors Serie, 445.
Giannotti, J., Devauchelle, G., and Vago, C. (1970). *Int. Congr. Microbiol., 10th, Mexico City* Abstr. 222.
Gourret, J. P., and Maillet, P. L. (1969). *Coton Fibres Trop.* **24,** 325.
Granados, R. R. (1969a). *Phytopathology* **59,** 1556.
Granados, R. R. (1969b). *Contrib. Boyce Thompson Inst.* **24,** 173.
Granados, R. R., and Chapman, R. K. (1968). *Virology* **36,** 333.
Granados, R. R., Maramorosch, K., Everett, T., and Pirone, T. P. (1966). *Contrib. Boyce Thompson Inst.* **23,** 275.
Granados, R. R., Maramorosch, K., and Shikata, E. (1968a). *Proc. Nat. Acad. Sci. U.S.* **60,** 841.
Granados, R. R., Gustin, R. D., Maramorosch, K., and Stoner, W. N. (1968b). *Contrib. Boyce Thompson Inst.* **24,** 57.
Hampton, R. O., Allen, T. C., and Stevens, J. O. (1969a). *Phytopathology* **59,** 1029.
Hampton, R. O., Stevens, J. O., and Allen, T. C. (1969b). *Plant Dis. Rep.* **53,** 499.
Harrison, B. D., and Roberts, I. M. (1969). *Ann. Appl. Biol.* **63,** 347.
Hayflick, L. (1965). *Tex. Rep. Biol. Med.* **23,** 285.
Hayflick, L. (1969). *In* "The Mycoplasmatales and the L-phase of Bacteria" (L. Hayflick, ed.), p. 15. Appleton-Century-Crofts, New York.
Hayflick, L., and Chanock, R. M. (1965). *Bacteriol. Rev.* **29,** 185.
Heimbeck, L. (1966). "A Letter to Plant Pathologists." Levanger, Norway.
Heinze, K., and Kunze, L. (1955). *Nachrichtenbl. Deut. Pflanzenschutzdienstes* **7,** 161.
Hibino, H., and Schneider, H. (1970). *Phytopathology* **60,** 499.
Hirumi, H. (1970). *Int. Congr. Microbiol., 10th, Mexico City* Abstr. 223.
Hirumi, H., and Maramorosch, K. (1963). *Contrib. Boyce Thompson Inst.* **22,** 141.
Hirumi, H., and Maramorosch, K. (1969a). *J. Virol.* **3,** 82.

Hirumi, H., and Maramorosch, K. (1969b). *Phytopathology* **59,** 1030.
Ishiie, T., Doi, Y., Yora, K., and Asuyama, H. (1967). *Nippon Shokubutsu Byori Gakkaiho* **33,** 267.
Jensen, D. D. (1959). *Virology* **8,** 164.
Jensen, D. D. (1968). *Virology* **36,** 662.
Jensen, D. D., and Nasu, S. (1970). *Int. Congr. Microbiol., 10th, Mexico City 1970,* 223. Abstr.
Jensen, D. D., Griggs, W. H., Gonzales, C. Q., and Schneider, H. (1964). *Phytopathology* **54,** 1346.
Jensen, D. D., Whitcomb, R. F., and Richardson, J. (1967). *Virology* **31,** 532.
Jensen, H. J., and Stevens, J. O. (1969). *J. Nematol.* **1,** 293.
Kahn, R. P., and Monroe, R. L. (1969). *FAO Plant Prot. Bull.* **17,** 104.
Kernaghan, R. P., and Ehrman, L. (1969). *J. Cell Biol.* **43**(2), Pt. 2, 67a.
Kernaghan, R. P., and Ehrman, L. (1970). *Chromosoma* **29,** 291.
Kitajima, E. W. (1965). *J. Electronmicrosc.* **14,** 119.
Kitajima, E. W. (1969). Personal communication.
Kitajima, E. W., and Lauritis, J. A. (1969). *Virology* **37,** 681.
Klein, M. (1970). Personal communication.
Klein, M., and Maramorosch, K. (1970). *Phytopathology* **60,** 1015.
Klieneberger, E. (1938). *J. Hyg.* **38,** 458.
Knudson, D. L., and MacLeod, R. (1970). *J. Bacteriol.* **101,** 609.
Kunkel, L. O. (1926). *Amer. J. Bot.* **13,** 646.
Kunkel, L. O. (1937a). *J. Bacteriol.* **34,** 132.
Kunkel, L. O. (1937b). *Amer. J. Bot.* **24,** 316.
Kunkel, L. O. (1938). *J. Econ. Entomol.* **31,** 20.
Kunkel, L. O. (1941). *Amer. J. Bot.* **28,** 761.
Kunkel, L. O. (1946). *Proc. Nat. Acad. Sci. U.S.* **32,** 246.
Kunkel, L. O. (1948). *Arch. Gesamte Virusforschung* **4,** 24.
Kunkel, L. O. (1955). *Advan. Virus Res.* **3,** 251.
Kunkel, L. O. (1957). *Science* **126,** 1233.
Laidlaw, P. P., and Elford, W. J. (1936). *Proc. Roy. Soc., Ser. B* **120,** 292.
Lawson, R. H., Kahn, R. P., Hearon, S., and Smith, F. F. (1970). *Phytopathology* **60.**
Lee, P. E., and Chiykowski, L. N. (1963). *Virology* **21,** 667.
Le Normand, M., and Gourret, J. P. (1969). *Ann. Phytopathol. (Paris)* **1,** 301.
Lesemann, D., and Casper, R. (1970). *Phytopathol. Z.* **67,** 175.
Lin, S.-C., and Lee, C.-S. (1968). *Annu. Rep. Taiwan Sugar Exp. Sta.* 1967/1968, 17.
Lin, S.-C., and Lee, C.-S. (1969). *Sugarcane Pathologist Newsletter (Taiwan)* **3,** 2.
Littau, V. C., and Maramorosch, K. (1956). *Virology* **2,** 128.
Littau, V. C., and Maramorosch, K. (1960). *Virology* **10,** 483.
Maillet, P.-L., and Folliot, R. (1968). *C. R. Acad. Sci., Ser. D* **266,** 923.
Maillet, P.-L., Gourret, J.-P., and Hamon, C. (1968). *C. R. Acad. Sci., Ser. D* **266,** 2309.
Maniloff, J. (1969). *J. Bacteriol.* **100,** 1402.
Maniloff, J., and Morowitz, H. J. (1967). *Ann. N.Y. Acad. Sci.* **143,** 59.
Maniloff, J., Morowitz, H. J., and Barrnett, R. J. (1965). *J. Bacteriol.* **90,** 193.
Maramorosch, K. (1950). *Proc. Soc. Exp. Biol. Med.* **75,** 744.
Maramorosch, K. (1951). *Phytopathology* **41,** 833.
Maramorosch, K. (1952a). *Phytopathology* **42,** 59.
Maramorosch, K. (1952b). *Phytopathology* **42,** 663.
Maramorosch, K. (1955). *Plant Dis. Rep.* **39,** 896.

Maramorosch, K. (1956). *Virology* **2,** 369.
Maramorosch, K. (1958). *Virology* **6,** 448.
Maramorosch, K. (1963). *Annu. Rev. Entomol.* **8,** 369.
Maramorosch, K. (1965). *Proc. Int. Conf. Plant Tissue Cult., 1963,* p. 541.
Maramorosch, K. (1969). *In* "The Virus Diseases of the Rice Plant" I.R.R.I. p. 179. Johns Hopkins Press, Baltimore, Maryland.
Maramorosch, K., and Jensen, D. D. (1963). *Annu. Rev. Microbiol.* **17,** 495.
Maramorosch, K., Shikata, E., and Granados, R. R. (1968a). *Trans. N.Y. Acad. Sci., Ser. II* **30,** 841.
Maramorosch, K., Shikata, E., and Granados, R. R. (1968b). *Phytopathology* **58,** 886.
Maramorosch, K., Shikata, E., and Granados, R. R. (1969). *In* "Viruses, Vectors, and Vegetation" (K. Maramorosch, ed.), p. 417. Wiley (Interscience), New York.
Matsumoto, T., Lee, C.-S., and Teng, W. S. (1969). *Proc. 13th Congr. Int. Soc. Sugar Cane Technol., Taiwan, 1968* (S.-C. Lin, ed.), p. 1090. Elsevier, Amsterdam.
Matthews, R. E. F. (1967). *In* "Methods in Virology" (K. Maramorosch and H. Koprowski, eds.), Vol. 3, p. 199. Academic Press, New York.
Matthews, R. E. F. (1969). Personal communication.
Matthews, R. E. F. (1970). "Principles of Plant Virology." Academic Press, New York. In press.
Morowitz, H. J. (1967). *Progr. Theor. Biol.* **1,** 35.
Morowitz, H. J. (1968). Personal communication.
Morowitz, H. J. (1969). *In* "The Mycoplasmatales and the L-phase of Bacteria" (L. Hayflick, ed.), p. 405. Appleton-Century-Crofts, New York.
Morowitz, H. J., and Maniloff, J. (1966). *J. Bacteriol.* **91,** 1638.
Müller, H. J. (1969). *Arch. Pflanzenschutz* **5,** 83.
Murayama, D. (1966). *Hokkaido Daigaku Nogakubu Hobun Kiyó* **6,** 81.
Musil, M. (1966). *Acta Virol. (Prague), Engl. Ed.* **10,** 273.
Nasu, S., Sugiura, M., Wakimoto, T., and Iida, T. T. (1967). *Nippon Shokubutsu Byori Gakkaiho* **33,** 343.
Nelson, J. B. (1935). *Science* **82,** 43.
Nelson, J. B., and Lyons, M. J. (1965). *J. Bacteriol.* **90,** 1750.
Newnham, A. G., and Chu, H. P. (1965). *J. Hyg.* **63,** 1.
Niederhauser, J. S., and Cervantes, J. (1950). *Phytopathology* **40,** 20.
Nocard, E., and Roux, E. R. (1898). *Ann. Inst. Pasteur, Paris* **12,** 240.
Ou, S. H., Iida, T. T., Maramorosch, K., Raychaudhuri, S. P., and Suzuki, N. (1969). *In* "The Virus Diseases of the Rice Plant" I.R.R.I. p. 339. Johns Hopkins Press, Baltimore, Maryland.
Peary, J. Y. (1969). *Turtox News* **47,** 66.
Pellegrini, S., Belli, G., and Gerola, F. M. (1969). *G. Bot. Ital.* **103,** 395.
Ploaie, P. (1968a). *20th Int. Symp. Crop Prot., Proc. Med. Rijks. Landb. Wet. Gent.* **33,** 1223.
Ploaie, P. (1968b). *Nat. Conf. Gen. Appl. Microbiol., Bucharest, Abstr. Commun.* p. 14.
Ploaie, P. (1970). Thesis, 280 pp. Univ. of Bucharest, Romania.
Ploaie, P., and Ionică, M. (1968). *Nat. Conf. Gen. Appl. Microbiol., Bucharest, Abstr. Commun.* p. 15.
Ploaie, P., and Maramorosch, K. (1969). *Phytopathology* **59,** 536.
Ploaie, P., Granados, R. R., and Maramorosch, K. (1968). *Phytopathology* **58,** 1063.
Pozděna, J. (1954). *Cesk. Biol.* **3,** 391.
Pozděna, J., and Čech, M. (1958). *In* "Stolbur a Príbuzné Vírusové Bezemenosti

Rastlín" (Stolbur and Similar Virus Diseases Causing Seedlessness of Plants) (E. Špaldon, C. Blattný, and V. Bojnanský, eds.), p. 198. Slovak Acad. Sci., Bratislava.
Purcell, R. H., Chanock, R. M., and Taylor-Robinson, D. (1969). *In* "The Mycoplasmatales and the L-phase of Bacteria" (L. Hayflick, ed.), p. 221. Appleton-Century-Crofts, New York.
Raine, J., and Forbes, A. R. (1969). *Can. J. Microbiol.* **15,** 1105.
Raychaudhuri, S. P., Varma, A., Chenulu, V. V., Prakash, N., and Singh, S. (1970). *Int. Congr. Microbiol., 10th, Mexico City* Abstr. 222.
Razin, S. (1969). *Annu. Rev. Microbiol.* **23,** 317.
Razin, S., Cosenza, B. J., and Tourtellotte, M. E. (1966). *J. Gen. Microbiol.* **42,** 139.
Reuss, K. (1967). *J. Bacteriol.* **93,** 490.
Richter, H. (1936). *Nachrichtenbl. Deut. Pflanzenschutzdienst (Berlin)* **16,** 66.
Rischkov, V. L. (1943). *C. R. Acad. Sci. URSS* **41,** 90.
Sabin, A. B. (1938). *Science* **88,** 575.
Schneider, H. (1970). *Phytopathology* **60,** 204.
Seiffert, G. (1937). *Zentralbl. Bakteriol. Parasitenk. Infektionskr. Hyg., Abt. 1: Orig.* **139,** 337.
Shikata, E. (1969). Personal communication.
Shikata, E. (1970). Personal communication.
Shikata, E., and Maramorosch, K. (1969a). *Phytopathology* **59,** 1559.
Shikata, E., and Maramorosch, K. (1969b). *In* "Viruses, Vectors, and Vegetation" (K. Maramorosch, ed.), p. 393. Wiley (Interscience), New York.
Shikata, E., Orenski, S. W., Hirumi, H., Mitsuhashi, J., and Maramorosch, K. (1964). *Virology* **23,** 441.
Shikata, E., Maramorosch, K., Ling, K. C., and Matsumoto, T. (1968). *Nippon Shokubutsu Byori Gakkaiho* **34,** 208.
Shikata, E., Maramorosch, K., and Ling, K. C. (1969a). *FAO Plant Prot. Bull.* **17,** 121.
Shikata, E., Teng, W. S., and Matsumoto, T. (1969b). *J. Fac. Agr. Hokkaido Univ.* **56,** 79.
Shinkai, A. (1960). *Nippon Shokubutsu Byori Gakkaiho* **25,** 42.
Shoetensack, H. M. (1934). *Kitasata Arch. Exp. Med.* **11,** 277.
Silvere, A.-P. (1970). *Int. Congr. Microbiol., 10th, Mexico City* Abstr. 222.
Silvere, A.-P., and Tiits, A. (1969). *Eesti NSV Tead. Akad. Toim., Biol.* **18,** 228.
Sinha, R. C., and Chiykowski, L. N. (1967). *Virology* **33,** 702.
Sinha, R. C., and Chiykowski, L. N. (1968). *Acta Virol. (Prague), Engl. Ed.* **12,** 546.
Sinha, R. C., and Paliwal, Y. C. (1969). *Virology* **39,** 759.
Smith, F. F. (1970). Personal communication.
Smith, R. E. (1902). *Hatch Exp. Sta., Mass. Agr. Coll. Bull.* **79.**
Staron, T., Cousin, M.-T., and Grison, C. (1968). *C. R. Acad. Sci., Ser. D* **267,** 2328.
Staron, T., Cousin, M.-T., and Kollmann, A. (1969). *Ann. Phytopathol. (Paris)* **1,** No. Hors Serie, 465.
Steere, R. L. (1967). *Phytopathology* **57,** 832.
Stoddard, E. M. (1947). *Conn. Agr. Exp. Sta., New Haven, Bull.* **506.**
"Stolbur and Similar Virus Diseases Causing Seedlessness of Plants" (1958). Proc. Sci. Conf., Smolenice, 1956. (E. Špaldon, C. Blattný, and V. Bojňanský, eds.), 244 pp. Slovak Acad. Sci., Bratislava.
Stoner, W. N. (1965). *U.S. Dep. Agr. Spec. Rep.* **33-99,** 35 pp.
Story, G. E. (1969). Ph.D. Thesis, Texas A and M Univ., College Station, Texas.
Story, G. E., and Halliwell, R. S. (1969). *Phytopathology* **59,** 118.

Sukhov, K. S., and Vovk. A. M. (1945). *C. R. Acad. Sci. URSS* **48,** 365.
Summers, E. M. (1951). *Plant Dis. Rep.* **35,** 266.
Tahama, Y. (1961). *Nippon Shokubutsu Byori Gakkaiho* **26,** 211.
Tahama, Y. (1963). *Nippon Shokubutsu Byori Gakkaiho* **28,** 195.
Tahama, Y. (1964). *Nippon Shokubutsu Byori Gakkaiho* **29,** 39.
Tahama, Y. (1967). *Nippon Shokubutsu Byori Gakkaiho* **33,** 156.
Tetracycline Research Group (1968). Effects of Tetracycline Antibiotics on Various Plants with Presumptive Mycoplasma Diseases. 20 pp., April, Tokyo. (In Jap.)
Tetracycline Research Group (1969). Effects of Tetracycline Antibiotics on Various Plants with Presumptive Mycoplasma Diseases. 80 pp., March, Tokyo. (In Jap.)
"The Virus Diseases of the Rice Plant" (1969). I.R.R.I. 354 pp. Johns Hopkins Press, Baltimore, Maryland.
Thomas, L. (1969). *Harvey Lect.* **63,** 73.
Uschdraweit, H. A. (1961). *Phytopathol. Z.* **43,** 320.
Uschdraweit, H. A. (1962). Personal communication.
Valenta, V. (1959a). *Acta Virol. (Prague), Engl. Ed.* **3,** 65.
Valenta, V. (1959b). *Acta Virol. (Prague), Engl. Ed.* **3,** 145.
Valenta, V., Musil, M., and Mišiga, S. (1961). *Phytopathol. Z.* **42,** 1.
Van Velsen, R. N. (1967). *Papua New Guinea Agr. J.* **18,** 126.
Varma, A., Chenulu, V. V., Raychaudhuri, S. P., Prakash, N., and Rao, P. S. (1969). *Indian Phytopathol.* **22,** 289.
Whitcomb, R. F., and Davis, R. E. (1969). *Phytopathology* **59,** 1561.
Whitcomb, R. F., and Davis, R. E. (1970). *Annu. Rev. Entomol.* **15,** 405.
Whitcomb, R. F., Jensen, D. D., and Richardson, J. (1968). *J. Invertebr. Pathol.* **12,** 202.
Williamson, D. L., and Ehrman, L. (1967). *Genetics* **55,** 131.
Williamson, D. L., and Ehrman, L. (1968). *Nature (London)* **219,** 1266.
Wilson, C. L. (1969). Personal communication.
Worley, J. F. (1969). *Phytopathology* **59,** 1561.
Worley, J. F. (1970). *Phytopathology* **60,** 284.
Wu, R. Y. (1969). Personal communication.
Zeyen, R. J., and Banttari, E. E. (1969). *Phytopathology* **59,** 1059.

VESICULAR STOMATITIS AND RELATED VIRUSES

A. F. Howatson

Ontario Cancer Institute and Department of Medical Biophysics, University of Toronto, Toronto, Canada

I. Introduction

Vesicular stomatitis virus (VSV), an agent causing periodic outbreaks of disease among cattle and horses in Central and North America, was originally classified as an arbovirus on the basis of its sensitivity to ether, its isolation from arthropods, and its ability to multiply in mosquitoes. Studies by Chow *et al.* (1954) and Bradish *et al.* (1956) established that the infectious particle was rod-shaped, and subsequently more detailed morphological studies (Reczko, 1961; Howatson and Whitmore, 1961, 1962; Stone *et al.*, 1961) showed that VSV had structural features that differentiated it clearly not only from other arboviruses but from all structurally characterized animal viruses. The virus also had a characteristic mode of assembly at the host-cell surface or intracytoplasmic membrane (Howatson and Whitmore, 1962). Shortly thereafter the application of recently developed electron microscope techniques showed that other well-known viruses, e.g., rabies and sigma virus of *Drosophila*, shared the characteristic structural features of VSV. There followed a veritable flood of publications describing viruses associated with diseases of vertebrates, invertebrates, and plants that were morphologically similar to VSV (Tables I and II).

It became apparent that these viruses form a newly recognized genus of viruses affecting very diverse hosts and linked primarily by the structural similarity of the virions. In many instances information about properties other than morphological is fragmentary or completely lacking. In view of the paucity of information on some of the viruses, their inclusion in the new genus as unique species should be regarded as tentative at present.

Since VSV has been much more extensively investigated than any other member of the group it is generally accepted as the prototype virus. Selection of a suitable name for the genus presents some difficulties. The name Stomatoviridae proposed by the Provisional Committee for Nomenclature of Viruses (1965) has been generally rejected as inappropriate for most of the newly discovered members. The term rhabdovirus (from *rhabdos* = a rod), suggested by Melnick and McCombs (1966), has been widely used and is the name recommended by a subcommittee of the International Committee on Nomenclature of Viruses. A decision on this recommendation will be made at the International Microbiological Congress to be held at Mexico City in August, 1970. In this review the name rhabdovirus will be used to denote the group.

The aim of this article is to summarize and review present knowledge of the properties of VSV and to collect together widely scattered information on some twenty-five other viruses (many of them only discovered

TABLE I

SOME PROPERTIES OF VERTEBRATE VIRUSES

Virus	Site of maturation	Shape	Dimensions (nm)	Cross-striations (periodicity, nm)	Surface projections (length, nm)	Host	References
Vesicular stomatitis	Plasma and intracytoplasmic membranes	Bullet	175 × 68	4.5	10.0	Mammals and arthropods	Howatson and Whitmore (1962)
Rabies	Plasma and cytoplasmic membranes; also cytoplasmic matrix	Bullet	180 × 75	4.5	6–7	Mammals	Hummeler *et al.* (1967)
Egtved	Plasma membrane	Bullet	180 × 60–70	5.5		Rainbow trout	Zwillenberg *et al.* (1965)
Flanders-Hart Park	Plasma and intracytoplasmic membranes	Bullet	218 × 65	4.0		Birds and arthropods	Jensen *et al.* (1967); Murphy *et al.* (1968)
Kern Canyon	Plasma membrane	Bullet	132 × 73	5.0	8.0	Myotis bats	Murphy and Fields (1967)
Mount Elgon bat	Plasma membrane	Bullet	230 × 70	5.0	8–10	Insectivorous bat, mosquitoes	Murphy *et al.* (1970)
Bovine ephemeral fever	Plasma and intracytoplasmic memmembranes	Bullet; conical	140 × 80 176 × 88			Cattle	Ito *et al.* (1969); Holmes and Doherty (1970); Lecatsas *et al.* (1969)

TABLE II

Some Properties of Insect and Plant Viruses

Virus	Site of maturation	Shape[a]	Dimensions (nm)[b]	Cross striation[c] (periodicity, nm)	Surface projections (nm)	Insect host	References
Sigma	Cytoplasmic membranes	Bul	140 × 70 (ns) 180 × 70 (sec)	+		*Drosophila*	Berkaloff *et al.* (1965); Teninges (1968)
Maize mosaic	Perinuclear: cytoplasmic membranes	Bac	242 × 48 (sec) 255 × 90 (ns)	+	7	Leaf hopper	Herold *et al.* (1960); Herold and Munz (1965, 1967)
		Bul	241 × 73 (ns)	5.2			
Lettuce necrotic yellows	Cytoplasm close to nucleus	Bac	200–245 × 65–70 (ns)[d]	+	6	Aphid	Harrison and Crowley (1965); Wolanski *et al.* (1967)
		Bul		4.5			
Gomphrena	Perinuclear: budding of intranuclear particles	Bac	220–260 × 80–100 (ns)	+	6–7		Kitajima and Costa (1966)
		Bul	230–250 × 75 (sec)	5.2			
Wheat striate mosaic	Perinuclear: no budding observed but intranuclear particles	Bul	270 × 65 (sec) 170 × 80 (ns) 90 × 80 (ns)			Leaf hopper	Lee (1964, 1967, 1968)
Potato yellow dwarf	Perinuclear: some evidence of intranuclear particles	Bac	380 × 75 (sec)	+		Leaf hopper	MacLeod *et al.* (1966)
Plantain	Unknown	Bul	330 × 63 (ns) 195 × 90 (ns)	+ 4.5			Hitchborn *et al.* (1966)
Sowthistle yellow vein	Perinuclear: intranuclear particles	Bac	161 × 95 (ns) 222 × 99 (ns)	+		Aphid	Richardson and Sylvester (1968)
		Bul	220 × 80 (sec)				

Broccoli necrotic yellows	Cytoplasmic membranes	Bac Bul	270 × 66 (ns)	+ 4.5			Hills and Campbell (1968)
Egg plant mottled dwarf	Perinuclear: nuclear membrane budding but no intranuclear particles detected	Bac Bul	221 × 66 (sec)				Martelli (1969)
Northern cereal mosaic	Cytoplasm	Bac Bul	300–350 × 60 (ns) 500–600 × 40 (ns)	+			Shikata and Lu (1967)
Rice transitory yellowing	Perinuclear	Bul Bac	120–140 × 96 (ns) 180–210 × 96 (sec) 325 × 93 (ns)				Chiu *et al.* (1968)
Melilotis latent	Perinuclear budding of intranuclear particles	Bac Bul	250–300 × 80–100 (ns) 300–350 × 80 (sec)	+ 4.5–5.0	10		Kitajima *et al.* (1969)

[a] Bul = bullet-shaped; bac = bacilliform.
[b] ns = negatively stained preparation; sec = thin section preparation.
[c] + = present.
[d] Other values reported in insect host cell (see text).

in the past few years) that on the basis of their morphology and other properties appear to be related to VSV.

II. Vesicular Stomatitis Virus

A. *Historical Background*

The early history of the disease now attributed to this virus has been reviewed by Hanson (1952). It was first reported as a disease of horses and mules in South Africa in the late nineteenth century (Theiler, 1901), but the disease was probably present earlier in the Americas and may have been carried from there to Africa. There is circumstantial evidence suggesting that VSV was responsible for an outbreak of a disease causing hoof and tongue lesions among army horses during the American Civil War. It was not until the time of the First World War that well-documented accounts appeared in the American veterinary literature. An outbreak occurred in 1916 affecting both cattle and horses: it was first seen in stockyards in Denver and spread rapidly northward and eastward. The disease was carried to Europe in shipments of American and Canadian horses.

The disease symptoms resemble closely those of foot and mouth disease. Affected animals show elevated temperature with loss of appetite and abnormal salivation. Vesicular lesions occur around the mouth and tongue and also on hoofs and udders. Unlike foot and mouth disease, VSV disease is seldom fatal, recovery being usually rapid and complete. Under natural conditions, VSV infects mainly horses and cattle, although other species including pigs, sheep, and raccoons can also be affected.

Sporadic outbreaks continued to occur in the United States from time to time. In 1925 cattle arriving in Richmond, Indiana, from Kansas City showed symptoms of the disease which was later transmitted to horses. The infectious agent was isolated from the latter and preserved by animal transfer. This strain of virus is now known as the VS Indiana strain.

In the following year, an outbreak occurred in New Jersey. Virus isolated from infected animals was found to be immunologically distinct from the Indiana virus isolated the previous year and the strain is known as the VS New Jersey strain. All subsequent isolates of VSV have been found to be one or other of these two serotypes.

Vesicular stomatitis virus is most prevalent in countries bordering the Caribbean Sea, especially Mexico, Venezuela, and Colombia. The disease appears to spread north each season, sometimes only a short distance, sometimes into the southern states of the United States, and occasionally as far north as Canada. In northern latitudes the disease generally reaches a peak in the late summer and fall and dies out in October. The seasonal incidence and pattern of spread of the disease has led to the suggestion that an insect vector may be involved in its transmission (Hanson, 1952). Indiana type virus was in fact isolated from a pool of mosquitoes collected during an outbreak of vesicular stomatitis in New Mexico in 1965 (Sudia *et al.*, 1967) and also from phlebotomous sandflies collected in Panama (Shelokov and Peralta, 1967). The theory that VSV is spread via arthropods has, however, been questioned by Jonkers (1967) who suggested that the virus persists in or on the soil or vegetation of pasture lands between outbreaks. The known lability of the virus, which would result in rapid inactivation under the temperature conditions likely to be encountered, argues against survival of unprotected virus over long periods. However, the recent discovery of the existence of plant viruses having a striking morphological similarity to VSV suggests the intriguing possibility that VSV may be capable of an intimate relationship with plant cells. However this may be, it is clear that during outbreaks, contact between animals is responsible, at least in part, for spreading the disease. Infection of human beings in close contact with diseased animals is also well established. In addition, numerous cases have been recorded of infection of laboratory personnel exposed to the virus. The symptoms in human beings vary in severity. In general, they resemble those of influenza, with fever, sore throat, and general malaise lasting for several days. Serological surveys of persons exposed to VSV both in the field and in the laboratory showed that a high percentage had detectable antibody to the virus (Patterson *et al.*, 1958), but only about half of these had clinical symptoms of the disease.

Nearly all mammalian species can be infected with VSV under experimental conditions. Common laboratory animals, rabbits, guinea pigs, rats, mice, hamsters, etc., develop lesions similar to those in cattle. Intracranial injection of virus in mice and guinea pigs produces encephalitis which may be fatal. Chickens, ducks, and geese can be successfully infected in the tongue and foot. VSV has also been shown to multiply in mosquitoes (Mussgay and Suarez, 1962) and in *Drosophila* (Périès *et al.*, 1966). A VSV strain adapted to *Drosophila* shortens their life-span and confers on them a sensitivity to exposure to carbon dioxide similar to that induced by sigma virus (see Section V,A).

Cocal virus, an agent first isolated in Trinidad from Gigantotaelaps mites collected from jungle rodents (rice rats) is serologically closely related to the Indiana strain of VSV (Jonkers *et al.*, 1964; Tables III and IV). The virions of Cocal and VSV are morphologically indistinguishable (Ditchfield and Almeida, 1964). Later isolates of the same virus have been obtained from rodents and a pool of mosquitoes in Trinidad and also from mites in Brazil. The virus was not associated with clinical stomatitis.

The relationship of Cocal virus to the Indiana serotype and other isolates of VSV was investigated by Federer *et al.* (1967). They included in their study isolates of virus obtained from equines in Argentina in 1963 and in Brazil in 1964. By complement fixation and cross-neutralization

TABLE III

NEUTRALIZATION TEST RESULTS[a]

Virus	Titer log LD_{50}	Mouse hyperimmune sera										Guinea pig serum Marburg
		VS Indiana	Cocal	VS New Jersey	Piry	Chan-di-pura	Hart Park	Flan-ders	Ra-bies	Kern Can-yon	Mt. Elgon	
VS-Indiana	7.1	$\geqslant$*6.2*[b]	4.2	1.9	0	2.6	0	0	0	0	0	0
Cocal	7.7	4.2	$\geqslant$*7.0*	2.7	1.7	1.8	0	0	0	0	0	0
VS-New Jersey	5.5	2.2	0	$\geqslant$*5.0*	0	0	0	0	0	0	0	0
Piry	7.9	2.3	2.6	2.5	*5.7*	3.4	0	0	0	0	0	0
Chandipura	7.3	2.5	2.7	0	4.6	$\geqslant$*5.7*	0	0	0	0	0	0
Hart Park	4.6	0	0	0	0	0	$\geqslant$*4.1*	$\geqslant$4.1	0	0	0	0
Flanders	4.4	0	0	0	0	0	$\geqslant$3.9	$\geqslant$*3.9*	0	0	0	0
Rabies	5.9	0	0	0	0	0	0	0	$\geqslant$*5.4*	0	0	0
Kern Canyon	5.4	0	0	0	0	2.2	0	0	0	$\geqslant$*4.9*	0	0
Mt. Elgon	5.8	0	0	0	0	0	0	0	0	0	$\geqslant$*5.3*	0

[a] Table supplied by F. Murphy.
[b] Log neutralization index; 0 = $\geqslant$1.5.

TABLE IV

RESULTS OF COMPLEMENT FIXATION TESTS[a]

Antigens	Hyperimmune mouse sera										Guinea pig serum Marburg
	VSV New Jersey	VS Indiana	Cocal	Piry	Chan-di-pura	Flan-ders	Hart Park	Rabies	Mt. Elgon	Kern Canyon	
VS-New Jersey	256/512[b]	0	0	0	0	0	0	0	0	0	0
VS-Indiana	0	256/512	32/128	0	0	0	0	0	0	0	0
Cocal	0	32/512	256/512	0	0	0	0	0	0	0	0
Piry	0	0	0	128/32	8/4	0	0	0	0	0	0
Chandipura	0	0	0	0	128/64	0	0	0	0	0	0
Flanders	0	0	0	0	0	64/16	32/4	0	0	0	0
Hart Park	0	0	0	0	0	32/16	256/64	0	0	0	0
Rabies	0	0	0	0	0	0	0	128/512	0	0	0
Mt. Elgon	0	0	0	0	0	0	0	0	64/64	0	0
Kern Canyon	0	0	0	0	0	0	0	0	0	256/512	0
Marburg	0	0	0	0	0	0	0	0	0	0	64/32
Normal	0	0	0	0	0	0	0	0	0	0	0

[a] Table supplied by F. Murphy.
[b] Titer of serum/antigen; 0 = no reaction at 1:4 serum dilution.

tests they showed that the Argentina and Cocal strains could not be differentiated antigenically from one another, but that each differed from the Indiana strain to the same degree as from the Brazil strain. The virus particles of the four strains were not distinguishable by electron microscopy. All four strains of virus were pathogenic for cattle, producing typical lesions. The Indiana and cocal strains were also pathogenic for pigs. Federer *et al.* (1967) proposed on the basis of their findings that the Indiana serotype should be divided into three subtypes, Indiana 1 for the classic strain, Indiana 2 for the Cocal and Argentina viruses, and Indiana 3 for the Brazil virus.

B. Structure and Mode of Development

The main structural features of the VS virion have been established by electron microscopy of thin sections of infected cells and virus pellets and of negatively stained viral preparations (Howatson and Whitmore, 1962; Simpson and Hauser, 1966; McCombs *et al.*, 1966; Bradish and Kirkham, 1966; Nakai and Howatson, 1968). There is general agreement that the

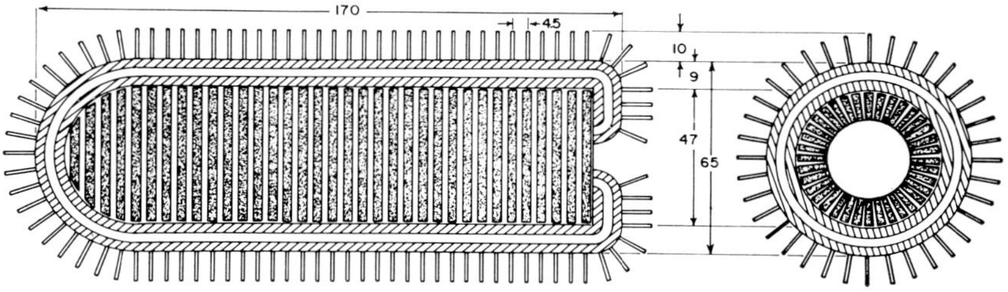

FIG. 1. Diagrammatic representation of structural features of VS virion observed by electron microscopy. Approximate dimensions are indicated in nanometers (nm). The internal nucleoprotein helix is represented on the left as a series of transverse striations (spacing 4.5 nm). In the crosssectional view on the right, individual protein subunits are shown.

particles are bullet-shaped, i.e., cylindrical with one hemispherical and one planar end, and consist of an internal helical structure which appears as a series of transverse striations, surrounded by a membranous envelope studded on its outer surface with fine projections. There is an axial channel which usually appears translucent in sections and is often partially penetrated by the stain in negatively stained preparations. Measurements of particle dimensions made in different laboratories are a fairly good general agreement. There appear to be no significant differences between virions of different serotypes (Bergold and Munz, 1967). Figure 1 is a diagrammatic representation of the VS virion as observed by electron microscopy; approximate dimensions are indicated. Occasionally abnormally long particles and particles with two rounded ends are observed, but these appear to be aberrant forms. In most preparations of VSV there are, however, in addition to the bullet-shaped (B) particles, numerous particles that are much shorter than the B particles but are otherwise similar. These are referred to as truncated (T) particles and are discussed in Section II,C. The T particles are extruded from the cell in a similar manner to the B particles.

Although the main structural features of the VS virion are not in dispute, there have been some differences in the interpretation of the structural details especially with respect to the conformation of the internal helix (or nucleoprotein core) in the intact particle. Several

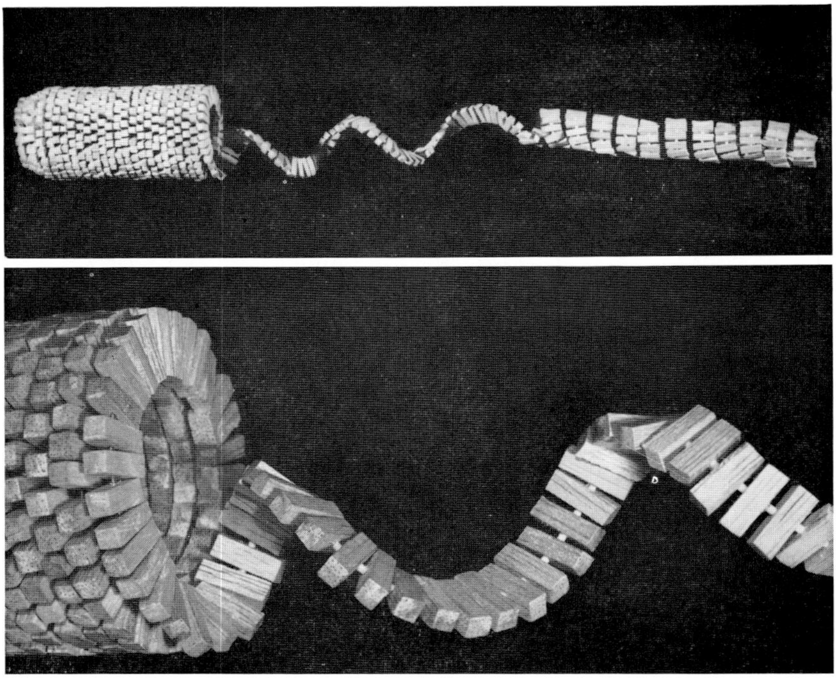

FIG. 2. Model, proposed by Nakai and Howatson (1968), showing three-dimensional arrangement of VSV nucleocapsid in intact and unwound state. The RNA molecule is represented by a wire on which blocks representing the protein subunits are strung.

different models of the virion have been proposed (Simpson and Hauser, 1966; Klimenko *et al.*, 1966; Bradish and Kirkham, 1966; Bergold and Munz, 1967; Nakai and Howatson, 1968). In the writer's opinion the one proposed by the last authors fits the observations most satisfactorily. According to this model, the nucleoprotein is in the form of a single helix of about 30 turns capped by four or five turns of diminishing diameter at the round end. The helix consists of about 1000 subunits of dimensions approximately 90Å × 30Å × 30Å, the long axis of the subunits being radially oriented. The continuity of the helix is presumed to be maintained by a single-stranded molecule of RNA (Fig. 2). The forces between adjacent rings of the helix are apparently weak for the helical configuration is readily destroyed by a variety of treatments including simple storage of the virus at 4°C. With loss of the stabilizing contacts between adjacent rings the helix reverts to a different configuration, that of an undulating ribbonlike strand or a loosely wound spiral. The latter structure which approximates to a helix of about half

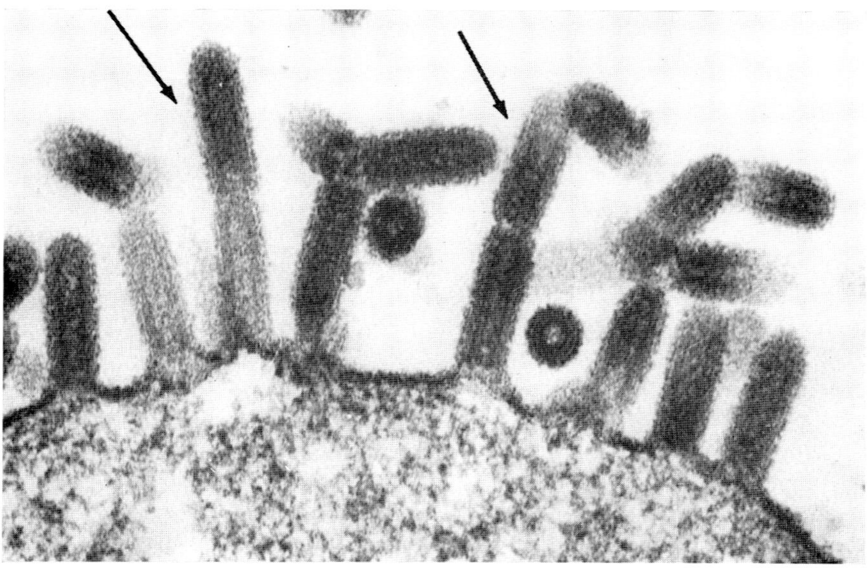

FIG. 3. Micrograph showing extrusion of VSV particles at surface of L cell. Examples of particles extruded in tandem formation are indicated by arrows. Micrograph by M. Betlem. Magnification 125,000 ×.

the diameter of the original helix is, according to our interpretation, essentially an artifact and does not exist as such in the virion, as proposed by some authors (Simpson and Hauser, 1966; Klimenko *et al.*, 1966; Bergold and Munz, 1967). Murphy *et al.* (1970) have recently obtained evidence in favor of the single helix model for another member of the rhabdovirus group, Mount Elgon bat virus.

The development and maturation of VSV in L cells grown in suspension was investigated by Howatson and Whitmore (1962) who showed that in this cell system the assembly of viral components occurs almost exclusively at the cell surface. Maturing virus particles are readily identified as fingerlike projections consisting of a dense striated core enveloped in a membrane continuous with the cell membrane. The outer surface of the membrane covering the budding particle is distinguished from that of the cell by the presence of an irregular layer of material which corresponds to the projections seen on the surface of negatively stained virions. The extrusion appears to be a rapid process as stages in budding are seldom seen. It is also difficult to determine how the particles sever their connection with the cell. In the severed particle the envelope presumably closes over the flat end, but appears to be weaker in this region than elsewhere since under the stress of negative staining procedures blebbing of the membrane frequently occurs at the flat end. Also the staining solution often penetrates some distance up the central canal from the flat end suggesting that the membrane is more permeable at this point than elsewhere. Occasionally severance of the particle fails to occur when the nucleoprotein core is completed and two or more cores are extruded in tandem enclosed within a single envelope (Fig. 3). Galasso (1967) has illustrated more extreme examples of this phenomenon, showing long lines of VSV particles attached end-to-end.

The site of maturation of VSV depends on the host cell line. Hackett *et al.* (1968) showed that the predominant site of extrusion of particles (VSV, New Jersey serotype) in chick embryo fibroblasts and in a pig kidney cell line was not at the cell surface, as it is in L cells, but at the membranes of intracytoplasmic vesicles. The budding of VS virions always occurs as preexisting cell membranes and formation of the viral envelope *de novo* in the ground cytoplasm [as reported for rabies virus (Hummeler *et al.*, 1967; Fig. 6)] has not been observed. Cytoplasmic aggregates of nucleoprotein are not readily detected in sections of infected L cells though analysis of polysome extracts of L cells shows that unenveloped nucleoprotein strands are present in appreciable quantities (Schincariol and Howatson, 1970). David-West and Labzoffsky (1968a) illustrated regular arrays of viral-specific material in the cytoplasm of VSV-infected L cells but the nature of the material was unknown.

Early stages in the viral growth cycle, viz., the adsorption of virions and their mode of entry into the host cell have been studied by electron microscopy by two groups (Heine and Schnaitman, 1969; Simpson *et al.*, 1969). The first authors claim that adsorption and penetration occur by an exact reversal of the extrusion process. The virion attaches to the cell surface usually at the flat end, the viral envelope and the cell membrane fuse, and penetration occurs by release of the nucleoprotein into the cytoplasm. Simpson *et al.* (1969), however, maintain that entry of VS virions is effected by viropexis, a process akin to phagocytosis. The virion attaches to the cell surface membrane which invaginates and closes around the particle to form an intracytoplasmic vesicle. Once inside the vesicle the virion is degraded and the nucleic acid or nucleoprotein enters the cytoplasm.

In the writer's experience phagocytosis of virions is readily observed but the mechanism whereby the viral genome crosses the barrier of the vesicle membrane is obscure. He has not been fortunate enough to observe the process described by Heine and Schnaitman (1969).

C. Truncated (T) Particles of VSV

Serial undiluted passage of VSV in cell cultures results in low yields of virus compared with those obtained by diluted passage. This phenomenon was investigated by Cooper and Bellett (1959) and Bellett and Cooper (1959) who concluded from an extensive series of experiments that the low yields resulted from the presence of a transmissible interfering component which they denoted by T. The effect resembles that described by Von Magnus (1954) for influenza virus and attributed by him to the presence of "incomplete" virus particles in infectious inocula. Prévec and Whitmore (1963) obtained evidence by density gradient centrifugation for the presence in VSV preparations of non-infectious particles of somewhat lower density than the infectious particles, but of similar chemical constitution. They did not, however, relate the "defective" particles to the interference phenomenon. The nature of the interfering component of VSV was clarified by Hackett (1964) who examined and compared by negative-contrast electron microscopy the particles present in virus preparations harvested after several diluted and undiluted passages. In the diluted-passage preparations most of the particles were bullet-shaped and of fairly uniform size, the lengths being in the range 155–185 mμ. In contrast, a high proportion of the particles in the undiluted-passage preparations were much shorter (average length 82 mμ) though they were otherwise similar in appearance to the bullet particles. Hackett suggested that the short particles were in all probability the physical equivalent of the interfering T component of Cooper and Bellett. The equivalence was confirmed and the nature of the T particles was further investigated by Huang *et al.* (1966) and Huang and Wagner (1966). These authors denoted the bullet-shaped and short particles by B and T, respectively. These designations for the infectious and interfering particles have become generally accepted and will be used in this article. The term T is now regarded as denoting "truncated particle" rather than "transmissible component" as originally defined by Cooper and Bellett (1959). Among the properties of the T particles that were elucidated or confirmed in the studies of Huang *et al.* were the following:

(1) Superinfection of cultures with purified and concentrated preparations of T completely inhibited growth of B; when the T preparation was diluted 1:100 the 8-hour yield was reduced to 1% of that of control cultures infected with B only.

(2) Superinfection with undiluted T (Indiana strain) caused incomplete inhibition of growth of B (New Jersey strain), i.e., inhibition was to some extent serotype specific.

(3) Undiluted T had no effect on replication of the unrelated encephalomyocarditis virus.

(4) The interfering action of T was expressed early in the replication cycle of B.

(5) UV-irradiation (25,000 erg/mm^2) destroyed the capacity of T to interfere with homotypic B, suggesting that functional T particle RNA was necessary for interference.

(6) B and T particles were antigenically indistinguishable and both incorporated radioactive uridine during growth.

Separation of infectious and interfering particles in sucrose density gradients has also been accomplished independently in other laboratories (Crick *et al.,* 1966; Hackett *et al.,* 1967). The conclusion from all these studies was that the T particles are responsible for most if not all the interfering effect; that the T particles are indeed truncated forms of B particles having similar structural features, antigenic properties, and chemical constitution; and that T particles are not infectious and replicate only in the presence of B particles.

The mode of action of T particles in the autointerference phenomenon is not understood. Some aspects of the problem have been considered by Schaffer *et al.* (1969) and Crick *et al.* (1969).

The T particles described by Huang *et al.* (1966) were somewhat shorter than those observed by Hackett (1964) who used the New Jersey serotype, being about 65 mμ in length and of the same diameter as the B particles (65 mμ). They had 8–10 internal striations compared with 14 in Hackett's T particles and about 35 in B particles of both serotypes. The T particles associated with the HR strain of VSV (Indiana) isolated in the writer's laboratory are significantly larger than those associated with the wild-type virus from which the HR strain was derived. Likewise, the mean length of nucleoprotein strands extracted from T particles of the HR strain was 1.6 $\pm$ 0.2 μ compared with 1.1 $\pm$ 0.1 μ for strands from wild-type T particles (Schincariol and Howatson, 1970). The B particle of both strains were identical. C. W. Ng (personal communication) has obtained evidence for the existence of a third distinct type of T particle intermediate in length between the two types described above.

D. Viral Antigens and Hemagglutinin

In an early study of the biophysical properties of VSV propagated in eggs, Bradish *et al.* (1956) identified four complement fixing (CF) components in infectious egg fluid having sedimentation coefficients of 625 S, 330 S, c. 20 S, and c. 6 S. Most of the infectivity was associated with the 625 S component which was shown to consist of rods of dimensions 165 × 65 mμ. The 330 S component was in the form of granules or spheres of diameter 62 mμ and had little or no infectivity. About 35% of the total CF activity was associated with the 625 S and 330 S components. It is now clear that the 625 S and 330 S components can be identified with B (infectious) and T (interfering) particles, respectively. Bradish *et al.* (1956) found a small amount of infectivity (0.1%) associated with the 20 S component which together with the 6 S component accounted for the remainder (65%) of the CF activity.

In more recent years these studies have been continued and extended by F. Brown and his collaborators who have examined the antigenic properties of VSV and their relationship to the structural components of the virus. Using sucrose gradient centrifugation, these workers (Brown *et al.*, 1966) found that, in agreement with Bradish *et al.*, the most rapidly sedimenting fraction consisted of complete bullet-shaped (B) particles with some disintegrated particles, and accounted for most of the infectivity. This fraction also possessed CF activity. Two other fractions having CF activity but negligible infectivity were also examined for their particle content. One contained "caps" (truncated or T particles) and fragments of particles; the other consisted of small "rosettes" (fragments of the viral envelope) and cellular debris. All three fractions possessed immunogenetic properties in guinea pigs, the middle one being the most active. Two further antigenic components of low molecular weight were detected by first removing larger antigens by centrifugation prior to fractionation by sucrose density gradient and filtration through Sephadex G-200 (Brown and Cartwright, 1966). Both components sedimented more slowly than 7 S γ-globulin.

Brown *et al.* (1967a) continued their investigation of the antigens of VSV by examining the activities of components derived from purified preparations of VSV by combined treatment with ether and the detergent Tween 80. The treatment reduced the infectivity of the preparation by about 4 logs but enhanced CF activity and immunogenicity for guinea pigs. Three fractions possessing CF activity were isolated from disrupted virions by sucrose density centrifugation; a "skeletonlike" structure with sedimentation coefficient greater than that of the intact virion (presumably the virion minus its envelope); rosettes (sed. coeff. 16 S) derived from the viral envelope; and material of sedimentation coefficient 3 S to 6 S presumed to consist of projections removed from the viral envelope. Brown *et al.* (1967b) found that the infectivity remaining after the Tween-ether treatment was resistant to further inactivation. They examined the nature of the material responsible for the residual infectivity and concluded from a study of its properties that it was not contaminating intact virus but consisted of virions lacking the outer envelope and associated fringe structure. From these results it would appear that after treatment with Tween-ether, the nucleoprotein helices of some of the virions remain intact and retain some infectivity. In our laboratory we have confirmed that residual infectivity remains after Tween-ether treatment. However, after treatment of concentrated virus suspensions with the combination 0.5 M urea, 0.1% SDS, and 0.1% 2-mercaptoethanol, infectivity was completely lost although CF activity remained unchanged. Unwound, but apparently otherwise unaltered nucleoprotein helices, were readily detectable by electron microscopy after the treatment (F. Shand, unpublished observations).

In further experiments, Brown and collaborators studied the effect of trypsin and phospholipase C on the structure and antigenic properties of VSV (Cartwright *et al.*, 1969). Treatment with trypsin (0.1 mg/ml) was found to reduce the infectivity by 5 logs in 5 minutes and to destroy immunizing activity. It also destroyed CF activity against antiserum to the virus but not against antiserum to the host cells. Surface projections on the viral envelope were removed but the envelope was otherwise unaffected. It was concluded that the immunizing and CF antigens are associated with the surface projections. Loss of infectivity was attributed to failure of the virus to attach to susceptible cells when the projections were removed. In contrast, treatment with phospholipase C reduced the infectivity only slightly and the immunizing activity was unaffected. CF activity against antiserum to virus was unaffected but CF activity against antiserum to host cells was greatly reduced. Electron microscopy showed that the projections remained but the rest of the envelope was removed. In line with this observation there was a loss of more than 50% of the radioactivity from virus in which the phospholipid component had been labeled with ^{32}P. From the combined observations it was concluded that the projections consist of virus protein and are responsible for the immunizing activity of the virus, and that a phospholipid component derived from the host cell is located in the regions between the projections. Other evidence indicating that a cellular component is present in the envelope of the virus was obtained by Cartwright and Pearce (1968).

The presence of a viral hemagglutinin in VSV, demonstrable by techniques similar to those developed for rabies virus, has recently been reported (Halonen *et al.*, 1968). Optimum conditions for titration of the hemagglutinin were described by Arstila *et al.* (1969); these included the use of goose erythrocytes at a low temperature and pH of 6.2, and replacement of the serum in the growth medium with 0.4% bovine albumin. The fraction showing peak HA activity in density gradients contained whole virions but the viral component associated with the hemagglutinin was not determined.

E. Viral RNA

Evidence that VSV is an RNA-containing virus was obtained by Prévec and Whitmore (1963). These authors first partially purified ^{32}P-labeled virus by differential centrifugation and then further purified it by equilibrium sedimentation in a cesium chloride density gradient. This resulted in two radioactive peaks, one of which (at density 1.20), contained all the infectious material. Chemical analysis of the materials in the radioactive peaks showed that they had very similar compositions; they both contained RNA and a high percentage of phospholipid. It is clear from subsequent work that centrifugation in cesium chloride had resulted in separation of the B and T particles of VSV. Use of cesium chloride, however, results in considerable damage to particles and loss of infectivity. Centrifugation in sucrose gradients is less damaging and is now generally preferred for separation of B and T particles, though complete separation is not achieved in a single centrifugation.

Huang and Wagner (1966) used this method of separation and obtained visible separated bands of B and T particles which they collected by puncturing the side of the tube. RNA, previously labeled with uridine-^{3}H, was extracted from purified B and T particles by adding 0.5% sodium dodecyl sulfate (SDS). The extracted RNA was then sedimented through a 0–15% sucrose gradient in the presence of *E. coli* rRNA which served as a sedimentation marker, its distribution being determined by absorbancy at 260 mμ. To determine the distribution of the radioactive viral RNA, fractions were collected from the bottom of each tube, the RNA precipitated with 10% cold trichloracetic acid, and the radioactivity of acid-insoluble material determined with a liquid scintillation counter. The sedimentation coefficients of RNA from B and T particles averaged 42 S and 25 S, respectively. Estimates of corresponding molecular weights were made, though these were subject to uncertainties because of difficulties of assessing the effects of pH, ionic strength, and temperature on the conformation of the RNA molecules. Using the relationship of Spirin (1963) the values obtained were 4.0×10^6 for B-particle RNA and 1.3×10^6 for T-particle RNA. Corresponding values based on Kurland's (1960) equation were 3.1×10^6 and $1.2 \times$

10^6. The RNA extracted from both B and T particles were readily solubilized by treatment with RNase, indicating that the molecules were single stranded. The RNA from B particles was tested for infectivity but none could be demonstrated.

Results similar to those described above were obtained independently by Brown *et al.* (1967c) using somewhat different methods and conditions. The viral RNA was labeled with ^{32}P by growing virus in actinomycin D-treated cells in a phosphate-deficient medium containing $^{32}PO_4$. Sedimentation in a sucrose density gradient resulted in four radioactive peaks, the most rapidly sedimenting containing the infectious (B) particles. The second fraction contained "caps" (T particles) and other viral components ("filaments and rosettes") and had most of the interfering activity. To separate the T particles from other components this fraction was further centrifuged in a potassium tartrate gradient. RNA was obtained from the B particle fraction by mixing with 1% SDS and extracting twice with phenol. The RNA was mixed with ribosomal RNA from BHK cells and centrifuged in a 5–25% sucrose gradient. From the distribution of radioactivity and absorbancy at 260 mμ it was found that the sedimentation coefficient of the virus RNA was 36–40 S. Under the same conditions, the RNA extracted from the T particle fraction sedimented in a sharp peak at 18–20 S. The RNA from both B and T particles was readily hydrolyzed by ribonuclease (0.01 mg/ml). The estimated molecular weight of B-particle RNA was 3×10^6 daltons. Brown *et al.* (1967c) also determined the base composition of the RNA obtained from B and T particles by paper electrophoresis. The percentage distribution of ^{32}P in the nucleotides was: A = 29.3, C = 21.1, G = 20.9, and U = 28.7 for B-particle RNA; and A = 27.1, C = 21.9, G = 20.3, and U = 30.7 for T-particle RNA. In view of the apparent single-stranded nature of the RNA, the approximate complementarity of the base composition was regarded as fortuitous. The difference in base composition between B and T particle RNA, though slight, was thought to be significant.

In another study Huppert *et al.* (1967) examined some properties of the RNA of VSV. The RNA, extracted from a ^{32}P-labeled virus preparation (presumably containing both B and T particles) by a variety of methods, was centrifuged on a linear gradient of glycerol or saccharose. Two main components with sedimentation coefficients of 45 S and 18 S were obtained. A third fraction having a sedimentation coefficient of about 7 S was sometimes present in variable amounts. Base composition analyses of the RNA components gave results in general agreement with those of Brown *et al.* (1967c), but the base composition of the 18 S component was said to be variable.

A different approach to determining the molecular weight of VSV RNA was used by Nakai and Howatson (1968) who measured the lengths of unwound nucleoprotein strands derived from disintegrated VSV particles. The average length of the nucleic acid molecules (assumed to be the same as the strand length) was 3.5 μ for B particles and 1.1 μ for T particles. From these figures, assuming that the linear density of single-stranded nucleic acid is 100 daltons/Å, the molecular weights obtained for the B and T particle RNAs are 3.5×10^6 and 1.1×10^6 daltons, respectively. These values are in good agreement with those obtained from sedimentation data.

F. Viral Proteins

Two separate reports have recently appeared on the analysis of the structural proteins of VSV by acrylamide gel electrophoresis (Wagner *et al.*, 1969a; Kang and Prévec, 1969). The latter authors isolated from supernatant fluids of VSV-infected L cell cultures four ^{14}C-labeled antigenic components corresponding to those described previously by Bradish *et al.* (1956); viz., B particles, T particles, 20 S antigen, and 6 S antigen. Each purified concentrated component was treated with SDS (1%), urea (0.5 *M*), and acetic acid (10%), followed by dialysis against SDS, urea, and mercaptoethanol. The resultant proteins were then analyzed by acrylamide gel electrophoresis. The B and T particle preparations both contained the same four protein components labeled 1, 2, 3, and 4 in order of increasing mobility (Fig. 4). The corresponding molecular weights were estimated to be 230,000, 84,000, 64,000, and 47,000 daltons. By using sodium deoxycholate to separate the envelopes from nucleoprotein cores and analyzing the fractions separately, the authors were able to show that protein 3 originated in the core and proteins 2 and 4 came from the envelope. The origin of protein 1 which was present in small quantities was not determined. The value obtained for the molecular weight of protein 3 agrees well with that to be expected if the molecules correspond to the subunits in nucleoprotein strands described by Nakai and Howatson (1968). The protein obtained from the 20 S component had the same mobility as protein 3. The origin of the 20 S component was not, however, established in these studies. The origin and function of the 6 S component was also undetermined. Its mobility was similar but not identical to that of protein 2. It could represent a viral coat component such as surface projections which might be released from completed virus or from infected cells.

Very similar experiments and results were reported independently by Wagner *et al.* (1969a,b). In their gel electrophoresis experiments these authors detected two minor, slow-moving protein fractions in addition to the minor protein 1 (using Kang and Prévec's terminology), and the major proteins 2, 3, and 4. Unlike minor protein 1, the additional minor proteins disaggregated in 8 *M* urea, suggesting that they might be polymers or mixed aggregates of the smaller proteins. The values for molecular weights obtained by comparing the electrophoretic migration

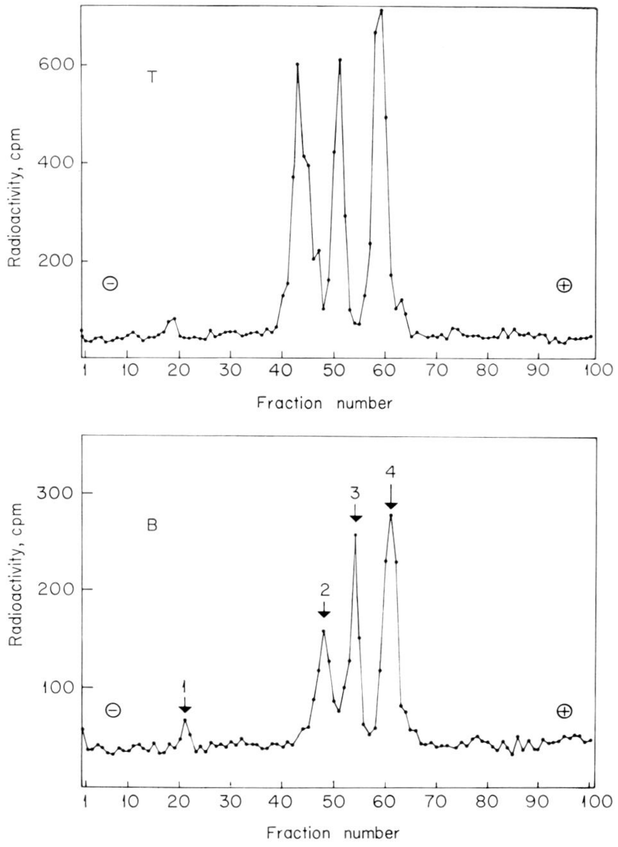

FIG. 4. Analysis of proteins of B and T particles of VSV by gel electrophoresis. The same four proteins are obtained from both types of particles (Kang and Prévec, 1969).

distances with those of known marker proteins were 275,000, 81,500, 59,500, and 34,500 for proteins 1, 2, 3, and 4, respectively, and 180,000 and 140,000 for the other two minor proteins. These authors used Indiana strain VSV grown in both chick and mouse cells. No differences were found in the electrophoretic patterns of virus grown in the different cell lines, indicating that none of the six proteins detected was of cellular origin. These authors also confirmed that the proteins released from B and T particles are indistinguishable. They analyzed proteins from the New Jersey strain of VSV and found that only the smallest protein (4) was distinguishable from the corresponding protein of the Indiana serotype. They suggested that protein 4 is probably a surface antigen and that differences in this protein might account for the marked antigenic dissimilarity of the two virus strains.

Wagner *et al.* (1969b) also described experiments designed to determine the origin of the proteins they had isolated in relation to the known structural components of the virion. They used both digitonin and sodium deoxycholate to disrupt purified virus and analyzed the products by gel electrophoresis and electron microscopy. They concluded, in agreement with Kang and Prévec, that protein 3 is located in the nucleocapsid and proteins 2 and 4 in the outer layers of the virion which they referred to as "shell" and "envelope."

G. The Infected Cell

As mentioned in an earlier section, many animal species are susceptible to infection with VSV. Likewise, *in vitro,* VSV can readily be adapted to grow to high titers in a great variety of cell types. Among the host cells that have been used in VSV studies are chick embryo fibroblasts, baby hamster kidney cells, simian cells (VERO and BSC-1), and Chinese hamster ovary cells.

The replication cycle of VSV is complicated by the presence in most viral lysates of noninfectious autointerfering T particles. The outcome of infection depends not only on the type and nutritional environment of the host cell but also to an important extent on the multiplicity of infection and the proportion of T particles in the inoculum (see Section II,C). Stampfer *et al.* (1969) have shown, for example, that the species of viral-specific RNAs present in infected Chinese hamster ovary cells differ according to whether infection is initiated by purified B particles alone or by a mixture of B and T particles. Under the usual conditions of infection, however, the inoculate contains both B and T particles. In our laboratory we routinely use an inoculum containing approximately 85% B particles and 15% T particles. The virus is a high-temperature resistant (HR) strain of the Indiana serotype (Schincariol and Howatson, 1970), and the host cell a line of Earle's L cells, L 60 T (Till *et al.,* 1963). A plot of a typical one-step viral growth cycle initiated by such an inoculum at a multicplicity of infection (m.o.i.) of 100 PFU/cell is shown in Fig. 5. The cycle is rapid for an animal virus, the latent period at 37°C being a little over an hour. This is followed by a period of exponential increase of progeny virus which continues for about 3½ hours after which the growth rate declines. The yield of virus is 10^8–10^9 PFU/ml, corresponding to 200–2000 PFU/cell. Nearly all the progency virus from L cells is released into the medium, only 1–2% remaining cell-associated. Approximately equal quantities of B and T particles are produced under the conditions described.

The replicaton of VSV is not affected by inhibitors of DNA synthesis such as bromodeoxyuridine nor by inhibitors such as actinomycin

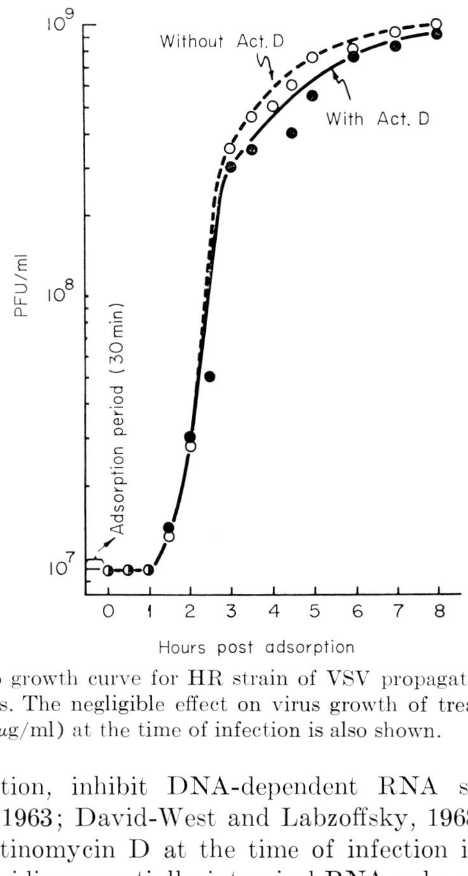

FIG. 5. One-step growth curve for HR strain of VSV propagated at a m.o.i. of 100 PFU/ml on L cells. The negligible effect on virus growth of treatment of cells with actinomycin D (5 μg/ml) at the time of infection is also shown.

which, in addition, inhibit DNA-dependent RNA synthesis (Prévec and Whitmore, 1963; David-West and Labzoffsky, 1968b; Fig. 5). Cells treated with actinomycin D at the time of infection incorporate radioactive-labeled uridine essentially into viral RNA only, so that the species of viral RNA synthesized in infected cells can readily be determined. In the L cell system described, species of RNA sedimenting at 13, 15, 21, 26, 31 and 38 S were found. The 26 S and 38 S species have the same sedimentation coefficients as the RNA extracted from T and B particles, respectively. The 13 S and 15 S species were associated with polysomes, suggesting that they function as messenger RNAs. Studies of hybridization of RNA from infected cells with RNA extracted from virions showed that large amounts of the single-stranded species, particularly the 13 S and 15 S RNA, were complementary to viral RNA (Schincariol and Howatson, 1970) in line with results obtained by Schaffer *et al.* (1968) using a different cell system. The nature of the 21 S and 31 S components is not known. In addition to the RNase-sensitive, single-stranded RNAs, other species that were RNase-resistant were observed at 13–15 S and 19–20 S. These were considered to be double-stranded replicative forms (RF) corresponding to T and B particles, respectively, and analogous to the replicative forms that are involved in the replication of RNA bacteriophages and picornaviruses (Franklin, 1967; Plagemann and Swim, 1968; Girard, 1969). A partially RNase-resistant, heterogeneous RNA component found in the range 13–50 S, had the characteristics of replicative intermediate (RI). RI, discovered also in studies of RNA bacteriophage and picornavirus replication, is a complex consisting of RF together with nascent molecules of single-stranded RNA (Baltimore, 1969).

Numerous species of viral-specific RNA have also been found during replication of VSV in other cell systems. Schaffer *et al.* (1968) observed RNase-sensitive RNAs sedimenting at 6, 15, 31, and 38 S in VERO cells. Newman and Brown (1969) using BHK-21 as host cell found five peaks of RNA which sedimented at <4, 12, 28, and 38 S, and contained varying amounts of RNase-resistant RNA. Stampfer *et al.* (1969) distinguished two groups of RNA species in VSV-infected Chinese hamster ovary cells; group I consisted of RNAs made when cells were producing mainly B particles and included single-stranded components sedimenting at 13, 28, and 40 S, and partially double-stranded 23–35 S RNA; group II consisted of RNA species made when predominantly T particles were produced, and included single-stranded 6 and 19 S, partially double-stranded 15 and 19 S, and a completely double-stranded 13 S species. It is difficult to compare results from different laboratories because of differences in experimental conditions and in the techniques used. Another factor that accounts for some of the differences in the sedimentation values reported is the existence of T particles of different size and RNA content. Thus, in our system, using the HR strain of VSV, the T-particle RNA sediments at 26 S and this species of RNA is also present in infected cells. The T particles of other strains of VSV are smaller and the RNA sediments at about 19 S.

The viral-specific proteins of the VSV-infected cell have not been studied as extensively as the viral RNAs. Wilson and Bader (1965) reported the existence of a cytoplasmic RNA polymerase which appeared in chick embryo cells following infection with VSV, and was not present in uninfected cells.

Baltimore *et al.* (1970) have recently reported the finding of RNA polymerase in association with the virion of VSV. The polymerase uses the viral RNA as template for the synthesis of complementary RNA which, in the infected cell, is thought to act as messenger for translation of viral proteins. The enzyme appears to act as a transcriptase rather than a replicase. It is not yet known whether the viral polymerase discovered by Baltimore *et al.* is the same as the polymerase reported by Wilson and Bader. The requirement of a virion-associated polymerase for viral replication would explain the lack of infectivity of RNA extracted from VSV (Huang and Wagner, 1966).

Further characterization of viral-specific proteins, including structural proteins, in the infected cell together with information now available on viral-specific RNA, should lead to a better understanding of the rather complex events occurring during the replication of VSV. These studies should also be aided by work on conditional lethal mutants of VSV which are discussed in the following section.

H. Temperature-Sensitive Mutants

The value of conditional lethal mutants in the study of bacteriophage genetics and physiology is well established (Epstein *et al.*, 1963). More recently conditional lethal mutants, especially those of the temperature-sensitive (ts) type have been used in physiological and genetic studies of animal viruses (Cooper, 1967; Fenner, 1969).

Temperature-sensitive mutants result from alterations in the nucleotide sequence of the parent (wild-type) virus which are such that the resultant protein is unable to function at one temperature (usually 38°–40°C), but is able to function normally at another temperature (e.g., 30°C). The former is referred to as the nonpermissive and the latter the permissive temperature. Normal or nearly normal yields of virus are obtained under permissive conditions but the yield of infectious virus under nonpermissive conditions is greatly reduced. Viral stocks can be grown at the permissive temperature and used to study the physiological defect associated with any particular mutant. A valuable feature of ts mutants is that the defect may involve any essential gene function so that in theory it should be possible to map the viral genome by means of complementation and recombination tests. In practice, certain difficulties arise in the study of ts mutants of animal viruses that are not encountered, at least to the same extent, in work on bacteriophages, e.g., complementation tests may be hampered by "leakiness" of mutants, recombination may be difficult to demonstrate, viral growth cycles are much longer.

The VSV system is a promising one for analysis by means of ts mutants. The relatively short growth cycle and efficient plaque formation of the virus facilitate isolation of mutants and other operations; the viral genome is of a size suitable for mapping, having an estimated 10–15 genes; and the virion has a well-defined, characteristic structure and mode of development. Work on ts mutants of VSV has, however, been reported only very recently. Flamand (1969) has described the isolation of 20 ts mutants from a stock of Indiana VSV. Some were obtained by treating the stock with nitrosoguanidine, others were isolated without any treatment. By infecting the host cells (primary chick fibroblasts) with selected pairs of mutants and measuring the complementation level (defined as yield of mixed infection/sum of yields of single infections) this author showed that the mutants could be classified into three distinct complementation groups. Some characteristics of a number of the mutants were investigated by Lafay (1969). Most of the mutants did not synthesize detectable amounts of RNA under nonpermissive conditions, though a few did so. The kinetics of the inactivation of infectious centers as a function of the time they were held at the nonpermissive temperature were also studied. With the RNA^- mutants the number of infectious centers decreased exponentially, two distinct slopes being obtained. The RNA^+ mutants behaved like the wild-type virus. Measurements of the production of virus (at 24 hours after infection) as a function of the time spent at the nonpermissive temperature gave three types of curves, one corresponding to RNA^+ mutants and the others to the two classes of RNA^- mutants previously distinguished. The separation of the mutants into three groups by these criteria agreed with the classification by complementation tests reported by Flamand (1969).

Holloway *et al.* (1970) isolated 24 ts mutants of Indiana VSV (HR strain) using nitrous acid, ethyl methane sulfonate, proflavine, and 5-fluorouracil as mutagens, and studied their characteristics. Only one mutant showed evidence of RNA synthesis at the nonpermissive temperature although all the mutants tested caused a marked inhibition of host-cell RNA synthesis. In temperature-shift experiments the mutant-infected cells were held at the permissive temperature for various times before being shifted to the nonpermissive temperature and the yield of infectious virus (at 8 hours) measured in each instance. On the basis of the average duration of the temperature-sensitive period for virus production the mutants were divided into three groups; those with a short ts period; those with a long ts period; and those with a ts period of intermediate duration. The mutants could also be grouped according to the pattern of their uptake of uridine following the shift. This grouping corresponded closely with that based on the duration of the ts period. The authors suggested that in mutants of the first group the genetic defect inhibits an early process that must be completed before RNA synthesis can begin, whereas in mutants of the second group the RNA synthesis, per se, is inhibited, possibly due to the heat lability of the RNA polymerase. The nature of the defect in the third (intermediate) group was not clear.

The isolation and genetic characterization of 105 ts mutants of VSV have been reported by Pringle (1970). The mutagen used was the base analog 5-fluorouracil. Complementation between mutants was found to be efficient and on the basis of complementation tests four groups of mutants were distinguished. Recombination frequencies were also measured. Between mutants of the same group recombination was very low (<0.02%). High values for recombination between representative mutants of different groups were obtained (0.29–2.31%). However, the values were not sufficiently additive to allow the construction of an unambiguous genetic map.

There is some evidence suggesting that the T particle of VSV contains a portion of the B particle genome (Huang and Wagner, 1966; Schaffer *et al.*, 1968). On this hypothesis, Pringle (1970) attempted to demonstrate complementation between B and T particles, but was unsuccessful. His negative result implies that none of the four groups of mutants described is located in the portion of the genome presumed to be present in the T particle.

It is clear that although much work remains to be done, a useful beginning has been made in exploiting ts mutants in the study of the replication of VSV.

III. Rabies Virus

A. *Introduction*

Since a separate chapter on rabies virus appears elsewhere in this volume, this section will be limited to a discussion of the basic characteristics of the rabies virion and its mode of development in host cells as a basis for comparing it with VSV and other members of the group.

Until fairly recently, study of the properties of rabies virus was hampered by the lack of satisfactory techniques for growing the virus *in vitro*. Before the early 1960's, practically nothing was known about the structure of the virus, its basic physicochemical properties, and its relationship to the host cell. However, the problems of growing rabies virus *in vitro* have been satisfactorily overcome (Hummeler and Koprowski,

1969) and the way is now open to investigation of its properties by modern virological techniques.

B. Structure and Mode of Development

The earliest studies by electron microscopy were by Matsumoto (1962) and Almeida *et al.* (1962). The former author examined thin sections of mouse nerve cells infected with street rabies virus, and observed elongated particles of diameter 110–130 mμ associated with a granular matrix in the cytoplasm. The latter group examined negatively stained specimens prepared from hamster kidney cells infected *in vitro* with fixed rabies virus. They observed membrane-bound particles having distinct surface projections but irregular shape. Disrupted particles released a wavy ribbonlike strand consisting of 50 Å subunits. Similar undulating strands were found in negatively stained preparations made from brains of rabies-infected mice (Pinteric *et al.*, 1963). These observations were confirmed and extended by several groups of workers who examined several strains of rabies virus in different cell lines and also in mouse brain (Atanasiu *et al.*, 1963a,b,c; Roots and Schultze, 1963; Matsumoto, 1963; Davies *et al.*, 1963). The results of most of these studies are summarized in the Proceedings of an International Symposium on Rabies held in Talloines, France, in 1965 (Symp. Ser. Immunobiol. Std., Vol. I. Karger, Basel, 1966). It was becoming clear at that time that rabies virus had more in common with VSV than with the myxoviruses, in which group it had been tentatively placed. Its shape and surface features resembled those of VSV, it matured by a similar budding process at the cell surface or cytoplasmic membrane, and the virion, when disintegrated, revealed a ribbonlike strand very similar to the internal component of VSV. There were, however, a number of differences between the two viruses. The rabies virions were often observed in association with a virus-specific cytoplasmic matrix; the internal component was not readily visible in negatively stained particles; and the shape of the virion sometimes departed from that of the standard "bullet," being in some instances bell-shaped and occasionally in the form of a long rod. These and other points relating to the structure and development of rabies virus have been clarified by Hummeler *et al.* (1967) who examined the maturation of virions of two fixed rabies virus strains (Flury and Pittmann-Moore) in baby hamster kidney cells (BHK-21). Exposure of the cells to diethylaminoethyl (DEAE)-dextran at the time of infection was used to enhance the uptake of virus and the viral yield. Matrix formation in the cytoplasm at 8–9 hours after infection was the first effect observed. Somewhat later (24–28 hours) particles identified as viral appeared within and especially at the periphery of the matrices. Budding of virus particles occurred later at the surface of the cell and

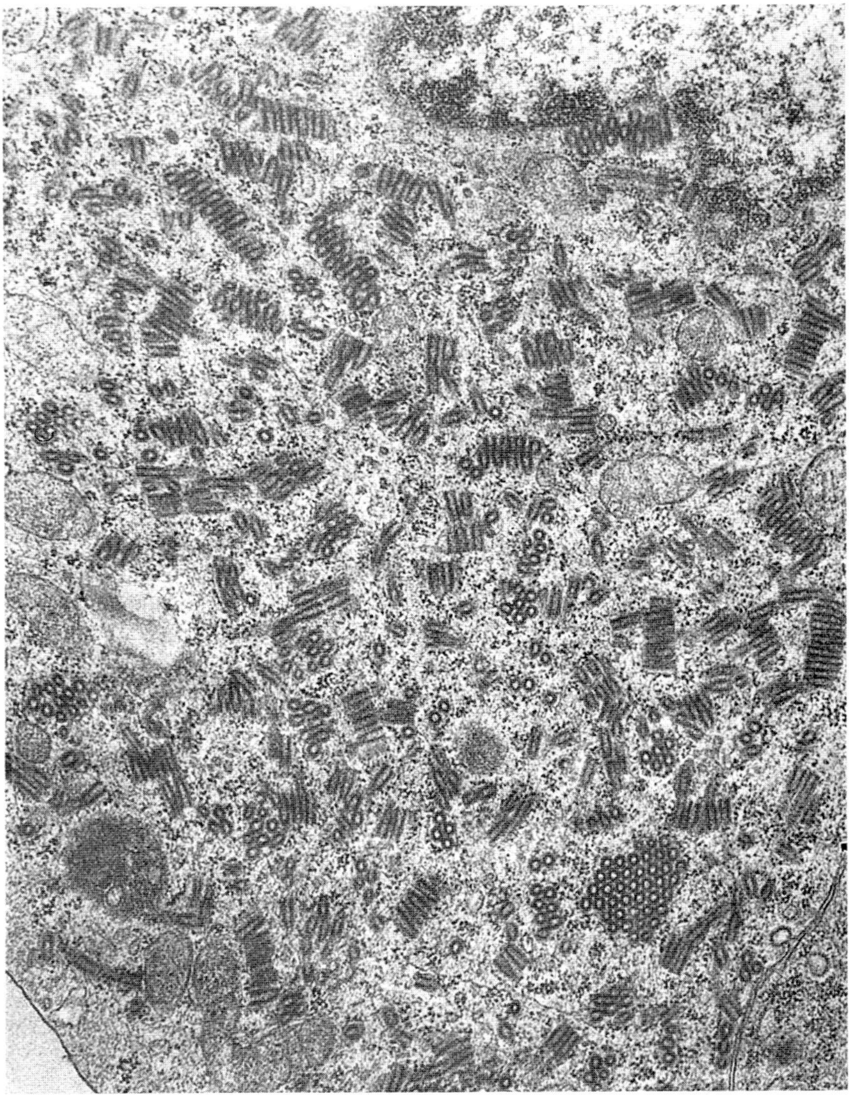

FIG. 6. Thin section of tissue culture cell 7 days after infection with the Flury (HEP) strain of rabies virus. A small portion of nucleus is visible at upper right; the rest of the area shown is cytoplasm. Many virus particles are seen sectioned in various planes; some are in close-packed array. The particles do not appear to be associated with cytoplasmic membranes (Hummeler *et al.*, 1967). Magnification 30,000 ×.

also within vesicles associated with the matrix areas, the mature particles acquiring the envelope from preexisting membranes. With these strains of virus (but not with the CVS strain grown in the same cell line), the authors observed many particles in which the envelope was apparently formed *de novo* within or at the edges of cytoplasmic matrices (Fig. 6). *De novo* synthesis of viral envelopes is not confined to rabies virus; it occurs also in the development of poxviruses (Dales and Siminovitch, 1961), but it has not been described for any other bullet-shaped virus. An interesting feature illustrated by Hummeler *et al.* (1967) and also in a recent paper by Matsumoto and Kawai (1969) is the occurrence of virus particles between the layers of the nuclear membrane. This is the site at which many of the bullet-shaped plant viruses congregate following the maturation process which occurs by budding of the nucleoprotein core from the inner layer of the nuclear membrane. However, in the case of rabies virus there was no evidence of nuclear membrane budding or of any involvement of the nucleus in viral development.

The rabies virus particles were described by Hummeler *et al.* (1967) as being in the form of a cylinder with one rounded end, resembling a bullet. An axial depression or hollow was often present at the flat end. The average dimensions determined both in sections and after negative staining were 180 × 75 mμ. The surface was covered with fine projections which were 60 to 70Å in length and had a knoblike structure at the distal end. In some particles the envelope appeared to be in the form of a regular honeycomb array of hexagonal elements. Short particles, possibly analogous to the T particles of VSV, were found among the viral progeny. Cylindrical particles having the same diameter and surface structure as the "bullet" particles but often of considerably greater length and lacking a rounded end were observed in negative contrast preparations. Corresponding long rods, sometimes partially segmented, were present in sections.

For reasons that are not completely clear, but may be associated with the permeability properties of the envelope, it has proved difficult to demonstrate an internal helix in intact rabies virions, although the nucleoprotein component is readily demonstrable in the form of a loose coil or wavy strand issuing from disintegrating particles. Transverse striations similar to those readily demonstrable in VS virions have, however, been detected, though with difficulty, in intact rabies virions (Atanasiu, personal communication). Hummeler has also recently observed cross-striations in negatively stained virions (Fig. 7). In view of the many similarities that have been observed in the structural and biophysical properties of rabies and VSV it is unlikely that the conformation of the nucleoprotein is different in the two viruses.

A major difference between rabies and VSV, however, is the ability of the former to complete its maturation intracytoplasmically in association with a viral matrix. The matrix-virus complex has been shown by Miyamoto and Matsumoto (1965) to correspond to the classical Negri body of rabies-infected cells. The extent of matrix formation depends on the strain of virus and the host cell type, and appears to be related to the efficiency of coating of the viral nucleoprotein which is present in the matrix. Infection of mouse brain with street virus results in large virus-matrix complexes which are readily detected by light microscopy as typical Negri bodies. Infection with fixed virus results in smaller matrix regions, and greater production of virus by budding, with concomitant cell damage and destruction (Miyamoto and Matsumoto, 1967). In fox salivary gland cells infected with a twice-passaged isolate of street virus,

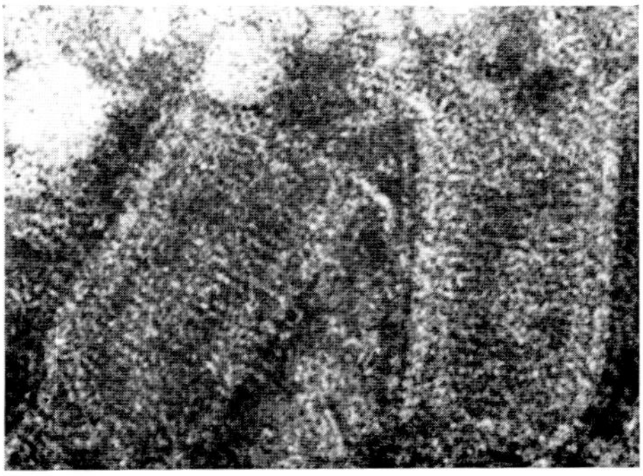

FIG. 7. Rabies virions negatively stained with PTA. Cross-striations and surface projections are similar to those of VSV. Micrograph supplied by K. Hummeler. Magnification 280,000 ×.

Dierks *et al.* (1969) observed massive formation and release of virus particles from marginal membranes of acinar cells in contrast to the exclusively intracytoplasmic maturation which occurred in nerve cells. Thus in salivary gland cells the maturation process of rabies virus resembles very closely that of VSV and other animal viruses of the group. With these viruses, accumulation of viral nucleoprotein in the cytoplasm in large quantities does not usually occur, though substantial aggregates have been observed in cells infected with VSV (Murphy, personal communication) and Egtved virus (Zwillenberg *et al.*, 1965).

C. Physicochemical Properties

Until recently very little was known about the physicochemical properties of rabies virus. From its sensitivity to ether it was deduced that the virus contained lipid and from the failure of DNA inhibitors to prevent viral growth that it was an RNA virus. Direct determination of the physicochemical properties became possible only when techniques were developed for obtaining high concentrations of the virus in purified form (Sokol *et al.*, 1968). Using highly purified viral prepartions, this group studied the properties of the nucleocapsid and nucleic acid of the virus (Sokol *et al.*, 1969). Rabies virions labeled with tritiated uridine were disrupted and the nucleoprotein component released by treating the viral suspension with dilute sodium deoxycholate (DOC). This treatment completely inactivated the virus and decreased the hemagglutinating (HA) activity 100 to 500-fold but did not appreciably alter the complement fixing (CF) activity. The nucleocapsid preparation obtained from the sucrose density gradient was further purified by equilibrium centrifugation in a cesium chloride (CsCl) gradient. The density of the nucleocapsids in CsCl was 1.32 gm/cm^3. After removal of the CsCl by dialysis, 60–75% of the radioactive label present in the original virus preparation was recovered. The nucleocapsids appeared by electron microscopy as loosely coiled or wavy strands similar to those observed in association with disintegrating virions. The lengths of uncoiled strands varied considerably, probably because of breakage during extraction and purification; the longest measured was 3.8 μ. The width varied from 20–65 Å according to the angle of viewing. No infectivity of the nucleocapsids could be demonstrated.

It was shown by chemical analysis that the nucleocapsids contained RNA, the ratio of RNA to protein being about 1:25. Most of the RNA extracted from purified virus or from nucleocapsids sedimented in a sharp peak with a sedimentation coefficient of 45 S. The origin of a small peak at 28 S, whether cellular or viral, was not determined. The viral RNA was deduced to be single-stranded from its sensitivity to degradation by ribonuclease and its density in cesium sulfate solution (1.66 gm/cm^3); the calculated molecular weight of the RNA was 4.6×10^6 daltons.

D. Hemagglutination and Complement Fixation

The presence of a hemagglutinin of rabies virus was demonstrated by Halonen *et al.* (1968). The optimum conditions for demonstrating hemagglutinin included low temperature, pH 6.2, and the use of goose erythrocytes. The same methods were successful in demonstrating hemagglutinin of VSV (Indiana, New Jersey, and Cocal strains) and Kern Canyon viruses. The hemagglutinating activity was associated with intact virions, there being no evidence of a "soluble" hemagglutinin (Murphy *et al.*, 1968; Sokol *et al.*, 1969). Complement fixing activity was associated with nucleocapsid fractions as well as with whole virions.

IV. Other Vertebrate Viruses

A. Salmonid Viruses

1. Egtved Virus

The rainbow trout (*Salmo gairdneri*), although native to North America, is now widely distributed throughout the world. In Europe, rainbow trout (and to a lesser extent other salmonids) are subject to a serious disease first described by Schäperclaus (1954) under the name "Nierenschwellung," later changed to "Infektiöse Nierenschwellung und Leberdegeneration." Schäperclaus showed that the disease was transmissible from fish to fish by bacteria-free filtrates and concluded that the causative agent was viral. Other workers confirmed his findings and conclusions (Ghittino, 1962; Jensen, 1963; Rasmussen, 1965).

In 1950 the disease was recognized in Denmark near the village of Egtved and the name Egtved virus was proposed by Jensen for the causative agent. At a symposium on fish disease held in Turin in 1962, it was agreed that the disease itself should be named viral hemorrhagic septicemia.

Jensen (1963) showed that the virus could be propagated *in vitro* on primary cultures prepared from immature rainbow trout ovaries and on a permanent cell line RTG-2 established by Wolf and Quimby (1962). Shortly afterward, Jensen collaborated with L. O. Zwillenberg and H. H. L. Zwillenberg (Zwillenberg *et al.*, 1965) in an electron microscopic investigation of Egtved virus isolated in RTG-2 cells from several independent outbreaks of viral hemorrhagic septicemia of rainbow trout. The virus was clearly shown to be morphologically very similar to vesicular stomatitis virus and to mature by a similar process at the cell surface. The particles were described as cylindrical and of average diameter 60 mμ in sections and 70 mμ in negatively stained specimens. The average length was 180 mμ by both techniques. The particles had a round end and a flat end to which, in some instances, a taillike appendage was attached. Around the axis of the particles there was a "ribbed sheath" of diameter about 50 mμ consisting of a series of striations about 30 Å in thickness and 55 Å apart. This was surrounded by an outer coat about 15 mμ thick. In these studies the authors did not detect surface projections but later they observed fine projections on Egtved virus particles (Zwillenberg *et al.*, 1968). The central region or core of Egtved particles usually appeared in cross sections as a dense circle or ring. This feature is not usually seen in sectioned VSV though examples of particles showing a central density are sometimes encountered. The overall picture is one of striking resemblance between Egtved virus and VSV.

An interesting feature of RTG-2 cells infected with Egtved virus was the presence of cytoplasmic inclusion bodies containing helices of diameter about 20 mμ (Zwillenberg *et al.*, 1965). The authors regarded the helices as probably the viral nucleocapsids which formed the internal striated component of the mature particle.

2. Other Salmonid Viruses

Diseases of fish attributed to viruses have been reviewed by Wolf (1966). Of these viruses, three causing hematopoietic necrosis in salmonid fishes, infectious hematopoietic necrosis (IHN), Oregon sockeye disease (OSD), and Sacramento River Chinook salmon disease (SRCD) have recently been studied by electron microscopy (Amend and Chambers, 1970). They were shown to be bullet-shaped and to bud from cytoplasmic membranes. The IHN virus was 90 mμ wide and 158 mμ long. It consisted of a core 60 mμ in diameter and a coat 15 mμ thick and had an axial channel 20 mμ in diameter. The other two viruses were morphologically indistinguishable from IHN virus. McCain (1970) examined the antigenic relationship between OSD, IHN, and SRCD viruses and showed that all three were related, OSD and IHN viruses being indistinguishable. McCain determined the base composition of nucleic acid extracted from OSD virus and showed that it contained single-stranded RNA.

From these studies, it can be concluded that these salmonid viruses are rhabdoviruses but their relationship to one another and to Egtved virus requires further clarification.

B. Flanders-Hart Park Virus

A virus isolated from mosquitoes and birds in New York State and called Flanders virus (Whitney, 1964) was shown to be related serologically to other strains of virus isolated in, among other places, Hart Park, California. The agent which has subsequently been isolated many times, especially from mosquitoes, is generally referred to as Flanders-Hart Park Virus (Murphy *et al.*, 1966). Murphy and his collaborators were the first to examine the morphology of the virus particles in infected mouse brain and found that they were similar to vesicular stomatitis virus. In sections of mouse brain, clusters of bullet-shaped particles were observed in intercellular spaces in association with cell membranes. The mean diameter of the particles was 65 mμ; the lengths varied considerably, the mean being 218 mμ. Similar particles of dimensions 209 × 65 mμ were found in specimens made by negatively staining a mouse brain suspension.

The serological relationship of the Flanders and Hart Park isolates was confirmed by Murphy and Fields (1967) who also showed that the virus does not cross-react with VSV and other bullet-shaped animal viruses (Tables III and IV).

Jensen *et al.* (1967) examined and compared by light and electron microscopy brain tissue of new-born mice inoculated intracranially with Flanders-Hart Park and rabies viruses. They observed both types of virus budding at cell membranes of neurons and glial cells and forming bullet-shaped particles. However, the typical cytoplasmic matrices present in rabies-infected cells were absent in cells infected with Flanders-

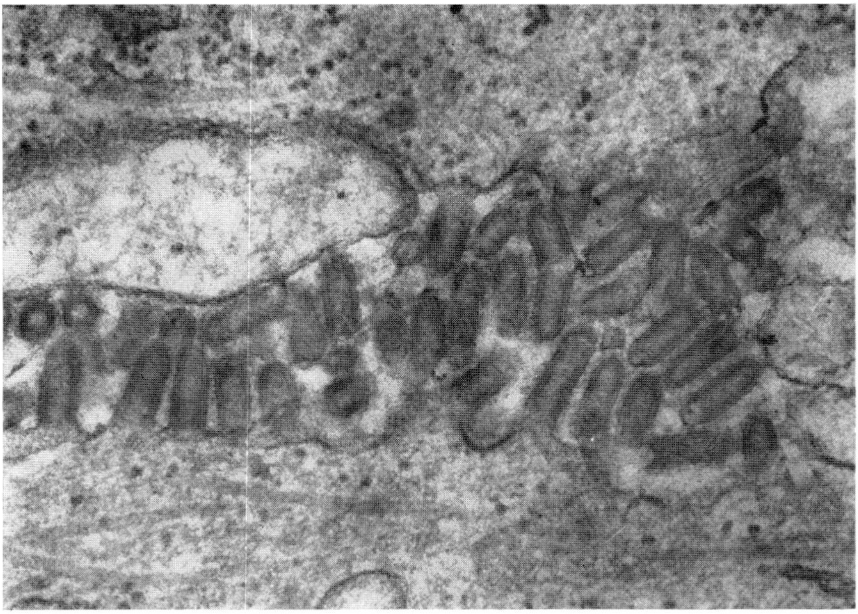

FIG. 8. Cell of mouse brain infected with Kern Canyon virus, showing maturation of virus by budding process at marginal cytoplasmic membranes (Murphy and Fields, 1967). Magnification 65,000 ×.

Hart Park virus. In this study, the latter virus was described as being in the shape of a bullet of diameter 60 mμ and of variable length.

C. Kern Canyon Virus (KCV)

Kern Canyon virus was isolated from bats (*Myotis yumanensis*) collected in Kern County, California (Johnson, 1965), and was found to be unrelated serologically to other viruses isolated in the area. Murphy and Fields (1967) examined the structure of the virus propagated in suckling mouse brain and in cultures of baby hamster kidney (BHK-21) cells and found that it was similar to that of VSV. This morphological resemblance prompted them to investigate the serological relationship of the virus to other members of the rhabdovirus group. Complement fixation, virus neutralization, and immunodiffusion tests all confirmed the distinct antigenicity of Kern Canyon virus (see Tables III and IV).

The structural details of the virus were shown best in negatively stained preparations of infected brain tissue. Large numbers of bullet-shaped particles were observed, many showing internal detail in the form of cross-striations of spacing 50 Å and a prominent axial channel. The surface of many particles was covered with projections 8 mμ long and many showed a trailing filament or bleb usually at the flat end. The average diameter of the particles was 73 mμ (excluding surface projections); the lengths were somewhat variable, the mean being 132 mμ. Very long particles and particles with two rounded ends were occasionally seen.

In sections of infected suckling mouse brain, particles were seen budding from plasma membranes and many groups of mature particles were observed in intercellular spaces (Fig. 8). Cross-striation and axial channels were visible in some particles. Similar observations were made in sections of infected BHK-21 cells. Numerous particles were observed in intercellular spaces and budding from plasma membranes but not from other cytoplasmic membranes. No indication of the presence of a matrix similar to that typical of rabies virus infection of mouse brain was detected in KCV infection. The authors commented on the ease of demonstrating cross-striations in KCV particles which appear to be readily penetrated by the negative stain, especially in comparison with rabies virus which is refractory to the same treatment.

D. Mount Elgon Bat Virus (MEBV)

This virus was isolated in Kenya from an insectivorous bat (Metsalaar *et al.*, 1969). The virus was shown to be capable of multiplying in new-born mice and also in *Aedis aegypti* mosquitoes; it was ether-sensitive and unaffected by rabies virus antiserum; it showed no antigenic relationship by complement fixation test to any virus known to occur in Africa and was provisionally classed as a new arbovirus (Metsalaar *et al.*, 1969).

Examination of infected mouse brain tissue by electron microscopy (Murphy *et al.*, 1970) showed that the virus was structurally similar to the rhabdoviruses. In negatively stained specimens prepared from an infected brain tissue suspension, bullet-shaped particles were found in small numbers in varying stages of preservation. Many particles were penetrated by the stain, revealing cross-striations of spacing 50 Å and, in some cases, axial channels. Surface projections 8–10 mμ long were observed on intact particles. The diameter was 70 mμ and the length approximately 230 mμ. The particles were described as having a surface membrane (with projections) surrounding a helically wound bullet-shaped core of diameter 44–50 mμ. In some disintegrating particles the core helix uncoiled in the form of a convoluted ribbon of width about 100 Å which often reformed as a helix of about half the diameter of the intact core in a fashion very similar to that observed with VSV (Nakai and Howatson, 1968). In addition to bullet-shaped particles, truncated forms analogous to the T particles of VSV were observed in moderate numbers.

In thin sections of infected mouse brain, virus particles were found in extracellular spaces and in the process of budding from plasma membranes. No budding from intracytoplasmic membranes was observed. During the budding process the viral envelope showed continuity with the cell membrane. In the cytoplasm at the base of budding particles there was in some instances a finely granular or filamentous matrix which was thought to be analogous to the matrix regions found in rabies-infected cells and to represent accumulations of viral nucleoprotein. The structure of the particles seen in sections was in agreement with that seen by negative staining. The average measured dimensions of longitudinally sectional particles were 226 × 68 mμ.

Complement fixation, neutralization, and immunodiffusion tests failed to detect any cross-reaction between MEB virus and other bullet-shaped animal viruses (Tables III and IV) and consequently MEB virus was considered to be an antigenically distinct member of the rhabdovirus group (Murphy *et al.*, 1970).

E. Bovine Ephemeral (or Epizootic) Fever Virus (EFV)

Strains of this virus have been isolated from cattle showing ephemeral fever syndrome in outbreaks occurring in Australia, South Africa, and Japan, and have been adapted to grow in mice and in BHK-21 cells (Holmes and Doherty, 1970). The Australian and South African isolates are serologically related but comparisons with the Japanese isolates have not been carried out. In three separate electron microscope studies of cells infected with EFV, particles having some of the characteristics of rhabdoviruses were detected. Ito *et al.* (1969) examined thin sections of infected BHK-21 cells and also examined virus preparations by negative staining. They observed bullet-shaped particles of mean length 140 mμ and diameter 80 mμ. Axial channels and surface projections were present but cross-striations could not be detected. Virus maturation occurred by budding from marginal membranes and from membranes of cytoplasmic vesicles. Lecatsas *et al.* (1969) also examined thin sections of infected

BHK-21 cells and observed budding from the cell surface and cytoplasmic vacuoles. During this process the core of the particle which, in some instances, appeared to form in the ground cytoplasm, acquired an enveloping membrane. The particles observed by these authors were not rod- or bullet-shaped but in the form of a cone of height 176 mμ and base diameter 88 mμ. Regular serrations were seen along the edge of the dense conical core or shell of the particles and were interpreted as rings of a spiral. The pitch of the spiral was 16.6 mμ. From this measurement and the dimensions of the cone it was deduced that the spiral had about 10 turns and a total length of approximately 2.2 μ.

Holmes and Doherty (1970), using Australian isolates of the virus, examined thin sections of infected mouse brain. They observed particles, 70 × 145 mμ, which were described as bullet-shaped but tapering slightly toward the round end. The viral envelope enclosed a dense shell of thickness about 12 mμ, but no internal striations could be detected. Most of the particles were extruded from marginal membranes of neurons but some particles of one strain appeared to form intracytoplasmically.

The EFV particles possess many of the characteristics of rhabdoviruses including elongated shape, formation by budding, ether sensitivity, and RNA genome (Lecatsas *et al.*, 1969). There are, however, significant structural differences that raise some question about the inclusion of EFV in the rhabdovirus group. The conical shape illustrated by Lecatsas *et al.* (1969) is unique. In the strain used by Holmes and Doherty (1970), however, only slight tapering was observed and Ito *et al.* (1969) did not mention any departure from the bullet shape in their strain. All three groups, however, comment on the unusual configuration of the inner, presumably nucleoprotein, shell which appears to be structurally different from the inner component of other rhabdoviruses. Pending further elucidation of the structural and other properties of EFV, it has been included here provisionally as a member of the rhabdovirus group.

F. Piry and Chandipura Viruses

These two viruses, the first isolated from an opossum in Belem, Brazil (Murphy and Shope, personal communication), the second from human serum in India (Bhatt and Rodriques, 1967), have recently been shown (Shope and Murphy, 1970) to have a VSV-like morphology and to form by a budding process at cell membranes. The observed dimensions of the particles were 188 × 73 mμ (Piry) and 180 × 71 mμ (Chandipura). Neutralization tests showed considerable cross-reaction between the two viruses and less cross-reaction between each virus and three strains of VSV (Table III). No cross-reaction with other vertebrate rhabdoviruses was detected. Complement fixation tests showed evidence of slight cross-

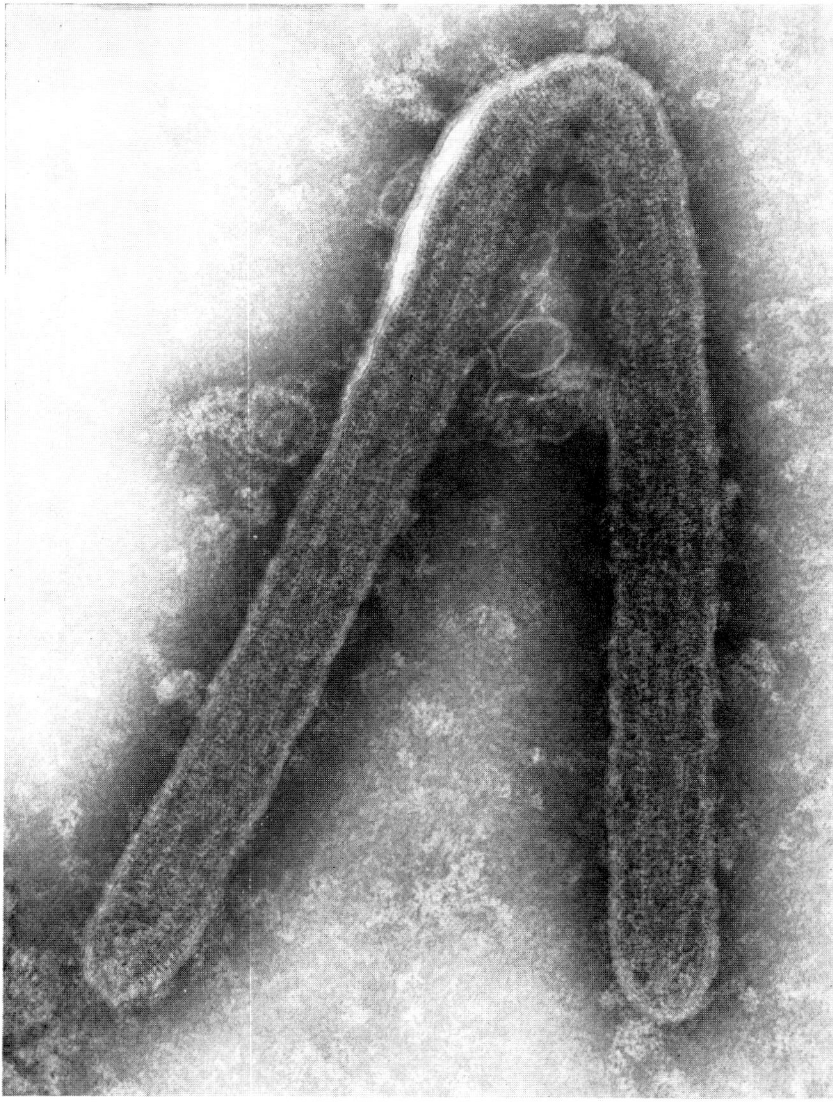

FIG. 9. Negatively stained Marburg virus preparation. The particles have some of the characteristics of rhabdoviruses but are of extreme and variable length. Micrograph supplied by F. Murphy. Magnification 190,000 ×.

reaction between the two viruses but no cross-reaction between either Piry or Chandipura virus and the other viruses tested (Table IV).

G. Recently Characterized Viruses

The number of candidates for inclusion in the rhabdovirus genus continues to increase at a rapid rate. Two further viruses of vertebrate source that have recently been shown to have rhabdovirus characteristics have been brought to the writer's attention (Murphy, personal communication). These are the Lagos (bat) virus isolated by Boulger and Porterfield (1958) and an unnamed virus denoted M-1056 isolated by Harald Johnson from a microtus rodent (Murphy and Shope, personal communication). Both of these viruses have a typical bullet shape and form by a budding process similar to that of VSV. They mature within neurons of mouse brain in association with a matrix, very much like rabies virus. The relationship of Lagos bat virus to rabies virus is under investigation. M-1056 is unrelated to any other rhabdovirus.

H. Marburg Virus

In the fall of 1967 illness and some deaths occurred in Germany and Yugoslavia among laboratory workers who had been handling tissues of African green monkeys. The disease was traced to a previously unknown agent which had many of the characteristics of a virus (Siegert *et al.*, 1968), and is now generally referred to as Marburg virus. The infection could be transmitted to guinea pigs and monkeys which succumbed within a few days. The virus could also be propagated in cultures of green monkey (VERO) cells and BHK-21 cells (Kissling *et al.*, 1968).

Electron microscopy of blood and liver tissue from infected guinea pigs and blood from sick monkeys revealed the presence of long cylindrical structures often bent in horseshoe shape (Siegert *et al.*, 1968). The cylinders consisted of a membranous coat surrounding an inner structure about 65 mμ in diameter which appeared as a series of cross-striations of spacing 62 Å and was probably in the form of a helix. The overall diameter was about 100 mμ and the length, which was very variable, averaged about 1 μ.

Kissling *et al.* (1968) observed similar structures in specimens obtained from infected BHK-21 cell cultures (Fig. 9). The dimensions measured by these authors were as follows. The cylinder diameter was uniform (90–100 mμ) but the length was variable (130 mμ to more than 2600 mμ). Both ends were usually rounded though frequently a blob of membranous material was attached at one end. The diameter of the striated core was 45 mμ and the striation spacing 5 mμ. Similar particles were observed in thin sections of infected guinea pig liver. Evidence of budding of particles from cytoplasmic membranes was obtained, though it was rather rare.

Peters and Müller (1969) also observed particles and budding processes in sections of livers of infected guinea pigs and monkeys, and also of VERO cells. In addition they observed intracytoplasmic inclusions which were shown by parallel light and electron microscopic studies to have staining properties similar to those of the Negri bodies of rabies-infected cells.

The agent of the disease was shown to be sensitive to ether and to heat, and its growth in BHK-21 cells was not inhibited by 5-bromodeoxyuridine, suggesting that the genetic material was RNA (Kissling *et al.*, 1968). These characteristics, together with its morphological features, indicate that the agent has much in common with the rhabdoviruses. However, the extreme length of many particles and the absence of any well-defined length distinguish the Marburg agent from all other animal viruses. The situation is complicated by the finding of Almeida *et al.* (1969) of long tubular structures resembling the Marburg particles in association with cultures of *Leptospira*. The origin and nature of these structures is not known but it seems most likely to the writer that they were formed during the preparation of the negatively stained specimen by a rearrangement or "crystallization" of the material in the leptospiral sheath. Somewhat similar structures have been seen in negatively stained preparations of *Bacillus subtilis* (Howatson and Russell, 1964).

Although Marburg Virus has been included in the rhabdovirus group by some authors (Maass, 1969; Peters and Müller, 1969), it would seem best to the writer, in view of the problems discussed above, to exclude it from the group until more information on its properties is available.

V. Insect and Plant Viruses

A. *Sigma Virus*

1. *Discovery*

The curious phenomenon of the sensitivity to carbon dioxide of a proportion of the population of a laboratory strain of *Drosophila* was discovered by L'Héritier and Teissier (1937). Several reviews on the subject have since appeared (L'Héritier, 1948, 1957, 1958; Seecof, 1968) and consequently only a brief account of the history of the discovery and earlier investigations of the phenomenon will be given here.

If *Drosophila* are placed in an atmosphere of carbon dioxide, narcosis occurs almost immediately. The effect continues as long as the insects are exposed to the carbon dioxide, but when they are returned to normal air, most of the flies rapidly awake and recover completely. Such flies are called CO_2-resistant. Other flies are sensitive to CO_2; when the CO_2

is removed they wake up from the narcosis but remain paralyzed and die a few hours later. Sensitive flies are present in natural populations of *Drosophila* as well as in laboratory strains. Sensitivity to the effects of CO_2 was shown to be heritable but not subject to Mendelian laws. At first the phenomenon was thought to be an example of cytoplasmic inheritance but later it became clear that the responsible agent was viral in nature (L'Héritier and Hugon de Scoeux, 1947; Plus, 1950). It was shown that an infectious agent could be extracted from sensitive flies that on injection into virus-free (resistant) *Drosophila* caused no apparent disease but brought about the development of CO_2 sensitivity. The agent went through a multiplication cycle characteristic of viral multiplication and was of a size consistent with its being a virus. L'Héritier (1954) gave it the name sigma (σ) virus.

2. Transmission

Sigma virus can be introduced into *Drosophila* in two different ways, artificially by inoculation, or naturally by hereditary transmission. In either case, the virus produces no noticeable effect in the flies, other than sensitivity to CO_2.* Sensitivity is of two different kinds termed stabilized and nonstabilized, the basis for the difference being in the relationship of the virus to the *Drosophila* cells. In a stabilized female *Drosophila*, the virus is integrated in some way with the host cells and is transmitted to the descendants which are all stabilized sensitives. Descendants of stabilized males, however, are of the nonstabilized type. Infectious virus extractable from stabilized flies and responsible for their CO_2 sensitivity plays no part in the transmission process. In nonstabilized *Drosophila* which includes all flies made sensitive by inoculation, the hereditary transmission of the virus is dependent on multiplication of the virus and subsequent infection of female germ cells. The rate of virus multiplication and the final virus yield are always greater in nonstabilized than in stabilized *Drosophila*. Thus the hereditary transmission of σ virus is very different according to whether or not the virus is integrated with the host cells. For further details of the rather complex relations involved in the transmission of σ virus the reader is referred to the review article by L'Héritier (1958) and to more recent articles by L'Héritier (1962), Ohanessian-Guillemain (1963), and de Lestrange (1963).

3. Assay

The titer of virus preparations can be determined by the limiting dilution method in *Drosophila*. When resistant flies are inoculated with an

* Slight deleterious effects on the fertility of infected females and on the survival of their progeny have been reported by Seecof (1964) and Jupin *et al.* (1968).

infectious extract the virus multiplies and symptoms of CO_2 sensitivity appear after, at most, 30 days. Batches of flies injected at increasing dilutions are tested for CO_2 sensitivity at 25 to 30 days after inoculation. At the limiting dilution not all flies in the batch give a positive result. An alternative method is to determine by daily testing the time after inoculation at which CO_2 sensitivity appears. It has been shown (Plus, 1954) that there is a linear relationship between the time interval from inoculation to onset of sensitivity and the logarithm of the number of infectious units, from a plot of which the infectious titer can be obtained.

4. Propagation in Vitro

Multiplication of σ virus in embryonic *Drosophila* cells cultivated *in vitro* has been described by Ohanessian and Echalier (1967). The embryonic cells, maintained in a medium simulating *Drosophila* hemolymph with the addition of 10% fetal calf serum, were subcultured in microdrops under paraffin oil. A suspension of virus, obtained by crushing infected flies in the culture medium, centrifuging, and filtering through 0.45 μ Millipore filters, was applied to the cultures which were maintained at 26°C with change of medium every 3 or 4 days. The viral content of the supernatant medium was assayed for several weeks. Regular virus production without any cytopathic effect was demonstrated. In one instance with an initial inoculum of 4×10^3 infectious units, the total virus collected after 2 months was 6×10^5 units.

5. Structure

The first indication that σ virus is similar to vesicular stomatitis virus came from electron microscopic studies. Berkaloff *et al.* (1965) examined thin sections of ovarian cysts of stabilized *Drosophila* and observed structures that were not present in similar preparations of virus-free *Drosophila.* The structures were described as having in longitudinal section the appearance of a "doigt de gant" and were shown to form by a budding process at a cell membrane. Their clear resemblance to vesicular stomatitis virus was confirmed by examination of negatively stained preparations in which regular cross-striations and surface projections were revealed. The particle dimensions were approximately 140×70 mμ. The authors did not give the striation spacing but it is clear from their illustrations that it is close to that of VSV.

These observations were confirmed and extended by Teninges (1968) who examined sections of testes from sensitive, stabilized *Drosophila.* Rod-shaped particles were observed budding from early spermatids but not from somatic cells (Fig. 10). The particle diameter was 70 mμ, the same as that recorded by Berkaloff *et al.* (1965), but the average length was somewhat greater, 180 mμ. A few particles were as long as 210 mμ. An interesting observation was the presence of what appeared to be viral matrix regions or viroplasm in the cytoplasm of infected cells. Dense material but no complete virions was present in these regions.

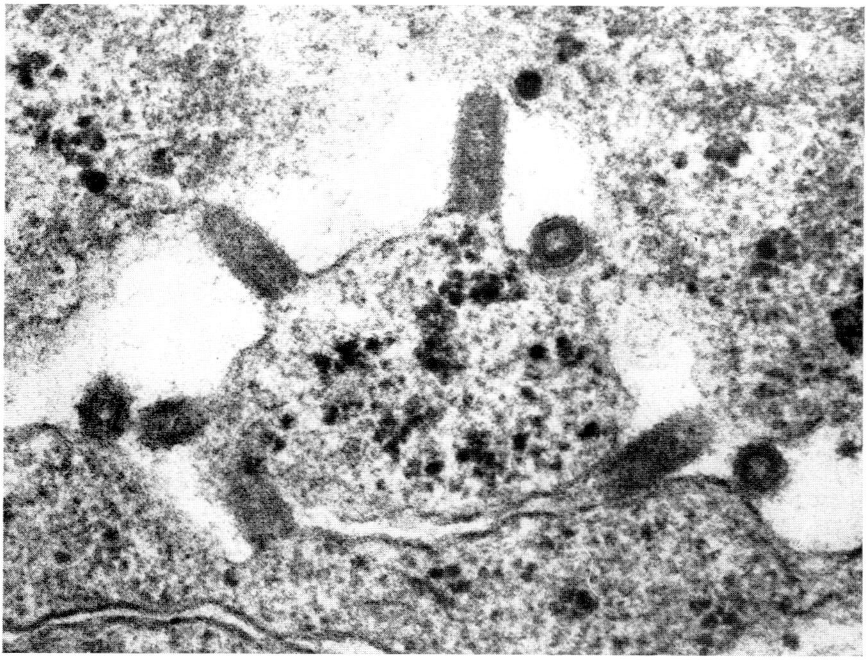

FIG. 10. Sigma virus particles budding from germinal cell of infected *Drosophila*. Micrograph by D. Teninges, supplied by A. Berkaloff. Magnification 110,000 ×.

6. Sigma Virus and VSV

The strong resemblance of sigma virus to VSV led to attempts to propagate VSV in *Drosophila* (Périès *et al.*, 1966). Multiplication of the virus (VSV, Indiana) in the insect was shown to occur in the first passage without producing any obvious pathological effects. After continued passage of VSV in *Drosophila,* however, there arose a variant, termed VSV_D, which conferred on the insects a sensitivity to CO_2 similar to that produced by σ virus. A minor difference was that although in some insects the VSV-induced sensitivity was immediate, as with σ, in others it was delayed, the insects recovering from the narcosis but dying within 24 hours. No sensitizing effect was observed with Sindbis virus which also multiplies readily in *Drosophila* (Herreng, 1967). These observations on VSV_D are of considerable interest in connection with the relationship between sigma virus and VSV since they indicate that the resemblance between the viruses is more than purely morphological.

The *Drosophila*-adapted strain of VSV reaches maximum titers of 10^6–10^7 infectious units per *Drosophila,* measured by the end point method, about 4 days after injection (Printz, 1969). The titer falls off slowly thereafter until the death of the insect. VSV_D has a more marked pathological effect on *Drosophila* than σ virus. It not only reduces the fertility of females but also markedly decreases the longevity of the flies. The adapted strain of VSV remains infectious for chick fibroblast cells but shows evidence of being temperature sensitive. Plaques are smaller and titers are lower by a factor of about 100 at 37° compared with 27°C. The plaque titer, even at the latter temperature is lower by a factor of ten than the infectious-unit titer measured in *Drosophila.*

No definite information has been obtained about the type of nucleic acid in σ virus but there is some suggestive evidence that it is RNA as would be expected from its close similarity to VSV and rabies viruses (Herforth, 1968).

B. Maize Mosaic Virus

Herold *et al.* (1960) undertook an electron microscopic investigation of sections of leaves of corn plants (*Zea mays L.*) infected with a virus-induced mosaic disease and discovered in infected cells numerous particles having a structure unlike that of any known plant virus. The particles were present in regular arrays, usually around the nucleus, and were rod-shaped, of average length 242 mμ and diameter 48 mμ. They were described as having two limiting membranes and a dense rod-shaped core in the center. Preparations obtained from the sap of diseased plants by differential centrifugation and also by treatment with fluorocarbon were examined after negative staining and metal shadowing. The specimens contained numerous particles having the same structure as those observed in sections. Since similar particles were never seen in uninfected materials the authors concluded that in all probability the rodlike particles represented the viral agent of the disease. Later the disease was correlated with maize mosaic virus I which is transmitted by the leaf hopper *Peregrinus maidis* (Ashm).

At the time these observations were made the structure of VSV and other similar animal viruses was not known in detail but it is now clear that the virus described by Herold *et al.* is structurally similar to VSV. Maize mosaic virus I was, in fact, the first of what is now a long list of plant viruses that are known to have structural characteristics similar to those of VSV and related animal viruses. In a subsequent report, Herold and Munz (1965) described an electron microscopic investigation of tissues from the leaf hopper vector of maize mosaic virus I. The insects were fed on infected corn plants, transferred for 10–12 days to healthy corn plants and finally transferred individually to healthy plants to determine which insects were able to transfer infectivity to healthy plants. The authors observed within cells of salivary glands and intestines of infective insects, but not in noninfective insects or insects reared on healthy plants, numerous rod-shaped particles similar to those seen in sections of infected plants. The particles were present within cytoplasmic cisternae and in the perinuclear space between the layers of the nuclear membrane. The authors assumed that the particles formed in association with membranes of the endoplasmic reticulum and nucleus but did not observe continuity of the viral envelope and these membranes. Some of their pictures, however, suggest that the particles may be budding from the inner layer of the nuclear membrane by a process that has since been clearly illustrated for other similar plant viruses.

A more detailed morphological study by negative staining and thin-sectioning methods was later made by Herold and Munz (1967). They observed bullet-shaped particles that measured 255 × 90 mμ in phosphotungstic acid (Pta) preparations and 241 mμ × 73 mμ in uranyl acetate (Uac) preparations. They also observed bacilliform particles of similar dimensions. The particles had an outer coat or envelope covered with fine projections 7 mμ long and an inner helical structure having about 40 turns separated by approximately 52 Å. This structure was thought to be the nucleocapsid of the virus. Similar features were observed in particles embedded and sectioned, though the dimensions were smaller, probably due to shrinkage of the embedded particles and flattening of negatively stained ones.

C. Lettuce Necrotic Yellows Virus (LNYV)

1. Structure

A disease of lettuce of some importance in Australia was shown by Stubbs and Grogan (1963) to be caused by a virus transmitted by aphids (*Hyperomyzus lactucae* L.). The virus is named after the disease it causes—lettuce necrotic yellows virus (LNYV). Stubbs and Grogan showed that the virus could readily be transmitted to lettuce plants and to several other plant species by manual inoculation of leaf sap.

Crowley *et al.* (1965) described a method for partially purifying the virus from infected leaf extracts. The properties of the purified virus were examined by Harrison and Crowley (1965). Among the techniques used was electron microscopic examination of purified preparations after negative staining with uranyl acetate (UAc). This revealed numerous bacilliform and bullet-shaped particles bearing a striking resemblance to vesicular stomatitis virions. The particles had about the same diameter as VSV (65–70 mμ) but were somewhat longer, the length of the majority of the particles being in the range 200–245 mμ. Particles penetrated by the stain showed an axial canal and cross-striations separated by 4.5 mμ. Other particles were not penetrated by the stain and showed only surface features similar to those of VSV. A third type of particle, roughly spherical, was thought to be a distorted form of the bacilliform particle. In later studies of the structure of LNYV, Wolanski *et al.* (1967) used both PTA and UAc and showed that, as in VSV, the striated component was in the form of a helix that was sometimes released from the particles in the form of a loose coil. They also noted that the envelope of the particles was covered with projections about 6 mμ long and 6 mμ apart. These authors concluded that various forms of damage were suffered by the particles during purification and specimen preparation. Bacilliform particles showing internal structure were regarded as the least damaged structurally, only the permeability of the envelope to the stain being affected. The bullet-shaped particles were thought to result from loss of part of the internal component from one end, with invagination of the envelope into the central canal. Particles with "tails" and pleomorphic forms were believed to result from more extensive damage.

Chambers *et al.* (1965) described an electron microscopic investigation of sections of LNYV-infected leaves of lettuce (*Lactuca sativa* L.) and *Nicotiana glutinosa* L. They observed in infected cells of both species, aggregates of rod-shaped particles within membranous vesicles. In a few instances they observed continuity between the envelope of the particle and the membrane of the vesicle. In lettuce cells the particles were very regularly arranged. Large crystalline inclusions were commonly seen in infected cells but these apparently were not viral-specific as they were present also in healthy plants. In sections of *Nicotiana* plants the particles were 52 mμ in diameter and of somewhat variable length, some being longer than 700 mμ. In lettuce the particles were much more uniform in length, the majority being between 340 and 380 mμ; the mean diameter was 44 mμ. The authors attributed the difference in diameter between sectioned and negatively stained particles to flattening of the latter during drying, but were unable to explain the difference in length. Virus particles were observed only in the cytoplasm, though many of them were situated close to the nucleus.

2. Other Properties

In addition to their structural studies, Harrison and Crowley (1965) examined other physical and biological properties of LNYV. They showed that the virus is less stable in organic solvents than most plant viruses, being rapidly inactivated by treatment with chloroform and diethyl ether. The susceptibility is no doubt related to its possession of membranous, presumably lipoprotein, envelope. Attempts to obtain infectious nucleic acid by treating infected leaves or partially purified virus with water-saturated phenol were unsuccessful. Harrison and Crowley further showed that different isolates of LNYV from widely separated regions of Australia were antigenically related. The buoyant density of the single viral component obtained after centrifugation in sucrose was 1.19–1.20 gm/cm^3 and the sedimentation coefficient was 943 $\pm$ 10 S. VSV has the same density, but in line with its shorter length the sedimentation coefficient of the particle is smaller, 625 S (Bradish *et al.*, 1956).

3. Insect Vector

O'Loughlin and Chambers (1967) were able to demonstrate by electron microscopy the presence of LNYV particles in tissues of the aphid vector *Hyperomyzus lactucae* L. which had acquired the virus by feeding on infected plants. Two types of rod-shaped particles were found within cells of numerous organs of the insects. One type appeared identical to that observed in infected plant tissues, the other was smaller in diameter (32–35 mμ compared with 48 mμ), and appeared to consist of the former type minus the coat or envelope. Both types of particles were present in the cytoplasm. A group of coated particles was observed between the layers of the nuclear membrane but no evidence of budding or conversion of one type of particle to the other was obtained. However, the smaller particles showed distinct cross-striations of spacing 4.5 mμ, similar to those observed in the internal component of LNYV, lending support to the interpretation that they were in fact the inner component of the larger particle. Although direct evidence of the replication and maturation of the virus in the insect host was not obtained, the large numbers of particles forming aggregates in cells of many organs of the aphids was a strong indication that viral multiplication occurred within the insect host.

D. Gomphrena Virus (GV)

A virus inducing local lesions similar to those produced by LNYV in globe amaranth (*Gomphrena globulosa* L.) and other host plants was isolated in Brazil by Kitajima and Costa (1966) and named *Gomphrena* virus. The morphology and mode of development of the virus were investigated by electron microscopy of thin sections and negatively stained preparations. In negatively stained dip preparations made from various infected host plants, bacilliform and bullet-shaped particles were consistently found. These were 220–260 mμ in length and 80–100 mμ in diameter and had an outer coat of thickness 8–10 mμ studded with projections 6–7 mμ long. Particles penetrated by the stain revealed a tubular core 60–70 mμ in diameter with an axial channel 35–40 mμ wide. The core consisted of 80–90 "light and dark bands" each 2.6 mμ wide. These appear from the illustrations to be identical to the cross-striations that have been described in other similar viruses. From the dimensions given by the authors the striation spacing is 5.2 mμ.

Electron microscopy of thin sections of infected cells revealed large perinuclear aggregates of bacilliform particles. These were visible by light microscopy as dense, apparently intranuclear inclusions, but electron microscopy showed that they were in fact situated outside the nucleus in distended regions between the outer and inner layers of the nuclear membrane. Less commonly, particles were observed also within cisternae of the endoplasmic reticulum. In longitudinal section the particles were mostly 230–250 mμ long, though occasionally longer particles were observed. In cross section the particles were ringlike, consisting of an outer dense layer 7–10 mμ in thickness and an inner core 35–40 mμ in diameter, separated from the outer layer by a clear zone 10 mμ wide. The overall diameter was 75 mμ.

Clear evidence of the involvement of the nucleus in the morphogenesis of the virus particles was described by these authors. They noted changes in the nuclei of infected cells, the most conspicuous being reduction or disappearance of chromatin and an increase in the size of the nucleolus which was usually vacuolated. Within the nucleus and often in close association with the nucleolus, rod-shaped tubular particles, similar in diameter and density to the core of the GV particles, were frequently observed. In some instances the tubular particles were orientated at random and the length was difficult to determine; in others they were very regularly arranged and of uniform length, this being approximately the same as that of the core of mature particles. The authors observed numerous examples of a budding process at the inner layer of the nuclear membrane. During the process the tubular particles acquired an envelope derived from the inner layer of the nuclear membrane and passed into the perinuclear space where they formed aggregates of mature GV particles. The budding process described by Kitajima and Costa differs from that of animal viruses such as VSV in several respects. It occurs at the nuclear membrane rather than at the cell surface or cytoplasmic membrane; the core is completed before the envelopment occurs; and the orientation of the long axis of the particle during the budding process is usually parallel to the surface of the enveloping membrane rather than perpendicular to it. The authors suggested that bacilliform particles might arise from the former and bullet-shaped particles from the latter type of budding.

E. Wheat Striate Mosaic Virus (WSMV)

A disease of wheat (*Triticum durum* Res.) was described by Slykhuis (1953) and shown to be due to a virus transmitted by the leafhopper *Endria inimica* (Soy). The virus, wheat striate mosaic virus (not to be confused with wheat streak mosaic virus), was later shown to be transmissible in extracts from both viruliferous insects and diseased plants (Lee, 1963).

Evidence for the multiplication of WSMV in its leafhopper vector was presented by Sinha and Chiykowski (1967).

The morphology of WSMV was first studied by Lee (1964) in thin sections of diseased plants. In parenchymal cells of diseased leaves he observed numerous cytoplasmic inclusions, some membrane-bound, consisting of arrays of rod-shaped particles of dimensions about 270 × 65 mμ (Fig. 11). The particle was described as having a dense core within a double membrane. In a later study, Lee (1967) amplified these observations and showed that many of the particles were localized between the layers of the nuclear membrane. As in the case of potato yellow dwarf and other viruses that accumulate in such perinuclear inclusions, the latter sometimes invaginated the nucleus and appeared in sections as membrane-bound, apparently intranuclear inclusions. Lee, however, observed some groups of particles without any apparent surrounding membrane and concluded that in these instances the virus was truly intranuclear. The intranuclear particles were not apparently different from the cytoplasmic particles and no evidence of a budding process at the inner layer of the nuclear membrane was obtained, although Lee suggested that the membrane might take part in the assembly of the particles. It would seem unlikely that this virus has a different maturation process from that of other morphologically similar plant viruses having an intranuclear and extranuclear phase. Further study concerning this point would be of value.

Lee (1967) also examined extracts from virus-infected plants by negative staining and observed particles of length 176 mμ and diameter 78 mμ, each having one round and one flat end. Extending from the flat end there was a central channel of diameter 23 mμ and of variable length. The particles were surrounded by a membrane 5 mμ wide showing indications of subunits on the surface. When extracts containing the particles were injected into insects, some of them were capable of transferring the disease to healthy seedlings. This, along with the absence of similar par-

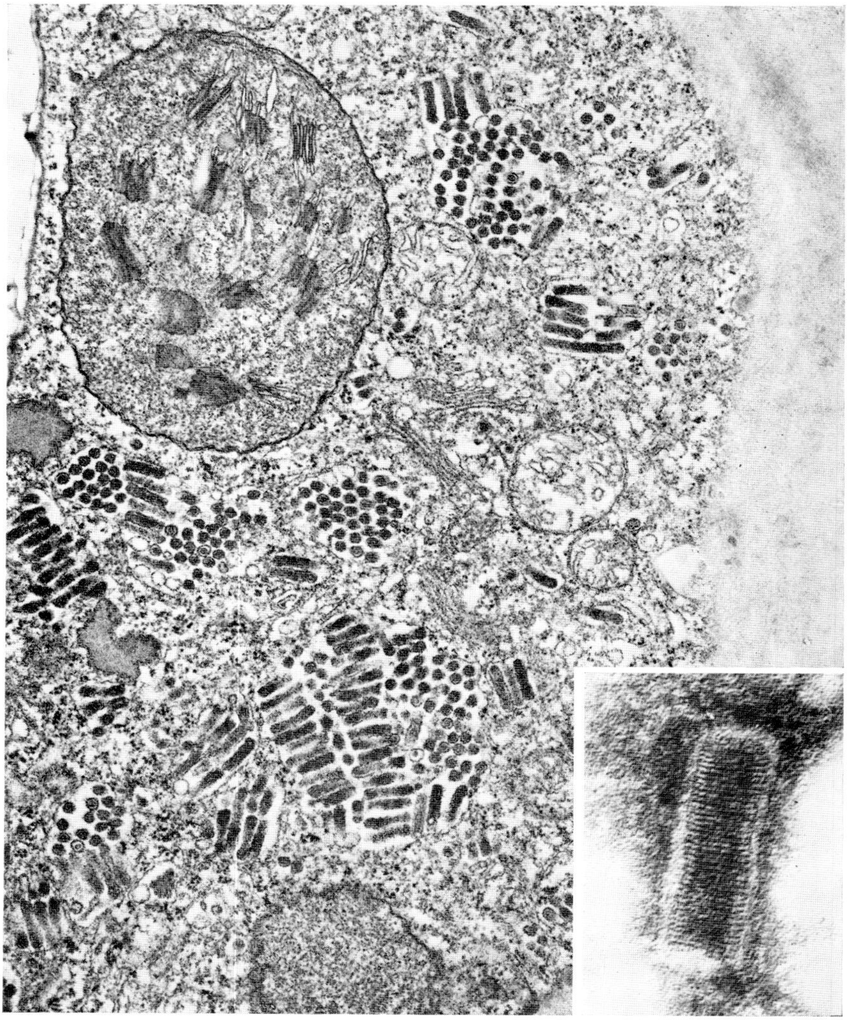

FIG. 11. Portion of parenchymal cell of plant infected with wheat striate mosaic virus. Semi-regular arrays of rod-shaped particles are present throughout the cytoplasm. Magnification 25,000 ×. *Inset:* Negatively stained particle showing regular cross-striations. Magnification 200,000 ×. Micrographs supplied by P. Lee.

ticles from extracts of healthy leaves, provided evidence that the particles were the agent of the disease.

In a later study, in which an improved method of extraction and purification of the virus was used, Lee (1968) examined fractions banded in a sucrose density gradient. Two types of particles were observed after negative staining; long particles of dimensions 170 ± 20 × 80 ± 10 mμ and short particles 90 ± 20 × 80 ± 10 mμ. Particles of both types had a round end and a flat end with a central channel extending from the flat end. No cross-striations were reported. In sections of pellets, however, the particles, sectioned longitudinally, were longer, 250–275 mμ, i.e., of the same length as particles seen in sections of infected cells, and they were rounded at both ends. Lee concluded that the 175 and 90 mμ bullet-shaped particles seen after negative staining were the result of fracture of the intact virus particles which were bacilliform and of length about 270 mμ. If this is so, the short particles of WSMV differ from the truncated forms of VSV which mature separately from the layer infectious particles and are not the result of fracture of the latter.

F. Potato Yellow Dwarf Virus (PYDV)

Early studies on the structure of this virus by metal-shadowing did not lead to definitive information about the structure of the particles which appeared to be easily distorted by the preparative procedures. The majority were flattened spheroids, though some rod-shaped particles were also observed (Black *et al.*, 1948; Brakke *et al.*, 1951). In a later study (Black *et al.*, 1965) in which negative staining was employed, most of the particles were distorted but they did reveal prominent projections on the viral surface and some evidence of a central body. The first clear indication that PYDV resembled VSV in structure was obtained by MacLeod *et al.* (1966) in a study by the thin section technique of infected tissues of tobacco (*Nicotiana rustica* L.) and clover (*Trifolium incarnatium* L.) and of pellets of purified virus. In the pellet preparations, profiles of randomly orientated bacilliform particles were observed, and particles of similar size and shape were found in abundance in sections of infected tissues; none were found in healthy tissues. The particles were seen especially in expanded spaces between the lamellae of the nuclear membrane. In some sections, aggregates of particles appeared to be in intranuclear inclusions but the presence of mitochondria and other cytoplasmic constituents within the inclusions indicated that they were in fact cytoplasmic invaginations. The particles had a diameter of 75 mμ and an average length of 380 mμ. Occasionally much larger particles were observed, perhaps consisting of two or more 380 mμ particles in tandem. Groups of particles were also found within cytoplasmic sacs which were thought to be derived from the outer layer of the nuclear membrane. The authors observed some particles in which the viral envelope was continuous with the inner layer of the nuclear envelope and also occasionally observed helical structures in the nucleoplasm near aggregates of virus particles at the periphery of the nucleus. Although cautious in their interpretation of these observations, the authors suggested that they might indicate that the helical core of the particles originated in the nucleus. In the light of more recent work on the morphogenesis of similar viruses, it would seem likely that this interpretation is correct.

In a later study, MacLeod (1968) succeeded in preserving the bacilliform shape of the particles in negatively stained preparations by fixing PYDV-infected tissues with osmium tetroxide or glutaraldehyde prior to staining. He observed transverse striations in many of the particles. The spacing was not given but from the published micrographs it appears to be about 55 Å. Spherical particles of about the same diameter as the bacilliform ones were also observed. These were thought to result from fracture of bacilliform particles near one end, leaving bullet-shaped particles.

G. Plantain Virus

Particles resembling vesicular stomatitis virions were observed by Hitchborn *et al.* (1966) in negatively stained preparations obtained from plantain (*Plantago lanceolata* L.) plants showing mottle or necrotic spotting of the leaves. The specimens were made by applying a strip of leaf tissue to a drop of PTA on an electron microscope grid. The particles were bullet-shaped and about 63 mμ in diameter. The most frequent length was 330 mμ, but shorter particles, probably the result of breakage of the longer ones, were common. The particles had a central canal, usually partly occluded, transverse striations of spacing 45 mμ and an enveloping membrane. Taillike appendages were sometimes present at the flat end of the particles. In one diseased plant there were, in addition to the particles described, bullet-shaped particles of distinctly different dimensions—195 mμ long × 90 mμ in diameter. These particles had a wide central canal and cross-striations having the same spacing as the first type. Attempts to transmit the disease by mechanical inoculation of the particles and also via aphids were unsuccessful. Although these negative results preclude the strict acceptance of the particles as viral, their association with diseased leaves and their characteristic rhabdovirus morphology leaves little doubt about their viral nature.

H. Sowthistle Yellow Vein Virus (SYVV)

A disease of sowthistle (*Sonchus oleraceus* L.) discovered in California and Arizona has been attributed to a virus, sowthistle yellow vein virus (SYVV) which is transmitted by the aphid *Amphorophora lactucae* L. (Duffus, 1963). Evidence of multiplication of the virus in this vector was obtained by Duffus (1963) and Richardson and Sylvester (1968). Subsequently, the latter authors (Sylvester and Richardson, 1969) presented further evidence for the multiplication of the virus in the aphid vector and for a low amount of transovarial passage of SYVV to larvae of the vector (Sylvester, 1969).

Richardson and Sylvester (1968) used electron microscopy to demonstrate viruslike particles on both infected plants and insect vector. Negatively stained preparations made by the leaf dip method and also from plant juice showed numerous bullet-shaped particles 95 mμ wide and 161 mμ long. Some showed cross-striations and evidence of an axial canal. Especially in centrifuged preparations there were also bacilliform particles which had well-defined cross-striations and were somewhat larger than the bullet-shaped particles (width, 99 mμ; average length, 222 mμ). Other ovoid particles found mainly in centrifuged preparations were thought to be damaged or distorted forms.

In sections of infected leaf tissue large groups of bacilliform particles were observed within membranous sacs in close proximity to the nucleus. The particles were uniform in size, being approximately 220 mμ long and 80 mμ wide. They possessed an outer coat with projections and there were indications of internal cross-striations.

In cells of salivary glands of infected aphids, numerous particles were found within the nucleus. These were smaller in diameter (63 mμ) than the particles seen in plant tissue but about the same length. Occasionally larger particles were seen; in these cross-striations were evident. In cross section the particles in insect tissue showed evidence of a core of dense material which was not present in the particles in plant tissue. Only a few scattered particles were observed in the cytoplasm of the insect cells.

The relationship of the particles seen in insect cells to those observed in plant cells was not clearly established in these studies. The former bear an obvious resemblance to the inner helical component of the latter and most probably represent uncoated SYVV particles. The situation is somewhat analogous to that described by O'Loughlin and Chambers (1967) for LNYV. Two types of LNYV particles, coated and uncoated, were, however, found in the cytoplasm of infected insect cells whereas in SYVV-infected cells only uncoated particles were found and these were almost entirely intranuclear.

The structure of SYVV was examined further by Sylvester *et al.* (1968) and a direct comparison made of the morphology of SYVV and VSV as observed by electron microscopy of negatively stained specimens. After phosphotungstate staining of mixed preparations both viruses appeared bullet-shaped, had axial canals and, in some instances, vesiclelike attachments at the flattened ends. The dimensions of the two viruses were, however, distinctly different, the modal value of the diameter of

VSV being about 60 mμ and of SYVV 93 mμ. The values for the particle lengths were not recorded. No evidence of cross-reaction of antisera prepared against VSV and SYVV was obtained, and immunodiffusion studies showed no common antigens. As the authors point out, these negative results may only reflect unrelatedness of the membrane coatings of the two viruses.

I. Broccoli Necrotic Yellows Virus (BNYV)

Bacilliform and bullet-shaped particles were found by Hills and Campbell (1968) in negatively stained preparations made from broccoli plants (*Brassica oleracea* L.) showing symptoms of cauliflower mosaic virus (CaMV) disease. Since CaMV particles are spherical, they were easily distinguished from the elongated particles. Preparations of BNYV free from CaMV were obtained and shown by mechanical transmission to be capable of inducing lesions in 4 other plant species (*N. clevelandii, N. glutinosa, Gomphrena globulosa* L., and *Datura stramonium* L.) Numerous other plant species remained symptomless and free from virus particles detectable by electron microscopy after inoculation with the virus. Attempts to transmit the virus via the aphid *Myzus persicae* were unsuccessful. In negatively stained preparations the BNYV particles had a general appearance similar to that of VS virions. Their average dimensions were 270 mμ in length by 66 mμ in diameter. The appearance varied according to the degree of penetration of the stain. In particles in which the stain had penetrated deeply a "helical layer" of diameter 44 mμ and axial repeat 4.5 mμ was visible. This appears from the micrographs to be identical to the striated internal component described for other similar viruses. Particles less penetrated by the stain showed a "hexamer layer" forming a tube of diameter 57.5 mμ around the helical layer. Outside this there was a "thin membrane" not further described. It appears to the writer from examination of the published micrographs that the thin membrane consists of the tips of surface projections similar to those that have been observed on the surface of many viruses of this type. The "hexamer layer" would then correspond to the envelope or phospholipid coat. Hexagonal arrangements of the materials forming the envelopes of other viruses have been detected after negative staining (Almeida and Waterson, 1967; Flewett and Apostolov, 1967). The significance of these arrangements and the conditions required to demonstrate them have not been fully explained. They may represent a basic structure of the envelope or may be induced by the negative staining procedure. The "helical layer" is very similar to the internal helix of VSV and other viruses and presumably, as in these viruses, consists of nucleoprotein.

In thin sections prepared from lesions in leaves of *D. stramonium*, rod-shaped particles rounded at both ends were observed within cytoplasmic sacs. No aggregates of virus between the layers of the nuclear membrane were observed. The evidence suggested that the virus particles were assembled at the membranes of the endoplasmic reticulum.

J. Eggplant Mottled Dwarf Virus (EMDV)

A disease of eggplant (*Solanum melongena* L.) discovered in southern Italy, results in stunting of the plants and mottling of the leaves. Since a virus was suspected as the causal agent, Martelli (1969) prepared and examined thin sections of infected eggplant tissues as well as tissues from healthy seedlings. Cells from infected tissues contained many bacilliform particles which occurred most frequently in paracrystalline arrays between the lamellae of the nuclear membrane. In numerous instances continuity of the envelope of particles with the inner layer of the nuclear membrane was observed. No evidence of the occurrence of particles within the nucleus was obtained. The bacilliform particles had rather constant dimensions (221 mμ × 66 mμ) and the profiles in section resembled very closely those of lettuce necrotic yellows and similar viruses. There were also present bullet-shaped particles of more variable length. Many of these were still attached at the flat end to the nuclear membrane or less commonly to a membrane of the endoplasmic reticulum and were thought by the author to represent immature particles.

The particles were clearly viral in nature and in the absence of information about possible relationships with known viruses the author suggested that it be regarded as a separate entity and proposed the name eggplant mottled dwarf virus.

K. Northern Cereal Mosaic Virus

A mosaic disease of barley recognized in Japan was shown to be caused by an insect-borne virus—northern cereal mosaic virus (Shikata and Lu, 1967). These authors examined partially purified and dip preparations of the virus by negative staining, and thin sections of infected cells from plants and insects. They observed two types of particles that were not present in preparations made from healthy insects and plants. The first type was in the form of "flexuous rods," 500–600 mμ in length and 40 mμ in diameter; the second was bacilliform or bullet-shaped, 300–350 mμ in length and 60 mμ in diameter. In some of the latter, cross-striations and a central canal were visible after negative staining. In thin sections similar bacilliform particles were observed within the cytoplasm of cells of diseased leaves of barley and Italian millet but were not detected in organs of infective insects. In salivary glands of the latter, however, there were numerous flexuous rods similar to those observed in both plant and insect preparations by negative staining.

The relationship between the flexuous rods and bacilliform particles was not clearly established in these studies; nor was it established which particle was the infectious agent. However, the bacilliform particles are clearly "rhabdoviruslike" and are tentatively included here as the probable agent of this mosaic disease.

L. Rice Transitory Yellowing Virus (RTYV)

A disease of rice in Taiwan, first described in 1965, was shown to be transmitted by leafhoppers (Chiu *et al.*, 1968). From this and other evidence it was concluded that the disease was caused by a virus—rice transitory yellowing virus. The morphology of the virus was investigated by Shikata and Chen (1969). Dip preparations of diseased leaves, examined by electron microscopy after negative staining, showed numerous, rather stubby, bullet-shaped particles, 96 mμ in diameter and 120–140 mμ in length. The particles had a central hollow and surface projections. In thin sections of diseased tissue numerous bullet-shaped particles were also detected. They were of the same diameter as those seen by negative staining but somewhat longer, 180–210 mμ. Bacilliform particles were also seen; these were 93 mμ in diameter and 325 mμ in length, with occasional longer particles. The virus particles were frequently found at the periphery of nuclei of infected cells but no information about their relationship to the nuclear membrane was given.

M. Melilotis Latent Virus (MLV)

During an electron microscopic investigation of bean yellow mosaic virus in sweet clover [*Melilotis alba* Desr. and *M. officinalis* (L.) Lam.], Kitajima *et al.* (1969) observed bacilliform particles in both infected and uninfected symptomless plants. The particles could be transferred from infected to uninfected plants only by grafting. However, because of this successful transmission and the characteristic morphology of the particles, the authors concluded that the particles were viral in nature and designated the virus melilotis latent virus (MLV).

In leaf-dip preparations, negatively stained with PTA, most of the MLV particles were bullet-shaped with a taillike appendage attached to the flat end. The particles were 250–300 mμ long by 80–100 mμ wide, and, in some instances, there was evidence of an inner striated component having a periodicity of 45–50 Å. The inner component was surrounded by a membraneous coat with surface projections about 100 Å long.

In thin sections of infected tissues bacilliform particles were observed in large numbers within perinuclear spaces and also occasionally within cytoplasmic vesicles. Individual particles or monomers were about 80 mμ in diameter and 300–350 mμ in length. Particles (dimers) of about twice this length were also seen. The continuity of the inner component (but not of the envelope) was interrupted at the midpoint of the long axis, suggesting that they could easily fragment into two units of equal length. The 45–50 Å striation periodicity could be observed in sections especially if the tissues were postfixed in uranyl acetate. In particles sectioned transversely the outer membranous coat (70 Å thick) could easily be distinguished from the inner component which appeared as a ringlike structure of external diameter about 600 Å. A central density corresponding in three dimensions to an axial rod of diameter about 100 Å was also visible. Tubular structures, identical morphologically to the inner component of the MLV particles were observed in groups within the nucleus. Stages in the extrusion of these particles through the inner layer of the nuclear membrane were clearly delineated. In this process, termed synhymenosis, the tubules acquired an outer coat derived from the inner layer of the nuclear membrane thus developing into complete virions which accumulated in the perinuclear space.

VI. Concluding Remarks

It is clear that a new and important family of viruses has emerged from recent studies of agents associated with diseases of vertebrates, invertebrates, and plants. Many of these studies have relied primarily on electron microscopic techniques to characterize the viral agents and their developmental sequence in infected cells. Members of the family infecting vertebrates range from the venerable rabies virus to viruses newly isolated from such diverse species as fish, bats, and man. Comparison of the known properties of vertebrate viruses (Table I) shows that despite some differences they form a homogeneous group distinct from other established viral groups. The most variable structural feature is the length, which varies from 130 nm for Kern Canyon virus to 218 nm for Flanders-Hart Park virus. The width is relatively constant. Distinguishing features of the group are the bullet shape and the cross-striations, representing the viral nucleocapsid, which have rather constant spacing of 4–5 nm in all members. The process of maturation by budding from a cytoplasmic membrane is also a common characteristic though rabies virus is exceptional in having an alternative mode of development that apparently does not involve budding. Other recently determined properties of rabies virus, however, emphasize its strong resemblance to VSV.

Some of the vertebrate viruses are known to multiply in insects, and insects also act as hosts for several of the plant viruses. No example is known of a virus that multiplies in all three types of host—vertebrate, invertebrate, and plant.

The inclusion of viruses causing disease in such diverse hosts as mammals and plants in a single genus is still a matter of discussion. The general consensus of opinion seems to be in favor of such a grouping if the physicochemical properties of group members are sufficiently similar, and distinct from those of other viruses. Certainly there are striking morphological resemblances between the plant and insect viruses listed in Table II and the vertebrate viruses of Table I. However, there are some differences. Several plant virologists insist that the plant virions are bacilliform in shape and that a bullet shape, if found, is a result of damage, whereas bacilliform virions are rare in animal virus preparations. This difference may be related to differences in the modes of development of plant and animal viruses. In several instances, e.g., in *Gomphrena* virus, and *Melilotis* latent virus, there is clear evidence of an intranuclear phase of virus development. Cores, presumably viral nucleoprotein helices, form within the nucleus and are extruded into the perinuclear space by a budding process at the inner layer of the nuclear membrane. In contrast, the nucleus does not appear to be involved in the formation of vertebrate viruses.

Clearly there is need for more information about the properties of many of these newly discovered viruses so that a more accurate assessment can be made of their relatedness to one another.

Acknowledgments

We wish to thank Drs. D. Baltimore, A. Holloway, B. McCain, F. Murphy, and C. Pringle for providing manuscripts prior to publication.

The writing of this article and research carried out in the author's laboratory were supported by grants from the Medical Research Council of Canada and the National Cancer Institute of Canada.

References

Almeida, J. D., and Waterson, A. P. (1967). *J. Gen. Microbiol.* **46,** 107.
Almeida, J. D., Howatson, A. F., Pinteric, L., and Fenje, P. (1962). *Virology* **18,** 147.
Almeida, J. D., Waterson, A. P., Berry, D. M., and Turner, L. H. (1969). *Lancet* **1,** 236.
Amend, D. F., and Chambers, V. C. (1970). *J. Fish. Res. Board Can.* **27,** 1285.
Arstila, P., Halonen, P. E., and Salmi, A. (1969). *Arch. Ges. Virusforsch.* **27,** 198.
Atanasiu, P., Lépine, P., and Dragonas, P. (1963a). *Ann. Inst. Pasteur, Paris* **105,** 813.
Atanasiu, P., Orth, G., Sisman, J., and Barreau, C. (1963b). *C. R. Acad. Sci.* **257,** 2204.
Atanasiu, P., Lépine, P., Sisman, J., Dauguet, J. C., and Wetten, M. (1963c). *C. R. Acad. Sci.* **256,** 3219.
Baltimore, D. (1969). *In* "The Biochemistry of Viruses" (H. B. Levy, ed.), pp. 101–176. Dekker, New York.
Baltimore, D., Huang, A. S., and Stampfer, M. (1970). *Proc. Nat. Acad. Sci. U.S.* **66,** 572.
Bellett, A. J. D., and Cooper, P. D. (1959). *J. Gen. Microbiol.* **21,** 498.
Bergold, G. H., and Munz, K. (1967). *J. Ultrastruct. Res.* **17,** 233.
Berkaloff, A., Bregliano, J. C., and Ohanessian, A. (1965). *C. R. Acad. Sci.* **260,** 5956.
Bhatt, P. N., and Rodriques, F. M. (1967). *Indian Med. J. Res.* **55,** 1295.

Black, L. M., Mosley, V. H., and Wyckoff, R. W. G. (1948). *Biochim. Biophys. Acta* **2,** 121.
Black, L. M., Smith, K. M., Hills, G. J., and Markham, R. (1965). *Virology* **27,** 446.
Boulger, L. R., and Porterfield, J. S. (1958). *Trans. Roy. Soc. Trop. Med. Hyg.* **52,** 421.
Bradish, C. J., and Kirkham, J. B. (1966). *J. Gen. Microbiol.* **44,** 359.
Bradish, C. J., Brooksby, J. B., and Dillon, J. F., Jr. (1956). *J. Gen. Microbio.* **14,** 290.
Brakke, M. K., Black, L. M., and Wyckoff, R W. G. (1951). *Amer. J. Bot.* **38,** 332.
Brown, F., and Cartwright, B. (1966). *J. Immunol.* **97,** 612.
Brown, F., Cartwright, B., and Almeida, J. D. (1966). *J. Immunol.* **96,** 537.
Brown, F., Cartwright, B., and Smale, C. J. (1967a). *J. Immunol.* **99,** 171.
Brown, F., Cartwright, B., Crick, J., and Smale, C. J. (1967b). *Virology* **1,** 368.
Brown, F., Martin, S. J., Cartwright, B., and Crick, J. (1967c). *J. Gen. Virol.* **1,** 479.
Cartwright, B., and Pearce, C. A. (1968). *J. Gen. Virol.* **2,** 207.
Cartwright, B., Smale, C. J., and Brown, F. (1969). *J. Gen. Virol.* **5,** 1.
Chambers, T. C., Crowley, N. C., and Francki, R. I. B. (1965). *Virology* **27,** 320.
Chiu, R. J., Jean, J. H., Chen, M. H., and Lo, T. C. (1968). *Phytopathology* **58,** 740.
Chow, T. L., Chow, F. H., and Hanson, R. P. (1954). *J. Bacteriol.* **68,** 724.
Cooper P. D. (1967). *Brit. Med. Bull.* **23,** 155.
Cooper, P. D., and Bellett, A. J. D. (1959). *J. Gen. Microbiol.* **21,** 485.
Crick, J., Cartwright, B., and Brown, F. (1966). *Nature (London)* **211,** 1204.
Crick, J., Cartwright, B., and Brown, F. (1969). *Arch. Ges. Virusforsch.* **27,** 221.
Crowley, N. C., Harrison, B. D., and Francki, R. I. B. (1965). *Virology* **26,** 290.
Dales, S., and Siminovitch, L. (1961). *J. Biophys. Biochem. Cytol.* **10,** 475.
David-West, T. S., and Labzoffsky, N. A. (1968a). *Arch. Ges. Virusforsch.* **23,** 105.
David-West, T. S., and Labzoffsky, N. A. (1968b). *Arch. Ges. Virusforsch.* **24,** 30.
Davies, M. C., Englert, M. E., Sharpless, G. R., and Cabasso, V. J. (1963). *Virology* **21,** 642.
de Lestrange, M. T. (1963). *Ann. Genet.* **6,** 39.
Dierks, R. E., Murphy, F. A., and Harrison, A. K. (1969). *Amer. J. Pathol.* **54,** 251.
Ditchfield, J., and Almeida, J. D. (1964). *Virology* **24,** 232.
Duffus, J. E. (1963). *Virology* **21,** 194.
Epstein, R. H., Bolle, A., Steinberg, C. M., Kellenberger, E., Boy De La Tour, E., Chevalley, R., Edgar, R. S., Susman, M., Denhardt, G. H., and Lielausis, A. (1963). *Cold Spring Harbor Symp. Quant. Biol.* **28,** 375.
Federer, K. E., Burrows, R., and Brooksby, J. B. (1967). *Res. Vet. Sci.* **8,** 103.
Fenner, F. (1969). *Curr. Top. Microbiol. Immunol.* **48,** 1.
Flamand, A. (1969). *C. R. Acad. Sci.* **268,** 2305.
Flewett, T. H., and Apostolov, K. (1967). *J. Gen. Virol.* **1,** 297.
Franklin, R. M. (1967). *J. Virol.* **1,** 64.
Galasso, G. J. (1967). *Proc. Soc. Exp. Biol. Med.* **124:** 43.
Ghittino, P. (1962). *Vet. Ital.* **8,** 457.
Girard, M. (1969). *J. Virol.* **3,** 376.
Hackett, A. J. (1964). *Virology* **24,** 51.
Hackett, A. J., Schaffer, F. L., and Madin, S. H. (1967). *Virology* **31,** 114.
Hackett, A. J., Zee, Y. C., Schaffer, F. L., and Talens, L. (1968). *J. Virol.* **2,** 1154.
Halonen, P. E., Murphy, F. A., Fields, B. N., and Reese, D. R. (1968). *Proc. Soc. Exp. Biol. Med.* **127,** 1037.
Hanson, R. P. (1952). *Bacteriol. Rev.* **16,** 179.
Harrison, B. D., and Crowley, N. C. (1965). *Virology* **26,** 297.
Heine, J. W., and Schnaitman, C. A. (1969). *J. Virol.* **3,** 619.

Herforth, R. S. (1968). *Genetics* **60,** 188.
Herold, F., and Munz, K. (1965). *Virology* **25,** 412.
Herold, F., and Munz, K. (1967). *J. Virol.* **1,** 1028.
Herold, F., Bergold, G. H., and Weibel, J. (1960). *Virology* **12,** 335.
Herreng, F. (1967). *C. R. Acad. Sci.* **264,** 2854.
Hills, G. J., and Campbell, R. N. (1968). *J. Ultrastruct. Res.* **24,** 134.
Hitchborn, J. H., Hills, G. J., and Hull, R. (1966). *Virology* **28,** 768.
Holloway, A. F., Wong, P. K. Y., and Cormack, D. V. (1970). *Virology* (in press).
Holmes, I. H., and Doherty, R. L. (1970). *J. Virol.* **5,** 91.
Howatson, A. F., and Russell, W. C. (1964). *J. Appl. Phys.* **35,** 3086.
Howatson, A. F., and Whitmore, G. F. (1961). *J. Appl. Phys.* **32,** 1639.
Howatson, A. F., and Whitmore, G. F.(1962). *Virology* **16,** 466.
Huang, A. S., and Wagner, R. R. (1966). *Virology* **30,** 173.
Huang, A. S., Greenawalt, J. W., and Wagner, R. R. (1966). *Virology* **30,** 161.
Hummeler, K., and Koprowski, H. (1969). *Nature (London)* **221,** 418.
Hummeler, K., Koprowski, H., and Wiktor, T. J. (1967). *J. Virol.* **1,** 152.
Huppert, J., Rosenbergova, M., Gresland, L., and Harel, L. (1967). *In* "The Molecular Biology of Viruses" (J. S. Colter and W. Paranchych, eds.), pp. 463–468. Academic Press, New York.
Ito, Y., Tanaka, Y., Inaba, Y., and Omori, T. (1969). *Nat. Inst. Anim. Health Quart.* **9,** 35.
Jensen, A. B., Rabin, E. R., Wende, R. D., and Melnick, J. L. (1967). *Expt. Mol. Pathol.* **7,** 1.
Jensen, M. H. (1963). *Bull. Off. Int. Epizimol.* **59,** 131.
Johnson, H. N. (1965). *Calif. Health* **23,** 35.
Jonkers, A. H. (1967). *Amer. J. Epidemiol.* **86,** 286.
Jonkers, A. H., Shope, R. E., Atkin, T. H. G., and Spence, L. (1964). *Amer. J. Vet. Res.* **25,** 236.
Jupin, N., Plus, N., and Fleuriet, A. (1968). *Ann. Inst. Pasteur, Paris* **114,** 577.
Kang, C. Y., and Prévec, L. (1969). *J. Virol.* **3,** 404.
Kissling, R. E., Robinson, R. Q., Murphy, F. A., and Whitfield, S. G. (1968). *Science* **160,** 888.
Kitajima, E. W., and Costa, A. S. (1966). *Virology* **29,** 523.
Kitajima, E. W., Lauritis, J. A., and Swift, H. (1969). *J. Ultrastruct. Res.* **29,** 141.
Klimenko, S. M., Uvarov, V. N., and Gajdamovich, S. J. (1966). *In* "Electron Microscopy" (R. Uyeda, ed.), Vol. II, pp. 183–184. Maruzen, Tokyo.
Kurland, C. G. (1960). *J. Mol. Biol.* **2,** 83.
Lafay, F. (1969). *C. R. Acad. Sci.* **268,** 2385.
Lecatsas, C., Theodorides, A., and Erasmus, B. J. (1969). *Arch. Ges. Virusforsch.* **28,** 390.
Lee, P. E. (1963). *Can. J. Bot.* **41,** 1617.
Lee, P. E. (1964). *Virology* **23,** 145.
Lee, P. E. (1967). *Virology* **33,** 84.
Lee, P. E. (1968). *Virology* **34,** 583.
L'Héritier, P. (1948). *Heredity* **2,** 325.
L'Héritier, P. (1954). *In* "Problemes Actuels de Virologie" (P. Hauduroy, ed.), p. 88. Masson, Paris.
L'Héritier, P. (1957). *Rev. Pathol. Gen. Physiol. Clin.* **57,** No. 692, 1471.
L'Héritier, P. (1958). *Advan. Virus Res.* **5,** 195.
L'Héritier, P. (1962). *Ann. Inst. Pasteur, Paris* **102,** 511.

L'Héritier, P., and Hugon de Scoeux, F. (1947). *Bull. Biol. Fr. Belg.* **81,** 70.
L'Héritier, P., and Teissier, G. (1937). *C. R. Acad. Sci.* **205,** 1099.
Maass, G. (1969). *In* "International Virology 1" (J. L. Melnick, ed.), p. 331. Karger, Basel.
McCain, B. B. (1970). Ph.D. Thesis, Oregon State Univ., Corvallis, Oregon.
McCombs, R. M., Benyesh-Melnick, M., and Brunschwig, J. P. (1966). *J. Bacteriol.* **91,** 803.
MacLeod, R. (1968). *Virology* **34,** 771.
MacLeod, R., Black, L. M., and Moyer, F. H. (1966). *Virology* **29,** 540.
Martelli, C. P. (1969). *J. Gen. Virol.* **5,** 319.
Matsumoto, S. (1962). *Virology* **17,** 198.
Matsumoto, S. (1963). *J. Cell Biol.* **19,** 565.
Matsumoto, S., and Kawai, A. (1969). *Virology* **39,** 449.
Melnick, J. L., and McCombs, R. M. (1966). *Progr. Med. Virol.* **8,** 400.
Metselaar, D., Williams, M. C., Simpson, D. I. H., West, R., and Mutere, F. A. (1969). *Arch. Ges. Virusforsch.* **26,** 183.
Miyamoto, K., and Matsumoto, S. (1965). *J. Cell Biol.* **27,** 677.
Miyamoto, K., and Matsumoto, S. (1967). *J. Exp. Med.* **125,** 447.
Murphy, F. A., and Fields, B. M. (1967). *Virology* **33,** 625.
Murphy, F. A., Coleman, P. H., and Whitfield, S. G. (1966). *Virology* **30,** 314.
Murphy, F. A., Halonen, P. E., Gary, G. W., Jr., and Reese, D. R. (1968). *J. Gen. Virol.* **3,** 289.
Murphy, F. A., Shope, R. E., Metselaar, D., and Simpson, D. I. H. (1970). *Virology* **40,** 288.
Mussgay, M., and Suarez, O. (1962). *Virology* **17,** 202.
Nakai, T., and Howatson, A. F. (1968). *Virology* **35,** 268.
Newman, J. F. E., and Brown, F. (1969). *J. Gen. Virol.* **5,** 305.
Ohanessian-Guillemain, A. (1963). *Ann. Genet.* **5,** 1.
Ohanessian-Guillemain, A., and Echalier, G. (1967). *Nature (London)* **213,** 1049.
O'Loughlin, G. T., and Chambers, T. C. (1967). *Virology* **33,** 262.
Patterson, W. C., Mott, L. O., and Jenney, E. W. (1958). *J. Amer. Vet. Med. Ass.* **133,** 57.
Périès, J., Printz, P., Canivet, M., and Chwat, J. C. (1966). *C. R. Acad. Sci.* **262,** 2106.
Peters, D., and Müller, G. (1969). *In* "International Virology 1" (J. L. Melnick, ed.), p. 312. Karger, Basel.
Pinteric, L., Fenje, P., and Almeida, J. D. (1963). *Virology* **20,** 208.
Plagemann, P. G. W., and Swim, H. E. (1968). *J. Mol. Biol.* **35,** 13.
Plus, N. (1950). *Exp. Cell Res.* **1,** 217.
Plus, N. (1954). *Bull. Biol. Fr. Belg.* **88,** 248.
Prévec, L., and Whitmore, G. F. (1963). *Virology* **20,** 464.
Pringle, C. R. (1970). *In* "The Biology of Large RNA Viruses." Academic Press, New York. In press.
Printz, P. (1969). *Arch. Ges. Virusforsch.* **27,** 209.
Provisional Committee for Nomenclature of Viruses (1965). *Ann. Inst. Pasteur, Paris* **109,** 625.
Rasmussen, C. J. (1965). *Ann. N.Y. Acad. Sci.* **126,** 427.
Reczko, E. (1961). *Arch. Ges. Virusforsch.* **10,** 588.
Richardson, J., and Sylvester, E. S. (1968). *Virology* **35,** 347.
Roots, E., and Schultze, I. M. (1963). *Zentralbl. Bakteriol., Parasitenk., Infektionskr. Hyg., Abt. 1: Orig.* **188,** 159.

Schäperclaus, W. (1954). *In* "Fischkrankheiten," pp. 537–543. Akademie Verlag, Berlin.
Schaffer, F. L., Hackett, A. J., and Soergel, M. E. (1968). *Biochem. Biophys. Res. Commun.* **31,** 685.
Schaffer, F. L., Hackett, A. J., and Soergel, M. E. (1969). *Fed. Proc. Fed. Amer. Soc. Exp. Biol.* **28,** 1867.
Schincariol, A., and Howatson, A. (1970). *Virology,* (in press).
Seecof, R. L. (1964). *Virology* **22,** 142.
Seecof, R. L. (1968). *Curr. Top. Microbiol. Immunol.* **42,** 59.
Shelokov, A., and Peralta, P. H. (1967). *Amer. J. Epidemiol.* **86,** 149.
Shikata, E., and Chen, M. (1969). *J. Virol.* **3,** 261.
Shikata, E., and Lu, Y.-T. (1967). *Proc. Jap. Acad.* **43,** 918.
Shope, R. E., and Murphy, F. A. (1970). Personal communication.
Siegert, R., Shu, H. L., Slenczka, W., Peters, D., and Müller, G. (1968). *Ger. Med Mon.* **13,** 1.
Simpson, R. W., and Hauser, R. E. (1966). *Virology* **29,** 654.
Simpson, R. W., Hauser, R. E., and Dales, S. (1969). *Virology* **37,** 285.
Sinha, R. C., and Chiykowski, L. N. (1967). *Virology* **32,** 402.
Slykhuis, J. T. (1953). *Phytopathology* **43,** 537.
Sokol, F., Kuwert, E., Wiktor, T. J., Hummeler, K., and Koprowski, H. (1968). *J. Virol.* **2,** 836.
Sokol, F., Schlumberger, H. D., Wiktor, T. J., Koprowski, H., and Hummeler, K. (1969). *Virology* **38,** 651.
Spirin, A. S. (1963). *Progr. Nucl. Acid. Res.* **1,** 301.
Stampfer, M., Baltimore, D., and Huang, A. S. (1969). *J. Virol.* **4,** 154.
Stone, R. S., Sellers, M. I., and Hiramoto, T. (1961). *J. Appl. Phys.* **32,** 1639.
Stubbs, L. L., and Grogan, R. G. (1963). *Aust. J. Agr. Res.* **14,** 439.
Sudia, W. D., Fields, B. N., and Calisher, C. H. (1967). *Amer. J. Epidemiol.* **86,** 596.
Sylvester, E. S. (1969). *Virology* **38,** 440.
Sylvester, E. S., and Richardson, J. (1969). *Virology* **37,** 26.
Sylvester, E. S., Richardson, J., and Wood, P. (1968). *Virology* **36,** 693.
Teninges, D. (1968). *Arch. Ges. Virusforsch.* **23,** 378.
Theiler, S. (1901). *Deut. Tieraerztl. Wochenschr.* **9,** 131.
Till, J. E., Whitmore, G. F., and Gulyao, S. (1963). *Biochim. Biophys. Acta* **72,** 277.
Von Magnus, P. (1954). *Advan. Virus Res.* **2,** 59.
Wagner, R. R., Schnaitman, T. A., and Snyder, R. M. (1966a). *J. Virol.* **3,** 395.
Wagner, R. R., Schnaitman, T. C., Snyder, R. M., and Schnaitman, C. A. (1969b). *J. Virol.* **3,** 611.
Whitney, E. (1964). *Amer. J Trop. Med. Hyg.* **13,** 123.
Wilson, R. G., and Bader, J. P. (1965). *Biochim. Biophys. Acta* **103,** 549.
Wolanski, B. S., Francki, R. I. B., and Chambers, T. C. (1967). *Virology* **33,** 287.
Wolf, K. (1966). *Advan. Virus Res.* **12,** 35.
Wolf, K., and Quimby, M. C. (1962). *Science* **135,** 1065.
Zwillenberg, L. O., Jensen, M. H., and Zwillenberg, H. H. L. (1965). *Arch. Ges. Virusforsch.* **17,** 1.
Zwillenberg, L. O., Pfitzner, I., and Zwillenberg, H. H. L. (1968). *Zentralbl. Bakteriol., Parasitenk., Infektionskr. Hyg., Abt. 1: Orig.* **208,** 218.

RABIES VIRUS

Seiichi Matsumoto

Institute for Virus Research, Kyoto University, Kyoto, Japan

I. Introduction

During the past 20 years, animal virology has become a quantitative science involving analysis of the virus-cell interaction at both the cellular and molecular level. Developments in the field of cell culture techniques have played a basic role in the application of many new valuable techniques which, in turn, have contributed to the rapid progress of animal virology. The use of cultured cell systems has made possible the isolation of many viruses, some of which are not yet known to be related to disease. Even the so-called "orphan" viruses have been extensively studied at the molecular and genetic level. Until recently a quite different situation existed in rabies research.

Rabies is a disease of great antiquity and its viral etiology was established early in this century (Remlinger, 1903). Since that time many significant advances have been made but most of this effort has been confined to the practical aspects of this virus infection. It has been evident that knowledge of the mechanism of viral replication at the cellular level and of the structure of virus particle would be increased by the establishment of a cell culture system highly susceptible to rabies virus. Accordingly, for this purpose, attempts have been made to adapt rabies virus to a cell culture system using non-nervous tissues, but in no case have high viral yields been obtained in the presence of a reproducible cytopathic effect. However, following the first report of Fernandes *et al.*

(1963), several cell culture systems have become available as tools for the quantitative study of rabies infection. Shortly thereafter, useful techniques of quantitative virology such as effective purification, antigenic analysis, and the demonstration of hemagglutinin were devised. With the development of these techniques in mind, we can anticipate the accumulation of much new knowledge of rabies virus in the near future, and, in particular, of the biological properties of the virus and its replication.

A number of reviews on the subject of rabies infection have been published since 1924 (Schweinburg, 1924). During the past few years three excellent concise reviews have covered recent findings in different fields of rabies research (Habel, 1964; H. N. Johnson, 1965; Campell *et al.*, 1968b). More detailed consideration of recent progress can be cited in the documents of International Symposium on Rabies held in 1965 which contains 48 papers classified under the following headings; nature of virus, pathogenesis and immune response, epidemiology and epizootiology, and new development in prevention and treatment. This essay will not cover the relatively older literature, most of which is concerned with practical control of the disease, but will be directed mainly toward laboratory investigations. However, since many new techniques have only recently become available, many of the present conclusions may be modified in the future.

II. Morphology of Rabies Virus

The application of negative staining to the rabies virion was first reported by Almeida *et al.* (1962), using crude materials obtained from infected hamster kidney cell cultured *in vitro*. Frozen thick sections were prepared from a pellet of infected cells, stained while in suspension with phosphotungstic acid and then photographed. Although the morphological units, probably disrupted during preparation, could not be positively identified as rabies virus, characteristic filaments consisting of repeating subunits were suggested as the internal component of rabies virus. The dimensions of the internal component were described as follows by the same group (Pinteric and Fenje, 1966) (Fig. 1): external diameter of the coiled helix 150–160 Å, internal diameter approximately 100 Å, the thickness of the ribbon from which the helix is wound 25–30 Å, the width of ribbon 55 Å, and the length along the ribbon 30–35 Å. The internal component of myxoviruses such as measles and Newcastle disease virus is similar to that of rabies virus, except that the external diameter of the helix is 180 Å and internal diameter is 50–60 Å. They also differ in the degree of rigidity of their helices. The helix of rabies viruses is more easily stretched and can be reduced to a diameter of about 55 Å. A filamentous internal component was also shown in the mouse brain infected with some fixed as well as street viruses (Pinteric *et al.*, 1963). Based on these findings and on the morphological feature of an enveloping membrane covered with fine projections about 100 Å long, the Toronto group proposed that the rabies virus be assigned to the myxovirus group, especially the Newcastle disease virus group. Other similarities support this classification. Some rabies virions are formed by budding from the cell surface (Davies *et al.*, 1963; Atanasiu *et al.*, 1963a; Hummeler *et al.*, 1967, 1968; Matsumoto and Kawai, 1969); the virions in cross section seem to have a lipid layer, which may account for the ether sensitivity of the rabies virus—a property common to all members of myxoviruses. It should be pointed out, however, that the proposal

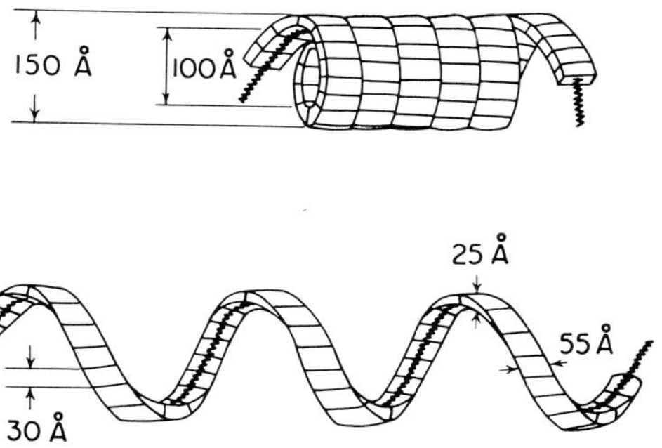

FIG. 1. The dimensions of the internal component of rabies virus. [Courtesy of Drs. L. Pinteric and P. Fenje (1966)].

originated when there was an incomplete understanding of the shape of the whole virion (Almeida *et al.*, 1962). It has since become evident that the complete rabies virus is bullet-shaped with one rounded and one flat end (Davies *et al.*, 1963; Pinteric and Fenje, 1966; Lépine *et al.*, 1966; Hummeler *et al.*, 1967) (Fig. 2). The diameter of the virion is 75–80 mμ and its length is variable, the longest measuring 180 mμ. Projections, 60–70 Å long, each with a knoblike structure at the distal end, cover the surface of the virion except for at the flat end where an indentation or an axial hollow is discernible. The hollow is roughly cylindrical, can be penetrated by phosphotungstic acid, and extends for a distance which varies up to one-half the length of the virus. These morphological features of the rabies virus are unique and quite different from those of any myxovirus. Since Reczko (1960) first reported the profile of the vesicular stomatitis virus, using the negative contrast method, some 15 bullet-shaped viruses have been discovered among animal and plant viruses, but not bacterial viruses (Table I). On the basis of the characteristic similarity of these viruses, it is preferable to allocate them to a new group, named "rhabdovirus" (*rhabdos* = rod in Greek; Melnick and McCombs, 1966). Preparation of purified rabies viruses with numerous virions of characteristic shape and structure, obtained from infective tissue culture fluid, were studied with the electron microscope by Sokol *et al.* (1968). However, partial or total breakdown of many viruses resulted from various steps in the purification procedure which is described in detail in the following section. A careful stepwise dialysis against decreasing concentration of sucrose prevented the disruption of the outer

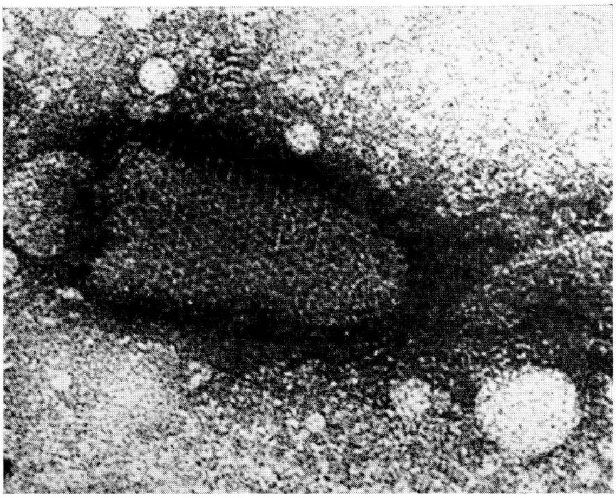

FIG. 2. Rabies virus (HEP Flury strain). × 200,000 (Courtesy of Dr. K. Hummeler).

viral membrane and it was concluded that the rabies virions are not pleomorphic but uniform in shape. The fine structure of other viral components was also studied by Hummeler *et al.* (1967). The envelope, closely associated with the underlying inner structure, was composed of two membranes of different densities. This finding was ascertained by a comparison of the end-on view of viruses, using negative staining, and the appearance of viruses cut in transverse section *in situ*. When virions were deeply penetrated by the stain, the core, presumably containing viral nucleoprotein, seemed to have cross striations with a ribbed appearance. The cross striation interval was about 4 mμ. The striated component, which certainly corresponds to the nucleocapsid of virus, has not yet been examined to the same extent as the striated component of the vesicular stomatitis virus described by Howatson and Nakai (1968), Howatson and Whitmore (1962), and Simpson and Hauser (1966). Given the general similarity in appearance, however, of the strands released from disintegrating viruses, the findings on the vesicular stomatitis virus seems applicable to the rabies virus: that is, the nucleoprotein is in the form of a ribbonlike strand consisting of a series of regular rodlike subunits; the continuity of the strand is maintained by the attachment of subunits to a thread of nucleic acid (Nakai and Howatson, 1968).

TABLE I
MEMBERS OF RHABDOVIRUS

Name	Natural host	Size (negative staining) mμ	References
Vesicular stomatitis	Bovine	69 × 175	Reczko (1960)
Rabies	Many mammals	75 × 180	Atanasiu *et al.* (1963d)
Marburg	Monkey	90 × 130–2600	Kissling *et al.* (1968)
Kern Canyon	Bat	73 × 132	Murphy and Fields (1967)
Egtved (viral hemorrhagic septicemia)	Rainbow trout	70 × 180	Zwillenberg *et al.* (1965)
Sigma	*Drosophila*	68 × 190	Berkaloff *et al.* (1965)
Cocal	Mite	60 × 170	Ditchfield and Almeida (1964)
Flanders-Hart Park	Mosquito, bird	65 × 209	Murphy *et al.* (1966)
Plantago lanceolata	Plantain	65–90 × 100–330	Hitchborn *et al.* (1966)
Gomphrena	Globe amaranth	90 × 220–260	Kitajima and Costa (1966)
Potato yellow dwarf	Potato	75 × 380	MacLeod (1968)
Lettuce necrotic yellow	Lettuce	66 × 227	Harris and Crowley (1965)
Wheat striate mosaic	Wheat	80 × 90–170	Lee (1968)
Maize mosaic	Corn	48 × 242	Herold *et al.* (1960)
Broccoli necrotic yellow	Cauliflower-headed broccoli	66 × 270	Hills and Campbell (1968)

In addition to these virions of fairly uniform structure, other structures of different shapes were observed at a relatively later stage of virus growth *in vitro*. The first type is a short form of virus frequently showing a bell-like shape. It is similar to the complete virus in other morphological details and resembles the truncated T particles of noninfectious vesicular stomatitis virus (Huang *et al.*, 1966). The second type is a long rod of varying length. In some cases, neither end of the long rod is covered by an envelope. Such long rods are also seen in thin-sectioned material as described in the later section. The last type has a more bizarre structure. It is branched or broken into small units, the length of which is nearly equal to that of the complete virus. Both the second and third types of rods are similar to the rabies virus in their structure and width.

From these observations it is concluded that the rabies virus, although its nucleoprotein appears to be arranged in helical symmetry, is constructed in an asymmetrical pattern as a whole, as in the tailed bacteriophages. A mere description of the morphology of the virions is, however, not sufficient, and it should eventually be correlated with the chemical and antigenic structure. To date, however, little or nothing is known about the biological function of the viral constituents.

III. Purification and Chemical Composition of Virus

Purification of rabies virus was first attempted using brains of infected animals. Most procedures, however, have not produced sufficiently purified virus in a reasonable quantity and comparable with the original titer. Thomas *et al.* (1965) used ion-exchange cellulose chromatography for this purpose. The adsorption of fixed rabies viruses, which had been centrifuged from a suspension of infected brains onto ECTEOLA-cellulose followed by elution with 0.3 M KCl, resulted in 240-fold recovery of purified virus. However, this procedure was not recommended by Turner and Kaplan (1967) since they found that total nitrogen was decreased by 90% in the eluates and that there was a loss of more than 10^4 LD_{50} of virus. Density gradient centrifugation has been utilized with infected brain tissue (Turner and Kaplan, 1967) and tissue cultures (Neurath *et al.*, 1966; Sokol *et al.*, 1968). The outline of the procedure, used for extracellular rabies virus released from cultured cells, is as follows: To avoid difficulties caused by binding of serum to the viruses, serum was replaced by bovine serum albumin (BSA) in the medium. Virus was precipitated from the infected culture medium and dissolved in EDTA-tris solution pH 7.8. Two to five percent of the protein contained in the medium was coprecipitated with the virus. After centrifugation at 1000 g for 20 minutes, the supernatant was filtered through Sephadex to remove low-molecular weight impurities, rather than BSA. BSA was also required for the stabilization of the biological activity of the virus during the centrifugation. The filtrate was centrifuged at 1000 g for 20 minutes and the supernatant was made up to 0.004 M with respect to $MgSO_4$ and then treated at 25°C for 40 minutes with RNase and DNase. After treatment with these enzymes, the virus was pelleted by high-speed centrifugation at 49,000 g for 60 minutes. This procedure reduced contamination of the preparation by nonviral nucleic acids and eliminated most of the BSA. With gentle shaking in buffer solution, the transparent, bluish-opalescent pellet instantly dissolved. With this step the preparation attained a purification of about 2640-fold (PFU/mg protein). Recovery tested by PFU was 110%. However, sucrose density gradient centrifugation at 61,000 *g* for 90 minutes was used for the removal of cellular materials (10 to 55%, w/w) and the virus band appeared in the middle of tube, while the band close to the bottom corresponded to cellular material. Peak turbidity coincided with the peaks of protein content, radioactivity of incorporated RNA precursor, hemagglutinating (HA) and CF activity, and infectivity of virus. This association, indicating that the population of virus was homogeneous, was limited to preparations harvested from cultures exhibiting no sign of cell degeneration. In contrast, when virus was harvested from relatively old monolayer cultures, these different viral activities were dissociated to some extent. The lighter virus particles showed little infectivity and a decreased HA activity. In preparations showing such heterogeneity, a small proportion (up to 10%) of the particles were as short as 75 mμ. It seems possible that these short particles corresponded to viruses sedimenting at a markedly lower rate than the complete virus and are characterized by lack of infectivity and decreased hemagglutinating activity. Sokol *et al.* found that this procedure also was not suitable for purification of cell-associated virus. However the authors compared the properties of intra- and extracellular viruses purified by the same method. Both preparations showed similar infectivity, HA:CF ratios. However, some preparations of intracellular virus showed much less HA activity and contained a large amount of light CF antigen. All these experiments were done with HEP Flury virus and BHK cell cultures. The final preparations were 1000–3000 times purer than the original tissue culture fluid, as judged by the ratio of infectivity to protein content.

The sedimentation coefficient of infectious rabies virus is approximately 600 S (Neurath *et al.*, 1966). The buoyant density of the purified virus, which was shown to be homogeneous by sucrose density gradient centrifugation, was found to be 1.17 gm/cm^3 after centrifugation at 61,000 *g* for 18 hours (Sokol *et al.*, 1968). The specific activities per milliliter of protein were 10^{10} PFU, 10^4 HAU, 5×10^3 CF. Precipitin tests in 1% agarose gel usually yielded a single line when purified virus was reacted with antirabic serum. Two additional specific lines considered to be breakdown products of the virus were often seen.

In spite of the progress in purification techniques for rabies virus, no direct analysis of its chemical composition was reported until August, 1969. Two reviews which appeared recently, refer briefly to chemical analysis being done at the Wistar Institute (Campbell *et al.*, 1968a; Hummeler and Koprowski, 1969). Detailed data have just recently been reported by Sokol *et al.* (1969). Purified uridine-^{3}H-labeled rabies virions were treated at 20°C for 10 minutes with 5 mg sodium deoxycholate per 1000 HAU of virus and then centrifuged in linear gradient of sucrose followed by equilibrium centrifugation in CsCl gradient. The nucelocapsid recovered in the middle of the gradient exhibited CF but not HA activity. The sedimentation coefficient of the nucleocapsid was approximately 200 S and its buoyant density in CsCl was 1.32. Examination under the electron microscope of nucleocapsids revealed that they are single stranded and right-hand helices. The nucleocapsid was composed of 96% protein and 4% RNA. Most of the RNA extracted either from purified virions or from nucleocapsid preparations sedimented as single component with a sharp peak. The sedimentation coefficient was 45 S and the molecular weight was about 4.6×10^6 daltons. Its sensitivity to RNase and its buoyant density being identical with that of ribosomal RNA, indicated that it was single-stranded.

IV. Hemagglutination

In spite of repeated attempts to demonstrate hemagglutination, it was not until 1968 that Halonen and his co-workers discovered the rabies virus hemagglutinin (HA). They had previously been able to demonstrate hemagglutinating activity of rubella virus preparations which had been propagated in serum-free suspension cultures of BHK-21/13S cells in order to avoid the effect of a serum inhibitor. They had also determined conditions for optimal HA titration (Halonen *et al.*, 1967a, b). Application of the same techniques yielded success with the rabies virus. They used the CVS strain of rabies virus propagated in BHK-21 cells which was maintained in medium containing 0.4% bovine albumin and no serum. Optimal conditions included an inhibitor-free medium, a low temperature (0°–4°C), a pH of 6.2, and the use of goose erythrocytes. Rubella HA titers at room temperature are only slightly lower than those at lower temperature and the patterns, once developed, are stable at room temperature. In contrast to rubella, the temperature requirement for rabies is so strict that the hemagglutination pattern rapidly changes to negative at room temperature, and even at a low temperature in higher dilutions starts to disappear in 60 minutes. Erythrocytes of various species were agglutinated but only 2-day-old chick (HA titer: 8 to 16) or goose erythrocytes (HA titer: 32) were practical for use. The optimal pH range was similar to that of arboviruses. It was shown that rabies HA inhibitor, present in high titer (1:10,000 to 40,000) in sera of many mammals, is difficult to remove and is adsorbed by 25% kaolin at pH 9.0 in tenfold dilution. Later, Kuwert *et al.* (1968) extended the search for HA to other rabies strains. By use of highly purified and concentrated viruses, it was found that the HEP Flury strain grown in BHK cells yielded the highest infectivity and HA titer. On the other hand, virus (PM strain) grown in mouse and hamster brain did not agglutinate goose erythrocytes. A similar HA has been demonstrated with other rhabdoviruses, such as vesicular stomatitis virus, cocal, and Kern Canyon viruses, but not with Flanders virus. These latter viruses were prepared from brains of infected suckling mice (Halonen *et al.*, 1968). Erythrocytes pretreated with rabies virus could still be agglutinated again by the same strain. Furthermore, receptor destroying enzyme or KIO_4 had no effect on receptors of the erythrocyte for rabies virus, probably because its capsid had no neuraminidase activity, in contrast to the myxoviruses. Results of density gradient centrifugation of extracellular rabies virus, as briefly described in the previous section, indicated that the hemagglutinating activity was a property of the virus particles and "soluble" HA was not present. Sokol *et al.* (1968) found that cell-associated and extracellular viruses (HEP Flury) sedimented at the same rate and showed similar ratio of infectivity to HA. However, the same group, using the same strain, reported that intracellular virus released from cells by freezing and thawing followed by sonication, showed much lower HA than extracellular virus; however, no HA inhibitor was detected. They proposed, therefore, that extracellular virus acquires HA during budding from cell membrane (Kuwert *et al.*, 1968). This proposal has been verified by the results of fractionation of the HA activity of DOC-disrupted rabies virus by centrifugation in sucrose density gradient (Sokol *et al.*, 1969). The component at the top of the gradient (viral envelope) exhibited HA activity. However, fractions 2 and 3 at the top retained a portion capable of binding hemagglutinin, as evidenced by loss of HA activity and acquisition of hemagglutination-inhibition activity.

Rabies virus HA was found to be sensitive to heating at 56°C and to treatment with proteolytic enzyme, lipid solvent, β-propiolactone, and compounds blocking sulfhydryl group, such as $HgCl_2$ and *p*-chloromercuribenzoate. KIO_4 did not affect HA, but decreased infectivity. Compounds capable of cleaving the —S═S— bounds, such as 2-mercaptoethanol, had no effect on HA and infectivity. Based on these results, it was concluded that HA is presumably protein or lipidprotein and the SH-groups may play an important role in attachment of rabies virus to the erythrocyte (Kuwert *et al.*, 1968).

V. Soluble Antigen

Like a number of other virus infections, the rabies virus-infected cells produce a complement-fixing soluble antigen which can be separated from the virus by centrifugation. The small particles of soluble antigen were found to be approximately 12 mμ in diameter as determined by diffusion (Polson and Wessler, 1953). Paralleling this measurement, centrifugation experiments showed a sedimentation coefficient of approximately 25 S. This latter value corresponded well with that calculated for a protein of 12 mμ diameter. From results obtained by zonal centrifugation, 23 S and 10 S were calculated for the two soluble antigens present in infected tissue culture fluid. The density of the antigens in cesium chloride solution was 1.26 gm/ml (Neurath *et al.*, 1966). This result is consistent with the two precipitation lines found by the Ouchterlony method (Grasset and Atanasiu, 1961). Mead (1962a) compared different methods for purifying rabies soluble antigen from brain tissue. He found that the initial step of precipitation at pH 4.5 was most effective. Batch adsorption of impurities on calcium phosphate from acid-precipitated purified extracts was a fairly efficient method; the product gave a single peak by electrophoresis, and this coincided with the CF activity. Chromatography on calcium phosphate or DEAE-cellulose was also recommended. The purity of Mead's best samples was 2 to 10 times that of the crude extract. Immunoprecipitation tests showed that this purified soluble antigen contained at least 2 and probably 4 specific antigens (Mead, 1962b). In the course of differential centrifugation of mouse brains infected with the Flury strain virus, the heavy fraction, which included practically all the infectivity, was almost entirely separated from the soluble antigen (van den Ende *et al.*, 1957). In turn, only a small amount of soluble antigen was subsequently released from the heavy fraction when this was exposed to repeated freezing and thawing or ultrasonic vibration. It was suggested that the latter probably came from some tissue component rather than the intact viruses. Sokol *et al.* (1968) have presented interesting data from their purification experiment of rabies virus grown *in vitro*. When crude preparations, harvested from infected cells, were fractionated by sucrose density gradient centrifugation, a large amount of light CF antigen, probably of cellular origin, was demonstrated at the same position as the band which contained RNA. On the other hand, almost as much CF antigen was found in the fraction exhibiting high infectivity and HA activity. Similar infectivity CF or HA:CF ratios were also demonstrated in the virus band prepared from extracellular virus materials. Under somewhat different cell conditions, the heavier virions had high infectivity, HA, and CF activities, whereas the lighter virions had little infectivity, decreased HA, but similar CF activity. Murphy *et al.* (1968) stated that approximately 23% of the total CF activity was associated with fractions containing normal and aberrant viral forms. Since highly purified virus materials were utilized as CF antigen, without treatment to release the internal component of the virus, it is possible that the CF antigenic site is in the membrane or envelope of virus. Another possibility is that soluble antigens leak out spontaneously from viruses distorted during the purification procedure. In either case, the evidence obviously contradicts van den Ende's results described above. Therefore, Campbell *et al.* (1968b) have raised the question as to whether soluble antigens represent structural components of the virus not yet incorporated into the virus particles, or whether they are enzymes induced by viral replication. Antibodies produced against purified split products of viruses, should be used to determine the site of formation of virus-specific antigens.

When centrifuged samples of mouse brains were tested at varying times after infection, the rise of infectivity preceded the appearance of soluble antigen. The soluble antigen, however, continued to increase after maximum titers of infectivity had been obtained. Soluble antigen was characterized as follows (van den Ende *et al.*, 1957): it was fairly stable at pH 6.0 to 10.0, and could be partially purified by precipitation at pH 4.3, even though only part of the original antigen can be recovered. It withstood heating at 56°C, and treatment with 0.5% phenol or 0.35% formaldehyde without loss of *in vitro* serological activity. The action of both crystalline trypsin and ribonuclease resulted in reduction of CF power of the antigen to approximately ⅔ or half of the original. Mead (1962b) demonstrated that the large antigen sedimenting slowly at 70,000 *g*, was resistant to trypsin, whereas smaller antigen was destroyed by trypsin and probably two antigens of intermediate size were also sensitive to trypsin.

VI. Biological Activities

An interference phenomenon has been shown with varying host systems infected with rabies virus, both *in vitro* and *in vivo* (Kaplan *et al.*, 1960, 1962; Fernandes *et al.*, 1964; Wiktor *et al.*, 1964; Selimov *et al.*, 1965; Stewart and Sulkin, 1966; Yoshino *et al.*, 1966b). All of these investigations, except that of Stewart and Sulkin, were carried out employing infected tissue cultures. Although rabies virus growth was accompanied by the production of a considerable amount of interferon in these tissue cultures, attempts to isolate an interferonlike substance from human diploid cell strain (WI-38) infected with HEP Flury virus as well as from rabbit endothelial cell-CVS virus system exhibiting endosymbiotic relationship, were unsuccessful (Wiktor *et al.*, 1964; Fernandes *et al.*, 1964). On the other hand, Stewart and Sulkin (1966), using an *in vivo* system, succeeded in isolation of rabies-induced interferon from hamsters infected intramuscularly with a large dose of CVS virus. The brain contained the largest amount of interferon, with lower levels of interferon, corresponding to the centrifugal spread of rabies virus from brain to different organs; blood, spleen, lung, kidney, and brown fat contained a little interferon but none was recovered from liver. When hamsters were intramuscularly inoculated with a strain of virus which was pathogenic only if inoculated intracerebrally, interferon was not induced in any of the tissue assayed. This clearly indicates that interferon is detected only in the presence of large amounts of infective virus. In general, it appears that titers of interferon induced by rabies virus grown *in vivo* are higher than those *in vitro*, as has been reported for Newcastle disease virus by Finter (1965).

When chick embryo fibroblast monolayers were infected with HEP Flury virus at a multiplicity of higher than 0.1 PFU/cell, no plaque developed (Yoshino *et al.*, 1966b). Although similar suppression of virus replication has been recognized in cells heavily infected with other viruses (Chambers, 1957; Chany, 1961; Uchida *et al.*, 1966), a complete absence of viral plaques, as produced by rabies virus, has never been observed with other systems. The authors concluded that this autointerference was not due to the presence of interferon in the seed virus suspension, nor to the presence of tissue components in the inoculum. Although autointerference may be due to production of interferon caused by a massive viral infection of cells, the mechanism underlying this phenomenon has remained unresolved. A similar autointerference phenomenon has also been observed during studies on pathogenic properties of Flury strain following prolonged cultivation in the chick embryo (Koprowski *et al.*, 1954). As depicted in Fig. 3, different susceptibilities to HEP Flury virus were shown in six species of mammals. The mortality rate indicates that adult mice, rabbits, and dogs were equally nonsusceptible, whereas rhesus monkeys and baby mice were highly susceptible to intracranial inoculation with this virus. In two other species, hamster and guinea pigs, there was, quantitatively, an intermediate susceptibility and the peak mortality appeared with low dilutions of the virus. From these results, Koprowski and co-workers assumed that HEP Flury virus represented a mixed viral population consisting of particles pathogenic for hamster and guinea pigs and of particles deprived of their pathogenic properties. The presence of the former became manifest only after the virus was used at higher dilutions. This phenomenon might be caused by interference produced by particles nonpathogenic for these animals with those that still remained pathogenic. In order to test this hypothesis, HEP Flury virus suspensions were used as diluent for titrations of a sample derived from LEP Flury virus. The results indicated that HEP Flury virus interfered with the hamster pathogen LEP Flury virus. However, in parallel experiments, when LEP Flury virus was replaced by street or by rodent-fixed viruses, no interference was observed. Although this latter failure of interference with an immunologically identical virus cannot yet be explained, the authors assumed that even in the early stage of adaptation of rabies virus to the chick embryo, viruses might multiply in cells other than those attacked by the unadapted street or rodent-fixed strains.

These investigations, using a chick embryo adapted rabies virus, demonstrated that the virus preparation was not homogenous; different forms

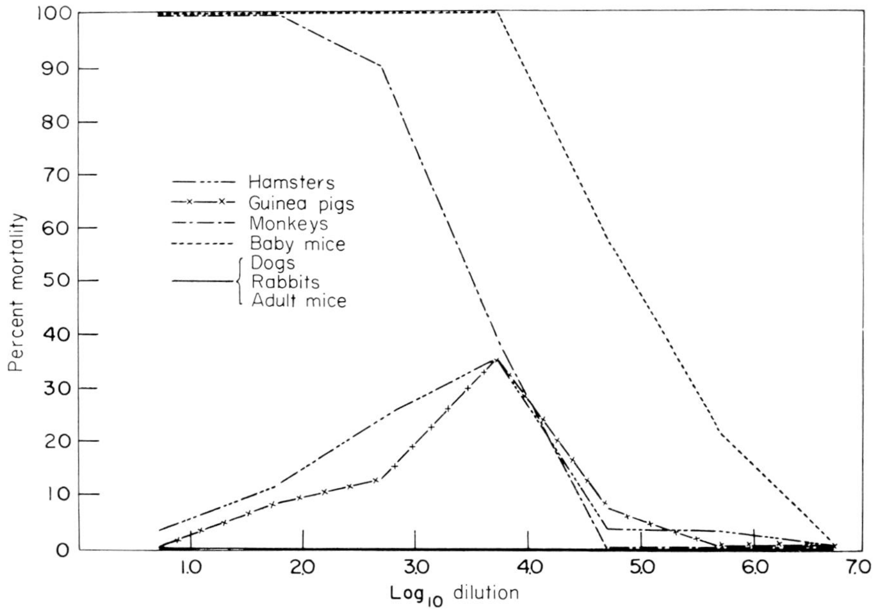

FIG. 3. Percentage mortality of test animals inoculated intracerebrally with dilutions of HEP Flury virus. [Courtesy of Dr. H. Koprowski *et al.* (1954).]

of virus were present each in varying stages of adaptation to the chick embryo. Since the establishment of the Pasteur strain, modified in its properties by intracerebral passage through rabbits, numerous efforts in the same direction have been made, mostly for the practical purpose of vaccination (Pasteur, 1885).

At present, the terms "street" and "fixed" virus are commonly used, implying a rather sharp differentiation. However, street rabies viruses vary greatly in their fixation, some becoming fixed almost at once, other strains after approximately 50 passages, and some strains never at all.

An unusual case was reported by Helman in which no fixation developed after 60 passages. With the 11th passaged brain, however, another parallel series of passages was initiated and then fixation occurred with this line of virus (van Rooyen and Rhodes, 1948). Because of these biological characteristics, Dean *et al.* (1963) questioned the use of the term "street" virus, since most isolates now originate from rural areas, and, in addition, the differences between street and fixed strains seem less important than was previously believed. However, we do not yet know the mechanism of adaptation which probably involves viral mutation or selection. The search for various markers of rabies virus will, in time, contribute to an analysis of this.

VII. Cytopathology of Infected Cells

Morphological aspects of the infection will be discussed in terms of both the light and electron microscopy. The main rabic lesions are localized in the nerve cells throughout the central nervous system. The degenerative changes of nerve cells are of varied degree, from chromatolysis and nuclear pyknosis to acidophilic necrosis. Many degenerative nerve cells, especially in the cord and spinal ganglions, are surrounded by mononuclear leukocytes, the cell is completely destroyed, and neuronophagia occurs. The grade of histological changes varies greatly depending upon many unknown and known factors, such as the strain of rabies virus, the period between the onset of clinical signs and death. These lesions are not regarded as characteristic of rabies infection, because they are very similar to those found in other viral encephalitides. In his search for the pathognomonic change of rabies, Negri (1903) described the inclusion body which now goes by his name. These bodies are eosinophilic masses measuring up to 10 μ and containing an internal structure with granules of chromatinlike material. They are usually found in more or less undamaged nerve cells, particularly in Ammon's horn, cerebral cortex, medulla, and cerebellum (Purkinje's cell). The significance of the Negri body is fully discussed later in this section.

Electron microscopic observations of thin sections of rabies-infected tissues have been carried out on both *in vivo* materials, such as brain and salivary gland tissues, or tissue culture preparations. They have all been consistent in that the viruses appear at various planes in the cut surfaces, are rod shaped and are regularly associated with a characteristic matrix (Matsumoto, 1962, 1963; Davies *et al.*, 1963; Roots and Schultz, 1963; Atanasiu *et al.*, 1963a,b; Johnson and Mercer, 1964; Jenson *et al.*, 1969; Hummeler *et al.*, 1967). These matrices are visible as eosinophilic inclusion bodies within the cytoplasm under the light microscope, especially well seen in infected cultured cells (Fernandes *et al.*, 1964) (Fig. 4). Under the electron microscope the homogeneous ground substance of the matrix is composed of relatively electron dense filamentous aggregates. Within or contiguous to these matrices are found the rabies virions, these in turn within the swollen vesicles of the endoplasmic reticulum (Fig. 5). In cross section, the virus appears to consist of a core surrounded by double membranes. The core, with an average diameter of 40 mμ, most often appears empty, but occasionally some material is found inside. The double membranes are electron opaque so that under a lower magnification they appear as a single thick layer. The outer membrane which is continuous with the membrane of the endoplasmic retic-

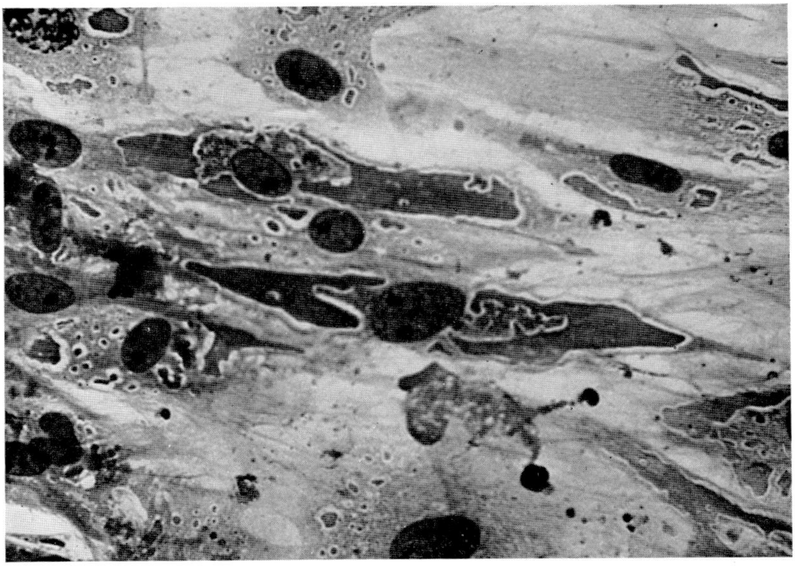

FIG. 4. Chick embryo fibroblasts infected with HEP Flury virus, 7 days after infection. Giemsa staining, $\times$ 800.

ulum is covered by surface projections about 8 mμ long. Thus, the size and shape of the virions in the cell are quite similar to that of extracellular viruses observed by negative staining. The identification of rabies virus by means of ferritin-labeled antibodies has been reported by Atanasiu *et al.* (1963c). Additional variations in morphology occur depending on the particular combination of virus strain and host cell.

Three types of elongated particles are found in close relationship to the matrix, when brain tissue infected with a street rabies virus is examined (Matsumoto, 1962, 1963; Matsumoto and Miyamoto, 1966). The largest particle is 120–130 mμ in width, has a single limiting membrane, and has a light interior with a ground substance similar to that of the matrix. The same structure has also been demonstrated within neurons also infected with street virus (Dierkes *et al.*, 1969). The medium sized particle is 110–120 mμ in width and has a moderately dense peripheral space bounded by parallel double membranes. Neither type of particle is related to any vesicular structure and both appear to be free within the matrix. The ends of the particles are open to the ground substance of the matrix at both sides. In addition to forming uniform rods, the same double membranous structures are found in an irregular arrangement (Matsumoto, 1963; Miyamoto, 1965; Jenson *et al.*, 1967). The last type

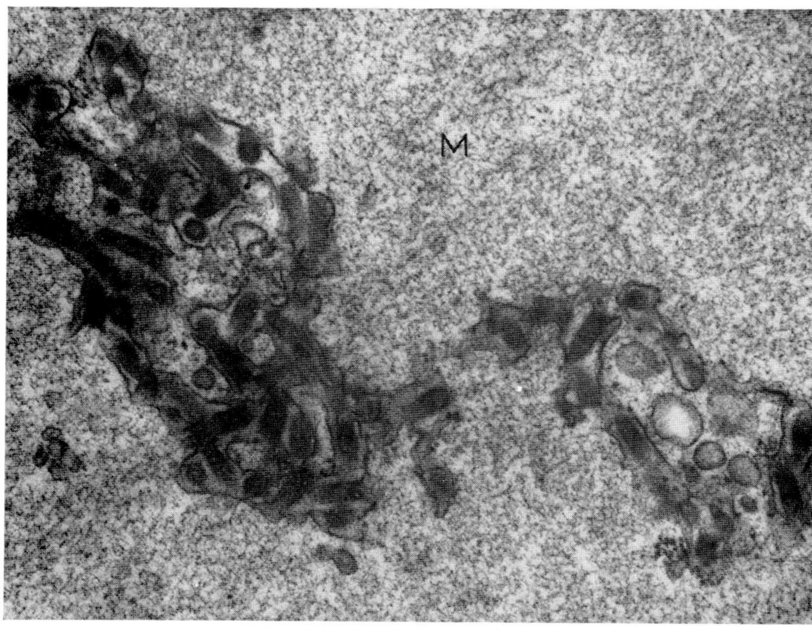

FIG. 5. A part of a nerve cell infected with a street rabies virus. A number of viruses are enclosed within swollen endoplasmic reticulum located in matrix (M). × 45,000.

of rod is the smallest and regularly appears within vesicles, as described in detail above. It has been noted by all investigators that most of the morphologically identifiable virus in both tissue culture and in the animal consists of forms which project from membranes of cytoplasmic vesicles or the cell surface. One exception was our study of the street virus (Matsumoto, 1962, 1963).

Branching and segmentation of long rods, which have been seen by negative staining, are also occasionally observed in some sections (Miyamoto and Matsumoto, 1967), as schematically shown in the Fig. 6.

However, it seems to be difficult to decide whether all projecting rabies viruses mature via the cell surface, because the frequency of appearance of such figures has been low compared with the large number of viruses which appeared within vesicles. In spite of similarities among these elongated particles, their morphological relationship to virus growth remains unknown.

The next problem is the site of virus assembly. The bullet-shaped virus of rabies appears to be formed by a process of budding within the host cells. In tissue culture systems, viruses are formed in variable quantites by budding from the cell surface. This would seem partly to sup-

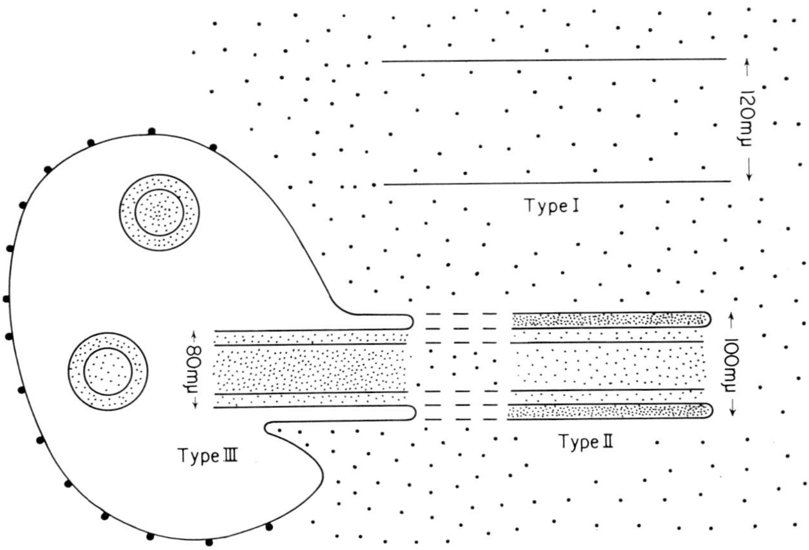

FIG. 6. Schematic diagram of three types of the rabies virus found in infected cells.

port the assumption that the rabies virus belongs to the myxovirus group. However, the participation of the cellular membrane system in virus assembly is more complicated in the case of rabies infection, than in myxoviruses which are only identified at the surface of infected cells. Hummeler *et al.* (1967) using cultured BHK-21 cells infected with four different strains, respectively, reported a disproportionately large ratio of viruses within the cytoplasm to that released from the cell surface. Recently, it was shown by Matsumoto and Kawai (1969) that virus assembly occurs at the cell membrane, (Fig. 7 and 8) especially in the later stage of infection, when the HEP Flury virus which was also utilized by Hummeler *et al.* (1968) was inoculated into chick embryo fibroblast monolayers. In contrast, when infected brain tissues were observed, formation of virus

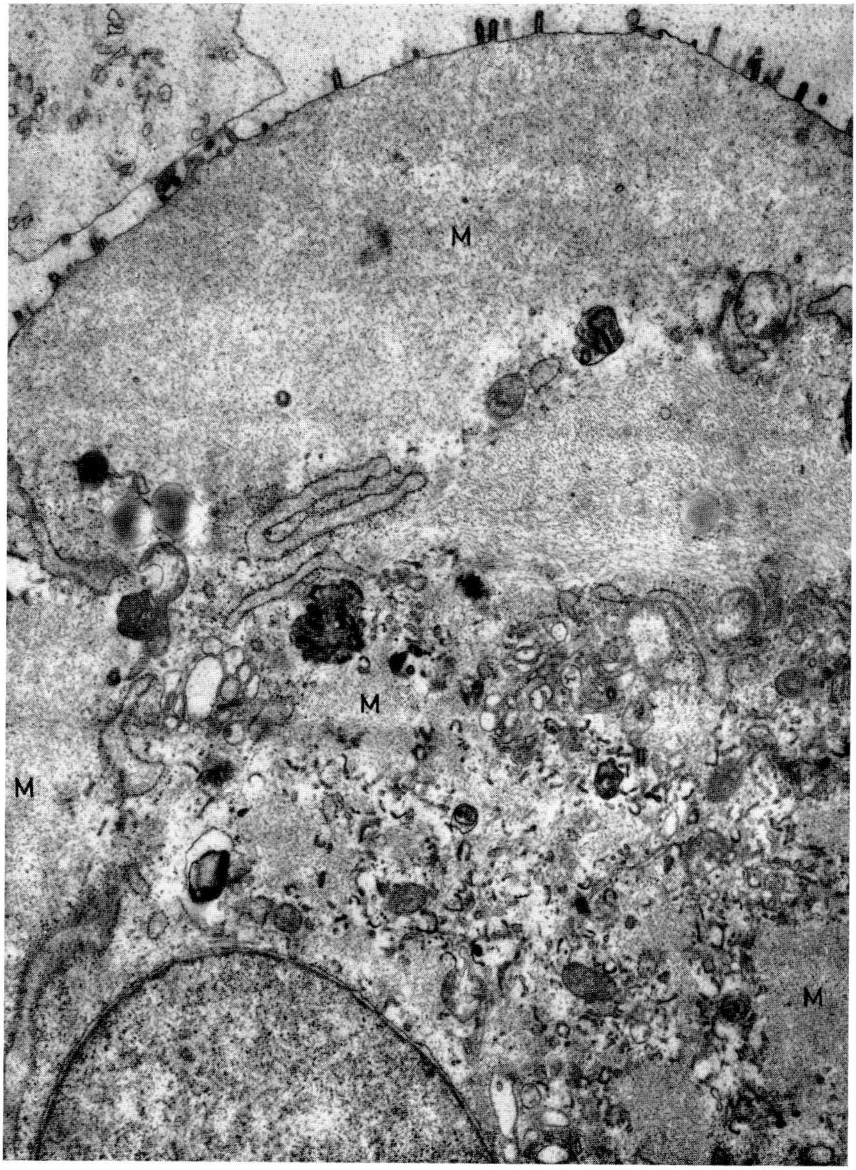

FIG. 7. Much of the cytoplasm of a chick embryo fibroblast is occupied by matrices (M). Virus particles bud out from a portion of the cell surface where a matrix is located near by; 7 days after infection. × 20,000.

was completely restricted to the inside of infected nerve cells and to some kinds of glia cells. These findings suggest that the site of virus assembly is not exclusively within the intracytoplasmic membrane systems but varies, depending on the combination of virus and host cell. In addition, it was recently shown by Dierkes *et al.* (1969) that numerous virus particles were released from the cell surface of salivary gland cells after intracerebral inoculation of a street virus. Of particular interest is the fact that no virus release from the cell surface was seen in electron micrographs of nerve cells in brain tissue of the same infected fox. As for this predeliction for virus formation inside nerve cells *in vivo*, at one time we sought an explanation in the histological topography of nervous tissue. Each nerve cell is entirely covered by parts of astrocytes and oligodendroglyiocytes at a definite interval of 80 Å. This compact attachment may make it difficult for progeny viruses to bud out into the extracellular space. However, such a simple interpretation is unlikely, since virus release from the cell surface of nerve cells has been clearly illustrated by Murphy and Fields (1967) in another rhabdovirus, Kern Canyon virus.

It is well known that two kinds of rhabdovirus, rabies and hemorrhagic septicemia of the rainbow trout, have been distinguished from other members of the group by the formation of the characteristic matrix (cytoplasmic inclusion body). This inclusion body had been described by Atanasiu and Laurent (1957) who examined infected mouse ependymoma cells in tissue culture. Concurrent with the appearance these eosinophilic inclusion bodies, specific immunofluorescence staining revealed brilliant masses within the cells (Fig. 9). Until now, however, most rabies studies using fluorescent antibody staining have not shown the fluorescent substances in detail because all studies have used immune sera stimulated by crude antigens. Some progress in this direction has been made by Hummeler *et al.* (1968) who applied immune serum prepared against a purified virus preparation, for immunological electron microscopy studies with ferritin-conjugated antibodies. They showed that the strands (filamentous structures) which constituted the ground substance of matrices were specifically and distinctly labeled. In addition, labeled strands appeared to be incorporated into the viruses leaving the cellular membrane. Thus, the assembly of viral components is similar to that of some paramyxoviruses, such as parainfluenza 2 or SV 5 (Howe *et al.*, 1967; Compans *et al.*, 1967). Hummeler *et al.* (1968) claimed that this incorporation of strands from the matrix into virions during morphogenesis and the diameter of about 15 mμ in sections made it obvious that the viruses are identical with the nucleoprotein of rabies virus which was seen in negative contrast.

Reports on the biosynthesis of the inclusion bodies which are contrary

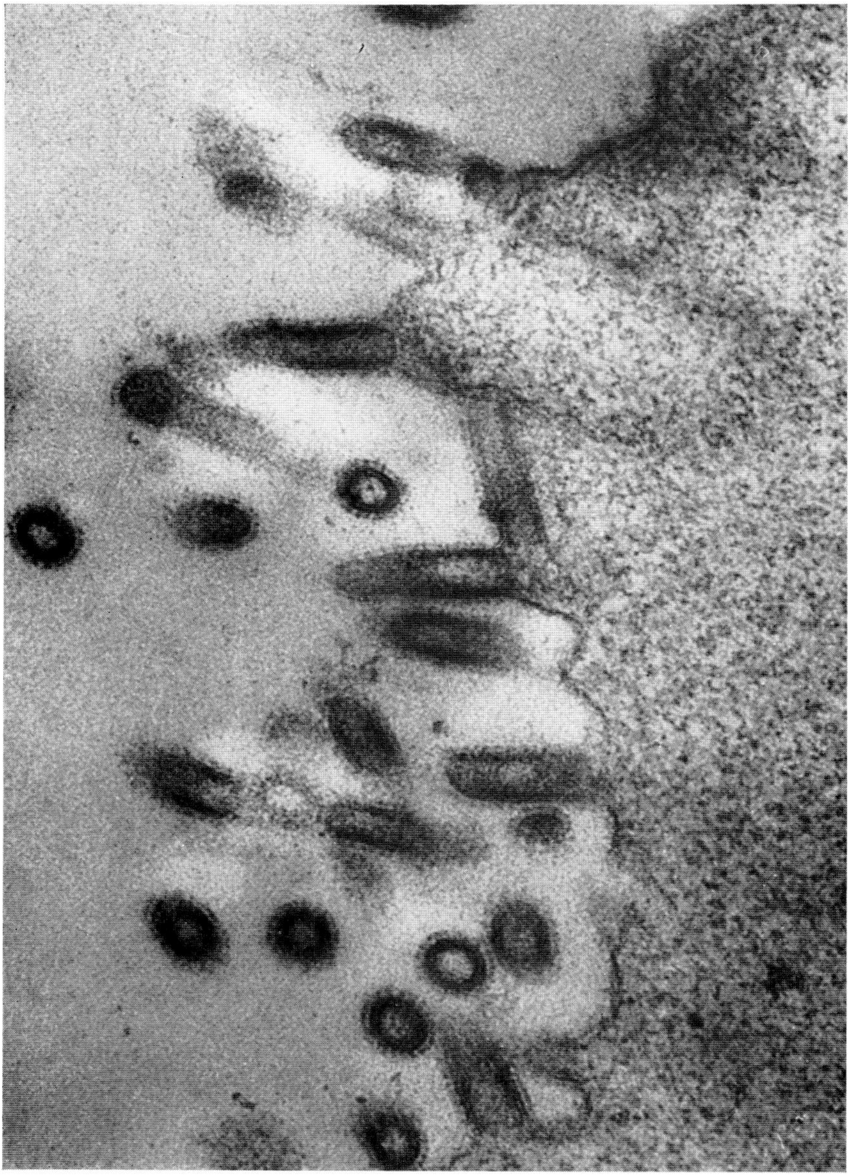

FIG. 8. Virus release from the cell membrane. Note the continuity between the cell membrane and the outer layer of the double membrane of the virus particle. × 120,000.

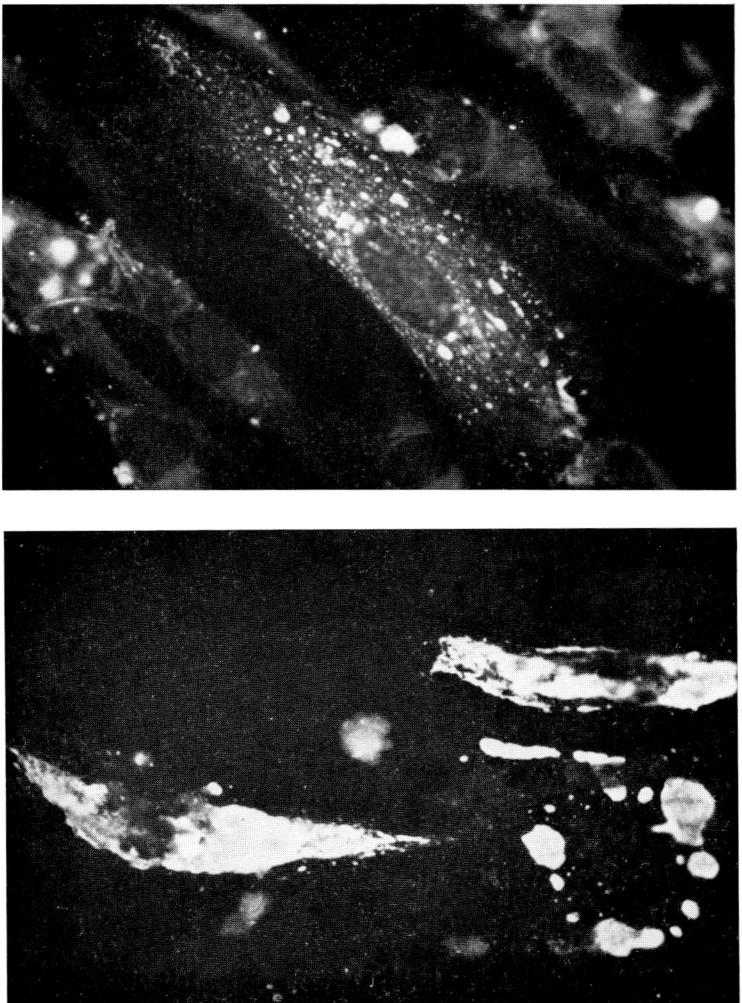

FIG. 9. Immunofluorescent antibody staining. (a) Numerous fluorescing granules are seen throughout the cytoplasm, 48 hours after infection. (b) Appearance of prominent large fluorescing inclusion bodies, 7 days after infection. × 800.

to this interpretation have been published. Fernandes *et al.* (1964) and Defendi and Wiktor (1966) examined autoradiographs of cultured rabbit endothelium cell chronically infected with rabies virus and found that the areas of the inclusion bodies had the same pattern of labeling by uridine-^{3}H as the other areas of the cytoplasm. After incubation with thymidine-^{3}H, no grain deposition was observed in the cytoplasm. These results seem to indicate that the inclusion bodies are not the site of viral nucleic acid synthesis and therefore cannot be regarded as virus factories. The rabies-infected rabbit endothelium cell line is particularly endosymbiotic compared to other cell systems infected with rabies virus, and all cells containing viral specific antigen can propagate normally without any detectable disturbance of cellular replication (Fernandes *et al.*, 1964). Therefore, one may argue that, since the nucleic acid metabolism of these cells is not affected by virus replication, no difference in the proportion of labeling is expected in the cytoplasm. Thus, if other rabies-infected cell systems which do result in cellular degeneration were

TABLE II
CYTOCHEMICAL REACTIONS COMMON TO CYTOPLASMIC INCLUSION BODIES BY RABIES INFECTION *in vitro* AND *in vivo*[a]

Staining method	Substance or group demonstrated	Result
Pauly	Imidazole (histidine), tyrosine, tryptophan	+
Dinitrofluorobenzene	SH, tyrosine, protein-bound amino	+
Alkaline fast green	Histones	−
Ninhydrin-Schiff	Protein-bound amino	+
Acrolein-Schiff	$-NH_2$, $-NH$, SH, imidazole	+
Morel-Sisley	Tyrosine	+
Feulgen	DNA	−
Alcian blue	Acid mucopolysaccharides	−
Dilute toluidine blue		
After nitrosation		+
After RNase digestion	RNA	−

[a] From Love *et al.* (1966a).

chosen, it might be possible to demonstrate the specific synthesis of viral RNA within the inclusion body, since in these cases virus has been shown by electron microscopy using ferritin-conjugated antibodies.

A number of cytochemical studies have been performed on rabies inclusion bodies appearing *in vivo* (Negri body) and *in vitro*. Contradictory findings have been reported in these relatively early studies on the nature of the Negri body as to whether or not it contains nucleic acid. Love *et al.* (1964, 1966a,b) carefully reinvestigated the cytochemistry of Negri bodies *in vivo* and also compared the inclusion bodies produced by the virus under different conditions. Their studies revealed that the ground substance of Negri bodies was stained similarly to the *in vitro* inclusion bodies by methods for protein-bound groups, by Feulgen test, alcian blue, and by dilute toluidine blue after nitrosation (Table II).

Both inclusion bodies were stained by all methods for protein-bound groups except that for histone. It was clear that the inclusion bodies contained small amounts of RNA, because they were weakly and orthochromatically stained by dilute toluidine blue after nitrosation and not stained by this method after digestion with ribonuclease. There was, however, one cytochemical difference between the ground substance of inclusion bodies *in vivo* and *in vitro*, i.e., lipid was present only in Negri bodies, but not in *in vitro* inclusions. This lipid was periodic acid-Schiff positive but did not stain by the direct Schiff reaction for preformed aldehydes. Digestion with diastase had no effect on the PAS reaction. The lipid, therefore, is probably phospholipid or glycolipid, or a mixture of the two. The authors supposed that the absence or presence of lipid was due to different environmental conditions. In the brain the infected nerve cells were surrounded by a milieu rich in lipids that was cytochemically identical to those of the inclusion bodies.

Given the similarities of cytochemistry and immunofluorescence staining between the Negri body and *in vitro* inclusion body, it seems likely that the Negri body is the site of virus replication. Numerous investigations have been carried out in the past in an attempt to elucidate the nature and origin of this inclusion body. The history of these studies up to the era of electron microscopy was reviewed in great detail by van Rooyen and Rhodes (1948) and Miyamoto (1965). The Negri body was alleged to be: (*1*) a colony of viruses, (*2*) degeneration products of nerve cells or, (*3*) reaction products of the cells. It is well known that the capacity of rabies viruses to form inclusion bodies is usually lost after serial passage through experimental animals. However, Negri bodies can still, in certain cases, easily be found in fixed virus infection of various animals (Lépine and Sautter, 1935, 1936). The population of Negri bodies is variable among the different strains of street virus. Johnson (1942) reported, for example, that the Negri body could not be demonstrated in approximately 10% of naturally infected animals and that under certain conditions this percentage might rise to 25%. Goldwasser and Kissling (1958) who first applied the fluorescence antibody technique to the diagnosis of rabies infection demonstrated specific fluorescent antibody staining of fixed virus as well as of street virus in strains which did not form Negri bodies. These unexpected findings have suggested, probably incorrectly, that the Negri body is not identical with the site of virus growth (matrix) but is secondarily derived from degenerative cellular constituents (Lépine and Croissant, 1951; Hottle *et al.*, 1951; Matsumoto, 1963). In order to determine the significance of the Negri body, Miyamoto and Matsumoto (1965) compared Negri bodies observed by light and electron microscopy in alternative thick (1 μ) and thin sections cut from the same nerve cell band of Ammon's horn. It was found that the eosinophilic ground substance of the Negri bodies is identical to the matrix seen in the electron micrographs and, hence, that the Negri body does correspond to the site of virus replication. In addition, observations of consecutive thick and thin sections revealed that the so-called inner body which is a characteristic constituent of the Negri body, is composed of virus particles associated with small amounts of cellular components. The presence of inner bodies within the Negri body was first described by Negri (1909). These internal basophilic granules have been given much attention taxonomically, since they permit differentiation of the Negri body from other viral or nonviral inclusion bodies. Therefore, the term "Negri body," strictly speaking, should refer only to bodies containing internal basophilic structures. Goodpasture (1925) recognized Negri-like bodies containing no internal structure in the brains of rabbits infected with street virus and termed them "lyssa bodies" for practical as well as theoretical reasons. He emphasized that lyssa bodies were, for the most part, small. A number of small inclusion bodies were found intermingled with typical Negri bodies. In addition small Negri bodies contained fewer inner bodies than large ones. The morphological appearance of inner bodies under the electron microscope is quite similar to that of the cytoplasmic areas where virus assembly occurs contiguous to the edges of the matrix. Therefore, it may be that Negri bodies are formed by the fusion of contiguous small inclusion bodies and, that during this process, the cytoplasmic portion close to them has been included to form the inner bodies. It seems likely, therefore, that the presence of the inner body is not essential and that the term "Negri body" may be used in a wider sense to include "lyssa body."

If the Negri body is identical with the matrix, which plays an essential role in virus growth, this immediately raises the question of why the fixed virus does not produce Negri bodies within the nerve cell. In an attempt to clarify this problem, Miyamoto and Matsumoto (1967) studied the comparative neuropathology of Ammon's horn produced by two strains of rabies virus; one which readily produces Negri bodies compared to the other which did not produce any (HEP Flury strain) (Figs. 10 and 11). As reported in earlier studies, nerve cells containing Negri bodies appeared otherwise very slightly damaged. In striking contrast, in the case of the fixed virus infection, nerve cells showed various grades of degeneration. The characteristic matrices were apparent within these cells in the electron microscope but were greatly reduced in volume. This evidence suggests that the fixed virus injures nerve cells so extensively that the full development of the typical Negri body as recognized by the light microscope, cannot occur.

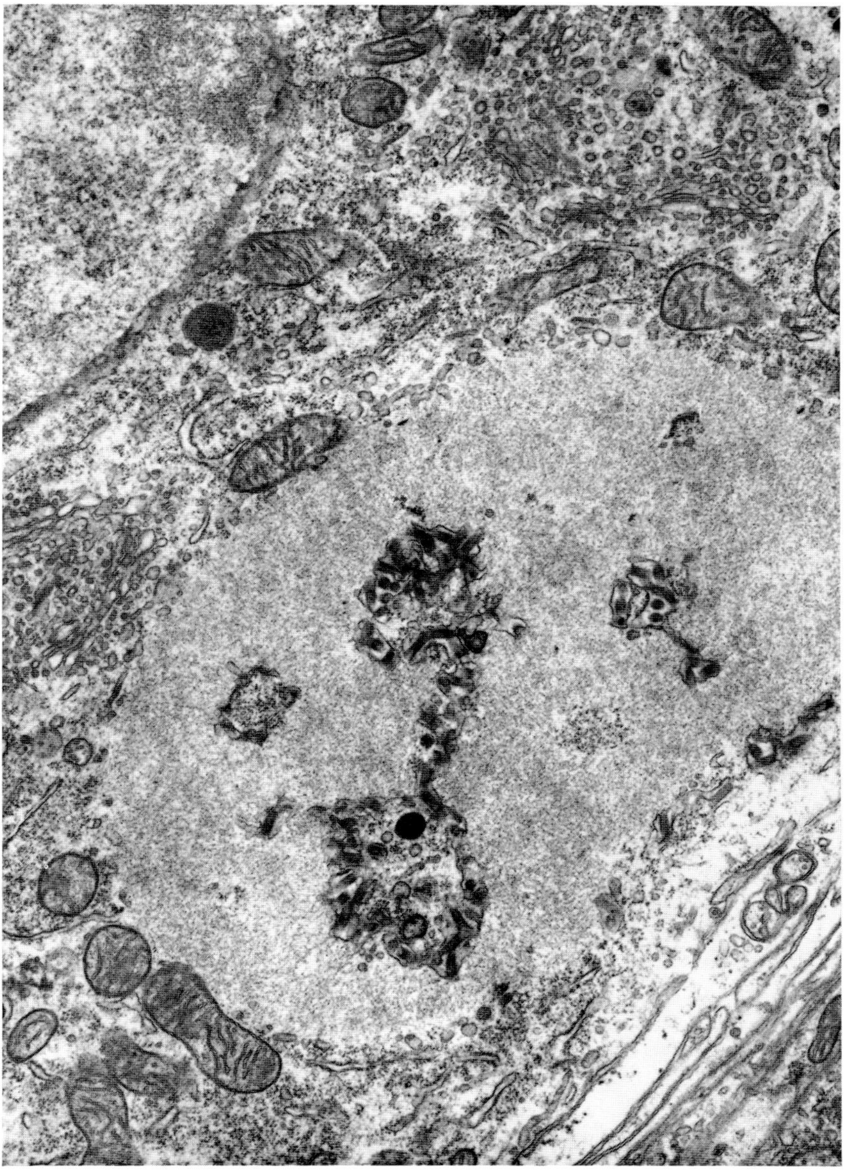

FIG. 10. A Negri body which contains several inner bodies. × 19,200.

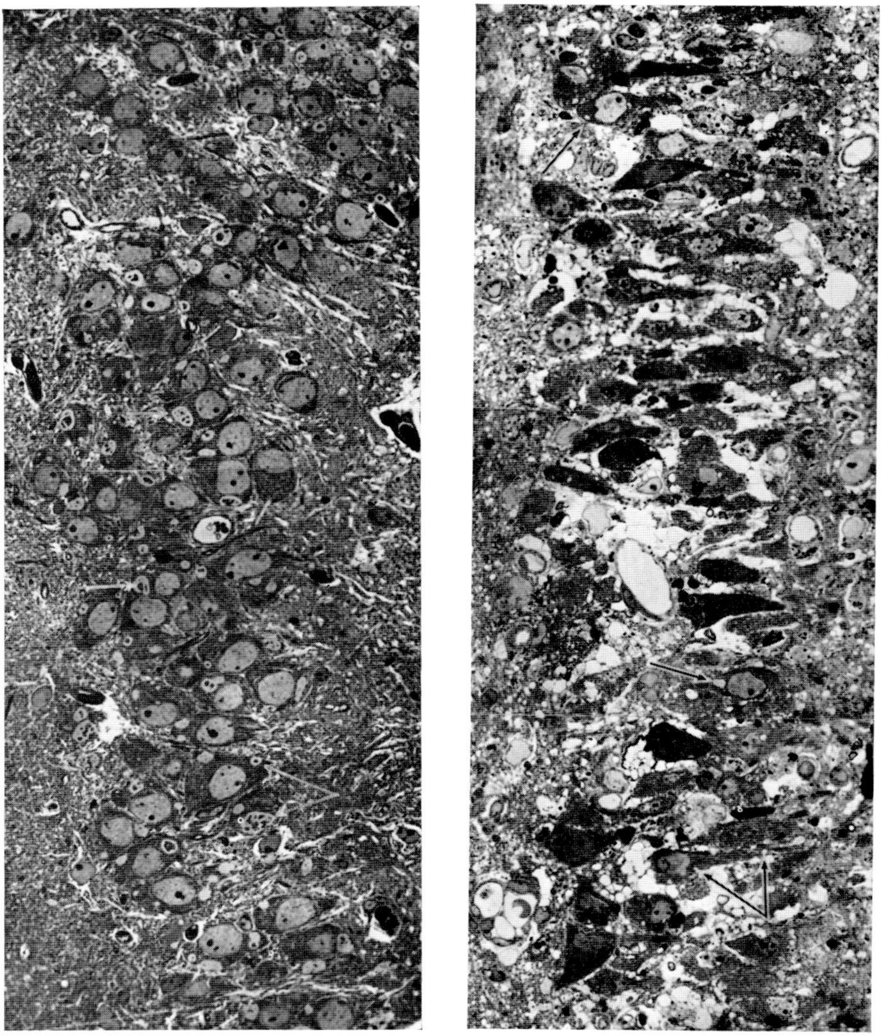

a b

FIG. 11. Light micrographs of Ammon's horn in the mouse hippocampus, fixed with osmium tetroxide, embedded in Epon, and stained with toluidine blue solution. (a) Street rabies infection. Nerve cells, most of which contain lightly stained inclusion bodies (Negri body), are closely packed. Several representative inclusions are indicated by arrows. Note little or no sign of degeneration of nerve cells, except for the occurrence of Negri bodies. (b) Fixed virus infection. In contrast to (a), marked degeneration of nerve cells is apparent. Inclusions are found within slightly damaged cells (arrows). × 280.

Lentz (1909) first observed structures which occur extracellularly, among nerve cells in the central nervous system of rabbits infected with fixed virus. Lentz bodies are similar to Negri bodies in that they are eosinophilic and contain blue inner structures. Light microscopic observation of fixed virus infection revealed that some degenerating nerve cells were reduced in volume and had an intensely eosinophilic cytoplasm (Miyamoto and Matsumoto, 1967). These necrotic cells, some of which had pyknotic nuclei, were found amidst normal or slightly damaged cells. It, therefore, seems likely that the Lentz bodies are severely damaged nerve cells.

VIII. Growth in Tissue Cultures

It took a long time and a great deal of work before tissue culture systems suitable for rabies research were established. The main goal has been, of course, to find the right combination of tissue culture and virus strain which gives high yields of progency viruses, comparable to that obtained from brains of infected animals, and in the presence of reproducible cytopathic effects. Earlier attempts summarized by Sanders *et al.* (1953) utilizing brain tissue from various sources did not reach a satisfactory level. Atanasiu *et al.* (1961) demonstrated cytoplasmic inclusion bodies in a mouse ependymal cell line within 2 days after inoculation of street virus. On the other hand, non-nervous tissue cultures have been also utilized to propagate rabies virus (Vieuchange *et al.*, 1956; Kissling, 1958; Fenje, 1960; Atanasiu *et al.*, 1963d; Sokolov and Parfanovich, 1965). Even though propagation of rabies virus produced a high yield of 10^5 to 10^7 by using hamster kidney cells, cytopathic effect was found only very sporadically (Fenje, 1960). The Wistar rabies research group, therefore, postulated that the mechanism of cell injury following infection with rabies virus might be different from that of other viruses grown in the same tissue culture systems. On the basis of this hypothesis, they carried out extensive studies on the rabies virus-cell relationship using 8 strains of fixed virus and 16 tissue culture systems of various types, such as primary cultures, cell lines, and cell strains (Fernandes *et al.*, 1963, 1964; Wiktor *et al.*, 1964; Wiktor, 1966). Propagation of rabies virus was achieved with all types of culture and all viruses tested. However, serial transfers of these materials resulted in a gradual decrease of infectivity, which was finally lost after several passages, depending on the tissue culture system and the virus strain. Subsequently better results were achieved when dispersed cells were exposed to virus, allowed to form monolayers, and growth then maintained by regular redispersion with trypsin and subdivision into new cultures at

3- to 4-day intervals. After several passages, the incidence of cells staining with fluorescent antibody steadily increased. Finally all cells exhibited large fluorescing inclusion bodies. As the proportion of this cell population increased, the cytopathic effect became pronounced with some culture systems, such as the BHK-21 cell line and the human diploid cell strain (WI-38). When infected cultures stopped growing, passage of virus could be continued by mixing infected cells with noninfected cells of the same type at each transfer. With this technique, adaptation of the virus continued, and ultimately at about the 50th passage, virus was transferred from culture to culture by the standard procedure of infecting new cells with medium or cell extract from previously infected culture. In addition to this chronic infection, eventually leading to lysis of cultured cells, different types of infection were encountered as follows: (*1*) infection representing an endosymbiotic relationship between virus and cell, and (*2*) a carrier-type infection. In the case of a rabbit endothelium cell line infected with the CVS strain of virus, cytoplasmic fluorescing inclusion bodies remained small in size and no cytopathic effect was noted throughout the 93 transfers of infected cells. Virus-specific inclusion bodies were detected in the cytoplasm of all cells including those in various stages of mitosis, but only 5% of the infected cells released infectious virus. It was emphasized that no difference between infected and control cultures was found in the growth rate, plating efficiency, morphological features, and nucleic acid synthesis. At higher passage levels, infectivity for other cell cultures was lost. The final result, therefore, was and continued to be a cell population completely infected and one completely noninfected.

Carrier-type infection was represented by BHK cells infected with the CVS strain and dog kidney cells infected with the LEP Flury strain virus. In these cultures, lysis of cells supervened and continuation of virus growth depended on addition of new cells to the culture, as described above. After a few additional passages, a state of infection became established in which only a portion of the cell population was infected. The incidence of infected cells, which served as a reservoir of virus, fluctuated cyclically through serial passages. Dog kidney cultures, maintained in the carrier state by regular medium change without subdivision, continued to yield infectious virus for periods up to 3 months. The serially passed virus gradually became less virulent for mice, as with other cell culture systems.

Rabbit endothelium cell line and human diploid cells infected with different strains of rabies virus were resistant to superinfection with other strains of rabies virus, Eastern equine encephalomyelitis, polio, and Mengo viruses, or vesicular stomatitis virus. Resistance appeared complete in cultures in which all cells contained viral antigen. It was asserted that resistance could not be attributed to production of an interferonlike substance, since all attempts to demonstrate such a substance failed. Further data concerning interferon has been discussed in the previous section.

Other rabies virus-tissue culture systems which yield relatively large amounts of virus in the presence of cytopathic effect have been described (Habel, 1964; Kondo, 1965a; Mikhailovsky and Iliasova, 1966; Mikhailovsky and Selimov, 1966; Hronovsky *et al.*, 1968). Except for the use of Kissling's hamster kidney culture virus (Kissling, 1958), there has been no detailed description of the technical procedure used by Habel. Kondo attempted to overcome the difficulty of the primary chick embryo fibroblasts often sloughing from the glass surface of culture vessels before viral growth reached a maximum. He found that deletion of serum from the maintenance medium eliminated this difficulty and permitted HEP Flury strain virus to adapt to CEF. After serial passages, this culture system yielded high titers (around 10^6 $TCID_{50}$/ml of culture fluid) and showed an intensified CPE about 7 days after inoculation. Mikhailovsky and Iliasova (1966) and Mikhailovsky and Selimov (1966), using the method of serial transfer of mixtures of infected and normal cells, obtained a cytopathic street virus in hamster kidney primary cultures. This pre-adapted virus was subsequently successfully propagated in newborn puppy and guinea pig kidney primary cultures and also in a stable line of swine embryo kidney cells. Hronovsky *et al.* (1966, 1968) also reported the process of adaptation of a street virus to dog kidney primary cultures. From the 4th passage on, the virus produced CPE constantly and the titer of virus yield reached a maximum of 10^7 $TCID_{50}$/ml by the 3rd passage. The ability to produce Negri bodies *in vivo* suddenly decreased after 12 passages *in vitro*, and parallel immunofluorescence staining studies demonstrated diffuse brain lesions in the form of small granules. Intracerebral pathogenicity for mice exceeded that of virus of the same strain propagated by brain passage. A tendency to a reduction in extraneural infection by the same virus was observed during 18 to 28 passages. The authors have supposed from their results that street rabies virus is more readily adapted to *in vitro* propagation than fixed virus.

Only one paper is available concerning application of culture of nervous tissue to rabies research (Fernandes and Pomerat, 1961). The authors presented ample evidence that virus growth, even though in low titer, was accompanied by the presence of inclusion bodies within neurons. In our unpublished experiments using cultured dorsal root ganglions of mouse fetus infection developed quite slowly and also remained in low titer, although a few degenerative neurons stained by fluorescent rabies antibody were observed amidst healthy neurons. There are many vexing problems in obtaining good culture conditions for nerve cells. Nevertheless, this system may offer interesting material for cytological studies of neurotropic virus infection, because each neuron can be successively viewed under high magnification for more than several months.

In vitro cultures of intrascapular brown adipose tissue of the bat supported the growth at 37°C of rabies virus for at least 2 months with no gross degenerative change (Allen *et al.*, 1964; Sulkin *et al.*, 1966). Sulkin *et al.* (1959, 1960) demonstrated that the virus yield in brown fat was relatively high compared to various organs of insectivorous bats infected with rabies virus via the intramuscular route. Given this and the fact that many species of Chiroptera sustain rabies infection in a persistent form, Sulkin *et al.* have proposed that besides the central nervous system, brown fat can serve as a site of replication and storage of virus, especially during periods of hibernation. In order to test this hypothesis, virus growth was measured in infected brown fat cultures at 8°C. Rabies virus persisted for more than 4 months but no conclusive evidence of replication was obtained at this temperature.

Thus, it appears that a low efficiency of infection is common to all the rabies virus-tissue culture systems. Although adsorption and penetration of fixed virus adapted to WI 38 human diploid cells was complete in a few seconds and 1 hour, respectively, the rate of appearance of infected cells determined by immunofluorescence remained 30% after 2 days of incubation (Wiktor, 1966). Such inefficient infectivity has now been overcome by the addition of polycations to the virus inoculum (Kaplan *et al.*, 1967). Small amounts of DEAE-dextran (50 μg/ml) or protamine markedly enhanced the infectivity of virus in some cultured cell lines. The action of polyions appears to be related to their ionic charge, because virus infectivity was inhibited by those having a negative charge (dextran sulfate and heparin). The exact mechanism of this action is unknown, but it was supposed that polycations act by binding to the cellular surface or by complexing with the virus particle at a very early stage or virus-cell interaction.

Reproducible plaquing systems for rabies virus have been discovered in parallel with the development of tissue culture applications (Habel, 1964; Kondo, 1965b; Yoshino *et al.*, 1966a; Sedwick and Wiktor, 1967). The first three papers were concerned with primary chick embryo fibroblast cultures. The efficiency of plaque formation was high, showing the same level of susceptibility as for baby mice and 1-day-old chick embryos (Yoshino *et al.*, 1966a). Recently Kondo (1969) obtained two clones of

HEP Flury strain virus which differ in plaque size. Conversion of small plaques into large ones was accomplished by addition of DEAE-dextran (75 μg/ml), as had been shown for encephalomyocarditis virus (Takemoto and Liebhaber, 1961). Except for plaque size, no other difference between these mutants has been found. Sedwick and Wiktor (1967) suspended rabies virus-BHK-21/13S cell mixture in a medium containing agarose and succeeded in producing plaques averaging 3 mm in diameter, after about 7 days. In this way, it was possible to dissociate contaminating colonies of mycoplasma from plaques of rabies virus and to obtain mycoplasma-free virus preparations (Zgorniak-Nowosielska *et al.*, 1967). It was emphasized that mycoplasma, which was not detected by the standard method using PPLO agar medium, were isolated by this method. After staining with neutral red, the mycoplasma colony appeared macroscopically as a small translucent area with a discrete opaque center. Virus plaques were usually distinguished from them by the absence of an opaque center. On the other hand, plaques of rabies virus which are produced on chick embryo fibroblast monolayers are characterized by the presence of a turbid center (Matsumoto and Kawai, 1969). The specificity of these latter plaques has been established by the following means: (*1*) specific antiserum to rabies virus abolished the plaques, (*2*) mycoplasma were not isolated, (*3*) not even a doubtful figure of mycoplasma characterized by a pleomorphic appearance was demonstrated under the electron microscope, and (*4*) characteristic auto-interference (which will be described later) was encountered in the titration procedure by plaque assay (Yoshino *et al.*, 1966b).

Contamination of LCM virus has occurred in rabies virus suspensions during passage through mouse brains (Wiktor *et al.*, 1965). As a result of this finding, these workers tested virus stocks harvested from a variety of tissue cultures and eventually showed the presence of LCM virus in most. In subsequent work they claimed that infection of cultured cells by rabies virus is enhanced by simultaneous exposure to live as well as UV-irradiated LCM virus. However, rabies virus-tissue culture systems free of LCM virus or other contaminants would seem to be preferable for the analysis of virus replication, especially when the mechanism of this curious phenomenon remains unresolved.

The kinetics of virus growth within tissue cultures has been studied only fragmentarily and there has been no systematic analysis of the metabolism of infected cells. In order to determine whether rabies virus belongs to the DNA or RNA viruses, the effect of various nucleic acid inhibitors on virus replication has been studied (Hamparian *et al.*, 1963; Kissling and Reese, 1963; Defendi and Wiktor, 1966; Maes *et al.*, 1967; Campbell *et al.*, 1968a). At present rabies virus is classified as an RNA-containing virus, because its growth is not inhibited by actinomycin D, mitomycin, fluorodeoxyuridine, or bromodeoxyuridine, but is enhanced, as shown by the high percentage of infected cells and high yield of infectious virus in cultures exposed to these inhibitors. However, 1-β-D-arabinofuranosylcystosine (ara-C), an inhibitor of DNA synthesis, was found to inhibit the replication of rabies virus (Maes *et al.*, 1967). The inhibitory effect of ara-C was completely reversed by the addition of deoxycytidine and cytidine, without concomitant reversal of the inhibition of all DNA synthesis. Afterward, it was found that this unique action of ara-C was partially or completely reversed when cycloheximide was added during the first 3 hours. The same phenomenon was observed with actinomycin D or puromycin. On the basis of these results, the authors have suggested strongly that ara-C requires the induction of a cellular protein which is necessary for its inhibitory action on rabies virus growth and that this protein exerts its inhibitory effect at an early stage in virus replication. Three other members of the rhabdovirus group, vesicular stomatitis virus, cocal virus, and Egtved virus were examined for the effect of ara-C. Vesicular stomatitis virus and cocal virus were inhibited but there was no effect on the growth of Egtved virus. In the case of Egtved virus, the authors supposed that the nonmammalian cell (RTG-2 cell line; rainbow trout; Wolf and Quimby, 1962) in which the virus was grown did not produce an inhibitory protein, since even mammalian cells appear to differ in this regard. The inhibitory effect seems to be similar to that of interferon with respect to the induction of a cellular protein which acts at an early stage of infection. Ara-C, however, acts against only a few viruses. The mechanism by which the induced protein inhibits rabies virus growth is as yet obscure.

The protein inhibitors, cycloheximide and *p*-fluorophenylalanine (PFA), also effectively inhibited the growth of rabies virus (Defendi and Wiktor, 1966; Maes *et al.*, 1967). The effect of PFA could be reversed by the simultaneous addition of phenylalanine to a phenylalanine-free medium. When cycloheximide was added as early as 7 hours after infection, new viral antigen, demonstrated by immunofluorescence staining, was nevertheless formed by 48 hours, suggesting that the synthesis of the viral antigen is already determined shortly after infection.

IX. Spread of Virus *in Vivo*

One of the characteristic features of rabies is a variable incubation period. The average is 30 days, but it can vary from 13 days to as long as 9 months. It used to be held that the nearer the bite to the central nervous system, the shorter the incubation time. Johnson (1943), however, suggested that the incubation period depends upon the amount of virus introduced and the type of tissue involved. For instance, the incubation period after head and face wounds is usually short because of severe laceration and exposure of sensory nerves (van Rooyen and Rhodes, 1948). It is still unsettled as to what the distribution of virus is in the body during the incubation period. In general, rabies virus introduced peripherally may remain at the site of injection up to 96 hours (Habel, 1941; Schindler, 1961; Dean *et al.*, 1963), this depending on the virus strain used. In studies of rats infected with the CVS strain of virus (Baer *et al.*, 1965), it was noted that virus remained at the site of inoculation at least until the central nervous system became infected, that is after 72 hours. The same authors also showed in their street rabies virus studies, that virus could not be recovered from the site of inoculation, the hind foot pad, 24 hours after challenge (Baer *et al.*, 1968). Although the rabies virus is usually transmitted by the bite of infected animals, natural transmission via other routes is known in exceedingly rare cases. In 1959, two men who had worked in a cave (Frio Cave, Texas) died of rabies with no history of exposure by bite. Since this suggested the possibility of transmission by aerosols under the atmospheric conditions of the cave which was inhabited by a number of rabies infected bats, Constantine (1962) exposed coyotes and foxes in the same cave for about 3 weeks in special cages designed for air exposure only. All animals developed rabies with an incubation period of 31 to 113 days. Recently, Atanasiu (1965) provided similar evidence, from one experiment with animals which inhaled aerosols of virus suspension. The virus titer of lungs of deceased animals was as high as $10^{3.5}$ LD_{50}. Up to now, reliable cases of rabies infection via the oral route, whether natural or experimental, have been extremely rare (Sulkin *et al.*, 1957; Soave, 1966; Fishman and Ward, 1968; Fishman, 1969). Fishman and Ward (1968; Fishman, 1969) inoculated relatively large amounts of virus suspension into various laboratory animals through a stomach tube. Oral administration of the CVS strain of virus proved to be highly infective in these animals (71 deaths out of 80 infected baby mice) with prolonged incubation periods, 5 to 13 days longer than infection by intracerebral route. Oral infection in baby mice required 83,000 mouse LD_{50} dose by intracerebral inoculation. Fluorescent antibody examination revealed a sequential development of rabies antigen in the nerve pathways of the intestine, with cells of Auerbach's and Meissner's plexuses positively stained. They also demonstrated that cannibalism of infected animals by their mothers resulted in frequent transmission when the CVS strain was used.

Although the spread of rabies virus from the site of exposure to the brain has remained a controversial matter since the days of Pasteur, it has gradually been accepted that the rabies virus is ordinarily transmitted through nerve paths. The evidence which supports this view has been obtained from many investigations. The presence of virus in different portions of peripheral nerves, such as the cranial or sciatic nerve, was determined by means of histological observation, titration by animal inoculation, or immunofluorescence staining at various times after peripheral injection into the region of peripheral innervation (Goodpasture, 1925; Krause, 1956, 1966; Schindler, 1961, 1966; R. T. Johnson, 1965). Goodpasture (1925) studied centripetal histological changes along the fifth cranial nerve after inoculation into the masseter muscle of rabbits. He found that lesions appeared in the medulla first, although by the time symptoms developed, lesions were fairly widespread in the central nervous system. These histological data, however, were not always consistent, because the signs of early involvement were frequently confused by widespread distribution of lesions in the central nervous system. Schindler (1961) inoculated both fixed and street virus into the calf muscle of the hind leg of mice and estimated the virus content of several organs (inoculated muscle, sciatic nerve, sciatic nerve of uninfected leg, nerve of foreleg, spinal cord, and brain). From statistical analysis of these results it was concluded that the rabies virus travels along or in the nerves from the periphery to the central nervous system and vice versa. The same kind of experiment was performed by R. T. Johnson (1965) utilizing fluorescent antibody staining in addition to conventional histological and virological methods. Fluorescent nerve cells were first detectable in the lumbar dorsal root and lumbar cord 3 days after subcutaneous inoculation. There was a more prominent involvement of ganglion and anterior horn cells ipsilateral to the inoculated foot, although fluorescence of contralateral cells was also present. During these experiments no specific fiuorescent granules were found in subcutaneous tissue and muscle at the inoculation site, local lymph node, or in peripheral nerves. The author also examined daily for the presence of virus in blood, liver, and spleen. At no time during the incubation periods could virus be isolated from blood or viscera.

In an attempt to verify the theory of nerve borne transmission, many workers have studied the sparing effect of neurectomy on rabies. They ligated or removed a segment of either or both the sciatic or saphenous nerve in animals and then inoculated the foot pad of the hind legs with virus (Dean *et al.*, 1963; Baer *et al.*, 1965, 1968; R. T. Johnson, 1965). All of these studies gave evidence in favor of a neural spread of the virus. For instance, Dean *et al.* (1963) reported typical data showing that whereas mortality in the controls was 38 of

40 mice (95%), none of the 32 and 40 mice on which combined sciatic and saphenous or just sciatic neurectomies were performed died, and only 24 of 34 (70.6%) with saphenous neurectomy succumbed. The inoculated extremity (approximately 12 mm) was amputated at various intervals after injection. As shown in Table III, only one mouse died of

TABLE III

EFFECT OF AMPUTATION OF INJECTED LIMB ON OUTCOME OF INFECTION IN MICE INOCULATED IN THE FOOT PAD WITH RABIES OR MOUSE ENCEPHALOMYELITIS VIRUS[a, b]

Interval between inoculation and amputation	Rabies virus (CVS strain)				Mouse encephalomyelitis virus	
	Experiment A		Experiment B		Experiment C	Experiment D
	Front limb	Hind limb	Non-neurectomized hind limb	Neurectomized hind limb	Hind limb	Hind limb
5 Minutes	—	—	—	—	8/28	—
15 Minutes	1/14	0/13	—	—	10/35	—
30 Minutes	—	—	—	—	9/36	—
1 Hour	0/10	0/15	0/25	0/25	9/33	20/41
2 Hours	0/12	0/14	—	—	—	—
4 Hours	2/11	6/14	0/18	0/21	—	21/40
8 Hours	15/15	15/15	20/23	0/19	—	—
12 Hours	14/15	15/15	25/25	0/21	—	—
24 Hours	14/15	14/14	—	—	—	25/39
72 Hours	—	—	—	—	—	19/43
Controls	13/15	14/15	25/25	3/25	6/41	29/42

[a] Results are expressed as the number of animals dying of rabies or mouse encephalomyelitis over the number inoculated. In experiment B neurectomy consisted in transection of the sciatic or saphenous nerves or removal of a nerve segment of not more than 2 mm at the distal end of the femur.

[b] From Dean *et al.* (1963).

rabies in those groups in which amputation was performed 2 hours or less after injection. Mortality from rabies was 18.2% for inoculation of the fore limb and 42.9% for the hind limb, respectively, in mice whose limbs were amputated after 4 hours; when amputation was delayed 8 hours or more, all mice, or all but one mouse, in each group died. The results suggest that rabies may be estimated to travel along nerve pathways at a rough rate of about 3 mm or more/hour, approximately the rate found for poliovirus by Bodian and Howe (1941). It is assumed that replication of virus in the nerve after injection is not essential. However, when neurectomized hamsters infected with the CVS virus were examined, the sparing effect was less marked due to the high susceptibility of the hamster to rabies virus; 6 out of 9 hamsters with neurectomy of both sciatic and saphenous nerves died of rabies. From this evidence, the authors deduced that blood-borne infection may occur in animals of known high susceptibility. According to Baer's experiments (1965, 1968), all inoculated animals were saved by removal of the nerve fasciculus prior to the injection. On the other hand, the perineural structures, including perineural lymph vessels did not seem to be involved. Complete demyelination of relatively long intervals, produced by mechanical crushing which brought about disintegration of axons, also has no detrimental effect on rabies pathogenesis. It would appear, therefore, that the Schwann cells, the endoneurium, or associated tissue spaces, all located within the nerve fasciculus, play a greater role than the axon cylinder in the central movement of virus. However, it was recently clearly shown by electron microscopy that virus particles are present either near or distant from the matrix within nonmyelinated axons of the trigeminal ganglion after intranasal inoculation with a virulent street strain of rabies virus (Jenson *et al.,* 1969). In their study, no evidence was obtained that Schwann and endoneural cells supported viral growth. It is hoped that more sensitive techniques will provide a more effective means of tracing virus progression in nerves.

Although the blood-borne transmission of rabies has been considered the exception rather than the rule (Dean *et al.,* 1963), there have been some reports supporting this idea (Krause, 1966). This author showed that soon after infection, rabies virus is transported by the blood to different organs such as liver, lung, or kidney. Zunker (1963) studied the spread of rabies virus using parabiotic rats possessing a common blood circulation but no neural connection. Street virus produced disease in 24 of 26 pairs when inoculated into the foot of one of these rats, whereas 7 of 37 pairs were infected with the fixed virus. With these contradictory data in mind, it seems to be difficult to draw any final conclusion about the mode of virus spread in the body. As pointed out by many researchers (Schindler, 1966; Campbell *et al.,* 1968b), the outcome of viremia caused by diffusion of the virus from tissue of animals is presumably dependent on the dose of rabies virus at the point of entry. It is possible, therefore, that viremia also occurs when rabies virus multiplies in non-nervous tissues at the point of entry.

The last important feature of the pathogenesis of rabies infection concerns centrifugal spread of virus along nerves. It was shown that salivary gland tissue sometimes contains as much rabies virus as brain (Vaughn *et al.,* 1965; R. T. Johnson, 1965). Large amounts of virus were observed within the acinar cells of this gland by immunofluorescence staining or by electron microscopy (Dierkes *et al.*, 1969; Yamamoto *et al.*, 1965). Schneider (1968) demonstrated the rabies antigen in corneal epithelium cells of rabies infected animals by immunofluorescence staining. Viral antigen was sometimes discernible during the incubation period, but was not found before the virus had multiplied in the central nervous system.

X. Immune Response and Abortive Infection

The last important feature of the pathogenesis of rabies infection with street virus become resistant to subsequent challenges of any strain of rabies virus. Although this immunological protection can be overcome by a virus challenge of a sufficiently large dose, especially if given by the intracranial route, rabies virus is considered to be a strong antigen. Most immunological studies have been carried out using crude materials of virus-infected brains or avian embryos, so that contamination of nonviral tissue constituents have probably made it difficult to initiate quantitative investigations on the antigenicity of rabies virus. Recently, the Wistar group briefly reported that rabbit sera, produced by injections of a total of 250 μg of purified virus inactivated β-propiolactone and emulsified in Freund's complete adjuvant, contained neutralizing antibody titers of up to 1:60,000 (against 20 LD_{50} of virus) and complement fixing titers up to 1:1,000. In the serum of animals infected with large amounts of rabies virus, 19 S neutralizing antibody appears in an early stage of infection (3 or 4 days) (Fujisaki *et al.*, 1968). The physicochemical properties of 19 S antibody (IgM) are quite similar to those produced by other viruses. The only difference is that a small amount of inoculum cannot bring about production of 19 S antibody, whereas a small inoculum of poliovirus can do so. Complement fixation, virus neutralization, and immunodiffusion tests, run against other viruses of the rhabdovirus group, confirmed the distinct antigenicity of rabies. For instance, the results of complement fixation tests are shown in Howatson's review on rhabdoviruses in this volume.

Fernandes *et al.* (1964) established the carrier state over a number of generations in tissue cultures derived from rabbit endothelium (RE) or hamster cells (BHK-21). When exposed to antibody in the serum, carrier cells lysed; the reaction was dependent on complement. Wiktor *et al.* (1968) gave a more detailed picture of this phenomenon. Neither antiserum nor fresh guinea pig serum alone was active. Fluorescein-conjugated antibody without complement stained the surface of infected cells even without fixation. In contrast, when cells were observed in the presence of fresh guinea pig serum, intracytoplasmic staining of rabies antigen was seen to be similar to that obtained when the cells were fixed before staining with fluorescent antibody. This indicates that complement is required for the immunocytolytic test and that it enables the antibody to penetrate the cell membrane. Both lytic and neutralizing antibodies were found in the 7 S immunoglobulin fraction (IgG). There seems to be no direct relationship between the budding rabies virus on the surface and lysis of infected cells, because cytolysis takes place before virus assembly is recognized, that is around 48 hours after infec-

TABLE IV
CROSS COMPLEMENT FIXATION TESTS BETWEEN ANIMAL VIRUSES OF THE RHABDOVIRUS GROUP[a]

Mouse hyperimmune ascitic fluids	Antigens[b]						
	Kern Canyon	VSV-N.J.	VSV-Indiana	Cocal	Flanders	Hart Park	Rabies
Kern Canyon	256[c]	<8	<8	<8	<8	<8	<8
Vesicular stomatitis-New Jersey	<8	64	<8	<8	<8	<8	<8
Vesicular stomatitis-Indiana	<8	<8	512	64	<8	<8	<8
Cocal	<8	<8	64	512	<8	<8	<8
Flanders	<8	<8	<8	<8	128	<8	<8
Hart Park	<8	<8	<8	<8	<8	32	<8
Rabies[d]	<8	<8	<8	<8	<8	<8	64

[a] From Murphy *et al.* (1967).
[b] Sucrose-acetone extracted mouse brain antigens were used except for rabies where the antigen was crude, clarified mouse brain suspension. Similar results were obtained with a complete series of crude mouse brain antigens.
[c] Reciprocal of ascitic fluid or serum dilution fixing 70% or more complement at the optimal antigen dilution as determined in box titration.
[d] Hyperimmune burro serum instead of mouse ascitic fluid.

tion. In fact, cytolysis was already detected 16 to 18 hours after the infection, at a time when rabies antigen had been shown to be within most cells by immunofluorescence staining. This phenomenon is similar to the lysis of murine leukemia cells. In studies of the cytolytic antigen, Defendi (1967) and co-workers reported that antigenic change occurs at the cell surface as demonstrated by a transplantation assay. When tumor cells or BHK-21 cells, both of which were infected with the rabies virus, were inoculated into mice previously immunized with the homologous virus strain, either enhancement or inhibition of tumor growth occurred compared with the control. From these results, they strongly maintained that a nontumor virus also confers on cells new antigenic determinants.

Neutralizing antibody against rabies virus has also been demonstrated in suspensions of brains of immunized animals (Johnson, 1957; Constantinescu and Birzu, 1957). Bell *et al.* (1966) applied the technique originally devised by Kubes and Gallia (1943) for evaluation of the immune state. Injection of rabies vaccine into mice induced the development of neutralizing capacity of brain tissue only after repeated doses. Although injection of live virus after the injection of killed vaccine served as a booster in that it increased the serum titer, it did not cause the development of appreciable brain neutralizing capacity. In contrast, inoculation of live virus alone by the intraperitoneal route caused the development of high brain neutralizing capacity in the 25% of mice (normal survivors) which did not develop detectable signs of rabies by the intraperitoneal inoculation of a street virus. This is comparable to the proportion (23%) of animals that survived rigorous intracranial challenge. Therefore, it was concluded that active infection is the critical stimulus for cerebral antibody formation. It appears that when the brain-neutralizing titer is a small fraction of the serum titer, this suggests vaccination, whereas when brain titers are comparable to serum titers, recovery from infection is implied. The substance responsible seems to be either serum antibody that has breached the blood-brain barrier or locally produced antibody present first in the brain and spleen and later released to the circulation (Schneider *et al.*, 1963). Based on these results, the cerebro-neutralization test might be useful for the differentiation of recovered animals from those which have been vaccinated or are in a prodromal stage of rabies infection.

Although rabies is considered to be uniformly fatal after clinical symptoms develop, evidence of recovered or abortive and even healthy carriers or inapparent infections of various animals has accumulated. Andral and Serie (1957; Serie and Andral, 1963) noted that abortive rabies infection of dogs may be more common than fatal rabies in Ethiopia. The authors isolated virus from a dog which was still alive 20 months later and also demonstrated neutralizing antibodies in the sera of apparently normal stray dogs. Similar abortive cases have been reported in various wild animals such as fox, raccoon, and bat (Webster, 1937; Yurkovsky, 1962; Sikes, 1962; Johnson, 1947, 1948; Tierkel, 1958; Pawan, 1936). Since survival following natural infection occurs in many species of animals, it might be expected that abortive infection also occurs in man. However, there are many practical problems which make it difficult to demonstrate unequivocally abortive infection in man. It has been inferred that naturally attenuated strains of rabies virus may produce in man an atypical infection (Ruegsegger *et al.*, 1961). Good's report of a child bitten by a rabid skunk, who survived in a comatose state for several months, is one unequivocal case of abortive rabies infection of man (Bell, 1964). In order to yield more information concerning the abortive infection, Bell (1964) attempted to produce an experimental curable rabies in mice inoculated intraperitoneally with a street virus from a local bat. He did obtain surviving mice in a relatively high incidence, for instance, 7 out of 100 inoculated mice survived with marked paralysis but were otherwise healthy. The surviving mice that did not develop detectable signs showed less resistance to the intracerebral challenge with fixed virus than another group of surviving mice with more or less severe sequelae. Tests for antibody in brain extract as well as the serum neutralization tests were consistent with the results of a challenge inoculation. Thus, the existence of latent rabies infection among many wild animals has been demonstrated, but it remains unknown as to how the virus multiplies within the body of these animals and is constantly excreted.

In this review we have omitted epidemiological topics of rabies with other practical subjects. Rabies is now found in the arctic regions, as well as the temperate and tropical countries of both hemispheres. Recent knowledge of rabies infection among wildlife in how it is transmitted to man has been summarized by Fenje (1968) and Kaplan (1969).

XI. Summary and Outlook for the Future

The ultrastructure of rabies virus and its relationship to morphological changes in the infected cell are now understood at a level comparable to those of other viruses, such as influenza virus, vaccinia virus, or herpes virus. In contrast, however, biochemical aspects need further systematic study. At present, we can only predict that much information concerning the metabolism of cells infected with the rabies virus will be forthcoming, because quantitative work with this virus has now become feasible due to establishment of tissue cultures which are highly susceptible. The relationship between the two complement fixing antigens each with a different sedimentation coefficient and the viral antigen, has not been clarified. Detailed study of rabies virus antigens will have to await their physical separation from infected tissue cultures.

Vaccine prepared in tissue cultures eventually should be suitable both in respect to a reduction of the proportion of cellular antigen and an increase in the relative and absolute amount of viral antigen. Thus, it may become possible to eliminate the risk of serious post-vaccinal encephalomyelitis.

Acknowledgments

The author is indebted to Dr. F. B. Bang for his kind help in revising this review.

REFERENCES

Allen, R., Sims, R. A., and Sulkin, S. E. (1964). *Amer. J. Hyg.* **80,** 11–32.

Almeida, J. D., Howatson, A. F., Pinteric, L., and Fenje, P. (1962). *Virology* **18,** 147–151.

Andral, L., and Serie, C. (1957). *Ann. Inst. Pasteur* **93,** 475–488.

Atanasiu, P. (1965). *Symp. Ser. Immunobiol. Stand.* **1,** 159–166.

Atanasiu, P., and Laurent, C. (1957). *C. R. Acad. Sci.* **245,** 2562–2564.

Atanasiu, P., Favre, S., and Collombier, M. (1961). *C. R. Acad. Sci.* **252,** 2029.

Atanasiu, P., Lépine, P., and Gragonas, P. (1963a). *Ann. Inst. Pasteur* **195,** 813–824.

Atanasiu, P., Lépine, P., Sisman, J., Dauguet, J. C., and Witten, M. (1963b). *C. R. Acad. Sci.* **256,** 3219–3221.

Atanasiu, P., Orth, G., Sisman, J., and Barreau, C. (1963c). *C. R. Acad. Sci.* **257,** 2204–2207.

Atanasiu, P., Lépine, P., and Dighe, P. (1963d). *C. R. Acad. Sci.* **256,** 1415–1417.

Baer, G. M., Shanthaveerappa, T. R., and Bourne, G. H. (1965). *Bull. W. H. O.* **33,** 783–794.

Baer, G. M., Shantha, T. R., and Bourne, G. H. (1968). *Bull. W. H. O.* **38,** 119–126.

Bell, J. F. (1964). *J. Infec. Dis.* **114,** 249–257.

Bell, J. F., Lodmell, D. F., Moore, G. J., and Raymond, G. H. (1966). *J. Immunol.* **97,** 747–753.

Berkaloff, A., Bregliano, J. G., and Ohanessian, A. (1965). *C. R. Acad. Sci.* **260,** 5956–5959.

Campbell, J. B., Maes, R. F., Wiktor, T. J., and Koprowski, H. (1968a). *Virology* **34,** 701–708.

Campbell, J. B., Kaplan, M. M., Koprowski, H., Kuwert, E., Sokol, F., and Wiktor, T. J. (1968b). *Bull. W. H. O.* **38,** 373–381.

Chambers, V. C. (1957). *Virology* **3,** 62–75.

Chany, C. (1961). *Virology* **13,** 485–492.

Compans, R. W., Holmes, K. V., Dales, S., and Choppin, P. W. (1967). *Virology* **30,** 411–426.

Constantine, D. G. (1962). *Pub. Health Rep.* **77,** 287–289.

Constantinescu, N., and Birzu, N. (1958). *Ann. Inst. Pasteur* **94,** 739–747.

Davies, M. C., Englert, M. E., Sharpless, G. R., and Cabasso, V. J. (1963). *Virology* **21,** 51–72.

Dean, D. J., Evans, W. E., and McClure, R. C. (1963). *Bull. W. H. O.* **29,** 803–811.

Defendi, V. (1967). "Cross-Reacting Antigens and Neoantigens," pp. 96–97. Williams & Wilkins, Baltimore, Maryland.

Defendi, V., and Wiktor, T. J. (1966). *Symp. Ser. Immunobiol. Stand.* **1,** 119–124.

Dierkes, R. E., Murphy, F. A., and Harrison, A. K. (1969). *Amer. J. Pathol.* **54,** 251–273.

Ditchfield, J., and Almeida, J. D. (1964). *Virology* **24,** 232–235.

Fenje, P. (1960). *Can. J. Microbiol.* **6,** 605–610.

Fenje, P. (1968). *Can. J. Pub. Health* **59,** 217–228.

Fernandes, M. V., and Pomerat, C. M. (1961). *Z. Zellforsch.* **53,** 431–437.

Fernandes, M. V., Wiktor, T. J., and Koprowski, H. (1963). *Virology* **21,** 128–130.

Fernandes, M. V., Wiktor, T. J., and Koprowski, H. (1964). *J. Exp. Med.* **120,** 1099–1116.

Finter, N. B. (1965). *Nature (London)* **206,** 597–599.

Fishman, H. R. (1969). Personal communication.

Fishman, H. R., and Ward, F. E., III (1968). *Amer. J. Epidemiol.* **88,** 132–138.
Fujisaki, Y., Sekiguchi, K., and Hirasawa, K. (1968). *Nat. Inst. Anim. Health Quart.* **8,** 132–139.
Goldwasser, R. A., and Kissling, R. E. (1958). *Proc. Soc. Exp. Biol. Med.* **98,** 219–223.
Goodpasture, E. W. (1925). *Amer. J. Pathol.* **1,** 547–582.
Grasset, N., and Atanasiu, P. (1961). *Ann. Inst. Pasteur* **101,** 639–647.
Habel, K. (1941). *Pub. Health Rep.* **56,** 692–702.
Habel, K. (1964). *Ergeb. Mikrobiol. Immunitaetsforsch. Exp. Ther.* **38,** 39–54.
Halonen, P. E., Stewart, J. A., and Hall, A. D. (1967a). *Ann. Med. Exp. Biol. Fenn.* **45,** 182.
Halonen, P. E., Ryan, J. M., and Stewart, J. A. (1967b). *Proc. Soc. Exp. Biol. Med.* **125,** 162–167.
Halonen, P. E., Murphy, F. A., Fields, B. N., and Reese, D. R. (1968). *Proc. Soc. Exp. Biol. Med.* **127,** 1037–1042.
Hamparian, V. V., Hilleman, M. R., and Wood, E. G. (1963). *Proc. Soc. Exp. Biol. Med.* **112,** 1040–1050.
Harrison, B. D., and Crowley, N. C. (1965). *Virology* **26,** 297–310.
Herold, F., Bergold, G. H., and Weibel, J. (1960). *Virology* **16,** 466–478.
Hills, G. J., and Campbell, R. N. (1968). *J. Ultrastruct. Res.* **24,** 134–144.
Hitchborn, J. H., Hills, G. J., and Hull, R. (1966). *Virology* **28,** 768–772.
Hottle, J. H., Morgan, C., Reers, J. H., and Wyckoff, R. E. G. (1951). *Proc. Soc. Exp. Biol. Med.* **77,** 721–723.
Howatson, A. F., and Whitmore, G. F. (1962). *Virology* **16,** 466–478.
Howe, C., Morgan, C., deVaux St. Cyr, C., Hsu, K. C., and Rose, H. M. (1967). *J. Virol.* **1,** 215–237.
Hronovsky, V., Benda, R., and Cinatl, J. (1966). *Acta Virol. (Prague), Engl. Ed.* **10,** 181.
Hronovsky, V., Benda, R., and Cinatl, J. (1968). *Acta Virol. (Prague), Engl. Ed.* **12,** 233–240.
Huang, A. S., Greenwalt, J. W., and Wagner, R. R. (1966). *Virology* **30,** 161–172.
Hummeler, K., and Koprowski, H. (1969).
Hummeler, K., Koprowski, H., and Wiktor, T. J. (1967). *J. Virol.* **1,** 152–170.
Hummeler, K., Tomassini, N., Sokol, F., Kuwert, E., and Koprowski, H. (1968). *J. Virol.* **2,** 1191–1199.
International Symposium on Rabies (1966). *Symp. Ser. Immunobiol. Stand.* **1.**
Jenson, A. B., Babin, E. R., Wende, R. D., and Melnick, J. L. (1967). *Exp. Mol. Pathol.* **7,** 1–10.
Jenson, A. B., Rabin, E. R., Bentinck, D. C., and Melnick, J. L. (1969). *J. Virol.* **3,** 265–269.
Johnson, H. N. (1942). *Ill. Med. J.* **81,** 382.
Johnson, H. N. (1943). "Oxford Loose Leaf Medicine." New York.
Johnson, H. N. (1947). *Ann. N. Y. Acad. Sci.* **48,** 380.
Johnson, H. N. (1948). *Amer. J. Hyg.* **47,** 189–204.
Johnson, H. N. (1957). *Viral Rickettsial Infec. Man* pp. 405–431.
Johnson, H. N. (1965). *Viral Rickettsial Infec. Man* pp. 814–840.
Johnson, R. T. (1965). *J. Neuropathol. Exp. Neurol.* **24,** 662–674.
Johnson, R. T., and Mercer, E. H. (1964). *Aust. J. Exp. Biol. Med. Sci.* **42,** 449–456.
Kaplan, M. M. (1969). *Nature (London)*, 421–425.
Kaplan, M. M., Wecker, E., Forsek, Z., and Koprowski, H. (1960). *Nature (London)* **186,** 821–822.

Kaplan, M. M., Cohen, D., Koprowski, H., Dean, D. J., and Ferrigan, L. (1962). *Bull. W. H. O.* **26,** 765–775.
Kaplan, M. M., Wiktor, T. J., Maes, R. F., Campbell, J. B., and Koprowski, H. (1967). *J. Virol.* **1,** 145–151.
Kissling, R. E. (1958). *Proc. Soc. Exp. Biol. Med.* **98,** 223–225.
Kissling, R. E., and Reese, D. R. (1963). *J. Immunol.* **91,** 362–368.
Kissling, R. E., Robinson, R. Q., Murphy, F. A., and Whitfield, S. G. (1968). *Science* **160,** 888–890.
Kitajima, E. W., and Costa, A. S. (1966). *Virology* **29,** 523–539.
Kondo, A. (1965a). *Virology* **27,** 199–204.
Kondo, A. (1965b). *Uirusu* **15,** 261–262.
Kondo, A. (1969). Personal communication.
Koprowski, H., Black, J., and Nelson, D. J. (1954). *J. Immunol.* **72,** 94–106.
Krause, W. W. (1956). *Zentralbl. Bakteriol. Parasitenk. Infektionskr. Hyg., Abt. 1: Orig.* **167,** 458–503.
Krause, W. W. (1966). *Symp. Ser. Immunobiol. Stand.* **1,** 153–158.
Kubes, V., and Gallia, F. (1943). *Bol. Invest. Vet. Maracay, Venez.* **1,** 103.
Kuwert, E., Wiktor, T. J., Sokol, F., and Koprowski, H. (1968). *J. Virol.* **2,** 1381–1392.
Lee, P. E. (1968). *Virology* **34,** 583–589.
Lentz, O. (1909). *Z. Hyg. Infektionskr.* **62,** 63–94.
Lépine, P., and Croissant, O. (1951). *Ann. Inst. Pasteur* **81,** 1–8.
Lépine, P., and Sautter, V. (1935). *C. R. Soc. Biol.* **119,** 805–807.
Lépine, P., and Sautter, V. (1936). *C. R. Soc. Biol.* **122,** 542–547.
Lépine, P., Atanasiu, P., and Sisman, J. (1966). *Symp. Ser. Immunobiol. Stand.* **1,** 31–43.
Love, R., Fernandes, M. V., and Koprowski, H. (1964). *Proc. Soc. Exp. Biol. Med.* **116,** 560–563.
Love, R., Fernandes, M. V., and Wiktor, T. J. (1966a). *Rev. Pathol. Comp.* **66,** 533–541.
Love, R., Fernandes, M. V., and Wiktor, T. J. (1966b). *Symp. Ser. Immunobiol. Stand.* **1,** 105–117.
MacLeod, R. (1968). *Virology* **34,** 771–777.
Maes, R. F., Kaplan, M. M., Wiktor, T. J., Campbell, J. B., and Koprowski, H. (1967). *In* "The Molecular Biology of Viruses" (S. J. Colter and W. Paranchych, eds.), pp. 449–462. Academic Press, New York.
Matsumoto, S. (1962). *Virology* **17,** 198–202.
Matsumoto, S. (1963). *J. Cell Biol.* **19,** 565–591.
Matsumoto, S., and Kawai, A. (1969). *Virology* **39,** 449–459.
Matsumoto, S., and Miyamoto, K. (1966). *Symp. Ser. Immunobiol. Stand.* **1,** 45–54.
Mead, T. H. (1962a). *J. Gen. Microbiol.* **27,** 415–426.
Mead, T. H. (1962b). *J. Gen. Microbiol.* **27,** 397–414.
Melnick, J. L., and McCombs, R. M. (1966). *Progr. Med. Virol.* **8,** 400–409.
Mikhailovsky, E. M., and Iliasova, R. S. (1966). *Symp. Ser. Immunobiol. Stand.* **1,** 99–103.
Mikhailovsky, E. M., and Selimov, M. A. (1966). *Acta Virol. (Prague), Engl. Ed.* **10,** 373.
Miyamoto, K. (1965). *Ann. Rep. Inst. Virus Res. Kyoto Univ.* **8,** 10–34.
Miyamoto, K., and Matsumoto, S. (1965). *J. Cell Biol.* **27,** 677–682.
Miyamoto, K., and Matsumoto, S. (1967). *J. Exp. Med.* **125,** 447–456.
Murphy, F. A., and Fields, B. N. (1967). *Virology* **33,** 625–637.

Murphy, F. A., Coleman, P. H., and Whitfield, S. G. (1966). *Virology* **30,** 315–317.
Murphy, F. A., Halonen, P. E., Gary, G. W., Jr., and Reese, D. R. (1968). *J. Gen. Virol.* **3,** 289–294.
Nakai, T., and Howatson, A. F. (1968). *Virology* **35,** 268–281.
Negri, A. (1903). *Z. Hyg. Infektionskr.* **43,** 507–528.
Negri, A. (1909). *Z. Hyg. Infektionskr.* **63,** 421–443.
Neurath, A. R., Wiktor, T. J., and Koprowski, H. (1966). *J. Bacteriol.* **92,** 102–106.
Pasteur, L. (1885). *C. R. Acad. Sci.* **101,** 765–772.
Pawan, J. L. (1936). *Ann. Trop. Med. Parasitol.* **30,** 401.
Pinteric, L., and Fenje, P. (1966). *Symp. Ser. Immunobiol. Stand.* **1,** 9–25.
Pinteric, L., Fenje, P., and Almeida, J. D. (1963). *Virology* **20,** 208–211.
Polson, A., and Wessels, P. (1953). *Proc. Soc. Exp. Biol. Med.* **84,** 317.
Reczko, E. (1960). *Arch. Ges. Virusforsch.* **10,** 588–605.
Remlinger, P. (1903). *Ann. Inst. Pasteur* **17,** 834–849.
Roots, E., and Schultze, I. (1963). *Zentr. Bakteriol. Parasitenk. Infektionskr. Hyg., Abt. 1: Orig.* **188,** 159–173.
Ruegsegger, J. M., Black, J., and Sharpless, G. R. (1961). *Amer. J. Pub. Health.* **51,** 706–716.
Sanders, M., Kiem, I., and Langunoff, D. (1953). *Arch. Pathol.* **56,** 148–225.
Schindler, R. (1961). *Bull. W. H. O.* **25,** 119–126.
Schindler, R. (1966). *Symp. Ser. Immunobiol. Stand.* **1,** 147–152.
Schneider, L. G. (1968). *Zentralbl. Veterinaermed., Reihe B* **16,** 24–31.
Schneider, R., Durand, M., Kchouk, M., Moktor, and Farhat. (1963). *Arch. Inst. Pasteur Tunis* **39,** 417.
Schweinburg, F. (1924). *Wien. Klin. Wochenschr.* **37,** 797–801.
Sedwick, W. D., and Wiktor, T. J. (1967). *J. Virol.* **1,** 1224–1226.
Selimov, M. A., Chuprikova, M., Kalinina, L., and Shrava, Z. (1965). *Acta Virol. (Prague), Engl. Ed.* **9,** 445–448.
Serie, C., and Andral, L. (1963). *Ann. Inst. Pasteur* **104,** 123–126.
Sikes, R. K. (1962). *Amer. J. Vet. Res.* **23,** 1041–1047.
Simpson, R. W., and Hauser, R. E. (1966). *Virology* **29,** 654–667.
Soave, O. A. (1966). *Amer. J. Vet. Res.* **27,** 44–46.
Sokol, F., Kuwert, E., Wiktor, T. J., Hummeler, K., and Koprowski, H. (1968). *J. Virol.* **2,** 836–849.
Sokol, F., Schlumberger, H. D., Wiktor, T. J., and Koprowski, H. (1969). *Virology* **38,** 651–665.
Sokolov, N. N., and Parfanovich, M. L. (1965). *Acta Virol. (Prague), Engl. Ed.* **9,** 191.
Stewart, W. E., II, and Sulkin, S. E. (1966). *Proc. Soc. Exp. Biol. Med.* **123,** 650-654.
Sulkin, S. E., Krutzsch, P. H., Wallis, C., and Allen, R. (1957). *Proc. Soc. Exp. Biol. Med.* **96,** 461–464.
Sulkin, S. E., Krutzsch, P. H., Allen, R., and Wallis, C. (1959). *J. Exp. Med.* **110,** 369–388.
Sulkin, S. E., Allen, R., Sims, R. A., Krutzsch, P. H., and Kim, C. (1960). *J. Exp. Med.* **112,** 595–617.
Sulkin, S. E., Allen, R., and Sims, R. (1966). *Symp. Ser. Immunobiol. Stand.* **1,** 81–97.
Takemoto, K. K., and Liebhaber, H. (1961). *Virology* **14,** 456–462.
Thomas, J. B., Ricker, A. S., Baer, G. M., and Sikes, R. K. (1965). *Virology* **25,** 271–275.
Tierkel, E. S. (1958). *Ann. N. Y. Acad. Sci.* **70,** 445-451.
Turner, G. S., and Kaplan, C. (1967). *J. Gen. Virol.* **1,** 537–551.

Uchida, S., Watanabe, S., and Kato, M. (1966). *Virology* **27,** 135–141.
Van den Ende, M., Polson, A., and Turner, G. S. (1957). *J. Hyg.* **55,** 361.
van Rooyen, C. F., and Rhodes, A. J. (1948). "Virus Diseases of Man," pp. 835–843. Nelson, New York.
Vaughn, J. B., Jr., Gerhardt, P., and Newell, K. W. (1965). *J. Amer. Med. Ass.* **193,** 363–368.
Vieuchange, J., Bequignon, R., Guest, J., and Vialat, C. (1956). *Bull. Acad. Nat. Med. Paris* **140,** 77.
Webster, L. T. (1937). *New Engl. J. Med.* **217,** 686–690.
Wiktor, T. J. (1966). *Symp. Ser. Immunobiol. Stand.* **1,** 65–80.
Wiktor, T. J., Fernandes, M. V., and Koprowski, H. (1964). *J. Immunol.* **93,** 353–366.
Wiktor, T. J., Fernandes, M. V., and Koprowski, H. (1965). *J. Bacteriol* **90,** 1494–1495.
Wiktor, T. J., Kuwert, E., and Koprowski, H. (1968). *J. Immunol.* **101,** 1271–1282.
Wolf, K., and Quimby, M. C. (1962). *Science* **135,** 1065–1066.
Yamamoto, T., Otani, S., and Shiraki, H. (1965). *Acta Neuropathol.* **5,** 288–306.
Yoshino, K., Taniguchi, S., and Arai, K. (1966a). *Arch. Gestamte Virusforsch.* **3,** 370–373.
Yoshino, K., Taniguchi, S., and Arai, K. (1966b). *Proc. Soc. Exp. Biol. Med.* **123,** 387–392.
Yurkovsky, A. M. (1962). *J. Hyg. Epidemiol Microbiol. Immunol.* **6,** 73.
Zgorniak-Nowosielska, I., Sedwick, W. D., Hummeler, K., and Koprowski, H. (1967). *J. Virol.* **1,** 1227–1237.
Zunker, M. (1963). *Zentralbl. Veteriaermed., Reihe B* **3,** 271–277.
Zwillenberg, L. O., Jenson, M. H., and Zwillenberg, H. H. L. (1965). *Arch. Gesamte Virusforsch.* **17,** 1–19.

VIRUS-INDUCED POLYKARYOCYTOSIS AND THE MECHANISM OF CELL FUSION

George Poste

Department of Virology, Royal Postgraduate Medical School, London, England

I. Introduction

A. The Problem

The development of cytopathic effects (CPE) in cells infected with viruses is the most obvious means by which their presence is detected. The nature of the CPE produced by viruses is often highly characteristic and provides an important criterion for their assay and classification. Polykaryocytosis, which is the formation of multinucleate cells—variously termed polykaryocytes, syncytia or giant cells—is one such characteristic type of cellular response to virus infection (Fig. 1). Evidence will be presented to show that most virus-induced polykaryocytes are formed by cell fusion. However, viruses represent only one of the many agents which can induce polykaryocytosis and cell fusion (Haythorn, 1929; Roizman, 1962a). In a broader perspective, the process of cell fusion itself merely represents a special example of fusion between biological membranes. For these reasons, although this review will be primarily concerned with virus-induced cell fusion, it will at the same time attempt to consider broader aspects of the process of cell fusion.

B. Historical Perspective

The massive literature that has accumulated on the morphology, function, and formation of polykaryocytes has paralleled the entire history of cytology, from the development of microscopic anatomy and pathology to the present sophisticated techniques for the analysis of subcellular organization. The introduction of the cell theory by the botanist Schleiden (1838) and the zoologist Schwann (1847) provided the basis for the interpretation of the structure of plant and animal tissues in terms of cells. The cell concept was more firmly established by Virchow (1858) in his classic treatise "Cellularpathologie." The cell theory was not accepted unreservedly at the time. The finding of multinucleate "syncytia" or "plasmodia" in many plant and animal tissues (Rohde, 1923), resulted in an attempt to replace the cell theory by another idea, in which the body was viewed as a single tissue unit in which the cytoplasm, containing nuclei, was continuous—the so called syncytial or symplasmic state (Stůdnička, 1934). Although the various theories proposing the syncytial state met with little final support (Cameron, 1951), they did at least establish that multinucleate cells were in fact present in many situations.

Faber (1893) credited Müller, 1838, who published a treatise on tumors, with the first description of multinucleate cells. When Langhans (1868, 1870) published his classical papers on multinucleate cells, their presence in a vast range of conditions had already been recognized. Following Langhans article, interest in multinucleate cells, particularly in pathological conditions, developed rapidly and a large literature appeared, dealing primarily with their diagnostic importance and their morphological similarities and differences (Haythorn, 1929). The first reports of polykaryocytes in virus infections appear to be those of Luginbühl (1873) and Weigert (1874) in smallpox, Unna (1896) and Tyzzer (1905) in varicella, and Kromayer (1889) and Hecht (1910) in measles.

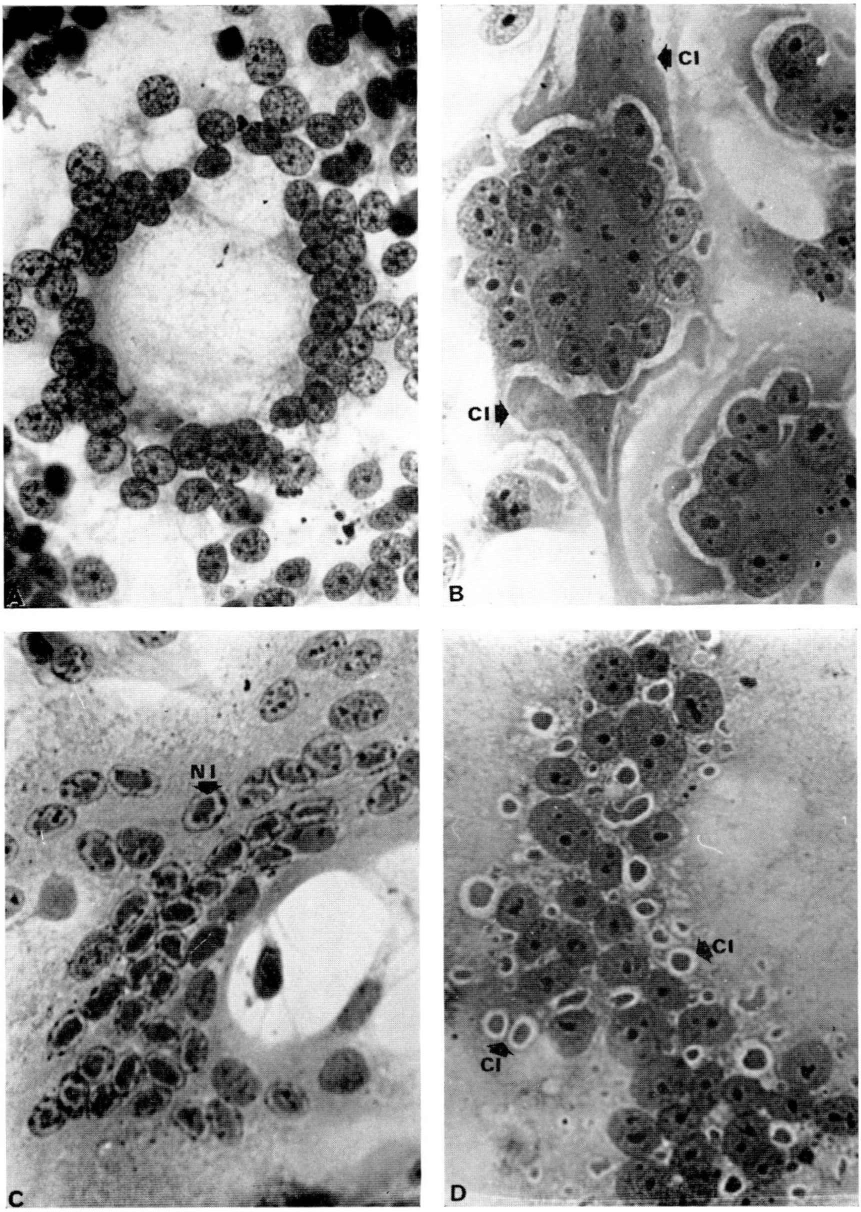

FIG. 1. Virus-induced polykaryocytosis. (A) Poxvirus-vaccinia virus in HeLa cells; (B) measles, distemper, rinderpest triad-measles virus in dog kidney cells; (C) herpesvirus—bovine herpes mammillitis virus in bovine kidney cells; (D) paramyxovirus—parainfluenza 3 virus in HEp-2 cells. CI = Cytoplasmic inclusion body; NI = Nuclear inclusion body.

Although it is probable that some of the polykaryocytes described in the early literature were caused by viruses, their viral etiology was not recognized until much later. A large number of viruses which can cause polykaryocytosis have now been isolated (Roizman, 1962a), and this has stimulated considerable interest in polykaryocyte formation and in the problem of cell fusion.

More recently, the ability of viruses to cause cell fusion has provided a technique with which problems in other aspects of biology can be investigated. Virus-induced fusion of different cell types, including cells from different species, has provided extremely important information on the fundamental control mechanisms operating in gene expression in differentiated cells (Weiss and Green, 1967; Harris, 1968; Defendi, 1969). Preliminary studies have also indicated that it may be possible to reduce the oncogenic potential of tumor cells by fusing them with normal cells (Harris *et al.*, 1969; Watkins and Chen, 1969). Virus-induced cell fusion has provided a method for the recovery of latent tumor viruses from transformed cells *in vitro*. Latent SV_{40} virus (Gerber, 1966; Koprowski *et al.*, 1967; Burns and Black, 1968; Kit *et al.*, 1969), polyoma virus (Fogel and Sachs, 1969), and Rous sarcoma virus (Shevliaghyn *et al.*, 1969; Svoboda and Dourmashkin, 1969) have been "rescued" by fusing transformed cells with permissive cells using inactivated Sendai virus. This technique may also find a possible application in the "rescue" of certain avidly cell-associated viruses, e.g., the EB herpesvirus found in Burkitt lymphoma cells. In another application to virology, virus-induced cell fusion has been used to introduce viruses mechanically into cells in which this cannot be achieved naturally. Viruses introduced into the cytoplasm in this way have been found to replicate well in cell types which were previously judged as unable to support their growth (cf. Enders *et al.*, 1967; Neff and Enders, 1968; Tegtmeyer and Enders, 1969).

It is obvious that the ability of viruses to cause cell fusion is important not only as a consequence of normal virus infection, but also as a biological tool which may be used to study more fundamental biological events. For this reason, investigations on cell fusion must become a field of increasing research interest.

C. Terminology

The term *syncytium* was introduced by Haeckel (1872) to describe the multinucleate ectoderm of the Calcispongia. The term *plasmodium* was introduced earlier by De Bary (1859) to describe the multinucleate structures formed in the developmental stages of the myxomycete, *Physarum*. Various other terms, e.g., *syndesmia, syncellia, symplasm, symplast,* and *symplasma* were also introduced at this time to describe multinucleate cells. Indeed, the term symplast is still commonly used in certain Eastern European literature to describe virus-induced polykaryocytes (cf. Dreizen *et al.*, 1967; Konovalova *et al.*, 1967). Bonnet (1903) attempted to introduce some order into this confusing nomenclature, and the meaning of the terms used today stem from the adoption of his recommendations.

Syncytium is now properly used to describe a multinucleate cell formed by the fusion of previously separate cells, while *plasmodium* is applied to multinucleate cells formed by repeated karyokinesis without cytokinesis. More recently, Roizman (1962a) has introduced the term *polykaryocyte* to describe, without reference to its mode of formation, any multinucleate cell, and this term will be used throughout the present article.

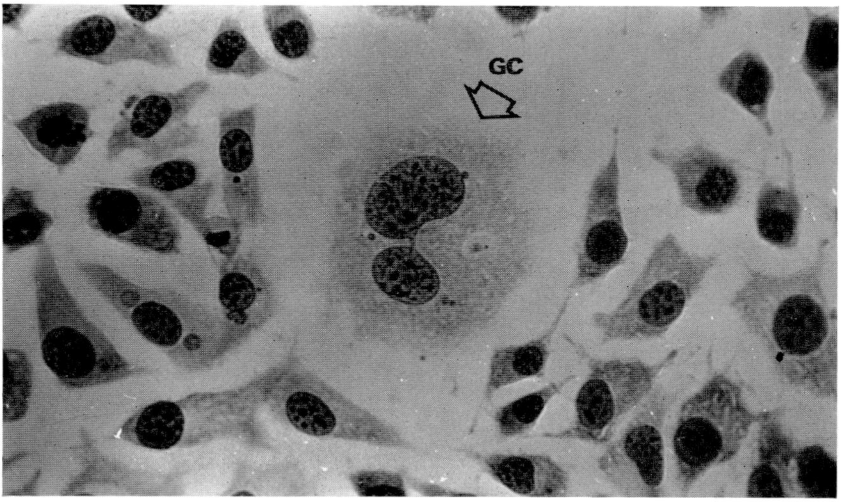

FIG. 2. True giant cell (GC) with pleomorphic nucleus in uninfected HEp-2 cell culture.

The term *giant cell* is still widely, but incorrectly, used to describe multinucleate cells, particularly those found in various pathological conditions. A few authors also use this term to describe polykaryocytes induced by viruses. However, this term is incorrect unless qualified as *multinucleate* giant cell, since a true giant cell only contains a single nucleus which is larger (giant) than the majority of nuclei within the cell population. Examples of true giant cells are commonly found in heteroploid established cell lines (Fig. 2) and in irradiated cell cultures.

II. Polykaryocyte Formation—Cell Fusion or Amitosis?

Langhans (1868) was the first to ask whether polykaryocytes were formed by repeated nuclear division of the same cell or by fusion of several cells. There is now considerable evidence that cell fusion is the more important mechanism in the case of virus-induced polykaryocytes, although nuclear division may be responsible in a few cases.

A. Polykaryocyte Formation by Cell Fusion

The evidence that viral polykaryocytes are generally formed by cell fusion is derived from a number of observations.

1. Time-Lapse Cinematographic Studies

Time-lapse microcinematographic studies have demonstrated that viruses can cause cell fusion. Studies on cell cultures infected with measles (Aoyama, 1959; Thomison, 1962; Tawara, 1965; Klöne *et al.*, 1966), SV_5 (Holmes and Choppin, 1966), mouse hepatitis virus (Allison, 1967), ectromelia (Habermehl and Diefenthal, 1961), herpesvirus hominis (HVH) (Barski and Robineaux, 1959; Bungay and Watkins, 1964), herpesvirus B (Falke and Richter, 1961a,b), and parainfluenza viruses (Marston, 1958; Lépine *et al.*, 1959) have all shown that polykaryocytes arise by cell fusion.

2. Electron Microscopy of Cell Fusion

Varying degrees of cell fusion have been recognized in ultrastructural studies of cells infected with Sendai virus (Okada, 1962; Hosaka and Koshi, 1968), Newcastle disease virus (NDV) (Meiselman *et al.*, 1967), canine distemper virus (CDV) (Poste, 1969), and vaccinia virus (Dales and Siminovitch, 1961). Ultrastructural studies on virus-induced heterokaryon formation have also provided evidence of cell fusion, since fusion between cells which have very different morphological characteristics can easily be recognized (cf. Harris *et al.*, 1966; Schneeberger and Harris, 1966; Svoboda and Dourmashkin, 1969).

These studies have shown that cell fusion starts with the formation of small cytoplasmic bridges between adjacent cells at points where the plasma membranes of the two cells are in direct contact (Fig. 3). The unequivocal demonstration of these bridges is not easy, because superimposition artifacts may occur because the membranes are so closely apposed. Very careful examination of material using a through-focus series is essential. For example, Hyde *et al.* (1969), in an ultrastructural study of intercellular contact in rat heart cell cultures, found apposed membranes which appeared both as fused and as separated segments within the same through-focus series.

The exact nature of the structural changes occurring in the plasma membrane which permit connecting bridges to be formed between cells cannot be established from electron microscopic studies.

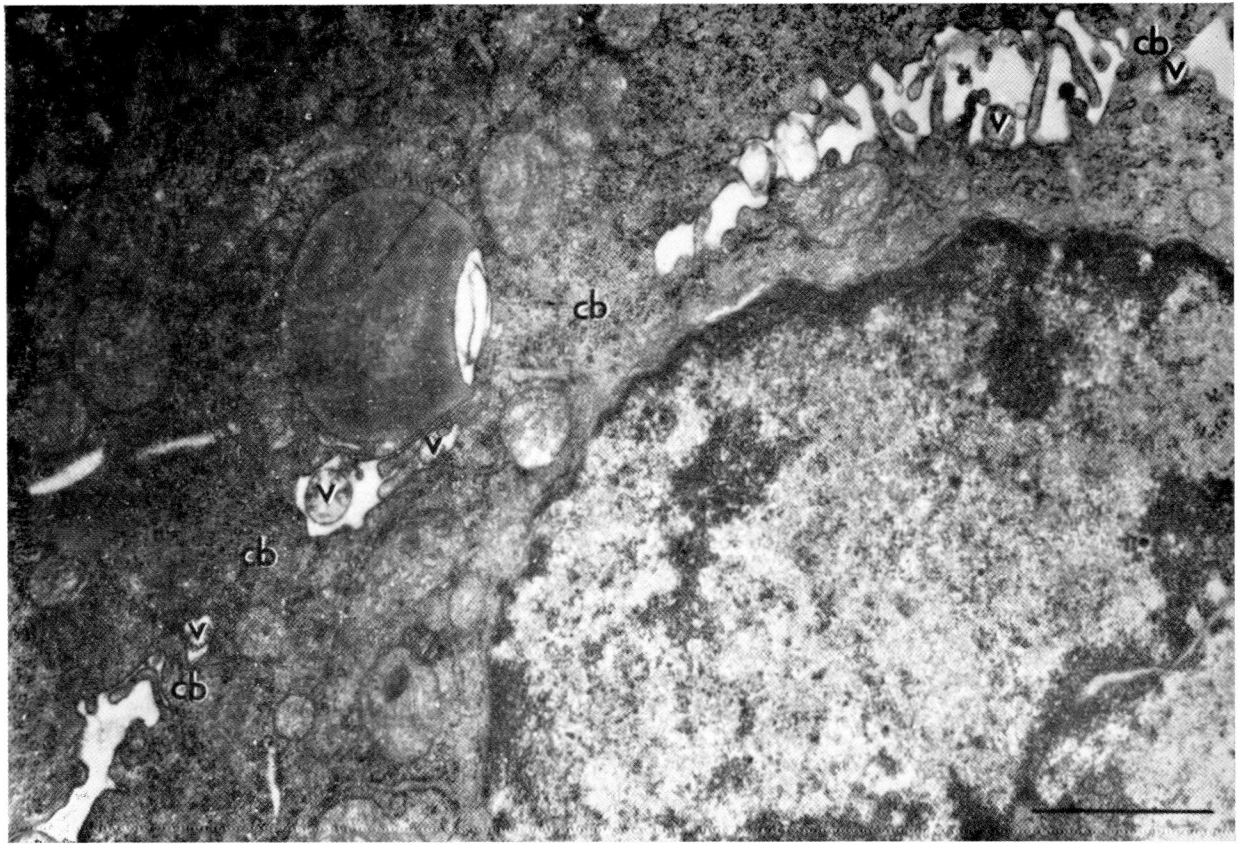

FIG. 3. Cytoplasmic bridges formed between adjacent Ehrlich ascites tumor cells following infection with the Z strain of Sendai virus. Reprinted with permission from Y. Hosaka and Y. Koshi, *Virology* 34, 419 (1968).

3. Studies with Cell Markers

The development of techniques whereby cells maintained as suspension cultures can be fused by viruses has provided further proof of the importance of cell fusion in polykaryocytogenesis. Using these methods, cells carrying specific markers or labels are mixed together in the presence of a polykaryocytogenic virus, and the formation of polykaryocytes containing both labeled and unlabeled cells is taken as evidence that fusion has occurred. Radioactive labeling of one cell type in a mixed cell culture has been used to demonstrate virus-induced cell fusion in several systems (Harris, 1965; Okada and Murayama, 1965; Harris *et al.*, 1966; Steplewski and Swierkowska, 1967; Dubbs and Kit, 1969; Svoboda and Dourmashkin, 1969; Weber and Stich, 1969). As an alternative to the use of artificial markers to identify cells, it is also possible to exploit natural cell markers for the same purpose. The more common specific cellular characteristics used in this way include: (*1*) morphological differences between the nuclei of the cell types fused together (Harris, 1965; Okada and Murayama, 1965; Burns and Black, 1969; Svoboda and Dourmashkin, 1969); (*2*) specific chromosome markers (Harris *et al.*, 1966; Ephrussi and Weiss, 1967; Silagi, 1967; Engel *et al.*, 1969); (*3*) cell-specific enzymes (Harris and Cook, 1969; Silagi *et al.*, 1969); (*4*) specific cellular synthetic products (Davidson, 1969); and (*5*) specific cell surface antigens (Watkins and Grace, 1967).

4. Nuclear Counts

If viral polykaryocytes were formed by successive amitotic nuclear division of the same cell, rather than by cell fusion, it would be expected that the numbers of nuclei in cultures containing polykaryocytes would be significantly increased. However, detailed counts have failed to reveal any increase in the number of nuclei in cell cultures containing polykaryocytes produced by mumps (Henle *et al.*, 1954), NDV (Butler, 1965), CDV (Poste, 1969), HVH (Ross and Orlans, 1958; Stoker, 1959), and measles (Matsumoto *et al.*, 1965) viruses. Further, the marked morphological similarity between the nuclei in polykaryocytes and those in single cells suggests that amitosis has not occurred on a large scale, since this would produce bizarre and highly pleomorphic nuclei (cf. Enders *et al.*, 1965).

5. Studies with Single Cells

If nuclear fission, instead of cell fusion, were responsible for the formation of polykaryocytes, virus infection of single isolated cells *in vitro* should lead to polykaryocyte formation. Unfortunately, very little work of this type has been done, presumably because of the technical difficulties involved. Wildy *et al.* (1959) infected single HeLa cells with the

HFEM strain of HVH. It was found that out of 40 cells exposed to the virus, only two divided in the following 33 hours and no polykaryocytes were found. This contrasts with findings obtained with the same virus strain grown in confluent HeLa cell monolayers where polykaryocytes were detected 9 to 12 hours after infection (Stoker, 1959). Although not providing a strict single cell system, Kohn (1965) found that the extent of polykaryocyte formation in FL cells infected with the HP strain of NDV was influenced by the cell population density. At low cell densities polykaryocyte formation was reduced, presumably as a result of the reduced opportunities for direct cell-to-cell contact and fusion.

6. Is Cell Fusion a Form of Phagocytosis?

As described above, most evidence indicates that cell fusion involves the formation of connecting bridges between adjacent cells, and the bridges subsequently enlarge to complete the fusion process. However, Lépine *et al.* (1959) and Chany and Cook (1960), from their studies on parainfluenza virus-induced fusion of KB cells, suggested that cell fusion was achieved by phagocytosis of one cell by another. They suggested that in this process, which they termed *cytophagia,* whole intact cells were engulfed and incorporated into polykaryocytes. Although cellular phagocytosis of whole cells does occur in certain situations (cf. Shelton and Rice, 1958; Bernkopf *et al.*, 1959), it is unlikely that the process observed by Lépine and Chany was true phagocytosis of cells since the outline of the allegedly engulfed cells could not be detected in the cytoplasm of polykaryocytes. Thus, the term cytophagia is probably misleading when applied to the cell fusion induced by viruses. However, very limited phagocytosis of intact cells by polykaryocytes has been noted in studies with measles virus (Kohn and Yassky, 1962; Nii *et al.*, 1964) and West Nile virus (Paul *et al.*, 1969). However, all these authors commented that this was a relatively uncommon finding in their material and they stressed that cell fusion, rather than phagocytosis, was involved in the formation of the polykaryocytes.

The process of *emperipolesis,* which involves the presence of intact, and often viable, cells within the cytoplasm of another cell might also be included in Lépine's concept of cytophagia. Nevertheless, some aspects of emperipolesis are relevant to the general problem of cell fusion, since ultrastructural studies have shown that fusion occurs between the interacting cells (Bedoya *et al.*, 1968).

B. Polykaryocyte Formation by Abnormal Nuclear Division

1. Amitosis

It is now generally acknowledged that amitotic division is not commonly involved in polykaryocytogenesis. As Roizman (1962a) pointed out, it is very difficult to envisage polykaryocytes containing several hundred nuclei being produced by repeated amitosis, since the parent nucleus would not have enough chromosomes to provide each nucleus in the polykaryocyte with one chromosome. Even assuming that the chromosomes doubled before each amitotic division, it is difficult to imagine how so many nuclei of normal morphology could arise by this process. True amitosis, which occurs normally in certain cells, involves exact nuclear division and genome segregation so that each nucleus receives an identical complement of genetic material (Grundmann, 1966). Polykaryocytes formed in this way would contain nuclei of equal size, i.e., isokaryocytosis. In its broadest sense, amitosis also includes nuclear budding and fragmentation. Polykaryocytes formed by these processes would probably contain macro- and micronuclei and thus show anisokaryocytosis.

Amitosis has been reported as responsible for the formation of *very small* polykaryocytes in cell cultures infected with widely differing viruses, including: measles (Thomison, 1962; Atherton *et al.*, 1965); rinderpest (Provost and Villemot, 1961); CDV (Poste, 1969); Sendai (Ho Yun-De, 1962); NDV (Johnson and Scott, 1964); myxoma virus (Maral, 1957); pseudorabies (Kaplan and Ben-Porat, 1959); herpes zoster (Weller *et al.*, 1958); herpesvirus B (Falke, 1961); and the HF (Cocuzza and Russo, 1966) and P (Scott *et al.*, 1961) strains of HVH. In all these reports, the authors also commented on the presence within the same cultures of much larger polykaryocytes which they suggested had arisen by cell fusion. It is perhaps pertinent to remember that amitotic nuclear division is also seen in cell cultures infected with viruses which do not cause cell fusion, e.g., Rous sarcoma virus (Levinson, 1967) and hog cholera virus (Pirtle and Woods, 1968). Examples of the formation of small polykaryocytes by amitosis, nuclear fragmentation, and mitotic nondisjunction are also commonly seen in virus-transformed cell cultures (cf. Moyer *et al.*, 1964; Kimoto and Grace, 1966). Furthermore, the type of cell can influence the frequency of amitosis induced by the same virus (cf. Nii and Kamahora, 1963). It would appear, therefore, that the induction of amitosis and/or nuclear fragmentation is a cytopathic effect common to a number of viruses, all of which do not ordinarily cause cell fusion.

2. Nuclear Division without Cytoplasmic Division

There are also a few reports where mitotic figures have been found in virus-induced polykaryocytes (Betz *et al.*, 1963; Cascardo and Karzon, 1965; Bonissol, 1966a; Holmes and Choppin, 1966). This has led to the suggestion that some small polykaryocytes can be formed from single cells by mitotic division of the nucleus without division of the cytoplasm. It is valid to point out that the incidence of mitotic figures given in these reports is very low and mitosis appeared to be confined to very small polykaryocytes, no mitotic figures being reported in the much larger polykaryocytes also present in the same cultures. Roizman and Schluederberg (1962) suggested that abnormal nuclear division of this type only occurred in cells where the mitotic apparatus had been damaged, but not destroyed, by the virus. Nevertheless, the incidence of this phenomenon appears to be extremely low and its importance in polykaryocytogenesis can be disregarded.

C. The Sequence of Events in Polykaryocyte Formation

1. The Requirements for Cell Fusion

Roizman (1962a,b) proposed that the polykaryocytes induced by viruses were formed by the fusion of infected and uninfected cells, or cells differing in the period since infection. He suggested that when all the cells in a culture were infected simultaneously differences would not exist between the cells and fusion could not occur. These suggestions arose from his findings that polykaryocytosis was the predominant CPE in cells infected with HVH at low multiplicities, while the same cells exposed to high multiplicities of the virus did not fuse. The view that polykaryocytogenesis involves fusion between infected and uninfected cells has been proposed on other occasions (Stoker, 1959; Bungay and Watkins, 1964; Tankersley, 1968). However, these suggestions can be disputed. First, there is an enormous amount of evidence to show that fusion occurs when all the cells are infected. Even studies with HVH, the virus used by Roizman, have shown that cell fusion can be induced readily with virus multiplicities greater than one (Nii and Kamahora, 1961a, 1963; Siminoff, 1964; Tokumaru, 1968). Similar examples can be quoted from studies with other viruses, in which large viral inocula were actually *necessary* to induce cell fusion (Henle *et al.*, 1954; Chany *et al.*, 1958; Black, 1959; Kaplan and Vatter, 1959; Bader and Morgan, 1961; Hosaka, 1962; Okada and Tadokoro, 1962; Demont *et al.*, 1963; McClain, 1965; Nasibov and Smorodintsev, 1968). Furthermore, Roizman's theory would not account for the numerous examples of so called "early" polykaryocytosis in which massive doses of virus cause extensive cell fusion within a few hours of infection (Section IV,B,1). Second, if cell fusion could only occur between infected and uninfected cells, it should not be possible to observe fusion between infected cells. However, Holmes and Choppin (1966), in their study of SV_5 virus infection in BHK21-F cells, showed by immunofluorescence that virtually all of the cells in infected cultures contained viral antigen 7 hours after infection when cell fusion was just beginning. This observation clearly indicates that fusion can occur between cells which were infected at the same time and which were at similar stages in the production of viral components. That fusion occurs between infected cells is also confirmed by observations from time-lapse studies where fusion between two or more polykaryocytes has been observed (Bonissol, 1966a; Holmes and Choppin, 1966; Klöne *et al.*, 1966).

When considering the effect of the virus dose on polykaryocyte formation, it is also necessary to remember that many virus populations are mixed and contain both particles which can induce cell fusion and others which cannot (see Section III,B,1). The proportion of each type within the virus population will determine the extent of the cell fusion produced by the inoculated virus.

2. *The Developmental Stages in Polykaryocyte Formation*

Roizman (1962a,b) also proposed that the polykaryocytes induced by viruses were formed in two stages; the propolykaryocyte stage followed by the true polykaryocyte stage. The propolykaryocyte described by Roizman was broken up by treatment with trypsin into elements numerically equivalent to the number of nuclei in the propolykaryocyte. The older true polykaryocyte was resistant to this treatment. Roizman suggested that the propolykaryocyte was still divided by membranes derived from the fused cells and that these membranes later disappeared to form the true polykaryocyte stage. Other studies have failed to confirm Roizman's findings. Treatment of virus-induced polykaryocytes with Versene (Stoker, 1959; Poste, 1969), trypsin (Toyoshima *et al.*, 1960; Cascardo and Karzon, 1965; Poste, 1969), and pronase (Poste, 1969) have failed to fragment polykaryocytes, even those formed within 1 to 3 hours of virus infection (cf. Toyoshima *et al.*, 1960).

The presence of small membrane segments partially separating the nuclei has been found in electron microscopic studies of polykaryocytes induced by viruses (Harris *et al.*, 1966; Meiselman *et al.*, 1967; Leestma *et al.*, 1969) and other agents (Gusek, 1962; Daniel, 1963; Grimley and Sokoloff, 1966). However, in none of these reports was complete membranous compartmentalization found of the type proposed by Roizman. It is not unknown, however, for large virus-induced polykaryocytes to fragment naturally into a number of smaller multinucleate units which are still viable (McClain, 1965; Holmes and Choppin, 1966; Paul *et al.*, 1969). Similar fragmentation has been reported with polykaryocytes induced by nonviral agents (Cohen, 1926; Schepers, 1959; Stephenson, 1969), and this phenomenon is commonly seen in multinucleate osteoclasts as part of their normal behavior (Hancox, 1965).

D. *Conclusions*

It can be confidently stated that the polykaryocytes induced by viruses are in most cases formed by the fusion of previously separate single cells. In a few cases, polykaryocytes of limited size can also be formed from single cells, either by repeated karyokinesis without cytokinesis or by multiple amitotic nuclear division. In any analysis of virus-induced polykaryocytosis, greater emphasis should be placed on the events which cause cells to fuse together. From the evidence reviewed it can be concluded that virus-induced cell fusion does not require that infected cells fuse only with uninfected cells. Fusion can occur also between infected cells and even between polykaryocytes. The polykaryocytes produced by cell fusion represent true multinucleate cells in which the cytoplasm is not subdivided by membranes.

III. Factors Influencing Polykaryocyte Formation

Any analysis of the factors concerned in the development of polykaryocytes, like other forms of CPE, demands consideration of a multiplicity of factors. However, as Melnick *et al.* (1957) commented: "Many of the factors which influence virus proliferation are often stumbled upon, rather than arrived at by inference." Acknowledging this, the following sections concern those factors which significantly influence polykaryocyte formation; the cell, the virus, and the culture environment.

A. *The Cell*

1. *Cellular Susceptibility*

In view of the limited host range and narrow tissue specificities possessed by most viruses, it is not surprising that the formation of polykaryocytes by viruses, like other forms of CPE, is influenced by the type of cell infected. Differences in the ability of various cells to fuse following virus infection are very striking, and provide important information on the basic mechanisms involved in cell fusion. A particularly interesting problem is posed by the many examples in which the same virus strain can cause extensive fusion of one cell type but not of another, yet replicate to equivalent infectivity titers in both cell types (Fig. 4).

Albanese *et al.* (1966) found that the P strain of HVH produced large polykaryocytes in HeLa cells but not in diploid human embryo lung fibroblasts. The latter cells, however, were consistently one hundred times more sensitive to the growth of the virus than the HeLa cells. Other strains of HVH are known to cause fusion of some types of cell but not others. For example, Roizman (1962b) found that the macroplaque (MP) strain of HVH produced twenty times as many polykaryocytes in HEp-2 cells as in ME cells. Waddell and Sigel (1966) found that the

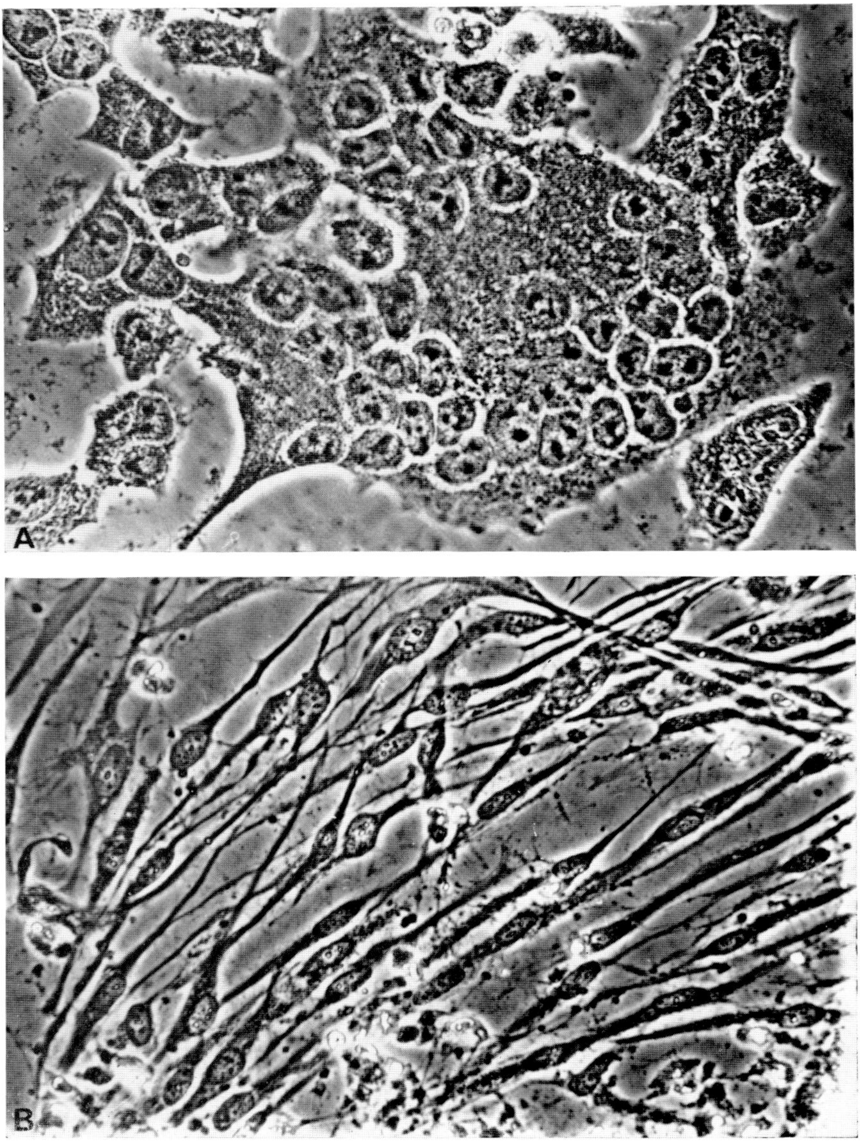

FIG. 4. Variation in cellular response to infection with the same strain of virus: (A) HEp-2 cells infected with an antigenic type II strain of herpesvirus hominis showing polykaryocyte formation; and (B) mouse L cells infected with the same virus and showing cell rounding vacuolation and degeneration.

GCA3 strain of HVH induced polykaryocytosis in rabbit kidney cells but not in KB cells. Tokumaru (1968) found that the H strain of this virus produced extensive cell fusion in rabbit kidney cultures, smaller polykaryocytes, and cell rounding in baby hamster kidney (BHK), while in human embryonic kidney (HEK), human amnion, and mouse MCN cells it only produced cell rounding. Another virus in the same group, herpesvirus T, has also been shown to produce markedly different degrees of cell fusion when grown in a range of cell types, even though virus production was comparable in all of the cultures (Daniel and Meléndez, 1968).

Variation in the ability of different types to fuse following infection has also been recognized with numerous other viruses including: mumps (Bader and Morgan, 1961; Brandt, 1961); SV_5 (Holmes and Choppin, 1966); NDV (Brandt, 1961; Butler, 1965; Kohn, 1965); measles (Moura, 1961); rinderpest (Plowright and Ferris, 1959); CDV (Bussell and Karzon, 1965); respiratory syncytial virus (Jordan, 1962; Anderson and Beem, 1966); visna (Harter and Choppin, 1967); Rous sarcoma (Moses and Kohn, 1963); avian infectious bronchitis (Lukert, 1966); rabbitpox (Appleyard *et al.*, 1962); and the parainfluenza viruses (McKinney *et al.*, 1959; Chany and Cook, 1960; Marston and Vaughan, 1960; Brandt, 1961; Love and Suskind, 1961; Okada and Tadokoro, 1963; Konovalova *et al.*, 1967). Marked differences in cell fusion capacity have also been recognized in systems using inactivated viruses, notably Sendai, to induce cell fusion (Okada, 1961; Okada and Murayama, 1965; Harris *et al.*, 1966; Guggenheim *et al.*, 1969; Dubbs and Kit, 1969).

2. The Influence of Cell Passage Level on Fusion Capacity

The evidence from the above reports indicates that malignant cells and cells from established cell lines have a higher fusion capacity than primary and secondary diploid cells. Okada and Tadokoro (1963) compared the abilities of different cells to fuse when infected with the Z strain of Sendai virus. They found that established cell lines (HeLa, KB, FL, ERK, and MS), mouse ascites tumor cells, and human leukemia cells all had a high fusion capacity, secondary bovine and monkey kidney cells and mouse and chick embryo fibroblasts had a low fusion capacity, but human, mouse, and rabbit leukocytes consistently failed to fuse. Cascardo and Karzon (1965) observed marked differences in the ability of cells to undergo rapid fusion following infection with massive doses of ultraviolet-inactivated Edmonston strain measles virus. Fusion was readily detected in cultures in established cell lines—AV_3 amnion, WS, HeLa, KB, HEp-2, Henle intestine, Chang conjunctiva, and several sublines of Detroit-6 cells. In contrast, primary cells from several human tissues, and primary cells from monkeys and lower animals, had a very poor fusion capacity. Similar variation in the ability of cells to undergo fusion after infection with high multiplicities of virus was reported by Kohn (1965) using the HP strain of NDV. He found that established cell lines (KB, HEp-2, FL, and BHK-21) were able to fuse while the various primary cells tested (human, mouse, and chick fibroblasts, guinea pig macrophages and human and guinea pig bone marrow cells) were not. Isogai (1961), in an investigation of the type of CPE produced by rinderpest virus strains grown in various primary, secondary, and established bovine and avian cells, found that cell rounding and necrosis was the principal type of CPE in the primary and secondary cells, while polykaryocytosis was the predominant CPE in the established cell lines. Harter and Choppin (1967) found that BHK-21-F cells were more susceptible to fusion by visna than primary choroid plexus cells derived from the natural host for this virus—the sheep. The BHK-21-F cells fused at lower virus input multiplicities than the sheep cells, and fusion in the BHK cultures was more rapid even with the lower virus dose. The extreme sensitivity of BHK-21-F cells to virus-induced cell fusion has also been described with SV_5 virus (Holmes and Choppin, 1966). At multiplicities of 2000–6000 plaque-forming units (PFU) per cell SV_5 caused extensive fusion of the BHK cells within 1 hour of infection, but the same dose of virus produced no visible effect on primary monkey kidney cells. The poor ability of primary monkey kidney cells to form polykaryocytes, compared with established cell lines, has also been reported in studies with measles (Moura, 1961) and parainfluenza 3 (PI_3) virus (McKinney *et al.*, 1959; Chany and Cook, 1960; La Placa and Moscovici, 1961; Love and Suskind, 1961; Szmigielski *et al.*, 1967).

Another example, derived from a nonviral system, which is also relevant to the low fusion capacity of certain primary cell cultures was made by Pomerat *et al.* (1957). These authors observed that following sublethal irradiation damage of cells *in vitro*, fusion often occurred between postmitotic daughter cells. However, cell fusion was not observed in primary cell cultures, and only occurred in cells from established cell lines and cells which had been cultured *in vitro* for at least 1 month.

Despite definite variation in the cell-fusion capacity between primary, secondary, and established cell lines in the above system, it must be pointed out that this is merely a general trend and not an absolute rule. For example variations in the fusion potential of established cell lines have also been reported. Ho Yun-De and Gorbunova (1962) found that HeLa, HEp-2, KB, and cynomologous monkey heart (CMH) cell lines were consistently susceptible to fusion by a number of Sendai virus strains, while the HLS (human lymphosarcoma) and 558-M (human salivary gland tumor cells) cell lines failed to fuse although all cells supported virus growth. McClain (1965) reported differences in the facility with which different cell lines were fused by wild-type rabbitpox virus and its various white-pock mutants. The FL, KB, Chang liver, and AT hamster cell lines showed a much greater tendency to fuse and form polykaryocytes than the L929 cell line. The low-fusion capacity of L929 cells has also been reported with other viruses. Toyoshima *et al.* (1960) found that massive doses of measles virus produced fusion of FL cells within 1 hour of infection, but L cells consistently failed to fuse under the same conditions. Bader and Morgan (1961) noted that the Enders strain of mumps virus produced polykaryocytes in HeLa cells but not in L cells. Brandt (1961) reported that polykaryocytes were produced by mumps, NDV and parainfluenza 2 viruses propagated in HEp-2 cells, but the same virus strains rarely produced this type of CPE when grown in L cells. Rabbitpox virus produces polykaryocytes in ERK-1 cells but not in L cells, despite replication to equivalent titer in both types of cell (Appleyard *et al.*, 1962). Studies in this laboratory with antigenic type II genital strains of HVH have shown that they were able to produce extensive cell fusion in HEp-2 and HeLa cells, but rarely in L cells (Poste and Underwood, unpublished). Even when polykaryocytes were found in L cell cultures they were always very small compared with those present in the other cell lines. Nevertheless, virus-induced fusion of L cells has been reported (Okada and Tadokoro, 1963; Hanafusa, 1964; Okada and Murayama, 1965; Vizoso *et al.*, 1966) and spontaneous fusion of L cells with other cell types has been observed in mixed cell cultures (Spurna and Hill, 1968).

3. Variation in Cell Fusion Capacity within the Same Cell Population

These differences in the fusion capacity of the same cell type, obtained by different workers using what is presumed to be a uniform cell type, adequately illustrates the point that more information should be given on the history of the cell types employed in any experiment. Further, the precise conditions used to produce fusion in any virus-cell system should be described. The influence of the genetic constitution of the host cell on the formation of polykaryocytes is illustrated by Rapp's (1960) study of the growth of measles virus in clones of HEp-2 cells. Clones varied both in their susceptibility to infection and in their ability to fuse. One clone produced many polykaryocytes after infection, but spindle-cell formation and lesser degrees of polykaryocytosis was seen in the other clones. These results indicate that the cell populations employed in virus experiments are often heterogeneous. This again stresses the dangers inherent in the assumption that a given cell type or cell line is similar when used in different laboratories. Cell cultures with a specifically reduced capacity to fuse have also been obtained by the selection and cultivation of those cells which did not fuse from cultures infected with polykaryocytogenic viruses (Poste, 1969).

4. The Influence of Cell "Age" on Fusion Capacity

There is some evidence to suggest that "young" cells are better able to fuse and form polykaryocytes than "aged" cells. "Age," in this sense, refers to the time for which cells have been cultured at any given passage level. Thus, ageing represents a continuous transition from newly seeded cells which are growing exponentially to confluent monolayers of aged cells in the stationary phase.

Tokumaru (1968) considered that 5 to 7-day-old rabbit kidney cell cultures were best for the formation of polykaryocytes with H strain HVH, cells more than 8 days old showing degenerative rounding rather than polykaryocytes. Other studies have shown that virus-induced polykaryocytosis is more extensive in cultures composed of cells in the logarithmic phase of growth than in stationary phase confluent cells (Imagawa and Adams, 1958; Plowright and Ferris, 1959; Underwood, 1959; Parfanovitch *et al.*, 1966; Khozinski *et al.*, 1967). Similarly, the subculture of infected "aged" cells, showing only a minimal nonprogressive CPE, results in the development of extensive polykaryocytosis in the young subcultured cells without further introduction of virus (Plowright and Ferris, 1959; Toyoshima *et al.*, 1959; Chabassol and Poussot, 1967). Age-related differences in cell-fusion capacity are also seen in nonviral systems. Bischoff and Holtzer (1969) found that the *in vitro* fusion of chick myoblasts to form multinucleate myotubes was significantly greater in 2-day-old cultures as compared with 4-day-old cultures.

It is likely that these differences in the development of CPE in young and aged cells reflect differences in the cellular metabolism in the two "age" conditions. The change in a cell culture from the logarithmic to the stationary phase of growth is accompanied by distinct alterations in cellular metabolism. Levine *et al.* (1965) found that the rates of cellular DNA, RNA, and protein synthesis decrease considerably as cells become confluent and enter the stationary phase. Another phenomenon which many accompany these changes involves the increased ability of certain aged cells to produce interferon (Carver and Marcus, 1967). Both these effects would tend to limit virus multiplication and the expression of viral CPE.

Changes might also occur in the lipid composition of the plasma membrane during "ageing" of the cell and could reduce the ability of old cells to fuse (Howe and Morgan, 1969).

B. The Virus

1. Variants Causing Different Cytopathic Effects

Although the formation of polykaryocytes in virus-infected cultures is influenced by the host cell, it is ultimately dependent upon the genetic constitution of the virus. For example, many virus populations have been shown to contain both particles which can cause cell fusion and others which cannot. Specific CPE variants producing either polykaryocytosis or some other type of CPE have now been isolated from such mixed virus populations. In some cases polykaryocytogenic variants were isolated from virus populations which did not normally produce this type of CPE. In other examples, polykaryocytogenic variants were obtained from a mixed virus population which produced several types of CPE, including polykaryocytosis. Gray *et al.* (1958) were the first to suggest that specific CPE variants existed within the same virus population. Using a strain of HVH isolated from a case of stomatitis, three major forms of CPE were observed in HeLa cells: *(1)* polykaryocytosis (GC); *(2)* cell proliferation (P); and *(3)* cell rounding. Using the same parent virus strain Scott *et al.* (1961) isolated virus strains producing only the "GC" and "P" types of CPE. Similar variants of HVH producing either one or the other of these forms of CPE have now been isolated (Hoggan and Roizman, 1959; Nii and Kamahora, 1961a,b; Kohlhage and Siegert, 1962; Munk and Donner, 1963; Wheeler, 1964; Kohlhage and Schieferstein, 1965; Hampar, 1966; Ejercito *et al.*, 1968; Germanov and Sokolov, 1969). Similar differences in CPE can also be demonstrated among primary isolates of HVH which appear to be correlated with the antigenic type of the virus. Two antigenic types of HVH are recognized: type I, generally found in labial lesions; and type II, generally found in genital infection. However, the type II viruses show a greater and more uniform tendency to produce polykaryocytes. (Nahmias and Dowdle, 1968; Kleger and Prier, 1969). This division is not absolute, since the emergence of polykaryocytogenic variants in antigenic type I populations has been reported (Schneweis, 1962).

CPE variants are not confined to HVH populations. Tokumaru (1957) isolated a polykaryocytogenic variant of pseudorabies virus in monkey kidney cells. Similar variants have also been obtained from populations of herpesvirus B (Falke, 1961), herpesvirus T (Daniel and Meléndez, 1968), herpeszoster virus (Taylor-Robinson, 1959), measles (Oddo *et al.*, 1967) and parainfluenza 3 virus (Dinter *et al.*, 1960). There are also a few reports where variants unable to cause cell fusion have been isolated from virus populations which normally caused polykaryocytosis (Okada and Hosakawa, 1961; Zhdanov and Bukrinskaya, 1962; McClain, 1965; Gharpure *et al.*, 1969).

2. *Properties of the Variants*

Despite the differences in CPE induced by the variants described above, most of their other properties resemble those of the parent virus population. However, the *macroplaque* (polykaryocyte CPE) and *microplaque* (cell rounding CPE) variants of HVH differ in buoyant density, ability to elute from ECTEOLA, and in their antigenic properties (Roizman and Roane, 1961, 1963). Similar differrences in buoyant density and elution from ECTEOLA were noted by Kohlhage and Siegert (1962) and Kohlhage (1964) in their HVH variants, but antigenic differences were not detected. Differences in the physicochemical properties of other CPE variants of HVH have been reported by Nii and Kamahora (1961a). However, it is important to recognize that even the CPE-specific virus populations are heterogeneous. Aurelian and Wagner (1966) found that the polykaryocytogenic macroplaque variant of HVH grown in HEp-2 cells contained at least two distinct types of virion separable by rate zonal centrifugation. These subvariants also differed in their DNA content, heat lability, envelope structure, and infectivity.

3. *Conclusions*

Virus populations are heterogeneous containing subpopulations differing in their ability to fuse cells. Moreover, such CPE specific subpopulations are still heterogeneous. Some antigenic and physicochemical differences have been detected between various subpopulations, but the significance of these differences in relation to the type of CPE produced is not known.

C. The Culture Environment

1. *The General Environment*

It is highly likely that many of the minor variations in the formation of polykaryocytes reported by different laboratories, using the same virus-cell system, result from differences in the *in vitro* culture environment. Most investigators tend merely to adopt a culture system which has proved successful in growing the type of cell used in the virus experiments, and assume that it is also optimal for the development of polykaryocytes. However, certain components of the culture medium and the culture technique are known to influence cell fusion.

2. *Serum Supplements*

Polykaryocytosis and virus yield have been reported to be greater in cell cultures maintained in medium with more than 5% serum supplement

(Reissig *et al.*, 1956; Kohn, 1965; Rweyemamu and Johnson, 1967). The species of serum may also influence polykaryocytosis. The replacement of calf by lamb serum increased the size and number of polykaryocytes induced by measles (Moura, 1961) and rinderpest (Liess and Plowright, 1963) viruses in HeLa cells. In contrast, Rweyemamu and Johnson (1967) found that calf serum was superior to lamb serum for the formation of polykaryocytes in bovine kidney cells infected with bovine herpes mammillitis virus. Marston and Vaughan (1960) reported that the polykaryocytosis produced by parainfluenza 3 virus in human and rabbit cells was reduced when calf serum, rather than human serum, was used in the medium. Variations between sera from different species probably reflect both batch variability and the extent to which the cells have been adapted to growth with that serum.

3. Glutamine

Reissig *et al.* (1956) and Frankel and West (1958) claimed that glutamine inhibited the formation of polykaryocytes in FL and HEp-2 cells infected with measles virus, but subsequent studies failed to confirm this (see Matumoto, 1966). In contrast, Marquez and Hsiung (1967) found glutamine to be essential for polykaryocyte formation in HEp-2 cells infected with respiratory syncytial virus, but other investigators reported that glutamine was not important in polykaryocytosis (Barski and Robineaux, 1959; Plowright and Ferris, 1959; Hoggan *et al.*, 1961; Jordan, 1962).

4. Culture Technique

The polykaryocytosis induced by herpes zoster virus (Weller *et al.*, 1958), rinderpest (Plowright, 1962), respiratory syncytial (Wulff *et al.*, 1964), and measles (Parfanovitch *et al.*, 1966) viruses is greater in roller cultures than in static cultures. One explanation for this effect is that frequent medium changes increase the rate of cellular RNA and protein synthesis (Becker and Levitt, 1968) and this could in turn increase virus production and also CPE.

IV. The Relationship Of Virus Multiplication to Cell Fusion

A. Early and Late Polykaryocytosis

The time at which cell fusion occurs after virus infection allows a distinction to be made between so called "early" and "late" polykaryocytosis. The early form involves rapid fusion of cells, usually within 3 hours of infection. This type of polykaryocytosis is essentially a laboratory artifact, since it is a nontransmissible form of CPE and can only be demonstrated in cells *in vitro* following infection at extremely high virus multiplicities. The capacity to produce early polykaryocytosis is largely confined to a group of RNA viruses sharing a common morphology, viz., Sendai (Okada, 1962), SV_5 (Holmes and Choppin, 1966), NDV (Kohn, 1965), and measles (Toyoshima *et al.*, 1960) viruses. Among DNA viruses, it has been reported only with HVH, again using high doses (Nii and Kamahora, 1963; Tokumaru, 1968), but Falke and Peterknecht (1968) could not produce this effect. Late polykaryocytosis is characterized by cell fusion beginning a number of hours or, more commonly, days after infection at moderate or low virus input multiplicities. In this type of polykaryocytosis, cell fusion coincides with the most intensive phases of virus multiplication.

It is difficult to assess whether an absolute distinction should be made between early and late polykaryocytosis. Both produce cell fusion which, in both processes, probably demands a common mechanism to effect fusion. However, it seems highly likely that the stimulus which initiates the fusion mechanism is different in early and late polykaryocytosis. Nevertheless, information obtained from studies on both types of polykaryocytosis has provided valuable data on the mechanisms involved in cell fusion. In the following sections evidence from both early and late polykaryocytosis will be considered together.

B. Dissociation of Cell Fusion from the Production of Infectious Virus

1. Rapid Cell Fusion

Many viruses can induce rapid cell fusion, particularly when massive inocula are employed. In many examples this effect has been produced by viruses rendered noninfectious by ultraviolet irradiation (see Section IV,B,2). This effect can also be produced with fully infectious virus. The rapid formation of polykaryocytes before the formation of new viral antigens or infectious virus has been reported with: SV_5 (Holmes and Choppin, 1966); Sendai (Hosaka, 1962; Zhdanov and Bukrinskaya, 1962; Demont *et al.*, 1963); measles (Toyoshima *et al.*, 1960); mumps (Nasibov and Smorodintsev, 1968); parainfluenza 3 (Chany and Cook, 1960; Cohen *et al.*, 1961); visna (Harter and Choppin, 1967); avian infectious bronchitis (Akers and Cunningham, 1968); HVH (Nii and Kamahora, 1961a; Siminoff, 1964); and rabbitpox (McClain, 1965) viruses.

2. Inactivated Viruses and Cell Fusion

Virus preparations rendered noninfectious by controlled ultraviolet irradiation still retain the ability to produce rapid, and often very extensive, cell fusion. The use of ultraviolet-inactivated Sendai virus to induce cell fusion is the classical example. Similarly, treatment of Sendai virus with β-propiolactone completely destroys infectivity but does not affect the ability to fuse cells (Burns and Black, 1968; Tegtmeyer and Enders, 1969). The persistence of the ability to fuse cells, despite loss of infectivity, has also been observed with ultraviolet-irradiated preparations of measles (Toyoshima *et al.*, 1960), mumps (Henle *et al.*, 1954); NDV (Bayreuther, 1966), and visna (Harter and Choppin, 1967) viruses.

The resistance of the viral cell fusion property to inactivation by ultraviolet irradiation may vary between viruses. In the "paramyxoviruses," using this term in its broadest sense to include measles virus as well as the parainfluenza group of myxoviruses, it is fairly resistant. However, ultraviolet treatment completely abolished the ability of HF strain HVH to fuse rabbit kidney cells (Cocuzza and Russo, 1966) and rabbitpox virus to fuse ERK cells (Appleyard *et al.*, 1962). In contrast, Hanafusa (1960) and Kaku and Kamahora (1964) found that ultraviolet-inactivated vaccinia virus could still fuse cells, although the morphology of the polykaryocytes induced by inactivated virus was different from those induced by fully infectious virus.

3. Abortive Infection and Cell Fusion

Viruses can also fuse cells in which productive infection does not occur. Aurelian and Roizman (1964) isolated a number of conditional lethal mutants of HVH which grew normally in HEp-2 cells and induced cell fusion, while in MDCK dog kidney cells fusion occurred without the production of infectious virus. In parallel with polykaryocyte formation in the MDCK cells small amounts of viral DNA, viral antigen, and interferon were detected. Virus-induced cell fusion in the absence of productive infection was also reported by Zhdanov and Bukrinskaya (1962) with Sendai virus; incomplete virus possessed the same ability to fuse cells as fully infectious virions. Stevens (1966) observed that infectious bovine rhinotracheitis virus induced cell fusion in MDBK bovine kidney cells grown at 37° and 42°C. However, infectious virus was only formed at 37°C; at 42°C the infection was abortive because viral proteins were not synthesized.

C. The Role of Virus-Induced Proteins in Cell Fusion

Chany and Cook (1960) proposed that the cell fusion produced by parainfluenza 3 virus was caused by "syncytine"—a substance presumed to be induced by the virus during the eclipse phase. Demont *et al.* (1963) also adopted this idea to explain Sendai virus-induced cell fusion. Although no information has been provided to support the existence of syncytine, many experiments have now been performed with metabolic inhibitors to test whether viruses can induce the synthesis of new proteins capable of causing cell fusion.

1. Inhibition of DNA Synthesis

The antibiotic mitomycin C causes structural changes in the DNA molecule which lead to its breakdown and thus prevent its replication (Shatkin *et al.*, 1962). Mitomycin C (40 μg/ml) completely inhibited DNA synthesis and the growth of the Lennette strain of HVH in rabbit kidney cells but polykaryocytes were still formed (Falke, 1967; Falke *et al.*, 1969). In the same system, inhibition of DNA synthesis by cytosine arabinoside and hydroxyurea also failed to inhibit the formation of polykaryocytes. Munk and Sauer (1964), using HeLa cells, found that mitomycin C (16 μg/ml) completely inhibited the production of infectious HVH but had no effect on cell fusion and polykaryocyte formation. Ben-Porat *et al.* (1961) showed that noninfectious "coreless" pseudorabies virus particles, produced by infection of rabbit kidney cells in the presence of mitomycin C (5 μg/ml), were able to induce cell fusion when adsorbed onto fresh cells. Moreover, incomplete virus formed polykaryocytes at lower multiplicities of infection than the fully infectious particles. Kaku and Kamahora (1964) reported the formation of polykaryocytes in L cell cultures infected with vaccinia virus in the presence of 10 μg/ml mitomycin C.

The halogenated pyrimidines, 5-bromodeoxyuridine (BUDR), 5-iododeoxyuridine (IUDR), and 5-fluorodeoxyuridine (FUDR), are also widely used to inhibit DNA synthesis. Tokumaru (1968) found that the formation of polykaryocytes by H strain HVH in rabbit kidney cells was not affected by IUDR (200 μg/ml), although virus production was completely inhibited. Polykaryocyte formation by the HF/C (Siminoff, 1964) and HFEM (Schneweis, 1967) strains of HVH was not inhibited by BUDR, although production of infectious virus was inhibited. Electron microscopic studies of the BUDR-treated cells demonstrated the formation of intracellular HVH subunits (Siminoff and Menefee, 1968). The formation of polykaryocytes in L-M cells infected with another herpesvirus, equine abortion, was not inhibited by 10^{-4} *M* to 10^{-6} *M* FUDR but, like HVH, virus production was inhibited (O'Callaghan *et al.*, 1968). In direct contrast to all these reports, Bungay and Watkins (1964) found that IUDR (200 μg/ml) inhibited both polykaryocyte formation and virus production in HeLa cells infected with the HFEM strain of HVH. Polykaryocytosis was only inhibited if IUDR was added during the first 6 hours after infection; by 7 hours after infection the IUDR-sensitive events were apparently completed since no inhibition was recorded thereafter. Falke (1965), using the Lenette strain of HVH in rabbit kidney cells, also found that IUDR and FUDR inhibited polykaryocyte formation, but only when added up to 2 hours after infection. Production of infectious virus, however, was susceptible to inhibition by these agents added up to 4 hours after infection. Using vaccinia virus, Kaku and Kamahora (1964) found that the polykaryocytosis in L cell cultures was inhibited by BUDR (10 μg/ml) added within 4 hours of infection.

Other analogs known to inhibit DNA synthesis have been investigated. Kaplan (1962) and Reissig and Kaplan (1962) reported that the formation of polykaryocytes by pseudorabies virus in rabbit kidney and ERK cells was not affected by preincubation of the cells with 5-fluorouracil (25 μg/ml) for 18 hours. Di Marco *et al.* (1968) found that daunomycin (4 μg/ml) added up to 9 hours after infection prevented polykaryocytosis in KB cells infected with the macroplaque strain of HVH. Interestingly, virus replication was only blocked by daunomycin if this was added not more than 3 hours after infection. Aminopterin, a folic acid antagonist which preferentially inhibits DNA synthesis, failed to inhibit the formation of polykaryocytes in chick kidney cells infected with avian infectious bronchitis virus (Akers and Cunningham, 1968).

2. *Inhibition of RNA Synthesis*

Actinomycin is an antibiotic which inhibits DNA-dependent RNA synthesis by combining with guanine residues on the DNA helix (Reich, 1964). It inhibits cellular RNA synthesis and the synthesis of mRNA for DNA viruses. It does not inhibit the replication of most RNA-containing viruses since the synthesis of their RNA is not DNA-dependent. Thus, not unexpectedly, the effect of this compound on polykaryocyte formation differs depending on whether a DNA- or an RNA-containing virus is responsible.

Falke and Peterknecht (1968) found that actinomycin C (0.5 μg/ml) prevented polykaryocytosis in rabbit kidney cells infected with HVH when added before, or up to 2 hours after, infection. Thereafter the polykaryocytes developed normally, but the synthesis of infectious virus could be inhibited by addition of actinomycin up to 4 hours after infection. Using vaccinia, another DNA virus, Kaku and Kamahora (1964) found the formation of polykaryocytes in L cells was prevented by actinomycin S (5 μg/ml) added within 5 hours of infection. In contrast, actinomycin has no inhibitory effect on polykaryocyte formation by RNA viruses (Mallucci, 1965; Holmes and Choppin, 1966; Okada *et al.*, 1966; Harter *et al.*, 1969; Hornsleth, 1969). Mirchamsy and

Rapp (1969) reported that the formation of polykaryocytes by the Schwarz strain of measles virus in BSC-1 cells was actually enhanced by treatment with 0.1 μg/ml actinomycin D. Enhancement of measles virus-induced polykaryocytosis was observed by Matsumoto *et al.* (1965) in FL cells treated with 0.06–0.12 μg/ml actinomycin D. The increase in polykaryocytosis in these systems was attributed to an increase in virus production following suppression of interferon synthesis by actinomycin.

Proflavine, an inhibitor similar to actinomycin D, inhibited polykaryocyte formation by HVH in rabbit kidney cells when added up to 2 hours after infection (Falke, 1965) but at smiliar concentrations (1 μg/ml) it had no effect on polykaryocyte formation induced by the Randall and Long strains of respiratory syncytial virus (Hornsleth, 1969).

3. Inhibition of Protein Synthesis

Virus-induced polykaryocytosis is also influenced by agents inhibiting protein synthesis. Puromycin, an antibiotic which interferes with polypeptide chain synthesis (Nathans, 1964), inhibited the formation of polykaryocytes in vaccinia-infected L cells when added within 7 hours of infection (Kaku and Kamahora, 1964). Inhibition of protein synthesis in rabbit kidney cells by cycloheximide (1.2 μg/ml) prevented polykaryocyte formation by HVH (Falke, 1965). Cycloheximide only prevented polykaryocytosis when added within 3 hours of virus infection, but production of infectious virus was blocked by this agent up to 5 hours after infection. In the same system, inhibition of protein synthesis by 120 μg/ml *p*-fluorophenylalanine (*p*FPA) also prevented polykaryocytosis but, in contrast to cycloheximide, this agent was only effective when added within 2 hours of infection. The picture was made no clearer by Falke's (1967) report that chloramphenicol, another inhibitor of protein synthesis, failed to prevent polykaryocytosis in rabbit kidney cells infected with the H4 strain of HVH. Akers and Cunningham (1968) briefly mentioned that 600 μg/ml *p*FPA inhibited polykaryocyte formation in chick kidney cells infected with avian infectious bronchitis virus. In the case of two RNA viruses, Sendai (Okada *et al.*, 1966) and SV_5 (Holmes and Choppin, 1966), puromycin had no effect on polykaryocyte formation.

4. Conclusions

The conflicting results obtained in these studies make it difficult to draw any firm conclusions about the importance of virus-induced molecular products in cell fusion. However, it can at least be stated that there is as yet no proof for the existence of specific virus-induced proteins which are capable of causing cell fusion. Even in those systems where the existence of such proteins was suggested (Kaku and Kamahora, 1964; Falke *et al.*, 1969), there is no evidence that any newly synthesized proteins were responsible for cell fusion *per se*. Besides "early" proteins, other products of viral gene action and replication could equally well be responsible for causing cell fusion, e.g., viral structural proteins, antigenic subunits, and factors which can arrest cellular nucleic acid and protein synthesis.

Even if the need for virus-induced proteins in causing cell fusion is accepted, certain fundamental questions remain unanswered. One such question is what determines the synthesis of these proteins. Obviously, protein synthesis will involve transcription from primary genetic information, and this would serve to differentiate viruses able to cause cell fusion from those unable to produce this effect. However, straightforward genomic transcription cannot explain cellular variation in the expression of polykaryocytosis, since a virus with a fixed genetic potential to cause cell fusion should produce this effect in any cell in which it is capable of growth. Furthermore, in many cases the synthesis of the proteins responsible for causing cell fusion would have to be completed very quickly after virus infection. For example, Hosaka and Koshi (1968), using electron microscopy, found that fusion of Ehrlich ascites tumor cells started within 5 minutes of infection with Sendai virus. Before the suggestions for the role of "early" proteins in cell fusion can be accepted, it will be necessary to identify these proteins. It will also be necessary to show that those virus strains or variants which fail to produce polykaryocytes (Section III,B,1) lack the ability to induce these early proteins. Considering the wide range of viruses which induce cell fusion, it is very difficult to think of a unifying concept for the role of specific virus-induced proteins in polykaryocytosis. Moreover, the ability of chemical and physical agents, such as silica and glass, to cause cell fusion, makes it even more difficult to acknowledge the need for the synthesis of specific proteins in order to cause cell fusion.

D. Attempts to Identify Virus Components Responsible for Cell Fusion

1. General

The ability of viruses to fuse cells has often been attributed to specific viral components, variously termed: fusion factor (Norrby *et al.*, 1964; Cascardo and Karzon, 1965); fusion-inducing factor (Meiselman *et al.*, 1967); cell fusion substance (Okada *et al.*, 1964); giant cell-forming character (Toyoshima *et al.*, 1960); cytolysin (Henle *et al.*, 1954); cell wall-destroying enzyme (Zhdanov and Bukrinskaya, 1962); and syncytium-producing toxin (Tokumaru, 1968). However, in none of these examples has the nature of the cell fusion factor, or its relationship to the virus been precisely defined.

2. Viral Hemolysin and Cell Fusion

The possibility has also been suggested that the cell fusing activities of viruses might be related to their ability to cause hemolysis. It has been postulated for Sendai (Okada, 1958; Ho Yun-De, 1962; Gorbunova *et al.*, 1963), mumps (Henle *et al.*, 1954; Russell and Morgan, 1959), measles (Toyoshima *et al.*, 1960; Cascardo and Karzon, 1965), and parainfluenza 3 (Bukrinskaya and Zhdanov, 1961) viruses that cell fusion and hemolysis were induced by the same component. These proposals were strengthened by the isolation from measles virus of a noninfectious fraction which had both cell fusing and hemolytic activity (Norrby *et al.*, 1964). The role of hemolysin as a *general* mechanism for inducing cell fusion is, however, discredited by the fact that certain nonhemolytic viruses, e.g., respiratory syncytial and the herpesviruses, commonly produce cell fusion. This criticism does assume, however, that all forms of virus-induced cell fusion are produced by a common mechanism, and that the hemolysins of different viruses have similar properties. The role of viral hemolysin in cell fusion is further discredited by the finding that the hemolytic and cell fusion activities of Sendai (Okada and Tadokoro, 1962) and NDV (Kohn, 1965) can be distinguished by their differential sensitivity to inactivation by heat and trypsin. Further the hemolysin of Sendai virus is inhibited by ultraviolet irradiation (Neurath, 1964), but the capacity to fuse cells is unaffected (Section IV,B,2). Finally, variation in the hemolytic activity of different strains of the same virus is not paralleled by variation in their capacity to fuse cells (Okada and Hosakawa, 1961; Hosaka, 1962; Ruckle-Enders, 1962, 1965; Demont *et al.*, 1963; Oddo *et al.*, 1967; Kohn and Fuchs, 1969).

3. Fusion Activity and Virus Structure

Kohn and his colleagues (Kohn, 1965; Kohn and Klibansky, 1967; Kohn and Fuchs, 1969) stated that the structural integrity of the viral envelope was necessary for NDV-induced cell fusion. Partial disruption of the virus envelope with phospholipase A or lysolecithin destroyed the capacity of NDV to fuse cells, without significantly changing the viral hemagglutinin, hemolysin, or neuraminidase activities. Treatment of NDV with other lipolytic agents (sodium dodecyl sulfate, ether, and desoxycholate), proteolytic enzymes, and sonication also reduced its ability to cause fusion. Kohn and Klibansky (1967) suggested that the fusion factor might be associated with an ATPase present in the viral envelope. Tokumaru (1968) reported rapid inactivation of the fusion capacity of HVH following treatment with lipolytic agents and proteases. He concluded that the physicochemical properties of the fusion factor were those of a lipoprotein.

It is, however, difficult to accept all the suggestions from these studies on the viral envelope. It is not at all surprising that degradation of the envelope should have fundamental effects on the ability of the virus to cause cell fusion. Drastic alteration on the envelope by lipases and proteases is likely to prevent even virus adsorption and thus exclude any interaction between virus and cell.

4. *Isolation of Noninfectious Viral Subunits with Cell-Fusing Properties*

There are a few reports where viral components inducing cell fusion have been isolated from the virus particle. Centrifugation of purified Sendai virus at 32,000 *g* for 30 minutes reduced its capacity to cause cell fusion, but the noninfectious supernatant possessed cell-fusing activity (Guggenheim *et al.*, 1969). Centrifugation of purified HVH on sucrose gradients revealed that fusion activity was associated with three components; one with the same density as infectious virus and two less dense noninfectious components (Tokumaru, 1968). A noninfectious component with cell-fusing activity has also been isolated from measles using cesium chloride gradients (Norrby *et al.*, 1964). Tokumaru (1968) was able to separate a lipoprotein from HVH which possessed fusion activity by filtration of purified virus through Biogel A-50 M and Sephadex G-200 gels.

5. *Conclusions*

Some progress has been made in the isolation of viral subunits which can cause cell fusion. However, the precise nature of the fusion-inducing components and their mode of action on the cell remains to be established. It must also be pointed out that distinct fusion factors associated with the virus particle appear to be important only in the rapid cell fusion encountered in "early" polykaryocytosis (Section IV,A,1). In this type of polykaryocytosis, viruses can cause cell fusion without entering the cell, the virus acting as a bridge between the membranes of apposed cells (Fig. 5)—fusion occurring between the virus and both cells (cf. Okada *et al.*, 1966; Hosaka and Koshi, 1968). Virus-associated fusion factors of the type considered in this section do not appear to operate in late polykaryocytosis, where the modifications of the cell surface which result in fusion are a direct consequence of intracellular virus replication.

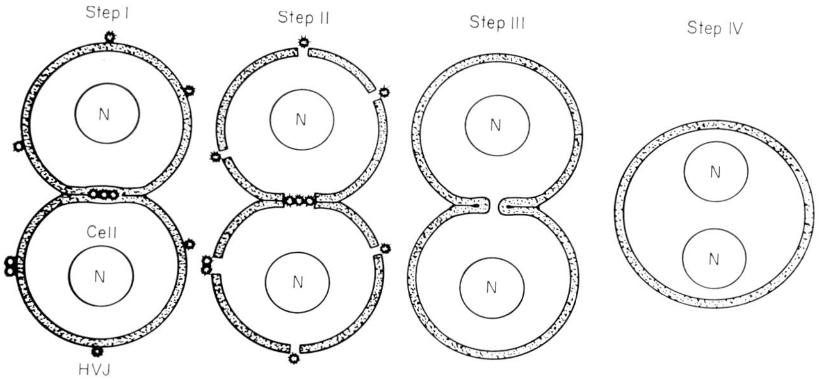

FIG. 5. A model (after Okada *et al.*) of the cell fusion reaction. Step I: adsorption of virus onto cells causing cell clumping and agglutination; Step II: "disconnection" of the cell surface by virus action; Step III: reconnection of the disconnected sites by fusion between apposed cells; Step IV: polykaryocyte formation. Reprinted with permission from Y. Okada, F. Murayama, and K. Yamada, *Virology* **27,** 115 (1966).

V. The Cytology of Cell Fusion

A. General Considerations

The plasma membranes of apposed cells both *in vivo* and *in vitro* are separated by 100–200 Å, except at specialized contact points (*zona occludens*) where the membranes are closely apposed or even fused. Thus in order for two cells to fuse by coalescence of their plasma membranes, the membranes must obviously be brought into direct apposition (<10 Å separation). The possible mechanisms by which membrane contact is achieved deserve consideration.

B. Biophysical Aspects of Cell Fusion

All animal cells so far examined carry a net negative charge at their surfaces (Weiss and Woodbridge, 1967). The contact between cells can be considered in a mathematical manner as contact between charged particles using the theory developed for the stability of lyophobic colloid particles by Derjaguin and Landau (1941) and Verwey and Overbeek (1948) (DLVO theory). The application of this theory to cell contact phenomena has been the subject of several reviews (Pethica, 1961; Curtis, 1966; Weiss, 1967a) which should be consulted for fuller details. Broadly speaking, according to the DLVO theory, electrostatic repulsive forces tend to keep cells apart while attractive forces, largely London van der Waals forces, tend to favor cell contact. The distance separating the plasma membranes of apposed cells therefore represents the point at which the forces of repulsion and attraction are balanced. Two types of balanced cell contact are recognized (cf. Curtis, 1966): (*1*) cells separated by 100–200 Å—this is termed adhesion in the secondary minimum; and (*2*) cells separated by 10 Å or less—termed as adhesion in the primary minimum. Thus, cells are normally adherent in the secondary minimum but adhesion in the primary minimum *must* be achieved before fusion can occur.

Bangham and Pethica (1961) and Pethica (1961) predicted from the DLVO theory that contact between cells by means of low radius of curvature (0.1 μ or less) microvilli would be the most effective method of achieving contact in the primary minimum, since microvilli of these dimensions would encounter significantly less electrostatic repulsion than the larger pseudopodial type of surface projection. Although not establishing a causal relationship, the approach and contact of cells via microvilli, of comparable size to those predicted on theoretical grounds, has been observed in numerous examples of cell-to-cell contact (Lesseps, 1963; Taylor and Robbins, 1963; Grant, 1965; Hughes *et al.*, 1968; Salsbury *et al.*, 1968; Chambers and Weiser, 1969; Cornell, 1969). In view of these considerations it is very interesting that large numbers of microvilli have been observed on the surfaces of fusing cells (Fig. 6), both in virus-induced polykaryocytosis (Okada, 1962; Harris *et al.*, 1966; Schneeberger and Harris, 1966; Meiselman *et al.*, 1967; Hosaka and Koshi, 1968; Poste, 1969; Svoboda and Dourmashkin, 1969) and in cell fusion produced by numerous nonviral agents (Ham and Leeson, 1961; Davis, 1963; Gusek, 1964; Policard *et al.*, 1965; Gol'tsman, 1966; Grimley and Sokoloff, 1966; Lockwood and Allison, 1966; Sutton, 1967; Smith, 1969).

C. The Influence of the Cell "Coat" on Fusion

If the association between microvilli and cell contact is valid, then it is highly likely that factors which influence the ability of a cell to form microvilli would also influence the ability of the cell to fuse. The formation of microvilli will be influenced by the mechanical deformability of the cell surface which will, in turn, be dependent upon the structural components at the cell surface. Weiss (1965, 1966, 1967b) concluded that the principal structural determinants of cell surface deformability were associated with the glycoprotein and protein components of the cell periphery. Poste (1969, 1970a,b) extended these observations, and examined the importance of the glycoprotein cell "coat" in the formation of microvilli. The glycoproteins of the plasma membrane exist as a distinct layer of coat (Fig. 7) situated on the outermost protein leaflet of the

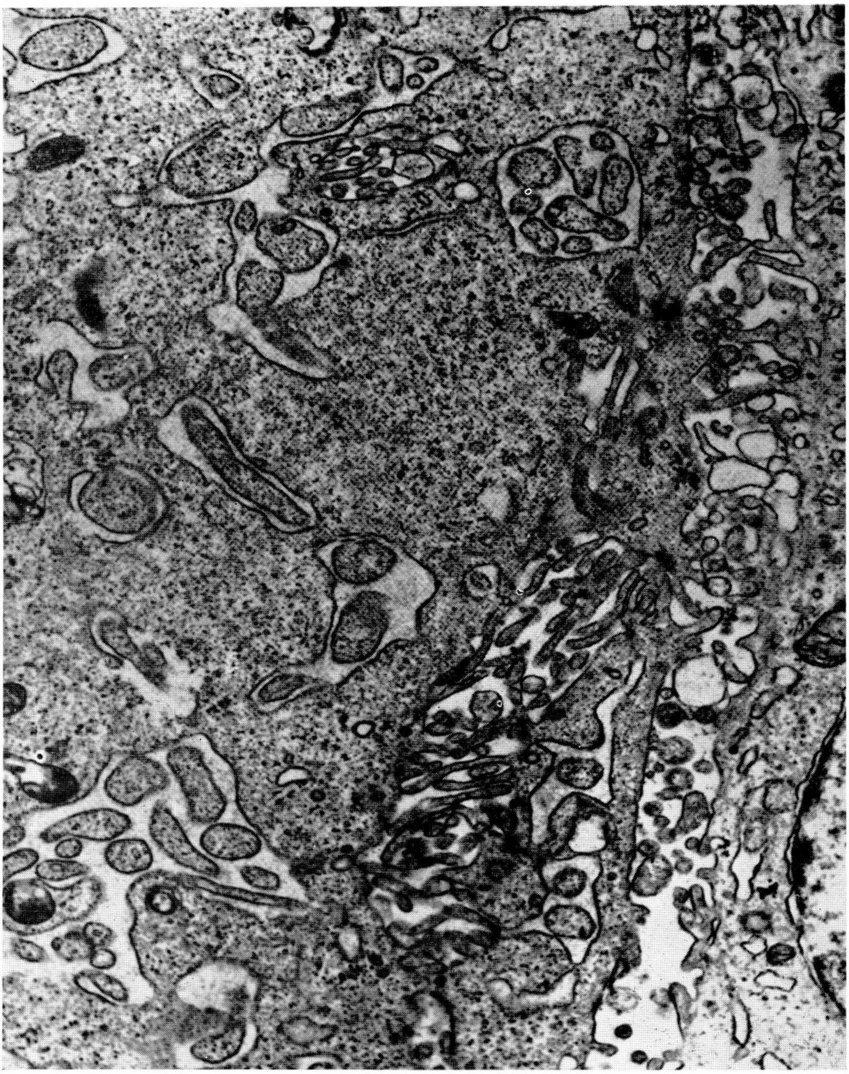

FIG. 6. Electron micrograph of part of the area of contact between two adjacent cells during ultraviolet-inactivated Sendai virus-induced cell fusion. Reprinted with permission from H. Harris, J. F. Watkins, C. E. Ford, and G. I. Schoefl, *J. Cell Sci.* **1**, 1 (1966).

trilaminar plasma membrane (for reviews, see Rambourg and Leblond, 1967; Revel and Ito, 1967). Poste, using electron microscopy and ellipsometry (an optical technique designed to measure the thickness of thin films by changes in the ellipticity of polarized light) found that the thick-

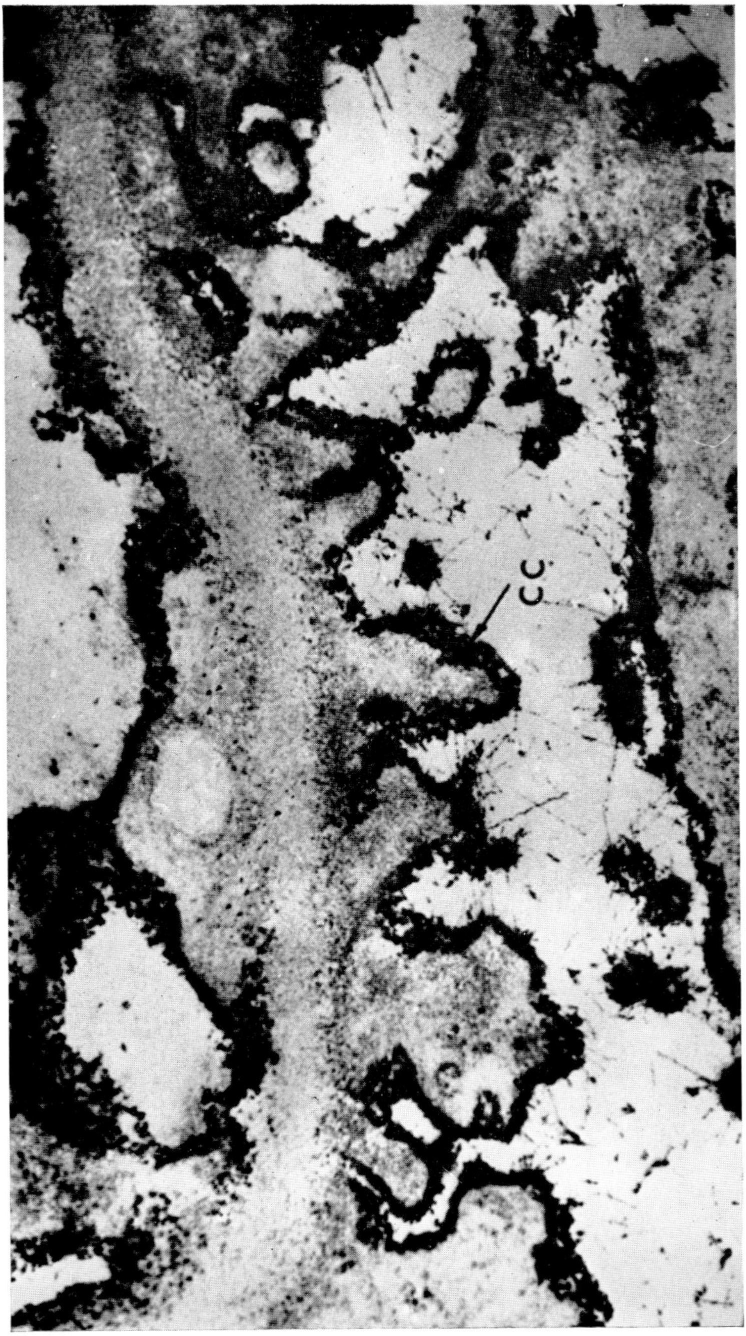

FIG. 7. Electron micrography of a human kidney cell process to show the presence of the cell "coat" (CC) stained with colloidal iron. Reprinted with permission from D. B. Jones, *Lab Invest.* **21**, 119 (1969). Copyright International Academy of Pathology.

ness of the cell coat influenced the formation of microvilli at the cell surface. It was found that microvilli were more easily formed when the cell coat was less than 35–40 Å thick. Experimental enzymic digestion and removal of the coat markedly increased the numbers of microvilli present on cells. Similarly by manipulating the coat thickness by alterations in the cell culture conditions it was possible to alter the number of microvilli; the number being always inversely related to coat thickness.

Extending these techniques to the study of virus-infected cells and, in particular, fusing cells, Poste (1969, 1970c,d) found that unless a cell had a coat thinner than 35 Å it was unable to fuse. It was proposed that cells which had a coat thicker than 35 Å were unable to fuse because they could not elaborate the microvilli necessary to establish contact in the primary minimum prior to actual membrane fusion. These findings, obtained from a range of cell types also provide a possible explanation for the cellular variations in fusion capacity discussed in Section III,A,1. For example, it was found that established cell lines generally had a significantly thinner (35 Å or less) coat than most primary diploid cells (coat thickness—60 to 70 Å), and this could account for the greater fusion capacity of established cell lines (Section III,A,2). It was also found that the subculture of several primary cells (coat thickness—60 to 70 Å) yielded secondary cells which had a significantly thinner coat (40 Å). Interestingly, the secondary cells had a much greater fusion capacity than the equivalent primary cultures, even though viruses grew to equal titer in both types of cell.

Measurement of the coat thickness in cells infected with polykaryocytogenic viruses (measles, CDV, parainfluenza 3, respiratory syncytial, and several herpesviruses) revealed that the coat thickness was significantly reduced compared with the uninfected controls. When the coat thickness was reduced below 35 Å in the infected cells, large numbers of microvilli appeared on the cell surface and fusion subsequently occurred. However, in those cell types which failed to fuse, despite viral replication, two types of changes were noted in the coat. In some cells no reduction in coat thickness was detectable. In others, a reduction in coat thickness, similar to that found in fusing cells, was found, but even with this reduction the coat was still thicker than 35 Å because these cells had a significantly thicker coat before infection than the cells which fused.

D. Lysosomes and Cell Fusion

The reduction in coat thickness recorded in the virus-infected cells was shown to result from digestion of the coat by lysosomal hydrolases liberated onto the cell surface (Poste, 1969, 1970c,d). Furthermore, by controlling the release of lysosomal enzymes with lysosomal stabilizing agents (hydrocortisone, chloroquine, diphenhydramine) it was possible to prevent digestion of the cell coat and also prevent cell fusion. Although cell fusion could be controlled and/or prevented in this way, normal virus replication was still obtained. These experiments have demonstrated that cell coat thickness, by influencing the capacity of the cell to form microvilli, is an hitherto unrecognized but highly important factor in the cell fusion process.

The concept of changes in the cell surface produced by lysosomal enzymes activated by virus infection is not new. Indeed, Allison (1967) suggested that lysosomal enzymes released from virus-infected cells could alter what he termed cell membrane "stickiness" and this could facilitate cell fusion. There is considerable other evidence for lysosomal labilization in cell fusion. Histochemically, lysosomal labilization, accompanied by a marked increase in lysosomal enzymes, has been detected in polykaryocytes produced *in vitro* by mouse hepatitis virus (Allison and Mallucci, 1965), ectromelia (Allison, 1967), HVH (Allison and Black, 1967; Tokumaru, 1968; Lesso and Szanto, 1969), respiratory syncytial virus (Bonissol, 1966b), measles virus (Atherton *et al.*, 1965), and parainfluenza viruses (Bonissol, 1966b; Szmigielski *et al.*, 1967). Increased lysosomal enzyme activity and lysosomal labilization has also been recorded in the polykaryocytes formed spontaneously in cultures of macrophages (Weiss and Fawcett, 1953; Goldstein and McCormick, 1957; Cohn and Benson, 1965; Allison, 1967) and in KB (Bonissol, 1966b) and HeLa (Fortelius *et al.*, 1961) cells. These *in vitro* observations agree with studies performed on polykaryocytes *in vivo,* where macrophages appear to be the main type of cell involved. Increased lysosomal enzyme activity has been recorded in polykaryocytes produced by: tubercle bacilli and other bacterial delayed type hypersensitivity states (Dannenberg, 1968); and by a wide range of chemical agents —heavy metals, silica, asbestos, carrageenan, and talcum powder (Gedigk and Bontke, 1957; Allison *et al.*, 1966; Niemi and Sylvén, 1968).

The inhibitory effect of lysosomal stabilizing agents on cell fusion mentioned above is in agreement with results from other studies. Bader and Morgan (1961) found that cortisone reduced mumps virus polykaryocytosis in HeLa cells, and Tokumaru (1968) found that hydrocortisone inhibited the formation of polykaryocytes by HVH. Allison (1967) reported that prednisolone prevented the spontaneous formation of polykaryocytes in chick embryo leukocyte cultures. Chloroquine diphosphate and diphenhydramine hydrochloride are also known to stabilize lysosomes and these agents prevented the cell fusion induced by mouse hepatitis virus grown in mouse macrophages (Vainio and Judah, 1962; Mallucci, 1966).

The proposed discharge of lysosomal enzymes onto the cell surface in cell fusion probably involves exocytotic fusion of the lysosomes with the plasma membrane. Electron microscopic evidence for this process is difficult to obtain since it would occur very quickly (cf. Daems *et al.*, 1969). It is of great interest therefore that Sutton (1967) in an ultrastructural study of macrophage fusion noted a large number of lysosomes around fusing membranes and, at a few sites, actual fusion of lysosomes with the plasma membrane was detected. Suggestive evidence of this process can also be seen in Hosaka and Koshi's study of Sendai virus-induced cell fusion (see plate 9).

Finally, it may well be significant that of the vast range of biological and chemical agents which can cause cell fusion (cf. Haythorn, 1929; Roizman, 1962a) a very high proportion are also known to labilize lysosomes (cf. Allison, 1968).

Despite the demonstrated importance of lysosomal labilization in producing the cell surface changes involved in fusion, it is clear that this alone is not sufficient to cause cell fusion. A wide range of agents can induce lysosomal labilization without causing cell fusion. This is particularly true of virus infection (for review, see Allison, 1967). However, there is some evidence (Poste, 1969) that the amount of lysosomal enzymes liberated onto the cell surface influences both the extent of the coat changes and the viability of the cell. Thus, the scale of enzyme release could provide one explanation as to why all those agents producing lysosomal labilization do not necessarily fuse cells. Thus, agents which induce massive enzyme release would probably not cause fusion because of rapid cytotoxicity and cell death, while agents which only induce minimal enzyme release might not cause sufficient reduction in coat thickness to permit fusion. The other explanation is that those agents which induce fusion must also cause specific effects on the plasma membrane which lead to fusion.

E. Conclusions

Cell fusion is influenced by the thickness of the glycoprotein cell coat. The available evidence suggests that only those cells which have a coat thinner than 35 Å can fuse. The effect of coat thickness on cell fusion is mediated indirectly via its ability to influence the formation of microvilli which are necessary for cells to achieve very close contact immediately before final membrane fusion. Viruses which induce cell fusion cause a reduction in the thickness of the cell coat to below 35 Å by the release of lysosomal hydrolases onto the cell surface. Digestion of the coat in this way can be prevented by lysosomal stabilizing agents. The same agents prevent cell fusion.

VI. Membrane Fusion

A. General Principles

Although fusion of lipoprotein membranes is of fundamental importance in cell biology, relatively little is known about the molecular mechanisms operating in this process. The fusion of two membranes can be expected to occur when the molecular interactions within the membranes become no greater than those across the gap between the membranes. This will arise if a reaction occurred within the membrane to decrease the cross-linking of the membrane molecules. This would increase the random rotation and vibration of the membrane molecules so that they could then interact with similar molecules in the membrane of the other cell. Kavanau (1965) proposed a scheme of this type to explain membrane fusion based on interaction between the outer protein leaflets of apposed membranes. He suggested that when membranes come into contact in the primary minimum most of the "hydration crust" associated with the proteins is freed. As a result of this change, the nonpolar side chains of the protein leaflets, which normally penetrate the lipid phase of the membrane, can slip out from the restraining lipid. This displacement of the protein leaflet molecules increases their molecular freedom and permits the formation of interbackbone and intersidechain linkages with similar protein molecules in the other membrane. Kavanau suggested that these changes would initiate reglobulation of the membrane proteins and establish a connecting bridge between the apposed cells of the type observed in virus-induced cell fusion (Section II,A,2). Once this stage has been reached, further enlargement of the connecting bridge would be favored by surface tension effects at the membrane interface. This suggested interaction between proteins in apposed membranes in order to initiate fusion implies either that the membrane proteins in fusing cells have a very similar structure or that such similarity is unecessary. This point is pertinent to the formation of heterokaryons, where fusion occurs between cells from different species.

Kavanau's scheme for fusion is based on the assumption that the protein leaflets of the plasma membrane exist in the extended β-configuration, as suggested in the original Davson-Danielli model for membrane structure. However, recent work using infrared and nuclear magnetic resonance spectroscopy and optical rotatory dispersal techniques indicates that the proportion of membrane protein in the β-configuration is very low (Chapman and Wallach, 1968). This, therefore, provides a potentially important criticism of Kavanau's hypothesis.

B. Surface Tension Effects and Cell Fusion

Early investigators considered that cell fusion occurred solely by surface tension effects (cf. Haythorn, 1929). A similar view was adopted by Warren *et al.* (1962) to explain measles virus-induced cell fusion. More recently, Dingle (1968) proposed that the fusion of lysosomes, phagocytic vesicles, and other membrane-bound bodies could be explained on the basis of surface tension effects. Dingle likened membrane fusion in biological systems to the coalescence and fusion of closed shells of fluid seen in foams and emulsions. Based on Dingle's analogy with the fusion of droplets in foams, two cell membranes which had a high surface tension would fuse on contact—unless certain stabilizing factors were present. However, it is difficult to accept that this type of spontaneous fusion could achieve the high degree of specificity and order observed in cell fusion and fusion between various organelles. Furthermore, it cannot be assumed that the forces operating at biological membranes give rise to exactly the same effects as the interfacial tension at liquid-liquid and liquid-gas interfaces found in foams (Pethica, 1961; Kavanau, 1965). It can also be argued that the low values for the surface tension at the surface of mammalian cells, invariably less than 1.0 dynes/cm and often less than 0.2 dynes/cm (Harvey, 1954), would not provide sufficient driving force to initiate membrane fusion. Although surface tension effects can be discounted as the primary mechanism in membrane fusion, they will undoubtedly play a role in the final merger of cells once connecting bridges have been formed between cells (Holmes and Choppin, 1968).

C. Fusion and the Presence of Viral Subunits at the Cell Surface

Several authors have proposed that the accumulation of virus or viral products at the cell surface induces changes in the membrane which lead to fusion. Roizman and his colleagues (Roizman, 1962a; Roane and Roizman, 1964; Ejercito *et al.*, 1968) proposed that the amount of HVH antigen present at the cell surface determines the type of cellular response induced by this virus. They suggested that the amount of antigen present in cells which fused would be different from that in cells which rounded up and this would again be different from that in cells which aggregated together. Although Roizman's team have made a valuable contribution in showing that antigenic alterations occur in HVH-infected cells, their results do not totally support the conclusion that the amount of antigen varies in cells showing different behavior. Indeed, recent evidence would suggest that it does not (Falke *et al.*, 1969). Bungay and Watkins (1964) also suggested that the presence of HVH antigen at the cell surface would be important in fusion, and suggested that the process of virus release might render the cell surface more susceptible to fusion. Although this suggestion cannot be totally discounted, it is unlikely since there are a large number of viruses, including some members of the herpesvirus group, which are released at the cell surface yet do not fuse cells.

D. Lipids and Membrane Fusion

Dingle (1968) suggested that unstable membranes susceptible to fusion might be achieved by the presence of a relatively high proportion of short-chain fatty acids, the incorporation of cis-isomers, and the presence of polar groups in hydrocarbon chains. Unfortunately, there is very little information on the quantitative analysis of lipids in fusing cells. Rubin (1967) and Howell and Lucy (1969) suggested that the formation or liberation of lysolecithin in the membranes of cells might promote structural changes responsible for fusion. However, analytical studies on the lipids of cells fused by Sendai (Hosaka, 1960), HVH (Falke *et al.*, 1967), and SV_5 (Elsbach *et al.*, 1969) viruses have shown that lysolecithin was not important in these particular systems.

Van Deenan *et al.* (1962) suggested that a high cholesterol to phospholipid ratio might promote order and rigidity in cell membranes. It is therefore of considerable interest that Klenk and Choppin (1969) found differences in the ratio of these components in the membranes of cells showing different fusion capacities with SV_5 virus. In monkey kidney (low fusion capacity) the molar ratio of cholesterol to phospholipid was high (0.81), while in the BHK and HaK hamster cell lines (high fusion capacity) lower ratios of 0.68 and 0.51, respectively, were found. Holmes *et al.* (1969), in a parallel study with the same cells, found that monkey kidney cells were also more resistant to osmotic shock, mechanical stress, and immune cytolysis than the BHK and HaK cells. Whether differences of this type in the membrane lipids can be correlated with differences in cell fusion capacity is not clear. Further investigations of this type with a wider range of viruses and cells should provide interesting results.

E. A Scheme for Membrane Fusion

1. The Significance of Membrane Fusion

Apart from the few reports considered above, there is no detailed information on the events which occur in membranes during fusion. However, membrane fusion is a common phenomenon and is not restricted merely to virus-induced cell fusion. The fusion of membrane-bound organelles, either with each other or with the plasma membrane, features prominently in the normal processes of cellular endo- and exocytosis (De Duve and Wattiaux, 1966), intracellular digestion (Dingle, 1968), and the secretion of specific cell products such as hormones (Stormorken, 1969). Although it cannot be assumed that the mechanism involved in virus-induced membrane fusion will be the same as that occurring in normal membrane fusion, there are a number of features common to all forms of membrane fusion which warrant a brief attempt to correlate them into a single scheme.

2. The Similarity between Events in Membrane Fusion in Subcellular Systems and Events in Cell Fusion

Woodin and Wieneke, in a series of papers (for review, see Woodin, 1968), developed a scheme to explain fusion between lysosomes and the plasma membrane in leukocytes treated with leucocidin. Based on the well known role of Ca^{2+} and adenosine triphosphate (ATP) in maintaining the structural rigidity and permeability of biological membranes (for reviews, see Abood, 1966; Manery, 1966), Woodin and Wieneke proposed that removal of Ca^{2+} and ATP from membranes would produce regions of decreased structural rigidity which would be susceptible to fusion. They suggested that the displacement of membrane-bound Ca^{2+} and ATP was initiated by hydrolysis of the ATP by a membrane-associated adenosine triphosphatase (ATPase). This reaction would create a localized high concentration of orthophosphate, and this would compete for and bind Ca^{2+}. There are similarities between this scheme and the events suggested to accompany membrane depolarization in excitable cells (for review, see Abood, 1966). In the latter, stimulation (neural or chemical) of excitable membranes is thought to induce displacement of Ca^{2+} and ATP from the membrane following ATPase-induced hydrolysis of ATP, resulting in a influx of ions and membrane depolarization. The similarities between these schemes is very striking. Indeed, Abood's scheme has been used to explain the mechanism whereby chromaffin and other secretory granules fuse with the plasma membrane during secretion (Poisner and Trifaró, 1967). More recently, Stormorken (1969), in an excellent review, has tentatively extended this sequence of events involving Ca^{2+}, ATP, and ATPase to explain the many examples in which hormones, enzymes, and other cellular products are released from the cell by fusion of the membrane of the secretory granule with the plasma membrane. Stormorken suggested that there was probably a common sequence and mechanism for the membrane changes involved in all forms of endo- and exocytosis.

These schemes, developed for membrane fusion in subcellular systems, can also be applied to whole cells. Membrane fusion, as described above, requires the displacement of Ca^{2+} and ATP from the membrane immediately prior to fusion. It would be expected therefore that the concentrations of Ca^{2+} and ATP available to the membrane at this time would be critical, since fusion should not occur if either Ca^{2+} or ATP were continually available to stabilize the membrane. Thus, Woodin and Wieneke (1964) found that the fusion of lysosomes with the plasma membrane was inhibited by high concentrations of ATP and Ca^{2+}. It is interesting therefore that the cell fusion induced by Sendai virus (Murayama and Okada, 1965; Okada and Murayama, 1966) and HVH (Tokumaru, 1968) was inhibited by similar high Ca^{2+} concentrations, and high concentrations of ATP inhibited NDV-induced cell fusion (Kohn and Klibansky, 1967). Also, in view of the possible parallel between events in membrane fusion and depolarization mentioned above, it is noteworthy that high concentrations of Ca^{2+} and/or ATP prevent depolarization and block conduction in nerves (Ritchie and Greengard, 1966).

The other principal feature of the proposed schemes for membrane fusion is that displacement of Ca^{2+} and ATP from the membrane requires a membrane-associated ATPase. If this suggestion is correct, it would be expected that inhibition of the ATPase would prevent fusion. For example, there is considerable evidence from subcellular systems that ATPase inhibitors prevent release of secretory granules by inhibiting fusion of the granules membrane with the plasma membrane (for references, see Poisner and Trifaró, 1967). It is therefore of interest that phlorizin, and ATPase inhibitor, inhibited the fusion of Lu106 and dog kidney cells infected with measles virus (Norrby, 1966). The nature of the ATPase implicated in fusion is also important. Studies on the fusion between the membranes of secretory granules and the plasma membrane have shown that the ATPase (present in the granule membrane) was not of the active transport type (Stormorken, 1969). On the basis of metal ion and nucleotide specificities, and inhibition by sucrose, but not by oubain, it is generally accepted that the ATPase associated with fusion in subcellular systems is a Ca^{2+} Mg^{2+} activated enzyme. Certain findings would suggest that a similar enzyme is involved in cell fusion. The inhibition of HVH-induced cell fusion by omission of Mg^{2+} from the culture medium (Falke, 1967) could be interpreted as involving inhibition of the Ca^{2+} Mg^{2+} ATPase which has an obligatory Mg^{2+} cofactor requirement (Duncan, 1967; Schatzmann, 1968). The inhibitory effects of Zn^{2+} on cell fusion in the same system might well result from inhibition of the ATPase (cf. Duncan, 1967). Also, the previously mentioned inhibitory effects of high Ca^{2+} concentration on cell fusion induced by Sendai (Okada and Murayama, 1966) and HVH (Tokumaru, 1968) could be due to inhibition of the ATPase, since quantitatively similar Ca^{2+} concentrations inhibited this enzyme in other systems (Duncan,

1967; Schatzmann, 1968). Suggestive evidence for the association of a Ca^{2+} Mg^{2+} ATPase with membrane fusion is provided by studies made on the fused membranes of the zona occludens type cell junction. Loewenstein (1967) showed that the function of this type of junction was dependent upon continuous displacement of Ca^{2+} from the fused membranes by a Ca^{2+} Mg^{2+} ATPase which could be inhibited by high concentrations of Ca^{2+} (Loewenstein, 1967) but not by oubain (Politoff *et al.*, 1967). Histochemical studies on fused zona occludens membranes in retinal cells revealed the presence of a nontransport type of ATPase at the sites of fusion but not where the membranes were separated (O'Daly, 1967).

Following displacement of Ca^{2+} and ATP from membranes during fusion, both these factors are necessary to stabilize the membrane once fusion has been completed. Okada *et al.* (1966), studying Sendai virus-induced cell fusion, proposed that ATP and Ca^{2+} were necessary for what they termed "reconnection" of the "disconnected" membranes; the latter representing the stage at which the membrane was susceptible to fusion. Okada and his colleagues showed that unless ATP and Ca^{2+} were replaced in the membrane, lysis occurred. The stabilization of the membrane by ATP after fusion means that fusion would be dependent upon viable cellular metabolism for the required energy input. This would explain the finding that virus-induced cell fusion is prevented by respiratory inhibitors and is retarded by anaerobic culture conditions (Okada *et al.*, 1966; Falke, 1967; Tokumaru, 1968). Kavanau (1965) commented on the large number of mitochondria found around fusing membranes and suggested that they were important in providing the energy required for fusion. Histochemically, increased activity of enzymes associated with oxidative metabolism has been noted in polykaryocytes induced by HVH (Felgenhauer and Stammler, 1962; Lesso and Szanto, 1969), respiratory syncytial, and the parainfluenza viruses (Bonissol, 1966b). Also in muscle cell fusion *in vitro*, Reporter (1967) found that the amount of ATP per milligram cell protein increased rapidly during fusion compared with the level in replicating cells.

These various similarities between events in virus-induced cell fusion and other forms of membrane fusion have not previously been commented upon. The parallels described between membrane fusion and membrane depolarization are also of interest, since the numerous drugs known to alter or prevent depolarization might be examined for their effect in cell fusion. In particular, the local anaesthetics, and the antihistaminic phenothiazines appear promising since they not only prevent depolarization but also protect cells against a variety of cytotoxic and cytolytic agents (for review, see Seeman, 1966). Indeed, the antihistamine, diphenhydramine hydrochloride, prevented the cell fusion induced by mouse hepatitis virus (Vainio and Judah, 1962) and parainfluenza 3, measles, CDV, and several herpesviruses (Poste, 1969).

The precise mechanisms by which Ca^{2+} and ATP are displaced from membranes cannot be entered into here (for reviews, see Tobais, 1964; Abood, 1966; Manery, 1966; Cavillito, 1967; Cuthbert, 1967; Duncan, 1967; Singer and Tasaki, 1968). However, there are a number of points about this process which must be considered. Displacement of Ca^{2+} from membranes, during fusion or depolarization, will produce conformational changes in the membrane lipids. Indeed, negative staining of fused membranes in zona occludens type junctions has revealed that the lipids had undergone a structural transformation from the normal lamellar bileaflet to a system composed of hexagonal micelles (Benedetti and Emmelot, 1968). This finding is very interesting since Dingle (1968) suggested that a primary requirement for the fusion of two membranes was that both of the membranes have a high proportion of their phospholipids in the micellar configuration. More recently, Howell and Lucy (1969) were even able to induce spontaneous fusion of hen erythrocytes simply by treating them with lysolecithin which is known to induce micellar transformation in the lipids of cell membranes (Lucy, 1968).

3. A General Scheme for Membrane Fusion

In summary, membrane fusion is considered to involve three stages.

Stage One: The Displacement of Ca^{2+} and ATP from the Membranes.

It is proposed that the displacement of Ca^{2+} *and* ATP from the membrane causes:

(*a*) A structural transformation in the membrane lipids, with a transition from the bimolecular lamellar form to a micellar form;

(*b*) a marked increase in the cation permeability of the membrane; and

(*c*) a reduction in the electrical resistance of the membrane.

This stage is initiated by the activation of a membrane-associated Ca^{2+} Mg^{2+} ATPase. It is inhibited by:

(a) factors which inhibit the ATPase enzyme system;

(b) conditions which provide a continuous supply of Ca^{2+} and/or ATP to stabilize the membrane; and

(c) conditions which prevent the displacement of Ca^{2+} and/or ATP from the membrane.

STAGE TWO: THE ESTABLISHMENT OF INTERMEMBRANE LINKAGES.

Actual membrane fusion involves the formation of stable chemical and physical linkages between similar molecules in apposed membranes. This molecular interaction between apposed membranes is only possible after Stage one (above) has been completed, since the removal of Ca^{2+} and ATP from the membrane will:

(*a*) increase the molecular freedom afforded to certain membrane macromolecules;

(*b*) produce conformational changes in membrane macromolecules; and

(*c*) increase the number of potential interaction sites by providing an increased number of free cationic and anionic sites.

All these factors will increase the possibility of interaction between molecules in apposed membranes. Various physical and chemical factors which influence molecular rotation and vibration could also affect this stage.

STAGE THREE: STABILIZATION OF THE MEMBRANE AFTER FUSION.

This stage is essentially the reverse of Stage one, and is concerned with the return of the Ca^{2+}/ATP depleted membrane to its normal state. This is achieved by replacement of ATP and Ca^{2+} at their binding sites within the membrane.

4. The Role of Cell Surface Patential in Membrane Fusion

One important deficiency in this hypothesis still remains, since the stimulus which initiates the events in Stage one has not been defined. In the case of fusion between secretory granules and the plasma membrane various hormones and neurotransmitter substances probably provide the stimulus. However, in virus-induced cell fusion the initiating stimulus is not as clear. In fusion between whole cells it is considered that contact in the primary minimum might alone be sufficient to initiate Stage one of the fusion process. This suggestion is prompted by recent observations made on the effect of the electrical potential at the cell surface on membrane structure and function (Gingell, 1967; Ambrose and Forrester, 1968; Wolpert and Gingell, 1968; Brewer and Bell, 1969). It has been suggested by these workers that changes in cell surface potential will alter the electrostatic potential within the membrane which will, in turn, result in reorientation of charged and dipolar groups within the membrane. These changes will markedly alter the membrane and its properties. Gingell (1967) examined the effect of cell contact on the cell surface potential. He showed that when cells achieved contact in the primary minimum there was a marked increase in the negative potential at the outer surface of each membrane. As Gingell pointed out, hyperpolarization of the membranes in this way could produce changes in membrane structure and permeability which could initiate all of the events suggested for Stage one of the fusion process.

This proposal that cell contact in the primary minimum initiates membrane fusion provides a final correlation in which the mechanical, chemical, and electrical energies of the plasma membrane are coupled within a single scheme. Further knowledge on the properties of the cell surface and a more complete understanding of the many factors involved may well alter all these proposals. Although very far from complete the scheme outlined here can at least be subjected to detailed experimental investigation. In this way it is hoped that it will provide some of the additional information required for a better analysis of the cell fusion process.

VII. Concluding Remarks

Many viruses have now been isolated which can induce the formation of polykaryocytes by cell fusion. As a result, an enormous literature has accumulated on this subject, much of it merely descriptive and uncritical. Furthermore, most authors have been very cautious in expressing any firm views on how cell fusion occurs. The viruses capable of fusing cells are largely confined to the paramyxo- and herpesvirus groups, and a few members of the poxvirus group. As yet no feature common to all these viruses can be unequivocally linked with their ability to fuse cells. The available evidence does not support the suggestion that these viruses can induce the synthesis of "early" proteins which cause cells to fuse. In a few cases, noninfectious viral subunits with cell fusing properties have been isolated from intact virions, but the extent of the cell fusion produced by these subunits is not comparable with that produced by intact virus.

Much of our present knowledge about cell fusion is merely descriptive, and there has been little experimental work concerned directly with the basic events which occur in cell fusion. However, cell fusion is no longer of significance only to virologists, since virus-induced cell fusion has emerged in recent years as an extremely useful tool for studying certain more fundamental problems in cell biology. The ability to fuse cells is not restricted to viruses, and many nonbiological agents can also produce this effect. In its broadest sense, cell fusion can be interpreted as a special example of fusion between two biological membrane systems. For these reasons, this article has attempted to examine cell fusion as a problem of general cell biology rather than as a purely virological one.

Thus, the mechanisms operating in cell fusion in viral systems are not necessarily pathological, and may have much in common with the events occurring in the fusion between biological membranes seen so commonly in normal cell function. Based on these considerations it has been viewed as justifiable in this article to seek a common mechanism for cell fusion whatever the inducing agent. Virus-induced cell fusion provides a useful model for studying this problem. As Weiss (1967a) points out, the cell periphery reflects much of the cellular organization. Thus, virus-induced changes in it are not expected to be unique since the virus "merely elects" ordinary cellular responses (including those which might be repressed) and to go outside this normal repertoire probably leads directly to degeneration. To this end, attention has been devoted to the basic events occurring at the cell surface during fusion. From the evidence presented in this article, a unitary theory has been proposed in which all forms of cell fusion, whether produced by viruses or not, are suggested to involve the same underlying mechanism. It is considered that cell fusion requires modification of the cell surface, notably the glycoprotein cell "coat," by lysosomal enzymes released onto the cell surface. The alteration of the cell surface in this way precedes the actual fusion of the membranes *per se*. The membrane fusion process involves fundamental reorganization of membrane structure and is an energy-dependent process. Obviously, many questions still remain unanswered. It is not known exactly what leads to lysosomal labilization and release of lysosomal enzymes onto the cell surface. Although a working hypothesis has been presented in this article for the events occurring in membrane fusion, there is little detailed knowledge of the biochemical and molecular events involved in this process. Some of the proposals put forward in this article can at least be subjected to experimentation. In this way, even though many of these proposals are speculative and certainly far from complete, it is hoped that these suggestions can contribute to the solution of some of the remaining questions in cell and membrane fusion.

Acknowledgments

I am indebted to Professor A. P. Waterson and Drs. P. Reeve and L. W. Greenham for their help in the preparation of this manuscript and for many valuable discussions on the material discussed here. Some of the research cited was supported by grants from the Animal Health Trust and the British Empire Cancer Campaign.

References

Abood, L. G. (1966). *Int. Rev. Neurobiol.* **9,** 213.

Akers, T. G., and Cunningham, C. H. (1968). *Arch. Gesamte Virusforsch.* **25,** 30.

Albanese, M., Bynoe, M. L., and Tyrrell, D. A. J. (1966). *Arch. Gesamte Virusforsch.* **18,** 256.

Allison, A. C. (1967). *Perspect. Virol.* **5,** 29–61.
Allison, A. C. (1968). *In* "The Biological Basis of Medicine" (E. E. Bittar and N. Bittar, eds.), Vol. I, pp. 209–242. Academic Press, New York.
Allison, A. C., and Black, P. H. (1967). *J. Nat. Cancer Inst.* **39,** 775.
Allison, A. C., and Mallucci, L. (1965). *J. Exp. Med.* **121,** 463.
Allison, A. C., Harington, J. S., and Birbeck, M. (1966). *J. Exp. Med.* **124,** 141.
Ambrose, E. J., and Forrester, J. A. (1968). *Symp. Soc. Exp. Biol.* **22,** 237.
Anderson, J. M., and Beem, M. O. (1966). *Proc. Soc. Exp. Biol. Med.* **121,** 205.
Aoyama, Y. (1959). *Jap. J. Exp. Med.* **29,** 535.
Appleyard, G., Westwood, J. C. N., and Zwartouw, H. T. (1962). *Virology* **18,** 159.
Atherton, I. G., Chaparas, S. D., Cremer, M., and Gordon, I. (1965). *J. Bacteriol.* **90,** 213.
Aurelian, L., and Roizman, B. (1964). *Virology* **22,** 452.
Aurelian, L., and Wagner, R. R. (1966). *Proc. Nat. Acad. Sci. U.S.* **56,** 902.
Bader, J. P., and Morgan, H. R. (1961). *J. Immunol.* **87,** 90.
Bangham, A. D., and Pethica, B. A. (1961). *Proc. Roy. Soc. Edinburgh, Sect. B* **68,** 43.
Barski, G., and Robineaux, R. (1959). *Proc. Soc. Exp. Biol. Med.* **101,** 632.
Bayreuther, P. (1966). Quoted in Harris *et al.* (1966).
Becker, Y., and Levitt, J. (1968). *Exp. Cell Res.* **51,** 27.
Bedoya, V., Rabson, A. S., and Grimley, P. M. (1968). *J. Nat. Cancer Inst.* **41,** 635.
Benedetti, E. L., and Emmelot, P. (1968). *In* "The Membranes" (A. J. Dalton and F. Haguenau, eds.), pp. 33–120. Academic Press, New York.
Ben-Porat, T., Reissig, M., and Kaplan, A. S. (1961). *Nature (London)* **190,** 33.
Bernkopf, H., Nishmi, M., and Rosin, A. (1959). *J. Immunol.* **83,** 635.
Betz, A., Gilgenkrantz, S., and De Lavergne, E. (1963). *Ann. Inst. Pasteur* **105,** 1047.
Bischoff, R., and Holtzer, H. (1969). *J. Cell Biol.* **41,** 188.
Black, F. L. (1959). *Advan. Virus Res.* **6,** 205.
Bonissol, C. (1966a). *Ann. Inst. Pasteur* **110,** 675.
Bonissol, C. (1966b). *Ann. Inst. Pasteur* **111,** 265.
Bonnet, R. (1903). *Monatsschr. Geburts. Gynaekol.* **18,** 1.
Brandt, C. D. (1961). *Virology* **14,** 1.
Brewer, J. E., and Bell, L. G. E. (1969). *J. Cell Sci.* **4,** 17.
Bukrinskaya, A. G., and Zhdanov, V. M. (1961). *Probl. Virol. (USSR)* **6,** 392.
Bungay, C., and Watkins, J. F. (1964). *Brit. J. Exp. Pathol.* **45,** 48.
Burns, W. H., and Black, P. H. (1968). *J. Virol.* **2,** 606.
Burns, W. H., and Black, P. H. (1969). *Int. J. Cancer* **4,** 214.
Bussell, R. H., and Karzon, D. T. (1965). *Arch. Gesamte Virusforsch.* **17,** 163.
Butler, M. P. (1965). *Virology* **25,** 454.
Cameron, G. R. (1951). "Pathology of the Cell," pp. 32–40. Oliver & Boyd, Edinburgh and London.
Carver, D. H., and Marcus, P. I. (1967). *Virology* **32,** 247.
Cascardo, M. R., and Karzon, D. T. (1965). *Virology* **26,** 311.
Cavallito, C. J. (1967). *Fed. Proc. Fed. Amer. Soc. Exp. Biol.* **26,** 1647.
Chabassol, C., and Pousset, A. (1967). *Rev. Corps Vet. Biol. Armees* **20,** 143.
Chambers, V. C., and Weiser, R. S. (1969). *Cancer Res.* **29,** 310.
Chany, C., and Cook, M. K. (1960). *Ann. Inst. Pasteur* **98,** 920.
Chany, C., Daniel, P., Robbe-Fossat, F., Vialette, J., Lépine, P., and Lelong, M. (1958). *Ann. Inst. Pasteur* **95,** 721.
Chapman, D., and Wallach, D. F. H. (1968). *In* "Biological Membranes" (D. Chapman, ed.), pp. 125–202. Academic Press, New York.
Cocuzza, G., and Russo, G. (1966). *Boll. Ist. Sieroter. Milan.* **45,** 228.

Cohen, M. (1926). *Amer. J. Pathol.* **2,** 431.
Cohen, S. M., Bullivant, S., and Edwards, G. A. (1961). *Arch. Gesamte Virusforsch.* **11,** 493.
Cohn, Z. A., and Benson, B. (1965). *J. Exp. Med.* **121,** 835.
Cornell, R. (1969). *Exp. Cell Res.* **57,** 86.
Curtis, A. S. G. (1966). *Sci. Progr. (London)* **54,** 61.
Cuthbert, A. W. (1967). *Pharmacol. Rev.* **19,** 59.
Daems, W. T., Wisse, E., and Brederoo, P. (1969). *In* "Lysosomes in Biology and Pathology" (J. T. Dingle and H. B. Fell, eds.), Vol. 1, pp. 64–112. North-Holland Publ., Amsterdam.
Dales, S., and Siminovitch, L. (1961). *J. Biophys. Biochem. Cytol.* **10,** 475.
Daniel, P. (1963). *J. Exp. Zool.* **154,** 231.
Daniel, M. D., and Meléndez, L. V. (1968). *Arch. Gesamte Virusforsch.* **25,** 18.
Dannenberg, A. M., Jr. (1968). *Bacteriol. Rev.* **32,** 85.
Davidson, R. (1969). *Exp. Cell Res.* **55,** 424.
Davis, J. M. G. (1963). *Brit. J. Exp. Pathol.* **44,** 404.
De Bary, A. (1859). *Z. Wiss. Zool.* **10,** 88.
De Duve, C., and Wattiaux, R. (1966). *Annu. Rev. Physiol.* **28,** 435.
Defendi, V., ed. (1969). Heterospecific Genome Interaction, *Wistar Inst. Symp. Monogr.*
Demont, G., Berkaloff, A., and Colobert, L. (1963). *Ann. Inst. Pasteur* **104,** 26.
Derjaguin, B. V., and Landau, L. D. (1941). *Acta Physicochim. URSS* **14,** 633.
Di Marco, A., Terni, M., Silvestrini, R., Scarpinato, B., Biagioli, E., and Antonelli, A. (1968). *G. Microbiol.* **16,** 25.
Dingle, J. T. (1968). *Brit. Med. Bull.* **24,** 141.
Dinter, Z., Hermodsson, S., and Bakos, S. (1960). *Acta Pathol. Microbiol. Scand.* **49,** 485.
Dreizen, R. S., Ponomareva, T. I., Rapoport, R. I., and Petrova, E. I. (1967). *Acta Virol. (Prague), Engl. Ed.* **11,** 533.
Dubbs, D. R., and Kit, S. (1969). *J. Virol.* **3,** 536.
Duncan, C. J. (1967). "The Molecular Properties and Evolution of Excitable Cells." Macmillan (Pergamon), New York.
Ejercito, P. M., Kieff, E. D., and Roizman, B. (1968). *J. Gen. Virol.* **2,** 357.
Elsbach, P., Holmes, K. V., and Choppin, P. W. (1969). *Proc. Soc. Exp. Biol. Med.* **130,** 903.
Enders, J. F., Gunalp, A., Gresser, I., Diamandopoulos, G. T., and Shein, H. M. (1965). *Arch. Gesamte Virusforsch.* **17,** 347.
Enders, J. F., Holloway, A., and Grogan, E. A. (1967). *Proc. Nat. Acad. Sci. U.S.* **57,** 637.
Engel, E., McGee, B. J., and Harris, H. (1969). *J. Cell Sci.* **5,** 93.
Ephrussi, B., and Weiss, M. C. (1967). *In* "Control Mechanisms in Developmental Processes" (M. Locke, ed.), pp. 136–169. Academic Press, New York.
Faber, K. (1893). *J. Pathol. Bacteriol.* **1,** 349.
Falke, D. (1961). *Virology* **14,** 492.
Falke, D. (1965). *Arch. Gesamte Virusforsch.* **15,** 387.
Falke, D. (1967). *Z. Med. Mikrobiol. Immunol.* **153,** 175.
Falke, D., and Peterknecht, W. (1968). *Arch. Gesamte Virusforsch.* **24,** 267.
Falke, D., and Richter, I. E. (1961a). *Arch. Gesamte Virusforsch.* **11,** 73.
Falke, D., and Richter, I. E. (1961b). *Arch. Gesamte Virusforsch.* **11,** 86.
Falke, D., Schiefer, H., and Stoffel, C. (1967). *Z. Naturforsch. B* **22,** 1360.

Falke, D., Bitter-Suermann, D., and Clauss, I. (1969). *Arch. Gesamte Virusforsch.* **27,** 317.
Felgenhauer, K., and Stammler, A. (1962). *Arch. Gesamte Virusforsch.* **12,** 223.
Fogel, M., and Sachs, L. (1969). *Virology* **37,** 327.
Fortelius, P., Levonen, E., and Saxen, E. (1961). *Acta Pathol. Microbiol. Scand.* **52,** 23.
Frankel, J. W., and West, M. K. (1958). *Proc. Soc. Exp. Biol. Med.* **97,** 741.
Gedigk, P., and Bontke, E. (1957). *Virchows Arch. Pathol. Anat. Physiol.* **330,** 538.
Gerber, P. (1966). *Virology* **28,** 501.
Germanov, A. B., and Sokolov, M. I. (1969). *Arch. Gesamte Virusforsch.* **28,** 85.
Gharpure, M. A., Wright, P. F., and Chanock, R. M. (1969). *J. Virol.* **3,** 414.
Gingell, D. (1967). *J. Theor. Biol.* **17,** 451.
Goldstein, M. N., and McCormick, T. (1957). *Amer. J. Pathol.* **33,** 737.
Gol'tsman, L. L. (1966). *Bull. Exp. Biol. Med. (USSR)* **62,** 1308.
Gorbunova, A. S., Yun-De, H., and Yershov, F. I. (1963). *Acta Virol. (Prague), Engl. Ed.* **7,** 308.
Grant, L. (1965). *In* "The Inflammatory Process" (B. W. Zweifach, L. Grant, and R. T. McCluskey, eds.), pp. 197–244. Academic Press, New York.
Gray, A., Tokumaru, T., and Scott, T. F. M. (1958). *Arch. Gesamte Virusforsch.* **8,** 59.
Grimley, P. M., and Sokoloff, L. (1966). *Amer. J. Pathol.* **49,** 931.
Grundmann, E. (1966). "General Cytology." Arnold, London.
Guggenheim, M. A., Friedman, R. M., and Rabson, A. S. (1969). *Proc. Soc. Exp. Biol. Med.* **130,** 1242.
Gusek, W. (1962). *Veroeff. Morphol. Pathol.* **64,** 1.
Gusek, W. (1964). *Med. Welt* **15,** 850.
Habermehl, K. O., and Diefenthal, W. (1961). *Arch. Gesamte Virusforsch.* **11,** 629.
Haeckel, E. (1872). "Die Kalkschwamme." Berlin.
Ham, A. W., and Leeson, T. S. (1961). "Histology," p. 253. Pitman, London.
Hampar, B. (1966). *J. Bacteriol.* **92,** 1741.
Hanafusa, H. (1960). *Biken J.* **3,** 191.
Hanafusa, H. (1964). *Virology* **22,** 591.
Hancox, N. M. (1965). *In* "Cells and Tissues in Culture" (E. N. Willmer, ed.), Vol. 2, pp. 261–272. Academic Press, New York.
Harris, H. (1965). *Nature (London)* **206,** 583.
Harris, H. (1968). "Nucleus and Cytoplasm." Oxford Univ. Press (Clarendon), London and New York.
Harris, H., and Cook, P. R. (1969). *J. Cell Sci.* **5,** 121.
Harris, H., Watkins, J. F., Ford, C. E., and Schoefl, G. I. (1966). *J. Cell Sci.* **1,** 1.
Harris, H., Miller, O. J., Klein, G., Worst, P., and Tachibana, T. (1969). *Nature (London)* **223,** 363.
Harter, D. H., and Choppin, P. W. (1967). *Virology* **31,** 279.
Harter, D. H., Rosenkranz, H. S., and Rose, H. M. (1969). *Proc. Soc. Exp. Biol. Med.* **131,** 927.
Harvey, E. N. (1954). *Protoplasmatologia* **5,** 1.
Haythorn, S. R. (1929). *Arch. Pathol.* **7,** 651.
Hecht, V. (1910). *Beitr. Pathol. Anat. Physiol.* **48,** 263.
Henle, G., Dienhardt, F., and Girardi, A. (1954). *Proc. Soc. Exp. Biol. Med.* **87,** 386.
Hoggan, M. D., and Roizman, B. (1959). *Amer. J. Hyg.* **70,** 208.
Hoggan, M. D., Roizman, B., and Roane, P. R. (1961). *Amer. J. Hyg.* **73,** 114.

Holmes, K. V., and Choppin, P. W. (1966). *J. Exp. Med.* **124,** 501.
Holmes, K. V., and Choppin, P. W. (1968). *J. Cell Biol.* **39,** 526.
Holmes, K. V., Klenk, H. D., and Choppin, P. W. (1969). *Proc. Soc. Exp. Biol. Med.* **131,** 651.
Hornsleth, A. (1969). *Acta Pathol. Microbiol. Scand.* **76,** 637.
Hosaka, Y. (1960). *Biken J.* **3,** 1.
Hosaka, Y. (1962). *Biken J.* **5,** 121.
Hosaka, Y., and Koshi, Y. (1968). *Virology* **34,** 419.
Howe, C., and Morgan, C. (1969). *J. Virol.* **3,** 70.
Howell, J. I., and Lucy, J. A. (1969). *Fed. Eur. Biochem. Soc. Lett.* **4,** 147.
Ho Yun-De. (1962). *Acta Virol. (Prague), Engl. Ed.* **6,** 202.
Ho Yun-De., and Gorbunova, A. S. (1962). *Acta Virol. (Prague), Engl. Ed.* **6,** 193.
Hughes, D., Raine, C. S., and Field, E. J. (1968). *Brit. J. Exp. Pathol.* **49,** 356.
Hyde, A., Blondel, B., Matter, A., Cheneval, J. P., Filloux, B., and Girardier, L. (1969). *Progr. Brain Res.* **31,** 283.
Imagawa, D. T., and Adams, J. M. (1958). *Proc. Soc. Exp. Biol. Med.* **98,** 567.
Isogai, S. (1961). *Nippon Densembyo Gakkai Zasshi* **35,** 417.
Johnson, C. F., and Scott, A. D. (1964). *Proc. Soc. Exp. Biol. Med.* **115,** 281.
Jones, D. B. (1969). *Lab. Invest.* **21,** 119.
Jordan, W. S., Jr. (1962). *J. Immunol.* **88,** 581.
Kaku, H., and Kamahora, J. (1964). *Biken J.* **6,** 299.
Kaplan, A. S. (1962). *Virology* **16,** 305.
Kaplan, A. S., and Ben-Porat, T. (1959). *Virology* **8,** 352.
Kaplan, A. S., and Vatter, A. E. (1959). *Virology* **7,** 394.
Kavanau, L. (1965). "Structure and Function in Biological Membranes," Vol. 2, pp. 415–430. Holden-Day, San Francisco, California.
Khozinski, V. I., Seibel, V. B., Panteleyeva, N. S., and Mazurova, S. M. (1967). *Acta Virol. (Prague), Engl. Ed.* **11,** 65.
Kimoto, T., and Grace, J. T. (1966). *Acta Med. Okayama* **20,** 215.
Kit, S., Kurimura, T., de Torres, R. A., and Dubbs, D. R. (1969). *J. Virol.* **3,** 25.
Kleger, B., and Prier, J. E. (1969). *J. Infec. Dis.* **120,** 376.
Klenk, H. D., and Choppin, P. W. (1969). *Virology* **38,** 255.
Klöne, W., Kulemann, H., Ward, E. N., and Salk, J. E. (1966). *Arch. Gesamte Virusforsch.* **19,** 91.
Kohlhage, H. (1964). *Arch. Gesamte Virusforsch.* **14,** 358.
Kohlhage, H., and Schieferstein, G. (1965). *Arch. Gesamte Virusforsch.* **15,** 640.
Kohlhage, H., and Siegert, R. (1962). *Arch. Gesamte Virusforsch.* **12,** 273.
Kohn, A. (1965). *Virology* **26,** 228.
Kohn, A., and Fuchs, P. (1969). *J. Virol.* **3,** 539.
Kohn, A., and Klibansky, C. (1967). *Virology* **31,** 385.
Kohn, A., and Yassky, D. (1962). *Virology* **17,** 157.
Konovalova, N. G., Blumkin, V. N., and Zakstelskaya, L. Y. (1967). *Vop. Virusol.* **6,** 729.
Koprowski, H., Jensen, F. C., and Steplewski, Z. (1967). *Proc. Nat. Acad. Sci. U.S.* **58,** 127.
Kromayer, E. (1889). *Virchows Arch. Pathol. Anat. Physiol. Klin. Med.* **117,** 452.
Langhans, T. (1868). *Virchows Arch. Pathol. Anat. Physiol. Klin. Med.* **42,** 382.
Langhans, T. (1870). *Virchows Arch. Pathol. Anat. Physiol. Klin. Med.* **49,** 66.
La Placa, M., and Moscovici, C. (1961). *Ann. Inst. Pasteur* **100,** 337.
Leestma, J. E., Bornstein, M. B., Sheppard, R. D., and Feldman, L. A. (1969). *Lab. Invest.* **20,** 70.

Lépine, P., Chany, C., Droz, B., and Robbe-Fossat, F. (1959). *Ann. N.Y. Acad. Sci.* **81,** 62.
Lesseps, R. J. (1963). *J. Exp. Zool.* **153,** 171.
Lesso, J., and Szanto, J. (1969). *Acta Virol. (Prague), Engl. Ed.* **13,** 278.
Levine, E. M., Becker, Y., Boone, C. W., and Eagle, H. (1965). *Proc. Nat. Acad. Sci. U.S.* **53,** 350.
Levinson, W. (1967). *Virology* **32,** 74.
Liess, B., and Plowright, W. (1963). *Arch. Gesamte Virusforsch.* **14,** 27.
Lockwood, W. R., and Allison, F., Jr. (1966). *Brit. J. Exp. Pathol.* **47,** 158.
Loewenstein, W. R. (1967). *Develop. Biol.* **15,** 503.
Love, R., and Suskind, R. G. (1961). *Exp. Cell Res.* **24,** 52.
Lucy, J. A. (1968). *In* "Biological Membranes" (D. Chapman, ed.), pp. 233–288. Academic Press, New York.
Luginbühl, D. (1873). Quoted in Harris *et al.* (1966).
Lukert, P. D. (1966). *Arch. Gesamte Virusforsch.* **19,** 265.
McClain, M. E. (1965). *Aust. J. Exp. Biol. Med.* **43,** 31.
McKinney, R. W., England, B. L., and Froede, S. (1959). *Amer. J. Hyg.* **70,** 280.
Mallucci, L. (1965). *Virology* **25,** 30.
Mallucci, L. (1966). *Virology* **28,** 355.
Manery, J. F. (1966). *Fed. Proc. Fed. Amer. Soc. Exp. Biol.* **25,** 1804.
Maral, R. (1957). *Ann. Inst. Pasteur* **92,** 742.
Marquez, A., and Hsiung, G. D. (1967). *Proc. Soc. Exp. Biol. Med.* **124,** 95.
Marston, R. Q. (1958). *Proc. Soc. Exp. Biol. Med.* **98,** 853.
Marston, R. Q., and Vaughan, E. R. (1960). *Proc. Soc. Exp. Biol. Med.* **104,** 56.
Matsumoto, M. (1966). *Bacteriol. Rev.* **30,** 152.
Matsumoto, M., Arita, M., and Oda, M. (1965). *Jap. J. Exp. Med.* **35,** 319.
Meiselman, N., Kohn, A., and Danon, D. (1967). *J. Cell Sci.* **2,** 71.
Melnick, J. L., Hsiung, G. D., Rappaport, C., Howes, D. W. and Reissig, M. (1957). *Tex. Rep. Biol. Med.* **15,** 496.
Mirchamsy, H., and Rapp, F. (1969). *J. Gen. Virol.* **4,** 513.
Moses, E., and Kohn, A. (1963). *Exp. Cell Res.* **32,** 182.
Moura, R. A. (1961). *Arch. Gesamte Virusforsch.* **11,** 487.
Moyer, A. W., Wallace, R., and Cox, H. R. (1964). *J. Nat. Cancer Inst.* **33,** 227.
Munk, K., and Donner, D. (1963). *Arch. Gesamte Virusforsch.* **13,** 529.
Munk, K., and Sauer, G. (1964). *Virology* **22,** 153.
Murayama, F., and Okada, Y. (1965). *Biken J.* **8,** 103.
Nahmias, A. J., and Dowdle, W. R. (1968). *Progr. Med. Virol.* **10,** 110.
Nasibov, M. N., and Smorodintsev, A. A. (1968). *Arch. Gesamte Virusforsch.* **24,** 319.
Nathans, D. (1964). *Fed. Proc. Fed. Amer. Soc. Exp. Biol.* **23,** 984.
Neff, J. M., and Enders, J. F. (1968). *Proc. Soc. Exp. Biol. Med.* **127,** 260.
Neurath, A. R. (1964). *Acta Virol. (Prague), Engl. Ed.* **8,** 154.
Niemi, M., and Sylvén, B. (1968). *Acta Pathol. Microbiol. Scand.* **72,** 205.
Nii, S., and Kamahora, J. (1961a). *Biken J.* **4,** 75.
Nii, S., and Kamahora, J. (1961b). *Biken J.* **4,** 215.
Nii, S., and Kamahora, J. (1963). *Biken J.* **6,** 33.
Nii, S., Kamahora, J., Mori, Y., Takahashi, M., Nishimura, S., and Okuno, Y. (1964). *Biken J.* **6,** 271.
Norrby, E. (1966). *Arch. Gesamte Virusforsch.* **18,** 333.
Norrby, E., Magnusson, P., Falksveden, L.-G., and Gronnberg, M. (1964). *Arch. Gesamte Virusforsch.* **14,** 462.

O'Callaghan, D. J., Hyde, J. M., Gentry, G. A., and Randall, C. C. (1968). *J. Virol.* **2,** 793.
O'Daly, J. A. (1967). *Nature (London)* **216,** 1329.
Oddo, F. G., Chiarini, A., and Sinatra, A. (1967). *Arch. Gesamte Virusforsch.* **22,** 35.
Okada, Y. (1958). *Biken J.* **1,** 103.
Okada, Y. (1961). *Biken J.* **4,** 145.
Okada, Y. (1962). *Exp. Cell Res.* **26,** 98.
Okada, Y., and Hosakawa, Y. (1961). *Biken J.* **4,** 217.
Okada, Y., and Murayama, F. (1965). *Biken J.* **8,** 7.
Okada, Y., and Murayama, F. (1966). *Exp. Cell Res.* **44,** 527.
Okada, Y., and Tadokoro, J. (1962). *Exp. Cell Res.* **26,** 108.
Okada, Y., and Tadokoro, J. (1963). *Exp. Cell Res.* **32,** 417.
Okada, Y., Yamada, K., and Tadokoro, J. (1964). *Virology* **22,** 397.
Okada, Y., Murayama, F., and Yamada, K. (1966). *Virology* **27,** 115.
Parfanovitch, M. I., Sokolov, N. N., Zmeeva, R. G., Gavrilov, V. I., Fadeyeva, L. L., and Mishin, L. N. (1966). *Acta Virol. (Prague), Engl. Ed.* **10,** 322.
Paul, S. D., Singh, K. R. P., and Bhat, U. K. M. (1969). *Indian J. Med. Res.* **57,** 339.
Pethica, B. A. (1961). *Exp. Cell Res. Suppl.* **8,** 123.
Pirtle, E. C., and Woods, L. K. (1968). *Amer. J. Vet. Res.* **29,** 153.
Plowright, W. (1962). *Ann. N.Y. Acad. Sci. U.S.* **101,** 548.
Plowright, W., and Ferris, R. D. (1959). *J. Comp. Pathol. Ther.* **69,** 152.
Poisner, A. M., and Trifaró, J. M. (1967). *Mol. Pharmacol.* **3,** 561.
Policard, A., Collet, A., Martin, J. C., and Reut, C. (1965). *Z. Zellforsch. Mikrosk. Anat.* **66,** 96.
Politoff, A., Socolar, S. J., and Loewenstein, W. R. (1967). *Biochim. Biophys. Acta* **135,** 791.
Pomerat, C. M., Kent, S. P., and Logie, L. C. (1957). *Z. Zellforsch. Mikrosk. Anat.* **47,** 175.
Poste, G. H. (1969). Virus-Induced Polykaryocytosis. Ph.D. Thesis, Univ. of Bristol, Bristol, England.
Poste, G. H. (1970a). *Cytobios* (in press).
Poste, G. H. (1970b). *Cytobios* (in press).
Poste, G. H. (1970c). *Microbios* (in press).
Poste, G. H. (1970d). *Microbios* (in press).
Provost, A., and Villemot, J.-M. (1961). *Ann. Inst. Pasteur* **101,** 276.
Rambourg, A., and Leblond, D. P. (1967). *J. Cell Biol.* **32,** 27.
Rapp, F. (1960). *Virology* **10,** 86.
Reich, E. (1964). *Fed. Proc. Fed. Amer. Soc. Exp. Biol.* **23,** 91.
Reissig, M., and Kaplan, A. S. (1960). *Virology* **11,** 1.
Reissig, M., and Kaplan, A. S. (1962). *Virology* **16,** 1.
Reissig, M., Howes, D. W., and Melnick, J. L. (1956). *J. Exp. Med.* **104,** 289.
Reporter, M. (1967). *J. Cell Biol.* **35,** 112A.
Revel, J.-P., and Ito, S. (1967). *In* "The Specificity of Cell Surfaces" (B. D. Davis and L. Warren, eds.), pp. 211–234. Prentice-Hall, Englewood Cliffs, New Jersey.
Ritchie, J. M., and Greengard, P. (1966). *Annu. Rev. Pharmacol.* **6,** 405.
Roane, P. R., Jr., and Roizman, B. (1964). *Virology* **22,** 1.
Rohde, B. (1923). *Z. Wiss. Zool.* **120,** 325.
Roizman, B. (1962a). *Cold Spring Harbor Symp. Quant. Biol.* **24,** 327.
Roizman, B. (1962b). *Proc. Nat. Acad. Sci. U.S.* **48,** 228.
Roizman, B., and Aurelian, L. (1965). *J. Mol. Biol.* **11,** 528.

Roizman, B., and Roane, P. R., Jr. (1961). *Virology* **15,** 75.
Roizman, B., and Roane, P. R., Jr. (1963). *Virology* **19,** 198.
Roizman, B., and Schluederberg, A. E. (1962). *J. Nat. Cancer Inst.* **28,** 35.
Ross, R. W., and Orlans, E. (1958). *J. Pathol. Bacteriol.* **76,** 393.
Rubin, H. (1967). *In* "The Specificity of Cell Surfaces" (B. D. Davis and L. Warren, eds.), pp. 181–194. Prentice-Hall, Englewood Cliffs, New Jersey.
Ruckle-Enders, G. (1962). *Amer. J. Dis. Child.* **103,** 297.
Ruckle-Enders, G. (1965). *Arch. Gesamte Virusforsch.* **16,** 182.
Russell, P. K., and Morgan, H. R. (1959). *J. Infec. Dis.* **104,** 38.
Rweyemamu, M. M., and Johnson, R. H. (1967). *Brit. Vet. J.* **123,** 482.
Salsbury, A. J., Clarke, J. A., and Shand, W. S. (1968). *Clin. Exp. Immunol.* **3,** 313.
Schatzmann, H. J. (1968). *Protides Biol. Fluids, Proc. Colloq.* **15,** 251–255.
Schepers, G. W. H. (1959). *Amer. J. Pathol.* **35,** 1169.
Schleiden, M. J. (1838). *Arch. Anat. Physiol. Wiss. Med. Leipzig* **ii,** 137.
Schneeberger, E. E., and Harris, H. (1966). *J. Cell Sci.* **1,** 401.
Schneweis, K. E. (1962). *Zentrbl. Bakteriol. Parasitenk Infektionskr. Hyg., Abt. 1: Orig.* **186,** 467.
Schneweis, K. E. (1967). *Deut. Med. Wochenschr.* **92,** 2313.
Schwann, T. (1847). "Microscopical Researches into the Accordance in the Structure and Growth of Animals and Plants" (transl. by H. Smith). Sydenham Soc., London.
Scott, T. F., McLeod, D. L., and Tokumaru, T. (1961). *J. Immunol.* **86,** 1.
Seeman, P. M. (1966). *Int. Rev. Neurobiol.* **9,** 145.
Shatkin, A. J., Reich, E., Franklin, R. M., and Tatum, E. L. (1962). *Biochim. Biophys. Acta* **55,** 277.
Shelton, E., and Rice, M. E. (1958). *J. Nat. Cancer Inst.* **21,** 137.
Shevliaghyn, V. J., Biryulina, T. I., Tikhonova, Z. N., and Karazas, N. V. (1969). *Int. J. Cancer* **4,** 42.
Silagi, S. (1967). *Cancer Res.* **27,** 1953.
Silagi, S., Darlington, G., and Bruce, S. A. (1969). *Proc. Nat. Acad. Sci. U.S.* **62,** 1085.
Siminoff, P. (1964). *Virology* **24,** 1.
Siminoff, P., and Menefee, M. G. (1968). *Exp. Cell Res.* **44,** 241.
Singer, I., and Tasaki, I. (1968). *In* "Biological Membranes" (D. Chapman, ed.), pp. 347–410. Academic Press, New York.
Smith, K. R., Jr. (1969). *J. Neurol., Neurosurg. Psychiat.* **32,** 348.
Spurna, V., and Hill, M. (1968). *Exp. Cell Res.* **50,** 223.
Stephenson, N. G. (1969). *Cell Tissue Kinet.* **2,** 225.
Steplewski, Z., and Swierkowska, K. (1967). *Fed. Proc. Fed. Amer. Soc. Exp. Biol.* **26,** 791.
Stevens, J. G. (1966). *Virology* **29,** 570.
Stoker, M. G. P. (1959). *Soc. Gen. Microbiol. Symp.* **9,** 142.
Stormorken, H. (1969). *Scand. J. Haematol. Suppl.* **9.**
Stůdnička, F. K. (1934). *Biol. Rev. Cambridge Phil. Soc.* **9,** 263.
Sutton, J. S. (1967). *Nat. Cancer Inst. Monogr.* **26,** 71.
Svoboda, J., and Dourmashkin, R. (1969). *J. Gen. Virol.* **4,** 523.
Szmigielski, S., Korbecki, M., Luczak, M., and Wilczynski, J. (1967). *Bull. Acad. Pol. Sci., Ser. Sci. Biol.* **15,** 211.
Tankersley, R. W., Jr. (1968). *Bacteriol. Proc.* p. 146.
Tawara, J. (1965). *Acta Med. Okayama* **19,** 155.
Taylor, A. C., and Robbins, E. (1963). *Develop. Biol.* **7,** 660.
Taylor-Robinson, D. (1959). *Brit. J. Exp. Pathol.* **40,** 521.

Tegtmeyer, P., and Enders, J. F. (1969). *J. Virol.* **3,** 469.
Thomison, J. B. (1962). *Lab. Invest.* **11,** 211.
Tobias, J. M. (1964). *Nature (London)* **203,** 13.
Tokumaru, T. (1957). *Proc. Soc. Exp. Biol. Med.* **96,** 55.
Tokumaru, T. (1968). *Arch. Gesamte Virusforsch.* **24,** 104.
Toyoshima, K., Hata, S., Takahashi, M., Kunita, N., and Okuno, Y. (1959). *Biken J.* **2,** 313.
Toyoshima, K., Hata, S., Takahashi, M., Miki, T., and Okuno, Y. (1960). *Biken J.* **3,** 241.
Tyzzer, E. E. (1905). *J. Med. Res.* **14,** 361.
Underwood, G. E. (1959). *J. Immunol.* **83,** 198.
Unna, P. G. (1896). "The Histopathology" of the Diseases of the Skin," p. 637. Clay, Edinburgh.
Vainio, T., and Judah, J. D. (1962). *Exp. Mol. Pathol.* **1,** 27.
Van Deenan, L. L. M., Houtsmuller, V. M. T., De Haas, G. H., and Mulder, E. (1962). *J. Pharm. Pharmacol.* **14,** 429.
Verwey, E. J. A., and Overbeek, J. T. G. (1948). "Theory of the Stability of Lyophobic Colloids." Elsevier, Amsterdam.
Virchow, R. (1858). "Die Cellularpathologie." Berlin.
Vizoso, A. D., Hay, R., and Battersley, T. (1966). *Nature (London)* **209,** 1263.
Waddell, G. H., and Sigel, M. M. (1966). *Arch. Gesamte Virusforsch.* **19,** 130.
Warren, J., Jensen, K., and Mason, R. (1962). *Ann. N.Y. Acad. Sci.* **101,** 520.
Watkins, J. F., and Chen, L. (1969). *Nature (London)* **223,** 1018.
Watkins, J. F., and Grace, D. M. (1967). *J. Cell Sci.* **2,** 193.
Weber, J., and Stich, H. F. (1969). *Exp. Cell Res.* **56,** 319.
Weigert, C. (1874). Quoted in Harris *et al.* (1966).
Weiss, L. (1965). *J. Cell Biol.* **26,** 735.
Weiss, L. (1966). *J. Cell Biol.* **30,** 39.
Weiss, L. (1967a). "The Cell Periphery, Metastasis and Other Contact Phenomena." North-Holland Publ., Amsterdam.
Weiss, L. (1967b). *J. Cell Biol.* **35,** 347.
Weiss, L. P., and Fawcett, D. W. (1953). *J. Histochem. Cytochem.* **1,** 47.
Weiss, L., and Woodbridge, R. F. (1967). *Proc. Fed. Amer. Soc. Exp. Biol.* **26,** 88.
Weiss, M. C., and Green, H. (1967). *Proc. Nat. Acad. Sci. U.S.* **58,** 1104.
Weller, T. H., Whitton, H. M., and Bell, E. J. (1958). *J. Exp. Med.* **108,** 843.
Wheeler, C. E., Jr. (1964). *J. Immunol.* **93,** 749.
Wildy, P., Stoker, M. G. P., and Ross, R. W. (1959). *J. Gen. Microbiol.* **20,** 105.
Wolpert, L., and Gingell, D. (1968). *Symp. Soc. Exp. Biol.* **22,** 169.
Woodin, A. M. (1968). *In* "The Biological Basis of Medicine" (E. E. Bittar and N. Bittar, eds.), Vol. 2, pp. 373–396. Academic Press, New York.
Woodin, A. M., and Wieneke, A. A. (1964). *Biochem. J.* **90,** 498.
Wulff, H., Kidd, P., and Wenner, H. A. (1964). *Proc. Soc. Exp. Biol. Med.* **115,** 458.
Zhdanov, V. M., and Bukrinskaya, A. G. (1962). *Acta Virol. (Prague), Engl. Ed.* **6,** 105.

AUSTRALIA (HEPATITIS-ASSOCIATED) ANTIGEN: PHYSICOCHEMICAL AND IMMUNOLOGICAL CHARACTERISTICS*

George L. Le Bouvier and Robert W. McCollum

Department of Epidemiology and Public Health, Yale University School of Medicine, New Haven, Connecticut

I. Introduction

The search for etiological agents in hepatitis has had a long and checkered history. From clinical, epidemiological, and controlled hu-

* This work was supported in part by Contract DA-49-193-MD-2062 under the sponsorship of the Commission on Viral Infections, Armed Forces Epidemiological Board, Office of the Surgeon General, United States Army Medical Research and Development Command.

man transmission studies two types of transmissible, presumably viral, hepatitis have been defined. The first, infectious hepatitis (IH; Type A) has a relatively short incubation period (15–45 days, but usually about 30–35 days), and may be transmitted by either the fecal-oral or parenteral route. Numerous common source epidemics attributable to contaminated food, water, or milk have been described. Secondary infections among close contacts are common, in households and, particularly, in large institutions for mentally retarded children in which IH may become established as an endemic problem. The second type, serum hepatitis (SH; Type B) has a long and highly variable incubation period (45 to more than 100 days). Until a few years ago, SH was thought to be transmissible only by parenteral inoculation. Recent transmission studies and epidemiological observations, however, have provided good evidence that the infecting agent may also be acquired by the oral route, and, like IH, may become endemic in institutional settings (Krugman *et al.*, 1967).

This review deals with the discovery, characterization, immunology, and etiological significance of "Australia antigen," a new antigenic specificity appearing in the serum of patients with serum hepatitis, and carried on characteristic lipoprotein particles. In addition to its original name, given before its relationship to viral hepatitis became known, the antigen has also been given the following designations: Au(1), SH antigen, Au/SH antigen, hepatitis antigen, and hepatitis-associated antigen (HAA). At this time, there is no clear evidence that these terms refer to more than a single entity.

II. Discovery and Early Studies

A. Identification of Australia Antigen

Sera from persons receiving multiple transfusions have proved of value in the detection of serum isoantigens. Using this approach, and the Ouchterlony technique of two-dimensional double immunodiffusion, Allison and Blumberg (1961) and Blumberg *et al.* (1962) were able to define a new lipoprotein polymorphism, the Ag system. [Details of the original and later immunodiffusion methods will be discussed below (Section V, C)]. Continuing the search, Blumberg and his co-workers, in 1963, identified a new precipitating antigen with the help of serum from two multiple transfused hemophiliacs (Blumberg, 1964; Blumberg *et al.*, 1965). These sera contained an antibody which reacted with the serum of an Australian aborigine to give a single line of precipitation. The precipitating component, designated "Australia antigen," appeared to represent a single antigenic determinant, and was clearly distinct from previously described human serum isoantigens. It was considered at first to be another example of a serum protein polymorphism. The possession of Australia antigen was held to distinguish the phenotype Au(1), reflecting the genotype Au^1/Au^1. The allele Au^1 was postulated to be autosomal and recessive. Thus, individuals lacking Australia antigen [phenotype Au(0)] would be either homozygous Au/Au, or heterozygous Au^1/Au, the dominant *Au* allele acting to prevent synthesis or detection of the antigen (Blumberg *et al.*, 1966; Blumberg *et al.*, 1967a). This hypothesis of a simple genetic determination of Australia antigen was later modified, with the discovery of its peculiar association with leukemia, Down's syndrome, and hepatitis (Blumberg *et al.*, 1969). In the meantime, however, it had led to a notable series of studies by Blumberg and his associates (Blumberg *et al.*, 1965, 1966, 1967a,b), in which they looked for the antigen in various populations in different parts of the world.

B. Geographical Studies

Early serum surveys soon revealed an uneven distribution of Australia (Au) antigen in different human populations. The data shown in Table I are taken from Blumberg *et al.* (1968). Possession, or expression, of the antigen was relatively common among the peoples of Southeastern Asia and the Pacific Islands, as well as in Australian aborigines (2–13%). By contrast, its frequency in the general United States population was low ($\leqslant$0.1%).

C. Genetic Studies

The variation between different populations appeared, at first sight, to provide possible support for the hypothesis of the genetic control of the synthesis of the Au(1) macromolecule. Further studies of families were made to test the suggestion that the antigen might be specified by an autosomal recessive gene (Blumberg *et al.*, 1966). The data obtained were not sufficient to provide firm support for this thesis, although they did not rule it out.

Two later pieces of evidence combined to make the early simpler genetic interpretation less convincing: (*1*) it began to be apparent that environmental factors significantly affected the detectability of Au antigen in the serum, and (*2*) it was observed by Prince (1968a), and soon generally confirmed, that the duration of antigen in the serum was usually transient (a few days to several weeks), but occasionally it persisted indefinitely (Giles *et al.*, 1969; Zuckerman and Taylor, 1969). The simple presence or absence of a gene product was inadequate to explain these findings.

More recently, however, the hypothesis has been modified to state (*1*) that the persistent presence of Australia antigen in the serum, i.e., the Au(1) phenotype, reflects a peculiar individual susceptibility to the development of chronicity after infection with a variety of agents, including that of serum hepatitis with its specific association with Au

TABLE I

FREQUENCY OF AUSTRALIA ANTIGEN IN DIFFERENT POPULATIONS

Population	Location	Number tested	Number Au^+	Percent Au^+
Americas				
Eskimos	Alaska (U.S.A.)	394	1	0.3
Indians, Sioux	South Dakota (U.S.A.)	130	0	0
Afro-Americans	Georgia and Maryland (U.S.A.)[a]	607	0	0
Caucasians		896	0	0
Indians, Maya	Yucatan	1417	4	0.07
Indians, Cashinahua	Peru	89	18	20.2
Oceania				
Micronesians	Marshall Islands	474	34	7.2
Melanesians	New Guinea	166	6	3.6
Aborigines	Australia	1807	38	2.1
Asia				
Filipinos	Cebu, P. I.	764	37	4.8
Japanese	Japan	1034	5	0.5
Israelis	Israel	340	4	1.2
Africa				
Pare	Tanzania	120	1	0.8
Ghanaians	Ghana	95	9	9.5
Europe				
Finns	Finland	924	1	0.1
Greeks	Greece	857	15	1.8

[a] In further surveys of hospital patients (serial admissions) and nonhospitalized "normal" controls in the U.S.A., 0.2% of the patients (2/1055), and 0.1% of the controls (2/2412) were positive for Australia antigen. Table modified from Blumberg *et al.* (1968).

antigen (*vide infra*); and (*2*) that it is this tendency toward development of a chronic carrier state which is affected by at least one autosomal recessive gene, still designated Au^1 (Blumberg *et al.*, 1969; Blumberg, 1970). The data in support of this expanded hypothesis were derived from studies of the island populations of Cebu (Philippines) and Bougainville (New Guinea) in which hygienic and sanitary conditions were such as to warrant the assumption that various orally transmitted infections, including both forms of viral hepatitis (Krugman *et al.*,

1967), would be endemic in the population so that there would be ample opportunity for exposure of all individuals, in time, to the infectious agents. The results, so far, do not appear to have disproved the hypothesis; but many more data from other presumably "hepatitis-saturated" populations demand analysis before this novel and provocative hypothesis can be accepted as nearing establishment.

D. Association of Australia Antigen with Different Diseases

In their studies of various groups within the United States, Blumberg and his colleagues (1965) observed early that Au antigen was unusually frequent in individuals with certain forms of leukemia. This association was later found to be true also for patients with Down's syndrome, lepromatous leprosy, and hepatitis (Blumberg *et al.,* 1967a,b). These workers further noted that among children with Down's syndrome, those in institutions showed a markedly higher frequency of Au antigen in their serum than those remaining at home (28 vs. 0%) (Sutnick *et al.,* 1968). Extending these observations, they and other investigators noted that the staff of mental hospitals and institutions likewise included more Au-positives than the general population. It became apparent that environmental conditions in such institutions were an important factor in determining the frequency of possession of Au antigen; and the suggested relationship with some acquired factor, or transmitted infectious agent, was strengthened by the finding of strikingly high proportions of antigen possessors among patients with diseases in which some depression or disturbance of immune function might be expected, e.g., leukemia and lepromatous leprosy (Blumberg *et al.,* 1968).

A more recent example of the tendency of nursing personnel, as well as patients, to acquire Au antigen is seen in the experience of chronic renal hemodialysis units (London *et al.,* 1969a; Turner and White, 1969).

III. Association of Australia Antigen with Hepatitis

The first indication of an unusually high prevalence of Au antigen in the serum of hepatitis patients was published by Blumberg *et al.* (1967a). Soon afterward, Prince (1968a), and Okochi and Murakami (1968) demonstrated the appearance of Au (or "SH") antigen in the serum of individuals, usually between 5 and 10 weeks after experimental inoculation or blood transfusion. In most cases, the antigen persisted for one to several weeks and then disappeared. But in 2 out of 7, and 1 out of 14 cases, respectively, it was still present in the latest serum tested (5–7 months after inoculation). Others have confirmed and amplified these findings, e.g., Hirschman *et al.* (1969), 4 of whose 46 Au-positive (Au+) cases of SH retained antigen for >10 months after onset; and

Giles *et al.* (1969), who reported persistence of Au for at least 3 years in 9 of 18 persons who received the MS-2 strain of SH agent. In these patients, the serum glutamic oxaloacetic or glutamic pyruvic transaminase rose to abnormally high levels, usually 5 to 15 days after the initial appearance of Au; but, thereafter, the correlation between elevated enzyme levels and serum antigen varied widely. In most of the cases with overt disease, symptoms began some 7–21 days after Au antigen first became detectable. These findings indicated a special temporal relationship of Au antigen with the SH form of viral hepatitis, as contrasted with its unchanging presence or absence in leukemia, Down's syndrome, and lepromatous leprosy.

The association of Au antigen with viral hepatitis has been confirmed in many laboratories. The principal point of disagreement has been the question of whether it is implicated in both forms of viral hepatitis, or specifically limited to the long-incubation SH form. Suffice it to say here that in those studies involving well-documented, experimentally produced infections, the antigen has been regularly found in all, or almost all, cases of SH, but has not been detectable in short-incubation disease of IH type (Prince, 1968a; Giles *et al.*, 1969; Le Bouvier *et al.*, 1969). Furthermore, in studies of several common-source outbreaks of IH type hepatitis, no Au antigen was demonstrable in any of the patients concerned (Prince *et al.*, 1970; Mosley *et al.*, 1970). It is noteworthy that none of a group of volunteers experimentally infected by mouth with the Akiba strain of IH (Neefe and Stokes, 1945) developed detectable antigen. One individual, who already possessed Au antigen in his serum before inoculation, continued to do so throughout the course of his experimental infection. However, a possible result of infection with the IH-type agent, in this case, was a decline in the concentration of the already circulating Au antigen between the fourth and eighth weeks after inoculation. It remains to be seen whether this was a coincidental fluctuation, or causally related to the experimentally introduced agent, e.g., as the result of interference with Au antigen synthesis at the cellular level, or due to the blocking effect of a circulating inhibitor or cross-reacting antibody. Initial experiments to test the second possibility have so far yielded negative results (Le Bouvier *et al.*, 1969).

Thus, while Au antigen is consistently found in cases of long-incubation viral hepatitis, the significance of its reported presence in sporadic cases designated as IH has still to be determined. London *et al.* (1969b) noted that Au was rarely detected in acute phase sera obtained from children with hepatitis, a finding supported by subsequent studies reported by Prince *et al.* (1970).

Among other forms of acute and chronic liver disease, including drug hepatitis, biliary cirrhosis, alcoholic cirrhosis, postnecrotic cirrhosis, and infectious mononucleosis, Au antigen is remarkably absent (Gocke and Kavey, 1969) with the exception of chronic active hepatitis in which Au antigen has been found, in the United States (Wright *et al.*, 1969; Gitnick *et al.*, 1969) and in Australia (Mathews and Mackay, 1970). However, it has so far not been found in such cases in England (Fox *et al.*, 1969), Denmark (Reinicke and Nordenfelt, 1970), or Chile (Velasco and Katz, 1970).

IV. Properties of Australia Antigen

A. Introduction

The serological reactions of Australia (Au) antigen and antibody are dealt with separately in the following section (p. 374). This section considers other properties of the antigen, and of the particles which carry the Au specificity.

B. Chemical Properties

In early studies, Alter and Blumberg (1966) investigated the staining properties of Au antigen-antibody precipitates in agar gel: a strong reaction was obtained with the protein stain azocarmine; there was also a weak and variable affinity for the lipid stain, Sudan Black, but the intensity of the reaction was less than that given by the serum lipoproteins. The participation of protein in the reactivity of Au antigen has also been shown by its sensitivity to trypsin (2.5%, 37°C, 2 hours), and to treatment with sodium dodecyl sulfate and 2-mercaptoethanol (1% of each, 37°C, 1 hour) (Le Bouvier, 1969). Treatment with diethyl ether, or fluorocarbon, has effects on the morphology of Au-antigenic particles, which are discussed below (p. 369); but their antigenic specificity is not altered, and the level of activity remains unchanged, or may even be increased (Barker *et al.*, 1969).

There appears to be no report of the presence of carbohydrate or nucleic acid associated with the Australia particles and their antigenic specificity. If indeed there be any nucleic acid, it is evidently not present in a concentration comparable with that of the ribonucleic acid in "full," D-antigenic poliovirions (~25%); for when immunodiffusion bands of "full" (D) and "empty" (C) poliovirions, and Au antigen, were stained with acridine orange (cf. Cowan and Graves, 1968) the poliovirus D band stained and fluoresced brightly, whereas the C and Au bands remained completely unstained (Le Bouvier, 1969).

C. Physical Properties

Long before its particulate nature was known, Au antigen was suspected of having a high molecular weight (Alter and Blumberg, 1966), since it was excluded from gels of Sephadex G-200. Moreover, the character of its precipitate band in agar indicated an antigenic particle, or macromolecule, distinctly larger than the presumably IgG antibody molecule with which it was reacting. Recent immunodiffusion studies have given a figure of $x_g \simeq 0.4$ for the equivalence position of Au antigen-antibody precipitates (i.e., the fractional distance between the antigen and antibody cups at which the precipitate forms when the reactants are meeting in optimal proportions). Here, the reacting antibody was known to be of IgG class. The diffusion coefficient, D_b, for the antibody was taken as 4.81×10^{-7} cm²/sec (cf., van Regenmortel, 1966). From the equation

$$x_b^2/x_g^2 = D_b/D_g$$

where $x_g = 0.4$, and $x_b = 1 - x_g$, the diffusion coefficient for Au antigen, D_g, was calculated to be $\sim 2 \times 10^{-7}$ cm²/sec (Le Bouvier, 1969).

In early studies of adsorption chromatography on DEAE-cellulose, Au antigen was eluted by 0.1–0.2 *M* phosphate, pH 7.0, after IgG, and together with, or slightly ahead of, β-lipoprotein, IgA, IgM, and albumin (Alter and Blumberg, 1966). When subjected to immunoelectrophoresis, Au antigen somewhat resembled in mobility an α_1-globulin (Alter and Blumberg, 1966).

The buoyant density of the antigen-bearing particles is intermediate between that of serum lipoproteins and most other proteins. In the first studies, done by flotation in KBr, the antigenic activity was associated with fractions of density >1.063 and <1.30 gm/ml (Alter and Blumberg, 1966). In recent studies, there has been general agreement about the intermediate density, but some discrepancy in the precise figures: in CsCl, the maxima were 1.20 (Gerin *et al.*, 1969), 1.21 (Le Bouvier and Hierholzer, 1969; Millman *et al.*, 1970a), and 1.24 gm/ml (Barker *et al.*, 1969); in sucrose, 1.16 (Gerin *et al.*, 1969) to 1.18 (Le Bouvier and Hierholzer, 1969); and in potassium tartrate, 1.15 (Gerin *et al.*, 1969). After treatment with ether, fluorocarbon, or sodium deoxycholate, the density increases, e.g., in CsCl, from 1.20 to 1.22 or 1.23 (Gerin *et al.*, 1969), or from 1.24 to 1.27 or 1.28 (Barker *et al.*, 1969); or from 1.18 to 1.20–1.21 in sucrose (Le Bouvier and Hierholzer, 1969). In one study (Gerin *et al.*, 1969), freezing and thawing, or treatment with Tween 80 of an Au antigen fraction, which had been twice banded in CsCl and then separated by rate sedimentation in sucrose, caused a fall in buoyant density from 1.20 to 1.18 in CsCl, and also resulted in the emergence of a "significant amount" of Au+ material with a density of 1.39 gm/ml. It is not yet known what this represents; but its density would be compatible with that of a nucleoprotein.

The sedimentation coefficient of Au-antigenic particles has been reported as 110 S in one study, in which adeno-associated virus (AAV-1), with $S_{20,w} = 104$, was used as a marker (Gerin *et al.*, 1969). The determination was made in sucrose (5–20% w/w, 39,000 rpm, 3 hours), using as test material Au antigen that had been purified by two sequential equilibrium centrifugations in CsCl density gradients. An identical sedimentation coefficient of 110 S was found by Prince (1970). In another study done under similar conditions, but using serum as the material under test (Le Bouvier, 1969), the S value of the Au antigenic activity was found to be intermediate between those of IgM (19 S) and "empty" poliovirus capsids (73 S). The reasons for these apparent discrepancies have still to be discovered.

Where the material under examination consists of a preselected segment of the population of Au-antigenic particles, e.g. the peak fraction from a CsCl isopycnic centrifugation, the values obtained for buoyant density and sedimentation coefficient may fall within quite a narrow range. But when the test material is untreated, unheated serum, these values show a greater spread, and sometimes more than one peak, suggesting considerable particle heterogeneity (Figs. 1 and 2).

It is clear that the degree of aggregation of Au-antigenic particles will affect the determination of their size, sedimentability, and diffusion characteristics, and likewise their capacity to react in serological tests (*vide infra*, p. 374). Purcell *et al.* (1969) have reported decreases of Au antigenic titer of up to 50%, as detected by immunodiffusion, after heating at 56°C for 30 minutes; this could be caused by aggregation without degradation, since the complement-fixing antigen was not destroyed by overnight incubation at this temperature (Gerin *et al.*, 1969). Other results have indicated no appreciable loss of antigenic activity, as tested by immunodiffusion, after heating at 56°C for 1 hour (Millman *et al.*, 1970a), or after 20 minutes at 59°C, or more than 1 year at room temperature (Hierholzer *et al.*, 1970). Gerin *et al.* (1969) reported a marked drop in Au antigen titer in some experiments, when Au antigen which had been fractionated by density in CsCl was subjected to velocity sedimentation in sucrose; and they pointed to particle aggregation as the probable reason for this loss. The complement-fixing activity of Au antigen was not affected, however, by incubation at pH 2.7 for 3 hours at room temperature, or by exposure to ether (20% v/v), either overnight at 4°C, or for 4 hours at room temperature.

D. Morphology

As the peculiar geographical distribution and disease associations of Au antigen began to be appreciated, the question arose whether the antigen might be related to, or might itself be, a transmissible agent and, in particular, a virus. Bayer *et al.* (1968) therefore examined in the electron microscope, by the technique of negative staining with sodium silicotungstate, Au+ fractions derived from a sample of serum which had been separated in a sucrose density gradient and then electrophoresced on cellulose acetate. They made the astonishing dis-

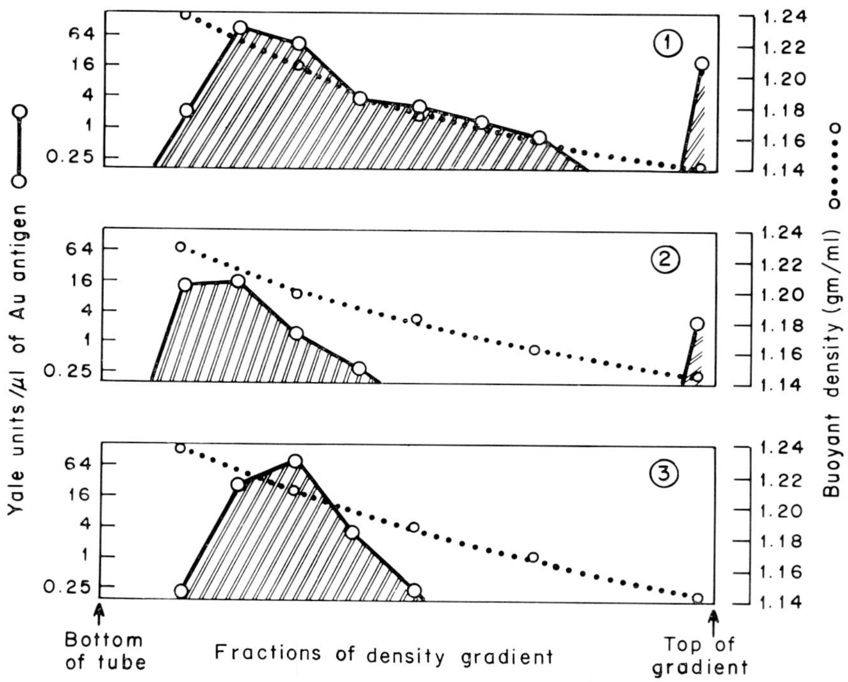

FIG. 1. Isopycnic centrifugation in cesium chloride of Au antigen in 3 different sera. Serum, 1 ml, mixed with 3.8 ml of 26% (w/w) CsCl ($\rho \simeq 1.24$); spun at 37,000 rpm for 21 hours at 5°C in Spinco SW 50 rotor; fractions of ~0.5 ml collected, and buoyant densities determined by weighing 100-μl aliquots.

covery of round and ovoid particles, 20 nm in diameter, possessing suggestive knoblike surface projections 3 nm in diameter. Some particles seemed to have a central 7-nm diameter core, while a few appeared to be "empty" shells filled with the stain. The particles were not seen in a heavier fraction lacking Au antigen, or in fractions of corresponding density derived from Au-negative sera. Furthermore, aggregates of these particles could be seen electron microscopically in mixtures of the Au+ fractions with rabbit antisera containing anti-Au precipitin.

These findings have been repeatedly confirmed by other workers (Figs. 3 and 4). In addition to the spherical and ovoid particles, tubular forms have been observed, their frequency varying from one serum

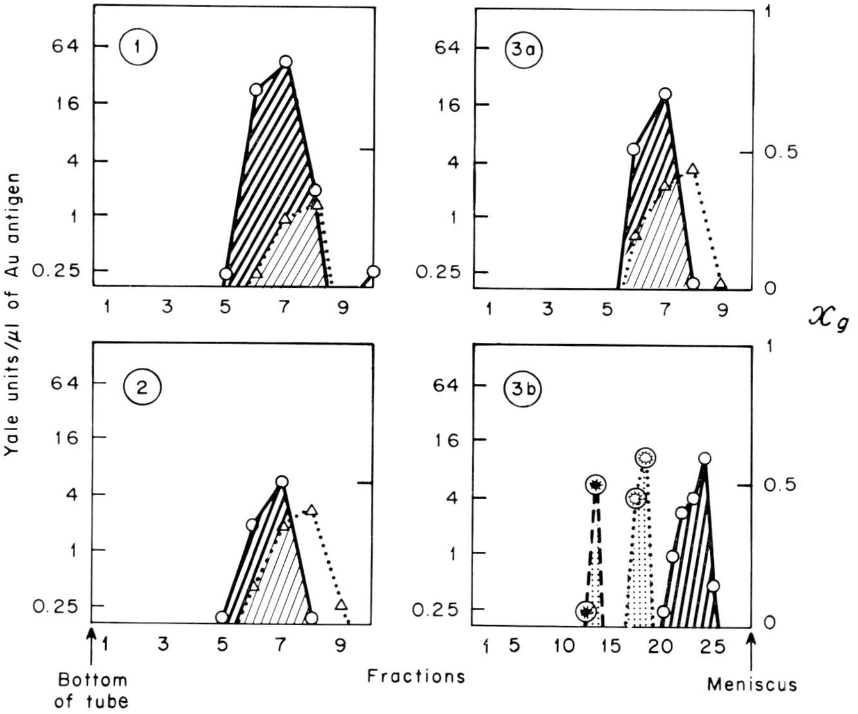

FIG. 2. Velocity sedimentation in sucrose of Au antigen and IgM in 3 different sera (parts 1, 2, and 3a). Serum, 0.25 ml, layered on 4.5 ml of a 10–30% (w/w) sucrose gradient; spun at 35,000 rpm for 2.5 hours at 5°C in Spinco SW 50 rotor; 0.5-ml fractions collected. Serum No. 3 was also rerun in parallel with poliovirus "full" (D) and "empty" (C) capsids (3b). Serum, 0.2 ml, or poliovirus concentrate (D + C), layered on 4.5 ml of 9–45% (w/w) sucrose gradient; spun at 30,000 rpm for 2.5 hours at 5°C in Spinco SW 50 rotor; 3-drop fractions collected. ○——○ = Au antigen; △····△ = IgM; ◉---◉ = poliovirus D antigen; ◎····◎ = poliovirus C antigen. Concentrations of the poliovirus antigens, and of IgM, have not been measured in units or milligrams, but are given as a function of x_g, the fractional distance between antigen and antibody cups at which precipitation is taking place (cf. p. 377).

to another (Almeida and Waterson, 1969). In these forms, an appearance of regular transverse striation can often be made out, with a periodicity of ~3 nm (Almeida and Waterson, 1969; Almeida *et al.*, 1969). These tubules may attain lengths of <50–200 nm or more, often having

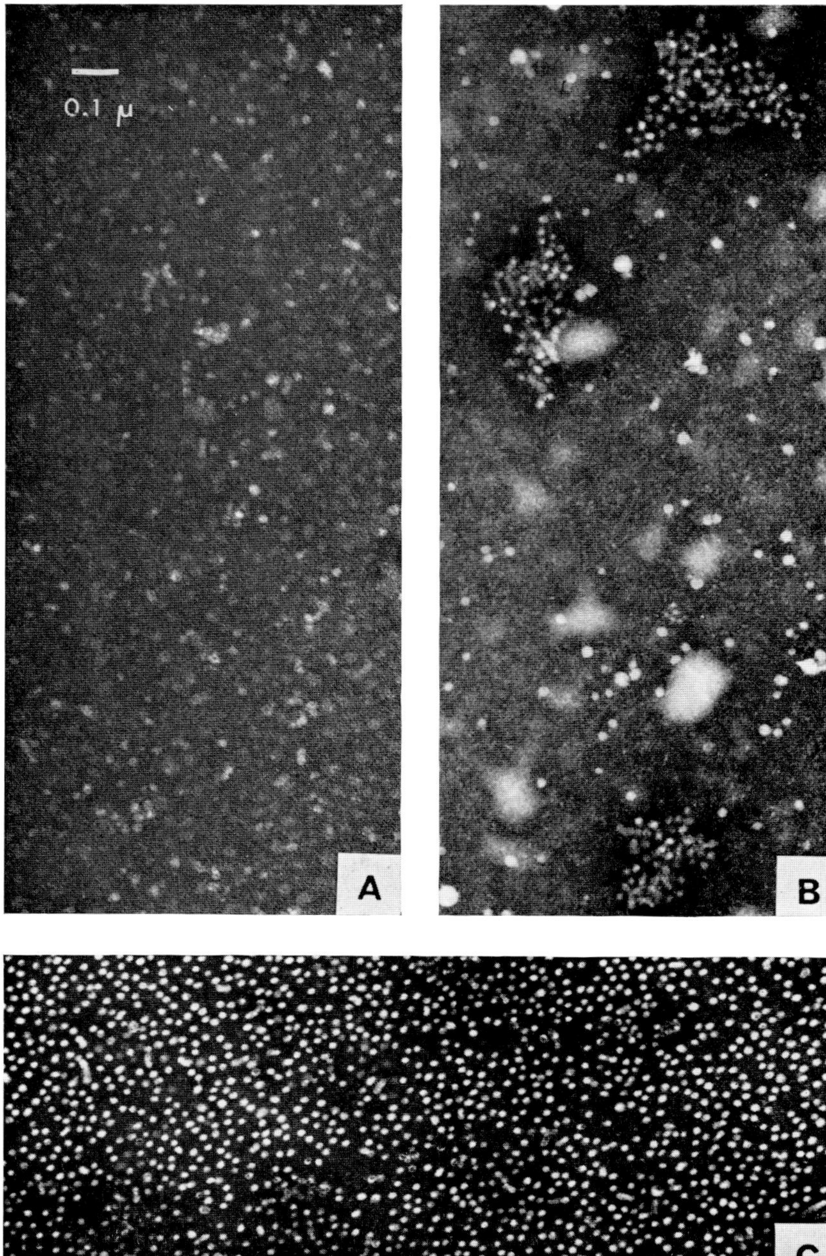

FIG. 3

variably wider rounded swellings, or bulbous formations, at one or both ends, and may exhibit sharply angled and even right-angled bends, as well as a lesser degree of smoother curvature (Bayer *et al.*, 1968; Almeida and Waterson, 1969; Almeida *et al.*, 1969; Zuckerman, 1969).

Barker *et al.* (1969) have studied the size distribution of the particles present in Au+ fractions from CsCl density gradients, both before and after treatment with ether or fluorocarbon (Genetron). The figure from their paper, with modifications, forms the basis of Fig. 5. It shows the larger modal particle diameter (20 nm) and broader spread of particle size in the untreated preparation. After treatment, the particles appeared smaller (modal diameter 16 nm), more sharply outlined and more evenly dispersed; there was a moderate increase in their buoyant density (*vide supra*); and virtually all the tubular forms had disappeared. The Au antigen titer, as measured by complement fixation, was, if anything, somewhat higher after the extraction. Barker *et al.* interpreted their findings to mean that an outer lipid coat ~2 nm thick, and in some cases probably also attached anti-Au antibody (Shulman and Barker, 1969), had been removed by the extraction.

Since treatment with lipid solvents did not appear to modify the antigenic specificity, it would seem that the putative lipid coat does not completely cover the particle surface. A further possibility might be that the bulk of the lipid is present as an interparticulate "cement," and that the larger rounded and ovoid particles are in fact made up of two or more "unit particles" (monads); some, at least, of the elongated forms

---

FIG. 3. Electron micrograph of Au particles from serum of a patient with post-transfusion hepatitis. Magnification: × 62,000. (We are indebted to Dr. Virginia Killby for the electron microscopic studies.) A. Au particles from untreated serum, negatively stained with 2% potassium phosphotungstate, pH 5.9. The serum was centrifuged at 35,000 rpm for 5 hours at 5°C in a Spinco SW 50 rotor, and the pellet resuspended at ~100× concentration in 0.15 *M* NaCl, 0.05 *M* Tris, pH 7.6. Note spherical and ovoid particles of diameter ~20 nm, with a few short tubular forms. The length of the bar is equivalent to 100 nm. B. Au particles agglutinated by anti-Au antibody. The same suspension as that seen in Fig. 3A was mixed with antibody-containing serum from a multitransfused patient, held at 4°C overnight, and examined by negative staining, as described above. Note aggregates of particles, which also include an occasional tubule. C. Au particles, concentrated and partially purified. The serum was fractionated by two sequential equilibrium centrifugations in CsCl density gradients (cf. Gerin *et al.*, 1969). The final Au antigen-containing fractions were diluted with 15 volumes of Tris-NaCl buffer, and the particles sedimented at 39,000 rpm for 4 hours at 5°C in a Spinco SW 50 rotor. The pellet was resuspended in buffer to give a concentration of ~100-fold with respect to the original volume of serum. A droplet of the particle suspension was examined by negative staining. In addition to the characteristic rounded particles, occasional short tubules are seen, as well as "empty" particles into which the stain has penetrated. (We are indebted to Dr. Walter Hierholzer for this preparation.)

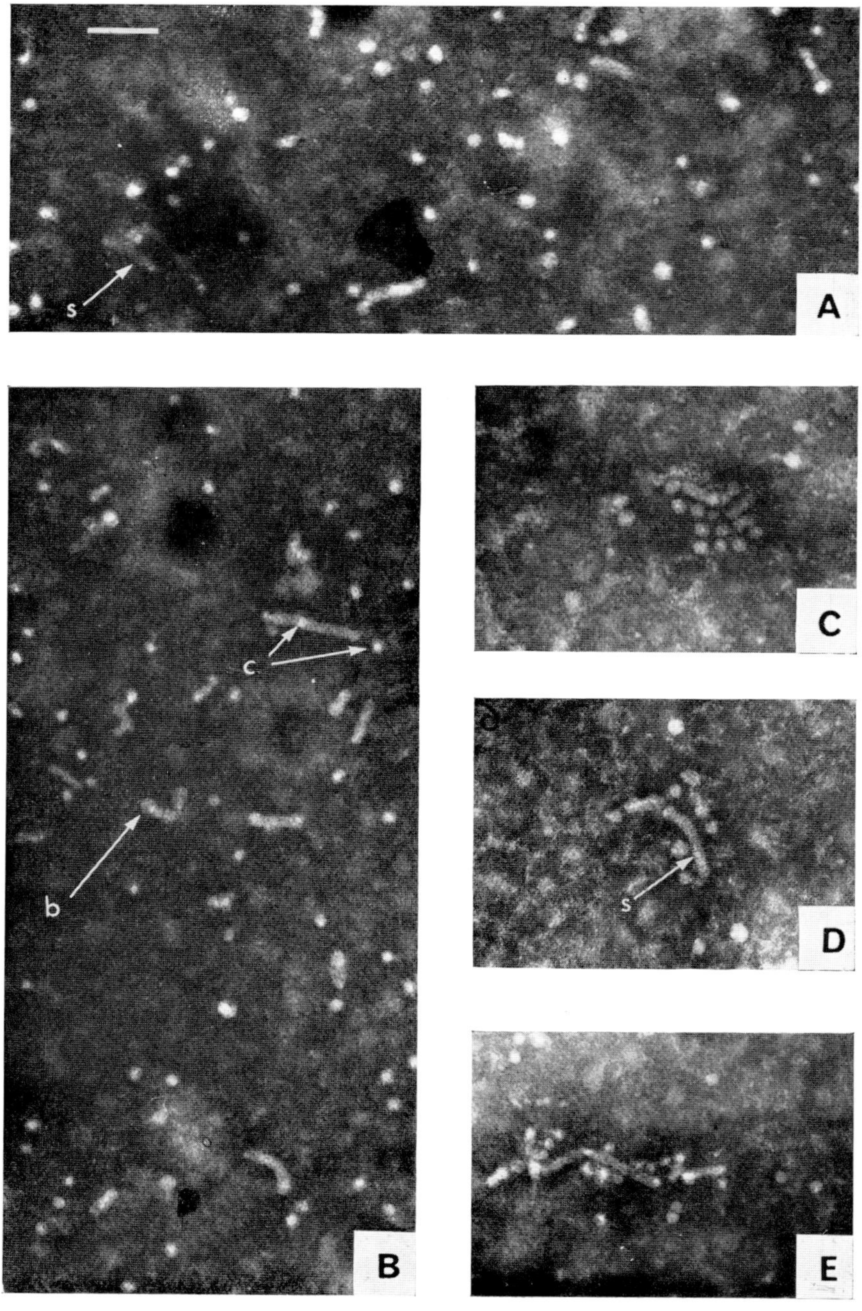

Fig. 4

might consist of strings of such monads, while others would be relatively "empty" lipoprotein sacs, possibly containing terminal and occasional intercalary monads. Based on this hypothesis, the lipid would be dissolved upon exposure to ether or fluorocarbon, and these larger structures—dyads, triads, etc., as well as the tubular pleiads—would be dismembered into their component monads.

A second class of particles has been observed in the serum of Au+ hepatitis patients by Dane *et al.* (1970). Of 16 patients whose serum contained 22-nm particles, 3 also showed lesser numbers of more complex, virus-like particles, ~42 nm in diameter, consisting of an inner body of 28-nm diameter, with a 2-nm shell, and an outer coat ~7 nm thick. The large and small particles formed mixed aggregates when treated with anti-Au sera, suggesting the sharing of a surface antigen, and the possibility that the larger form may be the SH virus, while the smaller particles and tubules may represent surplus virus-coat material. The finding of larger particles in certain Au+ sera has been confirmed by Cossart and Field (1970) and by Gust *et al.* (1970).

E. Biological Properties

The nature and significance of the Australia particles pose the biggest single question, at present, in the microbiology of hepatitis. Their surprisingly "viruslike" appearance has frequently led to the tacit assumption that these are indeed the virions responsible for the infection. The extreme opposite view, suggesting that they solely represent specifically modified, neoantigenic cell fragments produced in response to infection with an as yet undiscerned virus, will be considered later (p. 390). Also to be considered will be the view that the particles, while related to the causal virus, are not for the most part whole virions, but analogous, rather, to the envelopes of the myxoviruses, and composed of unaltered host-cell material as well as of virus-specified or virus-modified molecules, the great majority of these envelopes being

---

FIG. 4. Electron micrographs of Au particles from serum of a patient with chronic anicteric hepatitis. Magnification: × 92,000. (By the courtesy of Dr. Virginia Killby.)

A and B. Au particles from fraction No. 7 of the rate zonal sedimentation experiment illustrated in Fig. 2, part 1, examined by negative staining as indicated for Fig. 3. Note rounded particles ~20 nm in diameter, and tubules which are both more numerous and longer than those seen in Fig. 3, some showing sharp angulations. Note also the appearance of "cores" (c) in some spherical particles, and of cores and "bulbs" (b) in the elongated forms. An occasional tubule shows ill-defined, but apparently regular, transverse "striation" (s). The length of the bar in Fig. 4A is equivalent to 100 nm.

C, D, and E. The same fraction No. 7 mixed with serum containing anti-Au antibody. Note aggregates made up of both rounded and tubular Au particles. The tubule in Fig. 4D shows cross-striation (s).

"incomplete" or "empty," and different in structure, though presumably not markedly in size, from the infective particles (cf. McCollum, 1952; Barker *et al.*, 1970).

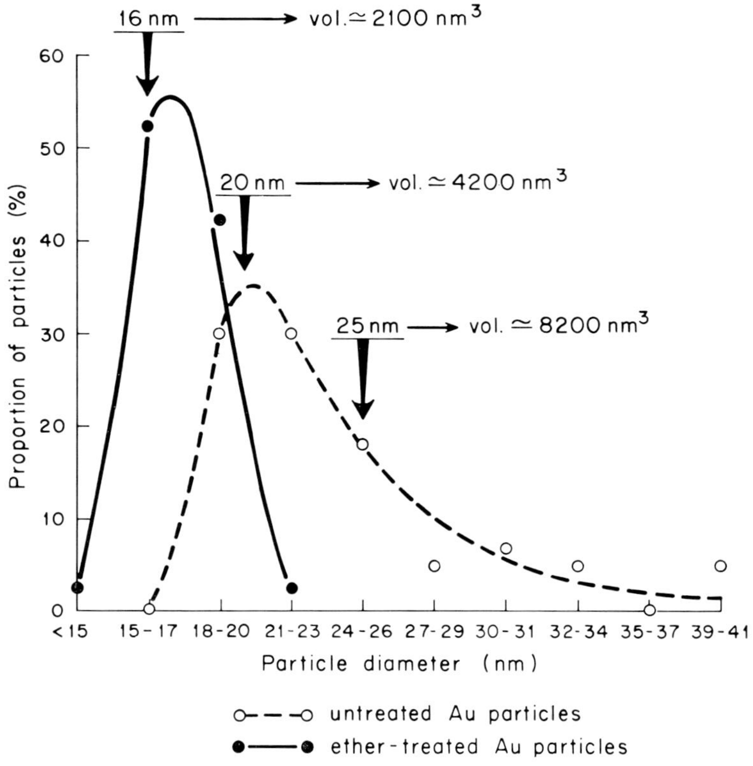

FIG. 5. Effect of ether treatment on the size of partially purified Au-antigenic particles (Barker *et al.*, 1969). Au-positive serum was passed through a Celite filter and fractionated by centrifugation in a CsCl gradient. Au^+ fractions were examined electron microscopically, by negative staining with phosphotungstic acid, before and after exposure to ether (equal parts, 1 hour, 0°C). Volumes are those calculated for *spherical* particles of the given diameters. On this basis, close to 40% of untreated Au particles, with diameters of 25–40 nm, have volumes ranging from 8000 to 34,000 nm^3, *i.e.*, 4 to 16 times the volume of the 16 nm-diameter "monadic" particle. (Figure modified from Barker *et al.*, 1969.)

The Au-antigenic particles must evidently attain impressive concentrations in the serum to be detectable so readily, whether as particles by electron microscopy, or as antigen reactants by immunodiffusion. By comparison with the corresponding concentrations required for poliovirus, one may calculate that individual sera must often contain up to

10^{13} particles—or ~40 μg—per milliliter of serum. There appear to be no published reports, as yet, of particle counts; but one serum examined was found to have ~10^{12} particles/ml (Melnick, 1969).

The tubular forms offer an additional ground for regarding Au-antigenic particles as conceivably related to some sort of "micromyxovirus." The proportion of such forms appears to vary considerably from one individual to another, and likewise within a given individual at different times. Almeida and Waterson (1969) have put forward the suggestion that the tubules represent a more mature form of the infective agent, elaborated particularly in patients with chronic hepatitis, or in asymptomatic persistent carriers; while the spherical, ovoid, and small pleomorphic particles would represent a less well organized form of the agent. The question of the significance of these different structures in different types of patient will be taken up again (p. 390).

The infectivity of particle concentrates *per se* has not been tested directly in human subjects; but previously identified icterogenic sera have been found to contain Au antigen. Inoculation of various primates, and attempts to produce detectable infection of a wide variety of cell and organ cultures, are currently being undertaken in various laboratories, but no findings have yet been published. Both Au antigen and morphologically characteristic particles have been found in occasional individuals of several primate species, including the chimpanzee, the orangutan, and the gibbon (Hirschman *et al.*, 1969). Serial serum specimens obtained, during earlier transmission attempts, from chimpanzees inoculated with materials known to contain Au antigen, have been tested by immunodiffusion. No evidence of circulating Au was detected (McCollum, 1970).

Au antigen has been reported in the liver cells of patients with hepatitis by means of immunofluorescence tests with a fluorescein-labeled IgG fraction from an anti-Au rabbit antiserum (Millman *et al.*, 1969). Liver biopsies from 9 patients were examined: 4 had some form of viral hepatitis, including one chronic anicteric, and all had Au antigen in their serum; the other 5 were controls without liver disease, except for one with hepatoma. The biopsy tissue was minced in culture medium, and drops of the resulting cell suspension were spread on slides, air-dried, and fixed with acetone. Discrete fluorescent granules were seen within or on the nuclei (1–30 per nucleus) of almost every cell in the biopsies from the 4 hepatitis patients; they were absent in the controls. The specificity of the reaction was shown by a blocking test with the unconjugated anti-Au antiserum: subsequent addition of labeled antibody produced no fluorescence. (See also Section V, F.)

Other tissues examined included sternal bone marrow from 14 Au+ Down's syndrome patients, and kidney, jejunum, and mesenteric lymph nodes from the chronic anicteric hepatitis patient referred to above. In none were the fluorescent granules detected.

Recently, Nowosławski *et al.* (1970) reported studies of liver cells obtained at autopsy from 12 patients with lymphoproliferative disorders. Six, whose serum contained Au antigen, all showed specific nuclear and/or cytoplasmic immunofluorescence, and also 20-nm diameter particles, sometimes in chains, within the nuclei. The other six, with Au− serum, showed neither specific immunofluorescence nor intranuclear particles.

V. Serology of Australia Antigen

A. Introduction

The method used for the original detection of Au antigen and antibody in serum, and still perhaps most widely used, is that of two-dimensional double immunodiffusion (ID). Recently, other serological techniques, with different attributes of sensitivity and specificity, have been turned to advantage in this connection, viz., complement fixation (CF), immunofluorescence (IF), reversed passive hemagglutination (RPHA) of antibody-coated red cells, immune electron microscopy (IEM), immunoelectroosmophoresis (IEOP), and radioimmunoassay (RIA).

By virtue of their first identification and characterization, Au antigen and antibody are defined in terms of the precipitating reactants used by Blumberg and his colleagues, to which all subsequent reactants have been referred. In like manner, when doubt or discrepancies arise during the use of other serological procedures, these demand resolution by comparison with the results obtained by ID.

B. Reactants

Antigen reactants have consisted principally of sera, or fractions derived therefrom; but also of cells, either naturally infected or experimentally exposed. Antibody reactants have comprised (*1*) human sera; and (*2*) sera from animals hyperimmunized with whole serum, or fractions, containing Au antigen. Human sera with anti-Au precipitins have come from multiple transfused patients (e.g., with hemophilia or various kinds of anemia), and from patients on hemodialysis because of chronic renal disease. In the course of their periodic transfusions, these patients presumably received repeated, and perhaps rather small, stimuli of Au antigen, with the result that some reacted to it as an immunizing protein rather than as an infecting agent, and responded with antibody instead of antigen formation. Animals used have included rabbits, guinea pigs, and mice.

Rabbits (Melartin and Blumberg, 1966) were given an intramuscular injection of alum-precipitated Au+ serum, followed by a similar injection 2 weeks later, and an intraperitoneal injection after a further 10 days. Serum was collected 7–10 days after the third injection. After a two week rest, the immunization schedule was repeated. The resulting antisera required absorption with Au− human serum to remove antibodies against normal components.

Guinea pigs and rabbits (Purcell *et al.*, 1970) were immunized with Au+ serum fractions separated by two CsCl density gradient centrifugations followed by a rate sedimentation in sucrose. The antigen preparation was emulsified with Freund's complete adjuvant (1:1) and injected into the footpads. Boosting injections of aqueous immunogens were given subcutaneously at 1- to 2-weekly intervals, starting 4–6 weeks after the initial injection. Of the animals that received purified Au fractions, rabbits responded with poor anti-Au antibody formation, and also developed low levels of antibodies against normal serum components; guinea pigs, however, produced good levels of seemingly unispecific anti-Au antibody, with no response to other serum components.

Ascitic fluids have been obtained from immunized mice with or without the aid of ascites tumor cells. Hierholzer (1969), in this laboratory, has injected mice intraperitoneally with Au+ fractions prepared as described for guinea pigs, mixed 1:1 with Freund's complete adjuvant, followed by similar booster injections into the footpads 2, 4, and 6 weeks later. At 6–8 weeks, the mice were given $\sim 10^6$ ascites tumor cells (Sarcoma 180/TG). The ascitic fluid was tapped 1 week after the injection of tumor cells, and thereafter every 2–3 days for ~ 2 weeks, at which time the mice died of the tumor. Moderate levels of anti-Au antibody were detected by CF, and by ID, after the second booster injection. The fluids so far obtained have usually contained low levels of non-Au antibodies and have required absorption with normal human serum.

Millman *et al.* (1970b) produced immune ascitic fluids by the injection of Au+ serum and Freund's complete adjuvant, without tumor cells. The proportions were 3 parts of adjuvant to 1 of serum (later reduced 2:1) in the first intraperitoneal injection, and 1:1 in the second given 6 weeks later. Over half the mice developed ascites 2–4 weeks after the second injection, and the rate of fluid production could be increased by periodic intraperitoneal injection of a saline-adjuvant mixture. To absorb nonspecific antibodies, fluids were mixed with normal human serum, or else were tested in wells from which normal serum had previously been allowed to diffuse into the agar ("in-well absorption"). Of 111 sera judged Au+ with a human antiserum, 84 also reacted with ascitic fluid; besides the 27 sera that were Au+ only with human antiserum, there were 6 others which reacted only with ascitic fluid. Some Au+ sera gave two precipitate bands with several of the mouse fluids, yet only one with human or rabbit antisera. Treatment of the ascitic fluid with 2-mercaptoethanol, as well as exclusion chromatography on Sephadex G-200, indicated that an appreciable part of the mouse antibody was apparently of IgM class. When fluids giving two bands were treated with mercaptoethanol, one of the bands was no longer seen. The suggestion of serological nonidentity between the human and certain of the mouse antibodies is discussed below (p. 385).

C. Immunodiffusion

The two-dimensional double diffusion procedures are based on the method of Ouchterlony (1958). Blumberg and his co-workers have used Oxoid Ionagar, 0.9% (w/v) in 0.07 *M* sodium phosphate, pH 7.4, with incubation of the test at 20°C for up to 1 week. Prince (1968b), to increase the sensitivity of antigen detection, modified the technique by using 1% agarose, made up in 0.1 *M* NaCl buffered with 0.01 *M* tris (pH 7.6 at 25°C), and adding 0.1% protamine sulfate and 0.001 *M* ethylenediaminetetraacetic acid to the gel. Protamine sulfate can cause clouding of the gel and occasional formation of obscuring haloes and opacities, and has accordingly been omitted in some laboratories. In our experience, the single most important factor in improving the detectability of tenuous precipitate bands was the use of a clear agarose in concentrations not exceeding 0.6% (w/v). The exact buffer used appeared to be less critical, except that it was preferable to exclude phosphate: we have used 0.1 *M* NaCl, buffered at pH 7.6 (25°C) with 0.1 *M* tris, and containing 0.1% (w/v) sodium azide as a preservative.

The questions of standardization and measurement, as is not unusual in the virological applications of ID, have scarcely been broached, let alone settled. Blumberg and his colleagues have employed the tube method of Preer and Preer (1959) to quantitate the Au antigen concentrations in their test sera. Unknown sera are tested in parallel against undiluted standard antiserum, and their content of Au antigen is expressed in Preer units, depending on the distance of the precipitate from the antigen-agar interface at a fixed time. For this purpose, the column of agar in the reaction tube is divided into 100 units.

In our laboratory, as a provisional method of assay, the roughly quantitative approach used for the measurement of poliovirus and rubella virus antigens (Le Bouvier, 1959) has been applied to the estimation of Au antigen and antibody. One serum pool containing Au antigen, and one containing anti-Au antibody, were selected as the reference standards. The position of equivalence for the Au system was found to be ~0.4 of the distance from the Au antigen cup to the homologous antibody cup. The positions of the leading edges of precipitates formed by various interacting pairs of antigen and antibody dilutions were measured from photographs, and standard curves were drawn. The highest dilution of the standard antibody reactant still giving a distinct band of precipitate in the equivalence zone, with any dilution of the standard (or any other Au-specific) antigen reactant, was defined as containing 1 "Yale unit" of anti-Au precipitin per μl. The particular dilution of the antigen preparation with which it gave this precipitate was taken to contain 1 "Yale unit" of Au precipitating antigen per μl. Unknown reactants are compared with the standards, and their antigen or antibody content is similarly expressed in Yale units per μl.

The strength of Au precipitating antigen has also been measured by making serial dilutions of the sera under test, and determining, as the titer, the highest dilution which still gives detectable precipitation with an undefined, but relatively high, concentration of the antibody reactant.

Factors which may help to enhance the sensitivity of ID tests include: the utmost possible clarity of the gel; a reasonably close spacing of the cups; the use of larger cups for the sera under test which are suspected of having minimal levels of antigen or antibody; prefilling of cups with the unknown reactants 1–4 hours before disposition of the standard reactants, at which time the test cups are refilled; the use of standard antigen and antibody reactants in approximately equivalent proportions, and at concentrations which are *(1)* adequate to give a clear arc of precipitate whose ends approach the cups containing the unknown reactants, but *(2)* not so strong that weak reactions given by the unknown sera are "forced back" into their cups.

The pattern we have adopted has been the familiar hexagonal arrangement, or a series of "fused hexagons" which becomes, in effect, a middle row of alternating cups of antigen and antibody standards, flanked by two rows of cups containing the unknown reactants.

D. Complement Fixation

The greater sensitivity of CF, as compared with ID, led to its use in the study of the Au system. In most kinds of CF tests, the unknown material is tested with both a specific positive reactant and an appropriate negative control—antigen or antibody, as the case may be. In the Au system, where the antigen being sought is present among a rich assortment of normal serum components, it is necessary to know that the standard antibody reactant will not fix complement with any of these other antigens. Human sera containing anti-Au antibody may not be the safest of reactants for this purpose; for it is clear that many, if not all, such sera from repeatedly stimulated donors may contain a variety of antibodies against different serum components. Animal hyperimmune antisera would seem to be preferable; and ideally, control antiserum should also be prepared against an early Au− serum specimen taken from the same individual who provided the Au+ serum which served, either as such or after fractionation, as the source of immunizing antigen.

The types of CF tests which can be used for the detection and measurement of Au antigen, or antibody, include: (*1*) relatively simple "linear" tests in which dilutions of the unknown serum are tested with an optimal concentration of known anti-Au antibody and a selected dose of complement (cf. Purcell *et al.*, 1969); (*2*) two-dimensional tests of the standardizing "chessboard" type, in which serial dilutions of both antigen and antibody reactant are tested against each other, using a single dose of complement; (*3*) tests of "quantitative CF," in which the unknown serum is tested in dilutions against a single optimal concentration of known serum—either antigen or antibody source, as the case may be—and in which the amounts of complement fixed are determined (cf. Shulman and Barker, 1969); or (*4*) three-dimensional tests in which the concentrations of antigen, antibody, and complement are all varied. From (*3*) or (*4*), curves can be drawn of the total amount of complement fixed by varying combinations of the standard and unknown reactants. For convenience, the strength of an unknown serum so tested may also be given as the highest dilution which fixes a chosen dose of complement, e.g., two 100% hemolytic units, in the presence of optimal standard antigen, or antibody, as the case may be.

Whereas an ID test may be set up so as to detect both antigen and antibody reactivity in each unknown sample, a CF test is of course usually designed to look only for one activity or the other.

While ID tests have the advantage over CF tests of confirming or refuting *ab initio* the Au identity of any antigen or antibody detected in an unknown serum, they are inherently less sensitive, the disparity in sensitivity increasing with the size of the reacting particle which must diffuse into the gel in the ID test. In the comparative study of Purcell *et al.* (1969), the linear CF test employed was about 24 times more sensitive than ID in detecting Au antigen, but no more than 4 times more sensitive in detecting antibody. They used a modified Prince (1968a) method of ID, in which protamine sulfate was omitted from the gel. In Shulman and Barker's (1969) comparison, their complement consumption test was 200–300 times better than their ID procedure for the detection of Au antigen, a quite remarkable degree of superiority. In our own series (Hierholzer and Le Bouvier, 1969), which employed a linear CF test with two 100% units of complement, the difference was ~16 times in favor of CF for detecting Au antigen; but there was at most only a 2 times difference in the ability to detect anti-Au antibody, and sometimes the ID method appeared to be slightly (~2 times) more sensitive than CF for this purpose.

Perhaps the greatest success of CF in the serological study of SH infection has been the identification, by Shulman and Barker (1969), of a transient phase in the later part of the incubation period, in most cases, during which the patient's serum becomes anticomplementary (AC). This AC activity rises to a peak from 4 to 6 weeks after infection, and then declines, at the same time as free Au antigen is first becoming detectable in the serum. In some cases, a second AC phase is seen after free Au antigen ceases to be detectable in the serum; and sometimes anticomplementariness is the only serological anomaly observed. It was suspected that this apparent AC effect might in fact be due to actual fixation of complement resulting from the simultaneous presence of circulating antigen and antibody, and the formation of immune complexes. This was confirmed by the finding that addition of further known Au antigen, or antibody, to the serum in question produced a situation of antigen or antibody excess, with a consequent prozone of diminished CF. The Au-specific character of the AC activity was further shown by fractionating such sera on CsCl gradients and finding Au particles apparently coated with antibody in the AC fractions. Treatment of these fractions with fluorocarbon, which dissociates virus-antibody complexes, reduced or eliminated their AC activity, and often doubled their Au-antigenic activity detectable by the addition of known antibody.

It is evident that CF is a good and sensitive means of looking for Au antigen, especially in experimental systems in which known antigen and antibody reactants are being manipulated, and the consequences assessed. For the detection of weakly antigen-positive sera it also comes into its own; but here there may be occasional situations in which the unispecificity of the reaction may need to be corroborated by ID, and perhaps by further CF cross-testing after absorption of the standard antiserum with the standard and the unknown antigen reactants.

E. Immune Electron Microscopy

The presence of Au antigen-antibody complexes in the serum of patients with hepatitis has also been demonstrated electron microscopically by Almeida and Waterson (1969), using the technique of negative staining with phosphotungstic acid (*vide supra*, p. 369). They described their findings in 3 different types of individual: (*1*) a chronic, asymptomatic carrier of Au antigen, in whose serum randomly distributed spherical and tubular particles were seen, with no sign of aggregation and no evidence of antibody molecules attached to the particles; (*2*) a patient with "chronic active hepatitis," who possessed many pleomorphic and tubular, as well as spherical, forms, and in whom both single particles and aggregates were present, some of them apparently comprising several hundreds of particles; (*3*) a fatal case of acute hepatitis, whose serum contained very few elongated forms, but many characteristic spherical particles, all coated with large amounts of antibody and forming numerous aggregates, some of quite small size.

The symptomless carrier exhibits the condition of persistent, apparently tolerant, carriage of Au particles, without any production of anti-Au antibody. The chronic active hepatitis case evidently possesses Au antigen in excess, but has succeeded in elaborating a minute amount of antibody. In the fulminating case, it is apparently the anti-Au antibody that is present in excess.

The authors discuss the possible significance of these diverse relative proportions of Au antigen and antibody in these dissimilar types of case. They suggest an analogy between acute SH and serum sickness, which has been shown to be caused by immune complexes present in the circulation (Dixon, 1963), and in which an excess of antibody may lead to an anaphylactic reaction, though failing to remove all circulating antigen. In the chronic case, the large immune complexes are seen as capable of initiating degenerative changes in the liver (and other organs too, perhaps?); while in the persistent carrier, a state of symbiosis and mutual forbearance seems to have been achieved, with neither any obvious reaction against the Au antigen, nor any detectable pathology in the host. These findings will be considered further in the concluding discussion.

F. Immunofluorescence

The use of IF by Millman *et al.* (1969) for the identification of Au antigen in liver biopsy cells from cases of hepatitis has been mentioned above (p. 373). A second paper by the same authors (Coyne *et al.*, 1970) extends and substantiates their earlier findings. They studied 61 patients with a variety of diseases, including 33 in whom there was evidence of viral hepatitis: of these, 24 had Au antigen in the serum; these 24, and a further 6, showed a positive IF reaction for Au antigen in their biopsied liver cells. Of the remaining 28 patients, only 2 had Au antigen in the serum—an inmate of a mental institution and a patient with chronic renal disease who had received many blood transfusions. These, and an additional 7 patients, had IF+ liver biopsies: the diagnoses included postnecrotic and biliary cirrhosis, biliary atresia, ? bile duct carcinoma, and hepatic metastasis of a renal carcinoma. The cell smears were prepared by mincing the liver specimens and spreading drops of the resulting suspension on slides, and fixing with acetone. They were stained directly with a fluorescein-labeled rabbit antiserum. Positive IF reactions took 3 forms: discrete particles within the nucleus; diffuse fluorescence of the whole nucleus; and fluorescence of the nuclear rim. Occasionally, particles of fluorescent antigen were also seen in the cytoplasm. Of various other tissues examined, the only positive findings were of a few cells in the bone marrow of 2 hepatitis patients, and of antigen in the liver, spleen, mesentery, and testis of a patient with chronic hepatitis who died of acute myeloid leukemia. Cells of other origin, including buffy coat cells and cells from peripheral lymphocyte cultures, were uniformly negative for Au antigen by IF.

The IF technique would be of particular value in observing the exposure of cells in culture to Au antigen, and following the subsequent events, including the potential synthesis of new Au antigen. Several workers have been attempting such studies, but definitive results are still awaited.

An ingenious IF slide test for Au antigen has been devised by Purcell (1970). Large drops of the blood (or serum) to be tested are spread in a film on glass slides, allowed to dry, fixed with acetone for 10 minutes at room temperature, and air-dried. Uninactivated guinea pig sera, with and without anti-Au antibody, are spread over part of the film, allowed to stand in contact for 30 minutes at 37°C, and then removed. The slides are then washed several times with phosphate-buffered saline (PBS), pH 7.4, exposed to fluorescein-labeled horse anti-guinea pig globulin, washed again, and examined with a low-power objective. Specimens containing Au antigen fluoresce with varying intensity, showing numerous bright points of light in the serum phase; the intact formed elements of the blood show no staining. The Au antigen content of sera can be roughly quantitated by testing drops of serial dilutions in the same way.

G. Reversed Passive Hemagglutination

Juji and Yokochi (1969) have made Au antigen-antibody precipitates, then washed and treated them with 3 *M* NaI to dissociate the anti-Au antibody, which they finally separated and recovered by exclusion chromatography on Sephadex G-200 equilibrated with 3 *M* NaI. After dialysis against PBS, the antibody was used to coat human group O, Rh-positive red cells which had been prepared by treatment with formalin and tannic acid. Control red cells were coated with normal human γ-globulin. For use as detectors of Au antigen, the antibody-coated red cells were suspended at 0.5% concentration in PBS, pH 7.2, containing 1% normal rabbit serum.

HA tests, done by the microtiter method, were considered to be more sensitive than ID for detecting Au antigen. Fifty-four assorted sera which were Au+, and 57 viral hepatitis sera which were Au−, by ID were tested by RPHA against both control and anti-Au-coated red cells. Four of the 54 Au+ sera agglutinated the control red cells as readily as the test cells, or more so. With the other 50 Au+ sera, the HA titer against antibody-coated cells was at least 16 times higher. On the other hand, 6 of the 57 Au− hepatitis sera had hemagglutinating titers against the antibody-coated cells which were considered significantly higher ($\geqslant 8$ times) than their titers against the control cells.

The method has not yet been tried for the detection of antibody, with the help of cells coated with Au particles or some solubilized fraction thereof. Unfortunately, the antibody-coated erythrocytes have so far proved unstable, and become denatured within a few weeks at 4°C. In theory, this could represent a sensitive and relatively simple way of detecting either antigen or antibody; and perhaps some modification of procedure, e.g., substituting activated Sepharose or another suitable immunoadsorbent vehicle, might provide a more stable test suspension.

H. Immunoelectroosmophoresis

The technique of IEOP has been introduced (Prince, 1970; Prince and Burke, 1970; Merrill *et al.*, 1970) in an attempt to increase both the speed and sensitivity of screening potential blood donors for the presence of Au antigen. It involves the forced diffusion of the sera under test into a gel in which the antibody reactant has either been incorporated, or else placed in multiple cups or troughs. The method is therefore as much as 10 times more expensive in standard antiserum than the usual immunodiffusion procedures. However, it can apparently detect ~3 times as many Au+ donors as ID, i.e., up to 4 in every 100 commercial donors, which is estimated to be about 90% of the probable carriers of SH agent in this group (Prince and Burke, 1970). The technique is critically dependent on a number of factors, including temperature, pH, type of buffer, ionic strength, and voltage. But if these can be reliably standardized and controlled, and the tendency to nonspecific precipitation minimized, it may prove to be the method of choice for donor screening, especially since the results are available within a few hours.

I. Radioimmunoassay

In the quest for a method more sensitive than CF in its ability to detect Au antigen, especially in the serum of prospective blood donors, workers from two laboratories (Walsh *et al.*, 1970; Coller and Millman, 1970) recently reported the successful application of the radioimmunoassay procedures which have already proved useful in the measurement of hormones. These entail the preparation of purified Au antigen, and its radioactive labeling with ^{125}I. The purification of Au antigen from serum was effected by either (*1*) two equilibrium centrifugations in CsCl, followed by a rate separation in sucrose (Gerin *et al.*, 1969), or (*2*) enzymatic treatment of Au particles concentrated by spinning, followed by gel filtration on Sephadex G-200, velocity sedimentation in a sucrose gradient, and centrifugation to equilibrium in CsCl (Millman *et al.*, 1970a). After the labeling with radioiodine, Walsh *et al.* refractionated the conjugated Au particles on a Sephadex G-200 column, determining the peaks of radioactivity and immunoreactivity by radioimmunodiffusion. They found that most of the ^{125}I was present in the albumin and iodide fractions, but that all the *immunoreactivity* (together with $\not> 5\%$ of the original label) emerged in the void volume.

In the preliminary standardization, mixtures containing constant amounts of radioiodinated Au antigen (^{125}I-Au) and standard anti-Au antibody reactant are combined with varying amounts of a selected unlabeled Au-positive serum. The effect of the different concentrations of unlabeled antigen in blocking immune aggregation of the ^{125}I-Au is measured by determining the distribution of radioactive counts between precipitate and supernatant, after these have been separated, e.g., by sedimentation, or by chromatoelectrophoresis (Berson *et al.*, 1956). Walsh *et al.* (1970) used an Au+ serum designated "JM," and assigned it a potency of 10^6 "JM units" of antigen per milliliter. They derived a standard curve by plotting the ratio, B/F, of antibody-bound ^{125}I-Au (B) to free ^{125}I-Au (F) as a function of the concentration of standard Au antigen "JM." This showed a marked change in B/F (from 0.5 to 0.25) over the range of Au antigen concentrations from 0 to 50 JM units/ml; then a reduction in B/F from 0.25 to 0.1 corresponding with the increase in Au from 50 to 200 JM units/ml; and above this antigen concentration, only a gradual decline in the value of B/F. It is evident, therefore, that the method is particularly sensitive in measuring differences in the Au antigen content of unknown specimens when the antigen is present in concentrations equivalent to those in 1/10,000 to 1/100,000 dilutions of the standard JM serum. The titer of this serum by CF was 1/1024, indicating that the radioimmunoassay method is some 10–100 times more sensitive for the detection of antigen than the CF technique used.

Walsh *et al.* separated the antigen-antibody complexes by chromatoelectrophoresis (Berson *et al.*, 1956). To separate all bound ^{125}I-Au, including soluble immune complexes, Coller and Millman (1970) precipitated the antibody with a rabbit antiserum against human IgG, and measured the amount of radioactive antigen in the precipitate. In this way, sera with CF titers of $\leqslant 1/32$ were found to have radioimmunoprecipitation equivalence titers of 1/5000 to 1/20,000; and antibody could still be detected at a serum dilution of 1/320,000.

Both groups of workers have shown that the method of RIA can thus measure Au antigen and anti-Au antibody in concentrations not detectable by CF, let alone ID. It can also show the concurrent presence of antigen and antibody in a given serum; in such cases, some binding of the ^{125}I-Au is observed in the control without added anti-Au (Walsh *et al.*, 1970). The method appears to hold great promise as the most sensitive means so far available for the detection and quantitation of exiguous amounts of Au antigen and its antibody.

J. *The Question of Multiple Antigenic Specificities Related to Australia Particles*

In view of the moderately complex nature of the Au particles, it would hardly be surprising if they were found to carry other antigenic determinant sites, in addition to the seemingly single one that has so far been firmly established. They could be present on the particle surface ("epitopes"), or "masked" and waiting to be revealed by suitable treatment ("hypotopes"). In addition, the polypeptides resulting from particle, and protein, disruption, e.g., by sodium dodecyl sulphate and 2-mercaptoethanol treatment, may be expected to have their own antigenic individualities ("cryptotopes"), when appropriate hyperimmune sera have been prepared against them.

The first findings suggestive of multiple antigenic specificities were obtained by Levene and Blumberg (1969). They hyperimmunized rabbits with 2 different antigen preparations: (*1*) an Au+ serum—containing "Au(1)"—from a patient with leukemia; and (*2*) serum from a patient with leukemic reticuloendotheliosis, which had given an "unusual and inconsistent reaction" with the aforementioned anti-Au(1) antiserum. The antiserum prepared against this second human serum was called anti-Au(2). By testing various combinations of antigen-containing sera with these two antibody reactants, the authors concluded that at least 3 distinct epitopes were involved, which they designated *a, b,* and *c.* The anti-Au(1) serum identified *a* and *c;* the anti-Au(2), *a* and *b.* They proceeded to test sera from different populations with these two antisera and obtained markedly divergent results, as shown in accompanying Table II.

If the two rabbit antisera were being used at dilutions selected to give roughly comparable concentrations of the unshared antibody specificities anti-*b* and anti-*c*, then antigenic specificity *b* is present and expressed in serum far more frequently than specificity *c*. However, reactions of specificity *a* would blur the picture. The authors did not absorb their antisera to try to obtain unispecific anti-*b* and anti-*c* reactants. Nor was it determined whether epitope *b*, or *c*, as the case may be, is present together with epitope *a* on the same particle, or whether at least two populations of particles are involved.

Millman *et al.* (1970b) have provided further information concerning the antigenic complexity of the Au particles, as reflected in the antibodies elicited in hyperimmunized animals. It was found that the previously described anti-Au(2) activity (Levene and Blumberg, 1969)

TABLE II
FREQUENCY OF AUSTRALIA ANTIGEN REACTING WITH ANTI-Au(1) AND ANTI-Au(2) RABBIT ANTISERUM IN DIFFERENT GROUPS[a]

Population	Total number	Percentage	
		Au (1)	Au (2)
Blood donors	293	0	7.2
Staff of institution for mentally retarded	114	0	52.6
Down's syndrome	209	31.6	74.2
Acute viral hepatitis	58	17.2	70.7
Thalassemia (transfused)	128	7.0	96.9

[a] All groups comprise individuals from the area of Philadelphia. Some of the thalassemic patients are from New York City and Northern Italy. Table modified from Levene and Blumberg (1969).

decreased with time on storage in the frozen state, disappeared after the immunized rabbits were reinjected with Au antigen, and, moreover, could not be found in the IgG fraction eluted from DEAE-Sephadex. However, it was apparently not demonstrated directly in the IgM fraction at this point. Ascitic fluids from immunized mice (see above, p. 375) generally showed reactions of identity with human and rabbit antisera, and were found to react with 84 of 111 sera (76%) that gave a positive Au reaction with a human antiserum. Six sera were found which reacted with mouse ascitic fluid, but not with human antiserum. By chromatography on DEAE-Sephadex, and gel filtration on Sephadex G-200, anti-Au activity was demonstrable in the apparent IgM as well as the IgG fractions.

Several such fluids formed two bands of precipitate with certain Au+ human sera, although these same sera gave only one band with other antibody reactants. The two antigens concerned both migrated as α_2-globulins. The two antibodies were not removed from one such ascitic fluid by absorption with normal human serum. Treatment of this fluid with mercaptoethanol eliminated one antibody, but not the other. These data are interpreted as additional evidence for multiple specificities among the populations of antibodies reacting with Au particles. However, the separate identity of the antigens has not yet been shown by absorption tests or possible physical fractionation.

A further possible indication of antigenic complexity was found by Millman *et al.* (1970a) in suspensions of Au particles purified by enzyme digestion, gel filtration, and zonal and isopycnic centrifugation. After treatment with ether or chloroform for 1 hour at room temperature, such a suspension gave two precipitate bands with a human and a rabbit anti-Au(1) antiserum, with which it had previously only given one. One of the two bands appeared to be common to both the ether- and the chloroform-treated Au particle concentrate; but the other bands, in each case, were distinct and crossed in a reaction of nonidentity.

Experiments in progress in this laboratory (Le Bouvier, 1969) likewise point to a "dissecting" action by trypsin on Au antigen. Exposure of Au+ serum to 2.5% (w/v) trypsin for 1–2 hours at 37°C caused the progressive degradation of a sensitive component (S), leaving a relatively trypsin-resistant component (R), which reacted with certain human anti-Au sera, but not with a rabbit or a mouse anti-Au(1) antiserum (kindly supplied by Dr. B. S. Blumberg), nor with a guinea pig antiserum (generously provided by Dr. R. H. Purcell). The S component would therefore appear to be Au antigen of generally recognized specificity; while the precise nature and relationship of the R component remain to be established.

VI. Immunology of "Australia-Positive" Hepatitis

A. Introduction

Blumberg and co-workers observed the presence of Au antigen in the serum of patients with hepatitis of presumed viral origin (Blumberg *et al.*, 1967a); and Prince (1968a), and subsequently other workers (see above, Section III), demonstrated the appearance of this antigen late in the incubation period of SH, as distinct from IH, its transient presence in most cases, and its apparently tolerated persistence in some. The following section deals with the problem of the immunological responses elicited by the agent of SH which is responsible for the appearance of Au antigen in the serum. Why is there no consistent and lasting production of high levels of antibody? What is the significance of the "immune complexes" detected in the acute phase, and again in later stages of the disease? And is there any evidence concerning the stimulation of cell-mediated immunity, and its relationship to the course of the infection?

B. Antibody Responses

The antibody response to Au antigen depends upon the method of stimulation and presumably on the dosage of antigen. In repeatedly transfused patients, relatively small amounts of Au antigen (together with subinfectious concentrations of the active SH agent) are administered at intervals, and result in immunization of the recipient with what is, in effect, an inert lipoprotein antigen preparation. The result is not the usual process of infection with production of Au antigen, but instead the elaboration of anti-Au antibody. In 11 of 12 sera examined (Shulman and Barker, 1969), the antibody resembled IgG in size; while in one serum, half of it was of molecular weight >200,000. Conceivably at an early stage of immunization IgM antibody may have been made in every case.

In patients undergoing SH-agent infection, it appears that anti-Au antibody may be—and perhaps regularly is—made in the middle of the incubation period, when it is generally not detectable in free form, but only complexed with antigen so as to produce a specific "anticomplementariness" of the patient's serum (*vide supra*). Shulman and Barker (1969) found this anticomplementary (AC) activity to be usually transient, and to precede the appearance of free Au antigen in the serum, though it could also coexist with, appear after, or occur without detectable free Au antigen. Purcell *et al.* (1969) reported AC activity in 4 of 32 hepatitis patients, which was temporally related to the disease, and declined without being replaced by free Au; while in one patient both AC activity and free Au antigen developed concurrently. Au antigen-antibody complexes would, of course, not be detectable by ID, unless dissociated before testing, as was shown by Millman *et al.* (1970c) (*vide infra*: Section VI,C); but such complexes have been seen in the electron microscope in a case of acute hepatitis (Almeida and Waterson, 1969). In 3 of 22 cases, during the month after their Au antigen declined and disappeared, free anti-Au CF antibody was ephemerally detectable (Shulman and Barker, 1969). In at least one patient, two such "cycles" of free antigen and free antibody succeeded one another over a period of a few weeks (Krugman and Giles, 1970). In general, however, free anti-Au antibody is not evident in SH infections, but only in the hyperimmunized recipients of Au+ blood transfusions. In two recipients of large amounts of blood (17 and 24 units, respectively), in whom no antibody was initially detected, a sharp rise in anti-Au CF antibody took place within 1–2 weeks of transfusion, suggesting a previous subliminal sensitization with Au antigen and a secondary antibody response on restimulation (Holland *et al.*, 1969).

Patients with chronic active hepatitis (CAH) often possess an antibody reacting with smooth muscle (SMA). In view of the differing observations on the presence of Au antigen in CAH, Wright (1970) has looked for Au antigen and SMA in sera from patients with CAH of insidious onset, as well as from patients with acute and prolonged viral hepatitis, and with subacute hepatic necrosis (SHN) which had progressed to cirrhosis. SMA was found in 19 of 78 patients with acute viral hepatitis, both early and late in the disease, and just as often in Au-positive as in Au-negative cases; but it was only present at low titer in 2 of 13 patients with prolonged classic viral hepatitis, 6 of whom possessed Au antigen. In the patients with SHN or CAH, Au antigen and SMA occurred together only in one case of SHN. Among the other 14 SHN patients, Au antigen was present in 3, and SMA in 8; while in the 23 patients with CAH, Au antigen was found in 6 and SMA in 10. There was no evidence that SMA behaves in any way as an antibody against Au antigen. These findings are taken to suggest that there may be at least two etiologically distinct forms of CAH, or that the disease, after being initiated by the SH agent (with production of Au antigen), may be perpetuated by some other mechanism such as an autoimmune process.

C. Formation of Immune Complexes

The presence of circulating Au particle-antibody aggregates in acute viral hepatitis has been mentioned (see above, Section V,E). In the fulminating case described by Almeida and Waterson (1969), the aggregates were comparatively small (e.g. <100 particles, and often <10), and all particles, including unaggregated ones, were seen to be coated with an ample supply of IgG antibody molecules. Here, therefore, the situation appeared to be one of antibody excess. These authors also reported the EM findings on the serum of 2 other cases: a patient with "chronic active hepatitis," with minor recurrent symptoms and raised, fluctuating transaminase levels; and an asymptomatic individual manifesting a persistent, and apparently tolerated, infection with SH agent, resulting in the continuing presence of high levels of Au antigen in the serum. In the former case, some antibody was continuing to be made, and caused the formation of large aggregates of spherical and tubular Au particles, together with some free particles not coated with antibody: the picture was one of antigen excess. In the persistent carrier, the Au particles were all free, uniformly dispersed, and without any evidence of attached antibody.

Millman *et al.* (1970c) demonstrated the presence of Au antigen-antibody complexes in the serum of two individuals: in one, a case of acute viral hepatitis, only antigen could be detected by ID; in the other, a mentally retarded patient, only antibody. Antibody was separable from "low affinity" complexes by centrifugation, and from "high affinity" complexes by treatment with a series of proteolytic and other enzymes. The suggestion is that Au complexes may be present, at some stage, in all individuals in whom free antigen or antibody is detectable.

D. Cell-Mediated Allergic Responses

The question of cellular immunity in relation to Au antigen has so far received little attention. In earlier studies, Mella and Lang (1967) reported an anergic response to phytohemagglutinin (PHA) in cultured peripheral lymphocytes from each of 12 cases of "acute infectious hepatitis;" it was not stated whether these included any examples of SH. Before the onset of the disease, 8–20% of cells were undergoing mitosis. At the height of the illness, the proportion had fallen to 0–0.5%. It rose again during convalescence to 13–20%, by which time various chromosomal anomalies had developed, including stickiness, multiple breaks, deletions, and additions.

Willems *et al.* (1969) tested the response to PHA of leukocytes from 15 patients with viral hepatitis, both IH and SH. In 8, there was a significant depression of DNA synthesis, as judged by thymidine-^{3}H uptake, in the cells after 3 days in culture in medium containing fetal calf serum; but after 6 days' incubation, there was no difference from the controls. The early hyporesponsiveness was unaltered when sera of healthy donors or hepatitis patients were added to the cultures, suggesting that it was inherent in the cells. It was seen in all samples taken within the first week after onset of jaundice, in both IH and SH cases. There was no correlation, in SH, between the detectability of Au antigen in the serum and the lack of lymphoblastic response to PHA after 3 days in culture. Acute phase sera from two IH and two SH patients inhibited the PHA response of normal leukocyte cultures slightly more than did sera of healthy donors; but this effect could not be serially transmitted to fresh cultures. Recently, Agarwal *et al.* (1970) have also confirmed the diminished response of cultured leukocytes to PHA, measured by reduction of DNA polymerase induction and of thymidine-^{3}H incorporation into DNA, in 7 patients with viral hepatitis of unspecified type.

It seems probable, therefore, that early in SH there does regularly develop a depression of the cell-mediated allergic response; and it remains to be seen if a similar, but persistent, anergy can be demonstrated in those individuals who go on to become chronic carriers of Au antigen.

No comprehensive comparisons appear to have been made, as yet, to determine the occurrence of an Au-specific, as distinct from a more general, anergy in the different kinds and phases of SH-agent infection. (This topic is discussed in Section VII: see below, p. 393). Although Au particles do not *seem* to act as potent stimulators of humoral immunity, it must be remembered that the enormous concentrations of available circulating antigen (estimated at up to 4–40 μg/ml of serum) would be adequate to sequestrate large amounts of antibody. In those cases in which immune aggregates are visible, and in which the concentration of circulating antigen falls relatively soon, it is quite probable that an active cellular allergy has also been elicited. In at least a proportion of the chronic particle carriers, on the other hand, it would appear that the formation of anti-Au antibody has been suppressed, and a state of tolerance induced. Since it is more usual, in states of "split tolerance," to find continued antibody synthesis in the absence of cell-mediated reactivity, it seems likely that in persistent possessors of Au antigen the cellular allergic response is likewise suppressed, and that a situation obtains which is analogous to that of mice persistently and tolerantly infected with lymphocytic choriomeningitis virus (cf. Volkert and Larsen, 1965).

VII. Conclusions and Speculations

There can no longer be any serious doubt that the synthesis of Au antigen, and its appearance in the serum, is specifically associated with infection by the causal agent of the SH type of viral hepatitis. The precise relationship of the Au-antigenic particles to the infectious agent is still not settled. There appear to be 4 main possibilities: (*1*) the smallest units, or "monads" (see above), i.e., those of ~16 nm modal diameter, may represent the virus particles, of which presumably only a minority would possess a full complement of nucleic acid, have a relatively high density, and be infective, while the elongated forms would in fact be aberrant, analogous to those seen, for example, among the papovaviruses; (*2*) most of the particles would represent incomplete virions, or even fragments of a viral envelope similar to that of the myxo- or herpesviruses, and the infectious unit would consist of a rare, relatively dense, "complete" particle containing a nucleocapsid within the membranous envelope; (*3*) the infectious entity may not be an "orthodox" type of virion at all, but rather some other kind of self-replicating macromolecule, e.g., a unit of lipoprotein membrane with associated carbohydrate residues, but devoid of essential nucleic acid, as in one of the forms that have been suggested for the agent of scrapie (Gibbons and Hunter, 1967); (*4*) the Au-antigenic particles may bear no structural relationship whatever to the SH infectious agent, but may be new or modified cellular components whose synthesis is specified by, or specifically derepressed by, the infecting virus.

At the present time, it is not possible to choose between these different hypotheses. The answers to a variety of questions, some of them hereafter adumbrated, will affect the balance of favor between them. Can a small proportion of particles be found, which do contain significant amounts of ribonucleic and/or deoxyribonucleic acid? If so, is infectivity associated with this fraction rather than with the less dense fractions which comprise the bulk of the Au+ particles? Do various forms of treatment, e.g., heat, ultraviolet irradiation, enzyme digestion, extraction with lipid solvents, exposure to sulfhydryl reagents or periodate, leave such infectivity essentially undiminished? Or is there a significant reduction in titer? Can infectivity (and antigenic reactivity) still be demonstrated in any subparticulate fractions? Can macromolecules of normal liver, or other, cells be detected in the particles possessing Au antigenic reactivity?

What is the significance of the relatively large particles reported by Dane *et al.* (1970) and by others (see above, Section IV, D)? Apart from these, and the usual, smaller Au-antigenic particles, are any other morphological entities discernible in sera from SH patients, e.g., comparable with the coronavirus-like particles that have been seen in the serum of certain cases of Au− chronic active hepatitis (Zuckerman *et al.*, 1970), and also in sera from healthy individuals (Deinhardt *et al.*, 1970)?

Clearly, the essential prerequisite for studies of this kind is a relatively simple and reproducible test of infectivity, either *in vivo* or *in vitro*. It is to be hoped that cultural manipulations of cells from different biopsied tissues, including co-cultivation, and perhaps imposed fusion, with diverse indicator cells and organ explants, and possibly also maintenance as heterotransplants, may permit the Au synthetic activity of the infectious agent to be expressed and recognized. And indeed, as Bang (1969) asks, when commenting on the hypothesis that persistent carriage of Au antigen is genetically determined (Blumberg *et al.*, 1969), is there in man, as in the mouse, a specific *cellular* basis for an inherited resistance or susceptibility to infection—and disease—caused by the hepatitis viruses?

Concerning the pathogenesis of SH, attention has been drawn to the possible role of circulating antigen-antibody aggregates (Almeida and

Waterson, 1969), since these were evident in both the acute and chronic disease, but were not seen in the asymptomatic persistent carrier of Au antigen. If the Au particles are being produced by hepatic, and perhaps also by lymphoreticular cells, the immune complexes might be expected to pass into the pulmonary capillaries and, if not there retained, into the systemic circulation, lodging in peripheral capillaries, e.g., in skin, central nervous system, and especially the renal glomeruli. There appear to be no reports, as yet, of lesions related to possible capillary trapping of aggregates, or of the presence of Au antigen or antibody in such situations, in cases of chronic hepatitis, whether in the active, aggressive type, or in the later stages of the relatively benign, persistent form. But such pathology might well be looked for, following the model of mice persistently infected with LCM virus, where the continuing, or slowly developing, production of antibody results in the formation of virus-antibody complexes and a consequent "late disease" of chronic glomerulonephritis (Hotchin and Collins, 1964; Oldstone and Dixon, 1969).

Probably even more important than circulating antibody as a potential pathogenetic factor in viral hepatitis is the cell-mediated allergic response. It seems clear that in the persistent possessor of serum Au antigen, there must be a rather firmly founded state of tolerance, involving not only the antibody synthetic mechanism, but also presumably the cellular immune mechanisms responsible for delayed-type hypersensitivity and the rejection of antigenically foreign or altered cells. Since it is precisely these chronic carriers of large concentrations of Au particles, lacking any detectable allergic response, who remain free from overt disease, suspicion is directed toward such responses as probable essential participants in the varying degrees of hepatic cell destruction that lead to elevation of serum transaminases, symptoms and signs of anicteric hepatitis, or the full-blown icteric disease.

The following model is therefore put forward to explain the differing manifestations of infection caused by the Au antigen-inducing agent of SH. Around the middle of the incubation period (e.g., some 3–7 weeks after inoculation), the infected cells, in the liver and perhaps elsewhere, begin to synthesize new macromolecules with Au antigenic specificity which are either the virion itself, or virus-associated lipoprotein particles, or antigenically altered cell-membrane fragments. These are released into the circulation, to some extent by disintegration of the more susceptible or heavily infected cells, but principally by shedding or budding from cells which otherwise continue to function relatively normally. As the number of disrupted cells increases, so the serum transaminase levels rise. However, there are at this stage no clinical symptoms; and the patient remains symptom-free, as long as his allergic responses remain minimal or imperceptible. But in many cases, the first-formed Au antigen has already evoked a low concentration of specific anti-Au antibody, all of which becomes bound to the growing numbers of Au particles. This antibody soon declines, to be followed by an excess of free Au antigen in the serum, which generally falls away, in its turn, within a few days to a few weeks. In some cases, there is then a detectable, usually transient, resurgence of antibody, which now begins to circulate in unbound form. In others, there may be subliminal levels of antibody, too low to be picked up by the methods of detection at present available.

Patients in the earlier phase, with "anticomplementary" immune complexes in their serum, do not yet show symptoms of hepatitis, despite their possession of bound, and sometimes also of free, antibody. It is therefore suggested that actual *clinical disease* is the result of a *cell-mediated allergic response against infected cells* which are in the process of producing Au particles, and whose surface membrane, and possibly also internal membranes, have acquired the specific new antigenic configuration. An active immunological attack on such hepatic, and other, cells would lead to massive cytolysis, with signs and symptoms indicating varying degrees of liver dysfunction. In many cases, this energetic reaction, assisted perhaps by the residual antibody-producing capacity, destroys all virus-harboring cells and terminates the infection. Such is the outcome usually seen in relatively healthy individuals, e.g., the personnel who staff renal hemodialysis units (London *et al.*, 1969a; Turner and White, 1969). In contrast to these are those other individuals, e.g., patients with chronic renal disease undergoing hemodialysis and maybe also treatment with immunosuppressive agents, in whom the allergic response may be depressed to a greater or lesser degree, and who therefore fail to eliminate the infection. These individuals go on to become partially, or in some cases totally, tolerant persistent carriers of the SH agent and of the Au particles which are its hallmark. In those with varying levels of incomplete tolerance, the cellular (and perhaps also humoral) responses may fluctuate; if so, these patients would be expected to show variations in their level of serum Au antigen, and would also experience corresponding exacerbations and remissions of their clinical condition. The more perfect and unbroken the tolerance, the smaller would be the clinical disturbance, and the more continuous and sustained the production of Au antigen. In some of these highly tolerant individuals, the SH agent might then indeed begin to behave as a "slow virus," causing a gradually progressive destruction of one or more kinds of tissue, either by its own replication alone, or with the help of periodic, local, minimal, and soon circumscribed allergic reactions.

The different aspects of this hypothetical model, though still for the most part untested, would seem to be consistent with the known facts; and they do point to several kinds of approach that might be expected to shed some light on the question of pathogenesis, such as studies of delayed-type hypersensitivity reactions and *in vitro* lymphoblast responses in the different clinical categories, and stages, of Au+ SH-agent infection.

References

Agarwal, S. S., Blumberg, B. S., Gerstley, B. J. S., Sutnick, A. I., London, W. T., and Loeb, L. A. (1970). *Clin. Res.* **18,** 436.

Allison, A. C., and Blumberg, B. S. (1961). *Lancet* **i,** 634–637.

Almeida, J. D., and Waterson, A. P. (1969). *Lancet* **ii,** 983–986.

Almeida, J. D., Zuckerman, A. J., Taylor, P. E., and Waterson, A. P. (1969). *Microbios* **2,** 117–123.

Alter, H. J., and Blumberg, B. S. (1966). *Blood* **27,** 297–309.

Bang, F. B. (1969). *New Engl. J. Med.* **281,** 1190–1191.

Barker, L. F., Smith, K. O., Gehle, W. D., and Shulman, N. R. (1969). *J. Immunol.* **102,** 1529–1532.

Barker, L. F., Shulman, N. R., Murray, R., Hirschman, R. J., Ratner, F., Diefenbach, W. C. L., and Geller, H. M. (1970). *J. Amer. Med. Ass.* **211,** 1509–1512.

Bayer, M. E., Blumberg, B. S., and Werner, B. (1968). *Nature (London)* **218,** 1057–1059.

Berson, S. A., Yalow, R. S., Bauman, A., Rothschild, M. A., and Newerly, K. (1956). *J. Clin. Invest.* **35,** 170–190.

Blumberg, B. S. (1964). *Bull. N.Y. Acad. Med.* **40,** 377–386.

Blumberg, B. S. (1970). *Perspect. Virol.* (in press).

Blumberg, B. S., Bernanke, D., and Allison, A. C. (1962). *J. Clin. Invest.* **41,** 1936–1944.

Blumberg, B. S., Alter, H. J., and Visnich, S. (1965). *J. Amer. Med. Ass.* **191,** 541–546.

Blumberg, B. S., Melartin, L., Guinto, R. A., and Werner, B. (1966). *Amer. J. Hum. Genet.* **18,** 594–608.

Blumberg, B. S., Gerstley, B. J. S., Hungerford, D. A., London, W. T., and Sutnick, A. I. (1967a). *Ann. Intern. Med.* **66,** 924–931.

Blumberg, B. S., Melartin, L., Lechat, M., and Guinto, R. A. (1967b). *Lancet* **ii,** 173–176.

Blumberg, B. S., Sutnick, A. I., and London, W. T. (1968). *Bull. N.Y. Acad. Med.* **44,** 1566–1568.

Blumberg, B. S., Friedlaender, J. S., Woodside, A., Sutnick, A. I., and London, W. T. (1969). *Proc. Nat. Acad. Sci. U.S.* **62,** 1108–1115.

Coller, J. A., and Millman, I. (1970). *J. Clin. Invest.* **49,** 20a.

Cossart, Y. E., and Field, A. M. (1970). *Lancet* **i,** 695–698.

Cowan, K. M., and Graves, J. H. (1968). *Virology* **34,** 544–548.

Coyne, V. E., Millman, I., Cerda, J., Gerstley, B. J. S., London, W. T., Sutnick, A. I., and Blumberg, B. S. (1970). *J. Exp. Med.* **131,** 307–319.

Dane, D. S., Cameron, C. H., and Briggs, M. (1970). *Lancet* **i,** 695–698.

Deinhardt, F., Holmes, A. W., Harris, W., Cline, J. B., and Ball, F. L. (1970). Unpublished observations.

Dixon, F. J. (1963). *Harvey Lect.* **58,** 21–52.
Fox, R. A., Niazi, S. P., and Sherlock, S. (1969). *Lancet* **ii,** 609–612.
Gerin, J. L., Purcell, R. H., Hoggan, M. D., Holland, P. V., and Chanock, R. M. (1969). *J. Virol.* **4,** 763–768.
Gibbons, R. A., and Hunter, G. D. (1967). *Nature (London)* **215,** 1041–1043.
Giles, J. P., McCollum, R. W., Berndtson, L. W., Jr., and Krugman, S. (1969). *New Engl. J. Med.* **281,** 119–122.
Gitnick, G. L., Gleich, G. J., Schoenfield, L. J., Baggenstoss, A. H., Sutnick, A. I., Blumberg, B. S., London, W. T., and Summerskill, W. H. J. (1969). *Lancet* **ii,** 285–288.
Gocke, D. J., and Kavey, N. B. (1969). *Lancet* **i,** 1055–1059.
Gust I. D., Cross, G., Kaldor, J., and Ferris, A. A. (1970). *Lancet* **i,** 953.
Hierholzer, W. J., Jr., (1969). Unpublished data.
Hierholzer, W. J., Jr., and Le Bouvier, G. L. (1969). Unpulished data.
Hierholzer, W. J., Jr., Le Bouvier, G. L., and Berndtson, L. W., Jr., (1970). Unpublished data.
Hirschman, R. J., Shulman, N. R., Barker, L. F., and Smith, K. O. (1969). *J. Amer. Med. Ass.* **208,** 1667–1670.
Holland, P. V., Walsh, J. H., Morrow, A. G., and Purcell, R. H. (1969). *Lancet* **ii,** 553–555.
Hotchin, J., and Collins, D. (1964). *Nature (London)* **203,** 1357–1359.
Juji, T., and Yokochi, T. (1969). *Jap. J. Exp. Med.* **39,** 83-88.
Krugman, S., and Giles, J. P. (1970). Personal communication.
Krugman, S., Giles, J. P., and Hammond, J. (1967). *J. Amer. Med. Ass.* **200,** 365–373.
Le Bouvier, G. L. (1959). *Brit. J. Exp. Pathol.* **40,** 452–463.
Le Bouvier, G. L. (1969). Unpublished data.
Le Bouvier, G. L., and Hierholzer, W. J., Jr., (1969). Unpublished data.
Le Bouvier, G. L., McCollum, R. W., and Mirick, G. S. (1969). Unpublished observations.
Levene, C., and Blumberg, B. S. (1969). *Nature (London)* **221,** 195–196.
London, W. T., Difiglia, M., Sutnick, A. I., and Blumberg, B. S. (1969a). *New Engl. J. Med.* **281,** 571–578.
London, W. T., Sutnick, A. I., and Blumberg, B. S. (1969b). *Ann. Intern. Med.* **70,** 55–59.
McCollum, R. W. (1952). *Proc. Soc. Exp. Biol. Med.* **81,** 157–160.
McCollum, R. W. (1970). Unpublished data.
Mathews, J. D., and Mackay, I. R. (1970). *Brit. Med J.* **i,** 259–261.
Melartin, L., and Blumberg, B. S. (1966). *Nature (London)* **210,** 1340–1341.
Mella, B., and Lang, D. J. (1967). *Science* **155,** 80–81.
Melnick, J. L. (1969). Personal communication.
Merrill, D. A., Kohler, P. F., and Cingleton, J. W. (1970). *26th Annu. Meet. Amer. Acad. Allergy* Progr. Abstr. No. 28, p. 42.
Millman, I., Zavatone, V., Gerstley, B. J. S., and Blumberg, B. S. (1969). *Nature (London)* **222,** 181–184.
Millman, I., Loeb, L. A., Bayer, M. E., and Blumberg, B. S. (1970a). *J. Exp. Med.* **131,** 1190–1199.
Millman, I., Ziegenfuss, J. F., Raunio, V., London, W. T., Sutnick, A. I., and Blumberg, B. S. (1970b). *Proc. Soc. Exp. Biol. Med.* **133,** 1426–1431.
Millman, I., London, W. T., Sutnick, A. I., and Blumberg, B. S. (1970c). *Nature (London)* **226,** 83–84.

Mosley, J. W., Barker, L. F., Shulman, N. R., and Hatch, M. H. (1970). *Nature (London)* **225,** 953–955.
Neefe, J. R., and Stokes, J., Jr., (1945). *J. Amer. Med. Ass.* **128,** 1063–1075.
Nowosławski, A., Brzosko, W. J., Madalinski, K, Krawczynski, K. (1970). *Lancet* **i,** 494–498.
Okochi, K., and Murakami, S. (1968). *Vox Sang.* **15,** 374–385.
Oldstone, M. B. A., and Dixon, F. J. (1969). *J. Exp. Med.* **129,** 483–505.
Ouchterlony, Ö. (1958). *Progr. Allergy* **5,** 1–78.
Preer, J. R., Jr., and Preer, L. B. (1959). *J. Protozool.* **6,** 88–100.
Prince, A. M. (1968a). *Proc. Nat. Acad. Sci. U.S.* **60,** 814–821.
Prince, A. M. (1968b). *Lancet* **ii,** 642–643.
Prince, A. M. (1970). *Perspect. Virol.* (in press).
Prince, A. M. and Burke, K. (1970). *Science* **169,** 593–595.
Prince, A. M., Hargrove, R. L., Szmuness, M. D., Cherubin, C. E., Fontana, V. J., and Jeffries, G. H. (1970). *New Engl. J. Med.* **282,** 987–991.
Purcell, R. H. (1970). Personal communication.
Purcell, R. H., Holland, P. V., Walsh, J. H., Wong, D. C., Morrow, A. G., and Chanock, R. M. (1969). *J. Infec. Dis.* **120:** 383–386.
Purcell, R. H., Gerin, J. L., Holland, P. V., Cline, W. L., and Chanock, R. M. (1970). *J. Infec. Dis.* **121,** 222–226.
Reinicke, V., and Nordenfelt, E. (1970). *Lancet* **i,** 141–142.
Shulman, N. R., and Barker, L. F. (1969). *Science* **165,** 304–306.
Sutnick, A. I., London, W. T., Gerstley, B. J. S., Cronlund, M. M., and Blumberg, B. S. (1968). *J. Amer. Med. Ass.* **205,** 670–674.
Turner, G. C., and White, G. B. (1969). *Lancet* **ii,** 121–124.
van Regenmortel, M. H. V. (1966). *Advan. Virus Res.* **12,** 207–271.
Velasco, M., and Katz, R. (1970). *Lancet* **i,** 779.
Volkert, M., and Larsen, J. H. (1965). *Progr. Med. Virol.* **7,** 160–207.
Walsh, J. H., Yalow, R. S., and Berson, S. A. (1970). *J. Infec. Dis.* **121,** 550–554.
Willems, F. T. C., Melnick, J. L., and Rawls, W. E. (1969). *Proc. Soc. Exp. Biol. Med.* **130,** 652–661.
Wright, R. (1970). *Lancet* **i,** 521–522.
Wright, R., McCollum, R. W., and Klatskin, G. (1969). *Lancet* **ii,** 117–121.
Zuckerman, A. J. (1969). *Nature (London)* **223,** 569–572.
Zuckerman, A. J., and Taylor, P. E. (1969). *Nature (London)* **223,** 81–82.
Zuckerman, A. J., Taylor, P. E., and Almeida, J. D. (1970). *Brit. Med. J.* **i,** 262–264.

IMMUNOSUPPRESSION AND EXPERIMENTAL VIRUS INFECTION OF THE NERVOUS SYSTEM*

Neal Nathanson and Gerald A. Cole

Department of Epidemiology, School of Hygiene and Public Health, The Johns Hopkins University, Baltimore, Maryland

I. Introduction

The fate of the host has long been an important concern of studies of parasitism by animal viruses. A critical component in this interaction is the complex of changes which constitute the response of the host to the infectious process. The immune response is probably the most extensively studied of these components, and a central theme of this discussion is the role of the immune response in the outcome of primary viral infections of the nervous system.

The altered responsiveness, usually favoring host survival, which occurs on second exposure to viruses, has been discussed in detail in reviews of immunization against viruses (World Health Organization, 1966; Fenner, 1968; Evans, 1969), and will not be considered here.

Descriptive studies of the sequential evolution of virus infection and of the immune response have shown that, with many host-virus combina-

* Work from this laboratory was supported by research grants NB 05363 and NB 07019, training grant NB 05627, and research career development award NB 21945 (N.N.) from the National Institute of Neurological Diseases and Stroke, United States Public Health Service.

tions, antibody can be detected early, often before clearance of virus. These observations have suggested that the outcome of infection may be due to a race between virus and the immune response (Mims, 1964; Fenner, 1968). However, such descriptive data are inevitably inconclusive (Bodian, 1961), and the subject has remained dormant for lack of more incisive experimental approaches. The recent burgeoning of immunology, and specifically of methods for immunosuppression, has reopened the question to productive exploration.

It should also be noted that, with a few exceptions, this review draws mainly upon results of experimental studies. Slow infections of the CNS, such as scrapie and visna, are not considered in any detail since the paucity of data on the role of the immune response during their progression does not justify extensive discussion.

II. Pathogenesis of Acute Virus Infections of the Central Nervous System (CNS)

The pathogenesis of CNS virus infection has been thoroughly discussed in an excellent recent discussion (Johnson and Mims, 1968) and additional useful information may be found in several other reviews (Bang and Luttrell, 1961; Mims, 1964; Albrecht, 1968; Fenner, 1968; Baer, 1969).

A. Peripheral Virus Infection and CNS Invasion

1. Routes of CNS Invasion

Since the CNS is considered to be a relatively sequestered tissue, the means by which viral invasion takes place has aroused recurring interest. Excellent reviews of this topic are presented by Wright (1953), Johnson and Mims (1968), and Baer (1969).

a. Viremia. In most instances, viral invasion of the CNS occurs from the blood. Passage across the blood-brain barrier can take place in several ways. A rather wide variety of viruses have now been reported to grow in endothelium of cerebral capillaries and small vessels (hog cholera virus, Seifried and Cain, 1932; herpes virus, Anderson, 1940; Bang, 1942; distemper virus, Coffin and Liu, 1957; infectious canine hepatitis virus, Cabasso, 1962; influenza virus, Hook *et al.*, 1962; arbovirus, Johnson, 1965b; K. P. Johnson and Johnson, 1968; reovirus, Kundin *et al.*, 1966; vesicular stomatitis virus, Bruno-Lobo *et al.*, 1968; rat virus, Cole *et al.*, 1970; vaccinia virus, Montasir *et al.*, 1966; adenovirus, Rabin and Jenson, 1967).

It seems likely that, in some instances, viruses may move passively across the cerebral capillaries, as suggested by the failure of careful observers to note endothelial infection (Albrecht, 1962, 1968), or across choroid plexus with subsequent infection of ependymal lining of ventricles prior to involvement of neural parenchyma (Mims, 1960c). Additional evidence of passive crossing of the blood-brain junction is the potentiation of invasion by treatments which increase vascular permeability. Among those shown effective have been carbon dioxide inhalation (Sellers and Lavender, 1962), bacterial endotoxin and hypernatremia (Rahman and Luttrell, 1963), provoking injections (Bodian, 1954), microembolism (Cooke *et al.*, 1942), and preceding parasitic or rickettsial infection of the brain (Mochizuki *et al.*, 1954; MacLeod, 1962).

b. Neural Spread. The other important route of CNS invasion is along peripheral nerves, following introduction of virus by parenteral or olfactory routes. There are probably relatively few instances of naturally occurring infection in which neural spread plays a role. Examples (Johnson and Mims, 1968) of parenteral infection include injection by bite (herpes virus simiae, Sabin and Hurst, 1935; rabies virus, Johnson, 1959) and by syringe inoculation (poliovirus, Nathanson and Langmuir, 1963). Olfactory or trigeminal invasion may be operative for herpes simplex encephalitis (Johnson and Mims, 1968; Kibrick and Gooding, 1965).

Experimentally, neural spread is readily demonstrated by direct immunofluorescent observations (Johnson and Mims, 1968) and, indirectly, by use of nerve section to prevent CNS invasion following either olfactory or parenteral virus introduction (Howe and Ecke, 1937; Nathanson and Bodian, 1961a; Dean *et al.*, 1963; Baer *et al.*, 1965).

Elucidation of the mechanism by which viruses move along nerve trunks has provided a challenge for over 40 years (Goodpasture, 1925; Hurst, 1933; Wright, 1953; Johnson and Mims, 1968; Baer, 1969). Viruses may move at high speed centripetally along nerve trunks to the CNS. Rates have been estimated at 2.4 and 3 mm per hour, respectively, for poliovirus and rabies virus (Bodian and Howe, 1941b; Dean *et al.*, 1963; Baer *et al.*, 1965). Such movement almost certainly implies passive transport of virions. More direct evidence is provided by observations on herpes virus (Sabin, 1937) and on rabies virus (Johnson and Mims, 1968) where neural spread was operative in the apparent absence of replication within the implicated nerve trunks.

There has been a longstanding debate as to the site of passive movement of virions within peripheral nerves (Johnson and Mims, 1968; Baer, 1969). The two sites considered most likely are tissue interspaces (extracellular space) and the axoplasm. Centripetal flow of certain components within the axoplasm has been described and can be of the same order of speed as movement of virus (Lubinska, 1964). The active contractions of myelin recently described (Singer and Bryant, 1969) suggest one possible mechanism for such movement. The clearcut replication of virus within the perikaryon of sensory ganglion cells without demonstrable involvement of supporting elements (Johnson, 1965a; Yamamoto *et al.*, 1965; ElDadah and Nathanson, 1967) is also consistent with axoplasmic spread. On the other hand, Baer *et al.* (1965), in a series of carefully executed experiments, concluded that the sciatic nerve could conduct rabies virus centripetally, following footpad inoculation, even though the axons had degenerated due to a prior nerve crush at the level of the sciatic notch (however, see Nathanson and Bodian, 1961a). Final resolution awaits further experimental evidence.

Concomitantly with neural spread, certain viruses replicate within Schwann cells and fibroblasts (endoneurium and perineurium) of the implicated peripheral nerves (Hurst, 1933; Sabin, 1937; Johnson, 1964a; Rabin *et al.*, 1968). It seems likely that, in some instances, infection of these supporting cells is secondary to axoplasmic movement of virus. In other virus-host interactions, it is possible that replication along a chain of supporting cells in the peripheral nerve is the primary mechanism of neural spread (Johnson, 1964a).

2. Relationship between Peripheral Phase of Infection and Behavior of Virus in the CNS

There is no regular relationship between the ability of a virus to replicate in nonneural tissues or to spread along peripheral nerves and its ability to gain access to the central nervous system. As a consequence, readily available experimental models may differ qualitatively as well as quantitatively in (*i*) the interval between initiation of infection in the periphery and in the CNS; (*ii*) the relative growth rates of virus in periphery and CNS; and (*iii*) the onset and acceleration of immune induction and other host defenses in relation to growth of virus in the CNS. Albrecht (1968) has reviewed these points in detail with respect to the arboviruses, and has collected examples of host-virus relationships in which (*i*) virus replicates readily in the peripheral tissues but only poorly in the CNS, so that even intracerebral inoculation of large doses produces a sublethal infection with a brisk viremia; (*ii*) virus replicates readily in CNS but relatively poorly in peripheral tissues; such virus strains have a high intracerebral titer, but a very low parenteral LD_{50} titer; (*iii*) arbovirus-host combinations in which virus replicates poorly in both peripheral tissues and in CNS (see ElDadah *et al.*, 1967, and references therein; Cole and Wisseman, 1969a); and (*iv*) finally, combinations in which virus replicates readily in both extraneural tissue and CNS, with regular occurrence of acutely fatal encephalitis.

B. Virus Replication in the CNS and the Pathological Response to Infection

1. Spread of Virus Within the CNS

The initial distribution of virus within the CNS following extraneural infection differs markedly from the distribution of virus which follows intracerebral inoculation. Mims (1960a) has shown that, in mice, an intracerebral inoculum is forcibly dispersed through the ventricular system and the subarachnoid space (as well as into the blood, Cairns, 1950) at the time of inoculation. Virus inoculated in this manner may invade the parenchyma both from the site of inoculation and through the ependymal and meningeal surfaces, particularly if it is capable of replicating in these superficial tissues (Mims, 1960b). In contrast, following extraneural infection, virus usually invades the CNS through (or across) the vascular wall, probably simultaneously at many sites. For viruses which can be identified replicating in endothelium, this widespread vascular distribution within the CNS can be observed directly (Cole *et al.*, 1970).

In those instances where a virus strain of high neurotropism invades the CNS along neural pathways, virus may at first be confined to one CNS area, with subsequent localization of early pathological changes or of early dysfunction to the same area (Bodian, 1959; Nathanson and Bodian, 1961a). Even where CNS invasion follows viremia, the earliest site of invasion may be somewhat circumscribed if there is an area of abnormally high vascular permeability (Bodian, 1954; see discussion in Nathanson and Bodian, 1961a).

Once CNS invasion has occurred, some viruses can spread rapidly through the parenchyma. Immunofluorescent observations (e.g., Johnson and Mercer, 1964; ElDadah *et al.*, 1967) indicate that infection develops simultaneously in parenchymal cells throughout the brain. Additional indirect evidence for ready dissemination is the widespread distribution of infection following intracerebral inoculation, even of viruses of low neurovirulence (Nathanson *et al.*, 1966; ElDadah and Nathanson, 1967).

There are several potential mechanisms of viral dissemination within the parenchyma of the CNS. Viruses which replicate in cytoplasm can be readily observed within dendrites of infected cells (e.g., ElDadah and Nathanson, 1967; Johnson and Mims, 1968). If axoplasmic streaming can passively transport viruses along peripheral nerves, the same mechanism could operate within the CNS. Movement within extracellular spaces, particularly for small viruses, is also possible (Boyse *et al.*, 1956; Brightman, 1965; Johnson and Mims, 1968).

2. Variation in CNS Localization of Infection

Widespread use of immunofluorescent staining has permitted detailed documentation of localization of viral antigen within the infected brain (Albrecht, 1968; Johnson and Mims, 1968). It is now clear that there are a number of sharply different patterns of localization of infection.

(*a*) Among the viruses which replicate within *neurons,* the proportion of infected cells may vary from very high to very low (ElDadah and Nathanson, 1967; Albrecht, 1968; Johnson and Mims, 1968). The proportion of infected cells can be relatively constant throughout the CNS (ElDadah and Nathanson, 1967) or there may be marked differences in the severity of infection in different CNS areas (Hurst, 1936). For instance, among arboviruses, there are some which severely attack cerebellum (louping ill, Hurst, 1931; Brownlee and Wilson, 1932), spinal cord (tick-borne viruses, particularly Russian spring-summer encephalitis, Silber and Soloviev, 1946; Zilber, 1962), or basal ganglia (Eastern equine encephalomyelitis, Nathanson *et al.,* 1969), while others produce more uniformly distributed lesions (Japanese B encephalitis, Nathanson *et al.,* 1966). Rabies virus produces spectacular infection of Purkinje cells (Johnson and Mercer, 1964); rat virus attacks cerebellar granule cells (Margolis and Kilham, 1968; Cole *et al.,* 1970); polioviruses produce their most severe lesions in spinal cord motoneurons (Bodian, 1959); and herpes simplex virus tends to select the olfactory and limbic systems of the forebrain (Hughes, 1969).

(*b*) Infection of *nonneuronal* cells also may vary greatly, without any necessary relation to location or severity of neuronal infection (Johnson and Mims, 1968). For instance, herpes virus encephalitis often involves all glial and neuronal elements in a devastating infection (Johnson, 1964a,b), while rabies virus may produce severe neuronal with little glial infection (Johnson, 1965a; Yamamoto *et al.,* 1965). Nonneuronal infection is considered in greater detail in the section on pathology.

3. Diversity of Pathological Lesions Produced by Virus Infection of the CNS

a. Individual Cells. (*i*) The most familiar cellular response to virus infection is *necrosis of the cell,* which may be produced by most classes of viruses. Tissue culture studies of the mechanisms by which virus infection causes cytopathic effects are reviewed by Fenner (1968) and Godman (1966). These include: (*i*) disruption of transcription or translation of host mRNA or of other essential cellular processes (Bablanian *et al.,* 1965a,b); (*ii*) activation and release of lysosomal enzymes (Allison, 1967); and (*iii*) insertion of virus-specific elements into the cell membrane, which causes "late" polykaryocytosis (Roizman, 1962).

There are innumerable descriptive studies of the evolution of virus-induced cytopathic changes, both in tissue culture (Bang, 1959; Pereira, 1961; Bernhard, 1964; Fenner, 1968) and in the nervous system (Hurst, 1936; Innes and Saunders, 1962; Johnson and Mims, 1968).

It should be recognized that virus-infected cells may undergo functional abnormalities prior to development of architectural changes; also early changes may not be recognized in the light microscope. Thus, in laboratory models in which rapid overwhelming infections occur, the heavily infected CNS may show relatively minor pathological changes (rabies virus, Johnson, 1965a; arboviruses, Albrecht, 1960; ElDadah and Nathanson, 1967).

Also cytolytic viruses may, upon occasion, produce nonnecrotic infection or infection from which the cell recovers. One example is poliovirus infection of motoneurons in the primate spinal cord (Bodian, 1948).

A cell population (even though homogeneous) may respond differently to infection than do the individual cells of which it is composed. Thus, individual cells may undergo lytic infection, and yet the population survives exposure to the virus. Such differences can arise when a relatively small proportion of the susceptible cell population is initially infected; if infection spreads sufficiently slowly to additional cells, host defense mechanisms may lead to eradication of the virus prior to infection of the whole population. Abortive arbovirus infection of the CNS (ElDadah and Nathanson, 1967; Cole and Nathanson, 1968) provides one example of this type of host-virus interaction in the brain.

A similar situation can be seen in certain persistent infections of tissue culture, but here the virus may be carried indefinitely, if the multiplication of uninfected cells occurs at a rate sufficient to replace infected cells (Wheeler and Canby, 1959; Lockart, 1960; Glasgow and Habel, 1962; Henle, 1963; Walker, 1968).

(*ii*) Many viruses are capable of producing *nonlytic* infections. In the CNS, immunofluorescent staining may indicate infection in certain areas in which no cellular destruction is seen (e.g., mumps, Johnson, 1968; certain arboviruses, Albrecht, 1962; rabies virus, Johnson, 1965a; Miyamoto and Matsumoto, 1967). Nonlytic infections have been most thoroughly documented in tissue culture, where they have been produced by a number of enveloped RNA viruses (Walker, 1964, 1968; parainfluenza, Choppin, 1964; Holmes and Choppin, 1966; mumps, Walker and Hinze, 1962a,b; rabies, Fernandes *et al.*, 1964; measles, Rustigian, 1966a,b; rubella, Downie and Oxford, 1969).

(*iii*) Certain viruses can affect cells, in the *absence of replication* of the virion or its components (Fenner, 1968). Among such phenomena, the one most relevant to this review is the cell-fusing action exhibited by a number of enveloped viruses (Roizman, 1962): measles, canine distemper, rinderpest (Hopper, 1959; Toyoshima *et al.*, 1960; Plowright, 1962; Warren *et al.*, 1962; Cascardo and Karzon, 1965); mumps, Newcastle disease (Henle *et al.*, 1958; Warren *et al.*, 1962; Kohn, 1965); parainfluenza (Okada and Tadokoro, 1962; Holmes and Choppin, 1966); herpes viruses (Roizman, 1962); and visna (Harter and Choppin, 1967). Virus-cell interactions of this type may be relevant to the pathogenesis of certain infections of the CNS in which demyelination is prominent (see discussion below).

b. Central Nervous System. (*i*) *Neuronotropic infection.* The most familiar pathological response of CNS to viral infection is the necrosis and outfall of neurons, together with an associated inflammatory response. Detailed descriptions of this type of response have been reviewed periodically over the last 30 years (Hurst, 1936; Bodian, 1959; Haymaker, 1961; Innes and Saunders, 1962; Johnson and Mims, 1968). A classical example is Bodian's studies of the sequence of changes which poliovirus produces in the anterior horn cell of the spinal cord (Bodian, 1948, 1959, 1964); principal stages are central chromatolysis followed by diffuse chromatolysis, nuclear changes culminating in pyknosis, and cytolysis followed by neuronophagia.

In addition to the necrobiotic sequence in neurons, a variety of other changes may be associated with neuronotropic infections, particularly when the CNS is subject to a devastating attack. These include: focal areas of demyelination or softening, sometimes perivascular in location; breakdown in the vascular wall with thrombi or small hemorrhages; and late atrophy, glial scars, or cysts (Haymaker, 1961; Innes and Saunders, 1962; Hughes, 1969). Variation in severity of neuronal destruction, duration of illness, physiological status of host, and probably other factors, account for the considerable individual differences in the pathologic picture.

(*ii*) *Primary attack upon meninges, ependyma, or vessels.* Attack upon meninges, ependyma, or vascular endothelium occurs in many CNS virus infections, but in some instances it stands out as the salient aspect of the disease process.

Leptomeningitis may be the site of most severe pathological change in certain experimental infections with virus strains which do not readily spread to the CNS parenchyma. Of particular note are unadapted strains of myxoviruses (Fraser *et al.*, 1959; Mims, 1960b; Johnson and Johnson, 1969) and of vaccinia virus (Rosenau and Andervont, 1931; Mims, 1960a; Kristensson and Sourander, 1969). The pathogenesis of influenza infection in the mouse is an interesting example which has been elucidated by the work of Mims (1960b). Unadapted strains of influenza, following intracerebral inoculation, infect the meninges, where they undergo a single cycle of replication, apparently producing progeny which are unable to infect additional cells, either meningeal or neuronal. A single large inoculum can infect enough meningeal cells to produce an acute leptomeningitis. The relative importance of leptomeningitis and of a "toxic" effect of the virus in producing the clinical syndrome is still unclear (Johnson, personal communication, 1969). Lymphocytic choriomeningitis and perhaps other related viruses (such as Machupo, Junin, Lassa) may also produce a selective meningeal infection under certain circumstances (Weissenbacher *et al.*, 1969). Certain distinctive clinical features often characterize leptomeningeal infections, particularly a marked convulsive diathesis such that animals often die in "status epilepticus."

Ependymitis may or may not be associated with simultaneous infection of leptomeninges. Severe ependymal infection has been described for myxoviruses (Johnson and Johnson, 1969) and for reoviruses (Margolis and Kilham, 1969; Kilham and Margolis, 1969). Of particular interest are the studies by R. T. Johnson and Johnson (1968) dealing with intracerebral inoculation of suckling hamsters with a benign nonneuroadapted strain of mumps virus. Immunofluorescent staining indicated that this strain of mumps produced an infection which involved ependyma, with essentially no infection of parenchymal cells. As a result of ependymal destruction the aqueduct was frequently obliterated, with subsequent development of internal hydrocephalus.

Endothelial infection can be associated with severe hemorrhagic lesions. If CNS parenchymal infection is minimal, a hemorrhagic encephalopathy results (rat virus in suckling rats, Cole *et al.*, 1970; Margolis and Kilham, 1970; NWS strain of influenza virus in chicken embryos, Hook *et al.*, 1962). If concomitant parenchymal infection occurs, hemorrhage is superimposed upon an encephalomyelitis (herpes, Bang, 1942; hog cholera, Seifried and Cain, 1932; infectious canine hepatitis, Cabasso, 1962; blue tongue, Young and Cordy, 1964; arboviruses in chicken embryo, Bang, 1943). It should be noted that it is not clear whether hemorrhages are simply due to cytocidal endothelial infection; it has been postulated that a consumptive coagulopathy may play a role in evolution of hemorrhage (Margolis and Kilham, 1970; Cole *et al.*, 1970). Furthermore, there are several instances where endothelial infection is not associated with hemorrhage (Coffin and Liu, 1957; Johnson, 1965b; Kundin *et al.*, 1966; Bruno-Lobo *et al.*, 1968).

(*iii*) *Demyelination prominent*. There are a number of CNS infections in which destruction of myelin is a prominent and regular aspect of the pathological process. Examples vary as to the severity of concomitant attack upon neurons or the intensity of inflammation. *Visna* is a slow infection; the etiologic agent is an enveloped RNA virus, with sufficient characteristics in common with conventional viruses to justify its inclusion. Following inoculation of sheep (the natural host) neurological symptoms develop in months to years; the CNS lesion is a severe infiltration of round cells which begins in perivascular, periependymal, and leptomeningeal sites; destruction of underlying tissue, including demyelination, usually appears later in the progress of the disease (Sigurdsson *et al.*, 1957, 1962). Harter has suggested that the membrane-fusing action of visna virus might play a role in production of the demyelinating lesion (Thormar, 1961; Harter and Choppin, 1967; Bunge and Harter, 1969).

Mouse hepatitis virus (a coronavirus) occurs in nature in neurotropic variants; these may also be produced by CNS passage. The most detailed description is presented in the original studies of Cheever and colleagues (Cheever *et al.*, 1949; Bailey *et al.*, 1949) of the JHM strain of MHV. This strain produced an acute necrosis of neurons of hippocampus and olfactory cortex, and simultaneous acute patchy demyelination in the brainstem and cord. White matter lesions appeared to commence with destruction of myelin, leaving axons relatively intact; inflammation followed breakdown of myelin; and giant cells were occasionally seen in a variety of tissues. Many of these features are similar to the demyelination produced by RNA viruses with cell-fusing properties (see above), and bring to mind the hypothesis of Harter and Choppin (1967) regarding the pathogenesis of visna.

Border disease is an infection of fetal sheep due to an agent, possibly a virus, transmitted across the placenta after parenteral inoculation of the pregnant ewe (Barlow and Gardiner, 1969). The pathological picture (Barlow and Dickinson, 1965; Cancilla and Barlow, 1968, 1970) is primarily one of severe demyelination; axons appear normal, but there is a decrease in myelin lamellae and degeneration of some myelin sheaths, as well as astrogliosis. There is little inflammation or involvement of neuronal perikarya.

(*iv*) *Panencephalitis.* An attenuated strain of *blue tongue* virus produced an asymptomatic immunizing infection in adult sheep, but if administered to pregnant ewes between 4 and 8 weeks of gestation caused a severe encephalopathy in the fetus (Cox, 1954; Schultz and Delay, 1955). The disease is characterized by an acute loss of neurons and other cells, producing severe atrophy with ventricular dilatation and large subcortical cysts; the architecture of the residual grey and white matter is loose and spongy, and diffuse round cell infiltrates and endothelial changes are present (Young and Cordy, 1964). The reports of Richards and Cordy (1967) and Svehag (1962) suggest that the overwhelming panencephalitis produced by blue tongue virus in fetal lamb or suckling mouse is similar to the lethal panencephalitis produced in suckling mice by many other viruses (for example, arboviruses, ElDadah and Nathanson, 1967; vesicular stomatitis virus, Bruno-Lobo *et al.*, 1968; herpes virus, Johnson, 1964a). The fetal lamb differs in that it may remain viable *in utero* for some time after the devastating panencephalitis, permitting pathological study of the late residua of widespread necrobiosis.

Subacute sclerosing panencephalitis (*SSPE*) is a rare disease which generally follows a progressive course leading to death (Sever and Zeman, 1968). The disease occurs in children who usually have experienced uneventful measles months to years before onset. During active disease, measles serum and CSF antibody titers are elevated; in the brain measles antigen, which stains specifically with measles immunofluorescent conjugates, is seen in the nucleus or cytoplasm of parenchymal cells, and may be visualized in the electron microscope as myxoviruslike nucleocapsids.

Although speculative, present knowledge suggests that SSPE is due to infection with a defective measles variant which is able to replicate once inside a permissive cell, but which cannot spread through extracellular fluids to infect potentially susceptible cells (Rustigian, 1966a,b; Baublis and Payne, 1968).

Histologically, the lesions of SSPE can be divided into two groups. In the grey matter there is cytolytic infection of neurons and glia with an associated inflammatory reaction. In the white matter there are large areas of partial demyelination with diffuse and perivascular infiltrations of cells. It appears that the demyelination may be due to destruction of oligodendroglia and that it cannot be explained as merely secondary to neuronal outfall (Herndon and Rubinstein, 1968).

The possibility of an immunopathological component in the pathogenesis of the disease, is supported by the studies of ter Meulen *et al.* (1969) and Saunders *et al.* (1969). Katz and associates (1968, 1970) have produced a subacute encephalitis in ferrets by intracerebral inoculation of brain homogenates from patients with SSPE. Since the affected ferrets fail to show evidence of measles antigen or myxovirions in the CNS, although they do develop measles antibody, the relationship of these findings to SSPE is not clear (for discussion see Johnson, 1970b).

Distemper occurs in nature as a respiratory infection of dogs; the causal agent is closely related to measles virus. A certain proportion of canine distemper infections involve the CNS, where several different pathological entities may be produced (Gorham, 1960; Gillespie, 1962; Innes and Saunders, 1962). The recent study by Appel (1969) helps to clarify this confusing situation. Susceptible dogs were infected by aerosol; after an incubation period of 3 to 4 weeks, about 50% of animals developed an acutely fatal disease with severe respiratory and intestinal symptoms.

These animals had a very widespread infection with a minimal antibody response; an acute encephalitis was present, with a pantropic (nondemyelinating) infection of meninges, ependyma, neurons, and glia. Most of the remaining animals underwent a mild or subclinical immunizing infection, with a detectable antibody response by 3 weeks; in these animals there was little or no infection of the CNS. A small number of dogs (2 of 55) also experienced an apparently silent immunizing infection; however, 40 to 60 days after infection they developed convulsions, with a panencephalitis, including demyelination as well as neuronal destruction and inflammation; at this time viral antigen was present in Purkinje cells and other neurons (but absent from most extraneural tissues); antibody titers were high in CSF as well as serum. The pathogenesis of distemper demyelination poses a number of challenging questions, including the hypothesized role of an immunopathological process (Choppin, 1968); the persistence of virus in spite of an active immune response; and the possible direct attack of virus on either oligodendroglia (Moulton, 1956) or on the myelin sheath itself (Gorham, 1960).

Postinfectious encephalitis. The rare occurrence of severe neurological symptoms shortly after acute infection with vaccinia, measles, and possibly other nonneurotropic viruses has been repeatedly reviewed (Miller *et al.*, 1956; Scott, 1967). This term has been used for a heterogeneous group of pathological entities (van Bogaert *et al.*, 1961), but is probably best limited to cases in which the cardinal pathological features are perivenular demyelination and cuffing, usually with minimal neuronal involvement (Turnbull and McIntosh, 1926, Perdrau, 1928; van Bogaert *et al.*, 1961; Blackwood *et al.*, 1967). Speculation about the pathogenesis of demyelination has included cytocidal infection of oligodendroglia, direct interaction of virus and myelin membranes, or an immunopathological process attacking myelin (Koprowski, 1962; Isacson, 1967; Choppin, 1968; Paterson, 1969). The similarities between postinfectious encephalitis, distemper, and SSPE suggest that there may be common factors in their pathogenesis.

C. The Inflammatory Response

1. Acute Neuronotropic Infections

An inflammatory response is regularly seen in the CNS as part of the pathological picture characteristic of infections with viruses which produce cytocidal infection of neurons and (often) also of glia. Detailed descriptions have repeatedly documented the salient features of inflammation. In experimental poliomyelitis (Bodian, 1948, 1959), histological changes in neurons occur first; these are followed by the appearance in the CNS of polymorphonuclear leukocytes and mononuclear cells (both lymphocytes and macrophages). Polymorphonuclear cells are usually most common in the first few days of the inflammatory response, and even then may be infrequent, while mononuclear cells may persist for months, particularly around blood vessels. Inflammatory cells typically assume several characteristic configurations: as perivascular cuffs, particularly around small vessels; as focal accumulations often at sites of neuronophagia; and as scattered cells distributed diffusely throughout the affected tissue. Inflammation is seen in both white and grey matter, but the most severe infiltrates are usually in grey matter.

Although excellent descriptions of the CNS inflammatory response have been available for over 50 years (Harbitz and Scheel, 1907), the mechanisms which underlie this response are not yet well understood.

(*a*) *Cellular destruction* may be an important *stimulus* to the response, since there is a general tendency toward correlation of distribution and severity of inflammation with severity of neuronal loss. The neuronophagia which is so prominently associated with neuronal destruction in some CNS viral infections (Bodian, 1948) indicates that cellular destruction is one of the stimuli responsible for inflammation. The inflammatory response to neuronal destruction due to toxins or anoxia is consistent with this view (Innes and Saunders, 1962). However, in local areas of the infected CNS there may be a marked discrepancy between cellular infection or cellular destruction and inflammation (Bodian, 1959; Johnson, 1968); likewise, inflammation may be seen in white matter distant from any apparent neuronal outfall (Nathanson *et al.*, 1965).

At present, there is no clear evidence whether the *immune response* plays any role in initiation of the viral inflammatory response; there are a few observations (Bodian and Howe, 1941a; Cole and Nathanson, 1968; Johnson, 1970a) which fail to indicate that the immune response is important, but these do not provide definitive information. It has been suggested by Webb (Webb and Smith, 1966; Webb *et al.*, 1968a,b; Webb, 1969) that the inflammatory response in neuronotropic viral encephalitides is associated with the formation of virus-antibody complexes in and around the small vessels of the CNS, but direct evidence for this association is lacking. Berge and associates (1961a) in an earlier series of studies also advanced a similar view.

(*b*) Recent observations by Johnson (1970a) shed considerable light on the *source and nature of cells* participating in the inflammatory response. Using tritiated thymidine and India ink to label, respectively, proliferating cells and phagocytic cells, it appears that the majority of inflammatory cells are recruited from outside the CNS; they are probably mainly monocytes, although some may be lymphocytes. Most inflammatory cells are derived from rapidly proliferating populations, and proliferation occurs both before and after they enter the CNS; cells with phagocytic activity are found, not only at sites of neuronophagia, but also in perivascular cuffs where they may be histologically indistinguishable from lymphocytes.

Zlotnik (1968) has recently described marked and regular astrogliosis accompanying acute rabies and arbovirus encephalitis in laboratory rodents, which was often seen as early as 24 hours after infection. Since earlier workers did not use stains appropriate for visualizing astrocytes, there is little information about the astroglial component of the inflammatory response. Further studies are needed to assess the significance of these findings.

(*c*) The relationship of *inflammation to outcome* of neuronotropic infection is currently controversial. There are at least two cell types in the inflammatory lesion which could play a role in recovery from infection; these are plasma cells (Bodian, 1948) and macrophages. Heremans (1968) has reviewed evidence that during infections of the CNS, immunoglobulins are produced locally which are specific for the infecting agent (Morgan, 1949a; Bell *et al.*, 1966). However, there does not seem to be any regular relationship between the outcome of infection (or titer of virus in the brain) and severity of inflammation.

Taking a quite different viewpoint, Webb and Smith (1966; Webb *et al.*, 1968a,b; Webb, 1969) have suggested that an immunopathological process is responsible for the inflammatory response (or at least certain components thereof), and that immunopathology or inflammation (Nahmias *et al.*, 1969; Hirsch and Murphy, 1968) may play a role in viral encephalitic death.

2. Other CNS Virus Infections

The diverse pathological syndromes which can be seen with nonneuronotropic virus infections of the CNS are associated with a variety of degrees and types of inflammation.

(*a*) *Inflammation is minimal* in certain infections of mesodermal elements in the CNS, such as the hemorrhagic encephalopathy produced by certain strains of influenza and rat viruses (Hook *et al.*, 1962; Cole *et al.*, 1970). Infections primarily of leptomeninges or ependyma are usually accompanied by inflammation; this is seen in the areas of cellular infection, but may also be present in the uninfected parenchyma of the CNS (R. T. Johnson and Johnson, 1968).

(*b*) *Demyelinating processes* may be associated with hypercellularity in affected areas of white matter. In some instances this is mainly due to increase in size or number of indigenous glial elements (Border disease, Barlow and Gardiner, 1969). In MHV-initiated demyelination, which is a more acute process, polymorphonuclear and mononuclear leukocytes are prominent initially, with later appearance of gliosis (Bailey *et al.*, 1949). In the slow infection, visna, hypercellularity is regularly seen in areas of demyelination, and may be the initial histologically apparent change (Sigurdsson *et al.*, 1962).

(*c*) *Panencephalitides* are regularly characterized by severe inflammation, both in grey and white matter. A heterogeneous population of cells is involved, which may represent several quite different pathological processes occurring simultaneously (Perdrau, 1928; Miller *et al.*, 1956; Innes and Saunders, 1962; Sever and Zeman, 1968; Appel, 1969).

D. Variables Which Influence the Outcome of CNS Infections

The course and outcome of CNS infection are influenced by the host, the virus, and the mode of infection. The effects of these variables are described below, but discussion of the underlying mechanisms is deferred to a later section.

1. Virus Variation

In recent years virus variation has become the province of workers interested in the genetics of animal viruses. Studies of this type, reviewed by Fenner and Sambrook (1964), Takemoto (1966), and Cooper (1967), have often been concerned with the biochemical mechanisms of genetic markers. In some instances, studies of mutants have produced instructive examples of the ways in which variations in the virus proliferative cycle can influence pathogenicity for host cells (Wagner *et al.*, 1963; Rapp, 1963; Finter, 1964a; Cooper *et al.*, 1966; Lwoff, 1969). Such studies suggest the type of information which should eventually be sought to explain the molecular basis of virus pathogenicity.

a. Origin of Virus Variants. More relevant to the theme of this review are virus variants which manifest differences in pathogenicity for experimental animals. Fenner and Cairns (1959) assembled a useful review of the older literature on this subject. Most variants presumably arise by mutation; the literature on their origin pertains mainly to the selection of variant subpopulations from heterogeneous parental populations.

It is convenient to consider variants as derived either by (*i*) segregation of individual infectious particles (plaque-forming centers) or small populations (terminal dilution), or by (*ii*) sequential passage of a heterogeneous population in a host which will support virus replication. No attempt will be made to catalog here the numerous histories of modified virus strains which have been published. Rather, a few selected examples will be noted.

(*i*) *Plaque mutants.* The search for attenuated virus variants optimal for human immunization against poliomyelitis involved one of the most extensive explorations of plaque mutants. Much of this work is summarized in Sabin (1957), Plotkin *et al.* (1962), and in two symposia (Live Poliovirus Vaccines, 1st and 2nd Int. Conf., 1959, 1960). Although no marker was found which invariably correlated with monkey neurovirulence, there was a rough correlation between the ability to replicate at high or low temperatures and virulence or avirulence, respectively (Lwoff, 1959, 1961, 1969; Dubes and Wenner, 1957; Sabin, 1961; Vonka *et al.*, 1967).

(*ii*) *Strains derived by passage.* Many of the "classical" strains used prior to the era of animal virus plaquing (Dulbecco, 1952) were derived by sequential passages in animals or cell cultures. Passage in the CNS, when sufficiently prolonged, yielded strains which were designated "fixed" or "obligatory neurotropes," referring to their tendency to replicate or spread only in the peripheral or central nervous system. However, it is not entirely clear whether such strains can infect glia, Schwann cells, or endoneural fibroblasts, in addition to neurons. Some examples are: the MV strain of poliovirus (Flexner, 1931; Bodian, 1959; Nathanson and Bodian, 1961a,b), the French neurotropic strain of yellow fever virus (Strode, 1951), and fixed strains of rabies virus (Johnson, 1959). Certain other viruses, even without many serial CNS passages, show a tendency toward obligatory neurotropism in certain hosts (herpes simplex virus, Sabin, 1937; Dean *et al.*, 1963; Wildy, 1967; vesicular stomatitis virus, Sabin and Olitsky, 1937a,b).

In contrast, strains of reduced animal virulence have also been derived by serial passage. Among these are the 17D strain of yellow fever virus (Strode, 1951), the LSc strain of poliovirus (Sabin, 1957), the E5 strain of Langat virus (Thind and Price, 1966), the MD-1 strain of dengue-1 virus (Wisseman *et al.*, 1963), and an attenuated strain of Venezuelan equine encephalitis virus (Berge *et al.*, 1961b). Experience has shown that attenuation for a given animal host is best achieved by passage in a different animal host or in tissue culture. Furthermore, passage leading to reduced virulence is often an irregular phenomenon, occurring in only a few of several parallel passage lines originating from a single virus stock (Thind and Price, 1966).

b. Comparative Pathogenesis of Viral Variants. The majority of studies reporting virus strain differences in animal virulence are limited to titrations of lethality and of infectivity. Detailed descriptions of the evolution of infection, which might suggest points of difference in comparative pathogenesis, are not often undertaken.

Attenuated poliovirus strains have been extensively studied in humans, chimpanzees, and monkeys (Live Poliovirus Vaccines, 1st and 2nd Int.

Conf., 1959, 1960); they are capable of regularly infecting oropharynx and intestine, but produce only minimal and infrequent viremia, in comparison with the most virulent wild strains (Melnick *et al.*, 1966). Growth of attenuated strains in the monkey spinal cord is greatly diminished in comparison with neurovirulent strains, and this in turn is reflected in mildness of histological lesions (Live Poliovirus Vaccines, 1st Int. Conf., 1959; Bodian, 1961).

A number of studies of arbovirus variants have been published. Thind and Price (1966) found that the attenuated E5 strain of Langat virus, when injected intraperitoneally, produced only trace viremia, and, occasionally, invaded the CNS where low levels of virus appeared for a short time; mice survived without symptoms. In contrast, the parent M3 strain produced a marked viremia, invaded the CNS early, and regularly replicated to high titer, with consequent fatal encephalitis. Cole and Wisseman (1969a) compared several passage levels of dengue-1 virus, following intracerebral inoculation of adult mice. The MP-3 strain (3 mouse passages) replicated slowly and then disappeared, often without producing clinical symptoms. The MP-125 strain replicated rapidly, to high titer, and regularly killed adult mice. Thus virulence may be associated both with greater neuro-invasiveness and with enhanced replication in the CNS. At present, little is known of the mechanisms which underlie such variations.

2. Host Variables

A number of host variables have been shown to markedly influence the pathogenesis of experimental virus infection. At a descriptive level, considerable information is available with regard to comparative pathogenesis (Bang and Luttrell, 1961).

a. *Age.* Because the dramatic effect of age on susceptibility to CNS viral infection is seen in so many laboratory models, this variable is probably the most thoroughly studied (Sigel, 1952). Age-related decrease in susceptibility has been measured in several ways: (*i*) intracerebral LD_{50} titer (Lennette and Koprowski, 1944; MacDonald, 1952; Schlesinger and Frankel, 1952; Nir and Goldwasser, 1961); (*ii*) intracerebral incubation period, and maximum titer attained by virus in infected brain (Meicklejohn *et al.*, 1952; Sabin, 1952; Overman and Kilham, 1953; Overman, 1954a,b; ElDadah *et al.*, 1967; Cole and Wisseman, 1969a); (*iii*) intracerebral susceptibility to viruses of relatively low virulence or freshly isolated strains prior to passage (Schlesinger and Frankel, 1952; Cole and Wisseman, 1969a); (*iv*) intracerebral susceptibility of relatively resistant rodent species (Duffy, 1951; ElDadah *et al.*, 1967); and (*v*) intraperitoneal LD_{50} titer (Lennette and Koprowski, 1944; Johnson, 1964b; ElDadah *et al.*, 1967), or severity of disease following other extraneural routes of infection (Sabin and Olitsky, 1937a,b).

b. Species. Animal viruses vary markedly in the breadth of their host range. Thus, human polioviruses are well known for their relative limitation to primate hosts (Holland, 1961; Plotkin *et al.*, 1962; Kunin, 1962). However, spider monkeys (genus *Ateles*) show a nonimmune resistance to types 2 and 3 (but not type 1) human polioviruses, even following intracerebral inoculation of highly virulent strains (Jungeblut and Bautista, 1956; Nathanson *et al.*, unpublished, 1969). In contrast, rabies virus, if inoculated intracerebrally, has high virulence for most mammalian species regardless of age (Johnson, 1959). Human enteroviruses show marked differences in their ability to infect mice: polioviruses usually fail to infect, group A coxsackie viruses produce a fatal poliomyelitis and severe myositis, and group B coxsackie viruses attack brain and brown fat. Group B arboviruses are much more virulent for certain species of laboratory rodents (mice and hamsters) than for others (rats and guinea pigs) (ElDadah *et al.*, 1967).

c. Genetic Differences Within Species. There may be dramatic differences in the viral susceptibility of different animals of the same species. Studies of the genetics of susceptibility have dealt mainly with mice, with particular references to mouse hepatitis virus (Bang and Warwick, 1960; Kantoch *et al.*, 1963), and group B arboviruses (reviewed in ElDadah *et al.*, 1967; Fenner, 1968). Arbovirus susceptibility has been studied by Webster and associates (Webster and Clow, 1936), Sabin and associates (Sabin, 1954), and Koprowski and associates (Goodman and Koprowski, 1962; Vainio, 1963; Groschel and Koprowski, 1965). Adult mice from resistant strains are not killed by intracerebral inoculation of certain group B arboviruses, although suckling animals are susceptible. Resistance is carried by a single dominant autosomal gene.

d. Physiological Status of the Host. Susceptibility can be markedly influenced by the physiological condition of the animal host. *Body temperature* can be raised or lowered by residence in a warm or cold environment. Elevated temperature usually favors the host, which may survive a potentially lethal infection (poliovirus, Lwoff *et al.*, 1960; coxsackie virus B1, Walker and Boring, 1958; Sindbis virus, Kirn *et al.*, 1967; dengue virus, Cole and Wisseman, 1969b; herpesvirus, Carmichael *et al.*, 1969; Carmichael and Barnes, 1969). Conversely, low temperatures may enhance susceptibility (Boring *et al.*, 1956).

Corticosteroids or stress can enhance susceptibility of experimental animals to infection (see discussions of poliovirus, coxsackie virus, and arbovirus in subsequent sections). *Sex* differences in susceptibility have been reported (encephalomyocarditis virus, Glasgow, unpublished, 1969) and *pregnancy* may be associated with increased risk (Siegel and Greenberg, 1955; Farber and Glasgow, 1968). Finally, *nutritional status* can affect the outcome of infection (Scrimshaw *et al.*, 1968; Woodruff, 1970).

Trauma of various types has been associated with enhanced risk of symptomatic CNS infection. The influence of several types of trauma upon poliomyelitis has received detailed epidemiological and experimental study (Habel, 1955). Parenteral injections, particularly of irritating materials, clearly enhance the risk of clinical poliomyelitis following extraneural virus infection (Hill and Knowelden, 1950; Bodian, 1954). Likewise, tonsillectomy enhances the risk of bulbar poliomyelitis, even years after the operation (Adams *et al.*, 1953; Paffenbarger and Wilson, 1955).

III. Effect of Immunosuppression on Selected Experimental Models of CNS Viral Infection

A. *Lymphocytic Choriomeningitis*

Lymphocytic choriomeningitis (LCM) of mice is of particular importance as the prototype of CNS viral infections in which the disease process is mediated by an immunopathological mechanism (Hotchin, 1962, 1965; Volkert and Larsen, 1965a). LCM is an unclassified, enveloped virus (Dalton *et al.*, 1968) which occurs in nature as an enzootic infection of mice (Traub, 1936b, 1939). Experimentally, the virus will produce symptomatic infections in a number of animal species (Findlay and Stern, 1936; Armstrong, 1942), but the following discussion is focussed on studies in mice.

1. Course of Infection in Mice

Depending on the age of mice, and upon numerous other variables, LCM infection can follow several markedly different courses:

(*a*) *Persistent infection with antigen excess* occurs following exposure to virus *in utero* or shortly after birth. Animals so infected carry high virus titers in blood, brain, and other tissues throughout their lives, and yet appear to develop and behave almost normally (Traub, 1936a,b, 1939; Hotchin, 1962, 1965; Pollard *et al.*, 1968a,b). Such carrier animals can transmit infection vertically, initiating persistent infections in their offspring (Pollard *et al.*, 1968a). In addition, they continually excrete virus in urine, resulting in occasional infection of other animals, including man (Farmer and Janeway, 1942). By conventional techinques it is difficult to demonstrate antibody in the serum; this type of infection was therefore termed persistent tolerant infection or PTI (Hotchin, 1962; Volkert and Larsen, 1965a). More recently, it has been shown that antibody is formed in this condition (Oldstone and Dixon, 1969; Benson and Hotchin, 1969). Such antibody may be bound to circulating infectious virus, and can be detected by use of antiserum directed against mouse immunoglobulins (Oldstone and Dixon, 1969).

(*b*) *Persistent infection with antibody excess* occurs in juvenile or adult mice inoculated by a parenteral route. Such animals usually undergo silent immunizing infection, with the disappearance of infectious virus and appearance of CF antibody within several weeks inoculation. Persistence of small amounts of virus may be demonstrated directly (Haas, 1954; Rowe, 1954), but special techniques can dramatically unmask virus. Thus, when such immune animals are treated with antilymphocyte serum (ALS) viremia reappears and persists until treatment is terminated (Volkert and Lundstedt, 1968). Likewise, animals in which neonatal "tolerant" infections have been "cured" by grafting immune isologous lymphoid cells, continue to show traces of virus in spite of high levels of circulating N and CF antibody (Volkert and Larsen, 1964, 1965a).

Finally, if an appropriate balance is struck between virus and antibody, persistent infections may be created in which both infectious virus and CF antibody can be found in the serum over long periods of time (Hirsch *et al.*, 1968).

(*c*) *Acutely lethal choriomeningitis* occurs in mice, 1 week or older, following intracerebral inoculation of virus. Typically, following an incubation period of about 1 week, nonspecific symptoms develop, accompanied by a characteristic convulsive diathesis. Paralysis or other localizing neurological signs are uncommon and animals often die during a seizure. Histologically, there may be lesions in liver and other viscera, but the salient lesions are found in the central nervous system, where a severe choriomeningitis occurs, consisting primarily of lymphocytes and other mononuclear cells (Findlay and Stern, 1936; Lillie and Armstrong, 1945).

A number of variables have been shown to play an important role in the outcome of LCM infection. Different *strains* of virus vary in their virulence; virulence is influenced by passage history (intracerebral-brain or intraperitoneal-visceral). An "aggressive" brain-passaged virus is more apt to kill acutely, while a "docile" visceral-passaged virus is more likely to produce persistent infection (Hotchin *et al.*, 1962; Hotchin, 1965). Host *species* is of importance, since persistent infections with antigen excess have not been reported in animals other than mice (Volkert and Larsen, 1965b), although choriomeningitis is readily produced in a variety of species (Findlay and Stern, 1936; Armstrong, 1942). More recently, it has been shown that there are marked differences between strains of mice, with respect to the titers which the virus reaches following neonatal infection. This, in turn, may play a critical role in the outcome of infection (Oldstone and Dixon, 1968, 1969). As noted above, *age* of host and *route* of virus injection are also critical determinants. Following intraperitoneal inoculation of adult mice, there is a variable mortality, depending upon strain of virus. Virus replicates in the brains of both fatally affected and surviving animals; however in survivors the titers are relatively lower and choriomeningitis, if present, is mild (Rowe, 1954; Lehmann-Grube, 1964).

2. Mechanism of Persistent Infection

Although persistent infection with LCM virus is not completely understood, several essential aspects have been delineated. LCM virus is enveloped; its interaction with host cells probably has features in common with other enveloped viruses, such as the myxoviruses and rhabdoviruses (Marcus, 1962; Lehmann-Grube *et al.*, 1969). Infected cells in culture can remain viable while supporting virus replication over an extended period (Benson and Hotchin, 1960; Benda and Cinatl, 1962; Seamer, 1965; Lehmann-Grube, 1967). The plasma membrane of such infected cells contains virus-specific antigenic determinants (Dalton *et al.*, 1968) which can bind antiviral antibody, thereby activating complement with subsequent cellular injury (Oldstone and Dixon, 1970). Cytopathology has also been observed in infected cultures to which have been added LCM immune lymphoid cells (Volkert and Lundstedt, 1968; Oldstone and Dixon, 1970) but, at present, evidence for the viral immunospecificity of this event is lacking.

In vivo a virus-cell interaction of this type could conceivably result in either persistent infection without pathological changes or in disease, depending on whether sensitized lymphoid cells and/or antibody and complement can gain access to infected cells. The fact that skin grafts from LCM carrier mice are rejected by uninfected syngenic recipients (Holtermann and Majde, 1969) is persuasive evidence for role of virus-specific surface antigen in the pathogenesis of disease.

Another factor of potential importance in persistence of LCM infection is the ability of the virus to infect susceptible cells even after it has been bound by virus-specific immunoglobulin. This is suggested by the observation that viral infectivity and CF activity may coexist in the blood over a long period (Volkert and Lundstedt, 1968; Hirsch *et al.*, 1968; Larsen, 1969a,b). More recently, it has been shown (Oldstone and Dixon, 1969) that in persistent infections with antigen excess, the bulk of infectious virus is inactivated by antiserum directed against mouse immunoglobulins. Analysis of the neutralization kinetics of other viruses (Notkins *et al.*, 1966, 1968; Ashe *et al.*, 1968; Krummel and Uhr, 1969) suggests that such infectious virus-antibody complexes may be a relatively common phenomenon.

3. Pathogenesis of Acute Choriomeningitis

a. Immunosuppression. Probably the most dramatic evidence that acute lymphocytic choriomeningitis is mediated by an immunopathological process comes from use of immunosuppression to manipulate the outcome of infection in adult mice. Originally Rowe (1954, 1956) and subsequently Hotchin and Weigand (1961) showed that X-irradiation converted a potentially fatal intracerebral virus inoculation into a benign infection. Similar results have since been reported for immunosuppressive drugs (Haas and Stewart, 1956; Hotchin, 1962; Gilden *et al.*, 1971); antilymphocyte serum (ALS, Lundstedt and Volkert, 1967; Gledhill, 1967; Hirsch *et al.*, 1967, 1968); and thymectomy (Rowe *et al.*, 1963; Levey *et al.*, 1963; East *et al.*, 1964).

Following immunosuppression with X-irradiation, intracerebally inoculated adult mice may develop persistent infections with antigen excess (Rowe, 1954; Hotchin, 1962). If short-term immunosuppression is applied, with ALS (Hirsch *et al.*, 1967; Gledhill, 1967) or cyclophosphamide (Gilden *et al.*, 1971), there can be either a transient sparing effect followed by fatal choriomeningitis upon the recovery of immunoresponsiveness, or permanent protection. Since the growth curve of virus in the CNS is similar in mice destined to die and in those protected by suppression (Rowe, 1954; Hotchin, 1962) protection cannot be attributed to differences in the number of infected cells in the brain.

Further evidence of the dynamic relationship between virus replication and immune induction is provided by the studies of Gilden *et al.* (1971), which demonstrate that, following intracerebral virus injection, the timing of immunosuppression is critical to the outcome. Thus, a single immunosuppressive dose of cyclophosphamide given to 6-week-old BALB/c mice between 3 to 5 days after LCM virus results in permanent survival of up to 20% of animals; drug given 1 or 2 days after virus increases mean survival time from 1 week (in controls) to 2 weeks, but all mice die of acute choriomeningitis.

b. Adoptive Immunization. To completely establish the immunopathological nature of choriomeningitis, it would be necessary to convert an asymptomatic persistent infection into overt choriomeningitis by immune serum or cells. Recently Oldstone and Dixon (1970) have shown that the intrathecal inoculation of immune serum into persistently infected mice can produce histologically apparent choriomeningitis, without death of animals. Additional evidence that choriomeningitis may in part be antibody-mediated is the observation that a proportion of adult mice, when fully depeleted of the third component of complement with cobra venom, are protected against intracerebral inoculation of LCM virus (Oldstone, 1970). Similar decomplementation experiments by others (Gilden *et al.*, 1969) have failed to show significant protection from acute LCM, indicating that precise experimental conditions are required to demonstrate this effect.

Warranting further explanation are the results of studies of the effect of adoptively immunizing persistently infected mice of the C3H strain (Volkert and Larsen, 1965a; Larsen, 1969a,b). Such animals, following inoculation of lymphoid cells obtained from immunized syngenic donors, develop persistent high levels of both CF and neutralizing antibodies but CNS disease does not occur. Infectious virus disappears from the blood as well as from the spleen and lymph nodes, where the bulk of the grafted cell inoculum apparently localizes. Infectivity persists in the kidneys and presumably in the brain.

Current observations by Oldstone and Dixon (1970) provide a possible explanation. They found that passive intravenous immunization of persistently infected mice, with either immune serum or syngenic cells from an immunized donor, did produce leptomeningitis and perivascular cuffing. These effects could be demonstrated in the SWR/J strain but not in the C3H strain of mice. It had been previously shown (Oldstone and Dixon, 1968) that persistently infected SWR/J mice carried much higher levels of virus than did persistently infected C3H mice. However, Lehmann-Grube (1969) has failed to find any effect of mouse strain on the titers of virus in the brain.

At present it is difficult to assess the relative contributions of the humoral and cellular components of the immune response to the pathogenesis of acute LCM. Although the available evidence suggests that both components can play a role in the immunopathological process, the precise cause of death needs further study.

c. Intraperitoneal Virus Inoculation. The inability of some strains of LCM virus to produce fatal CNS disease following peripheral inoculation of adult mice, particularly when involvement of the brain is regularly demonstrable, is still not entirely explained (Rowe, 1954; Lehmann-Grube, 1964). Here, infection of the CNS is secondary to visceral infection. Under these conditions the initiation of extraneural immune induction, before infection of the CNS reaches a critical threshold, may serve to abort the infectious process; clinical choriomeningitis does not occur, but relatively mild inflammatory lesions can be observed histologically. Apparently, the absence of acute disease is due to insufficient amounts of virus or viral antigen on "target" cell surfaces which can subsequently interact with virus-specific humoral and/or cellular components of the immune response of the host.

4. *Late Disease and Glomerulonephritis*

Although not central to the subject of this review, it should be noted that persistent LCM infection with antigen excess may, under certain circumstances, result in an immune complex disease. Originally called "late" disease by Hotchin (1962), since it often develops after many months after infection, it may be accelerated under circumstances which favor the formation of high levels of circulating antigen-antibody complexes (Hirsch *et al.*, 1968). Oldstone and Dixon (1967, 1969) have shown that the glomerulonephritis which is a cardinal feature of this disease is associated with deposits of LCM virus, LCM antibody, and complement components in the mesangial zone just outside the basement membrane of the glomerular capillary.

B. Arbovirus Encephalitis

1. *Pathogenesis*

Because of their marked ability to produce CNS infections in several rodent and primate species, arboviruses (Chamberlain, 1968), particularly those in groups A and B, have been extensively employed in studies of the pathogenesis of experimental viral infections of the CNS. Selection of appropriate host-virus combinations permits the study of different variables, with respect to their influence upon the course and eventual outcome of experimental infection. Age and species of host, route of infection, dose, strain, and passage history of virus, can be manipulated to provide laboratory models of CNS infections which range from inapparent and abortive to progressive and lethal. Abortive infections are particularly interesting since they probably represent the analog of many naturally occurring viral infections of man, in which virus gains access to the CNS, undergoes a limited period of replication, and is then eliminated.

2. *Effect of Immunosuppression on Factors Related to Resistance*

a. Rationale. A number of studies of abortive CNS infections produced by arboviruses have documented an association between the appearance of detectable humoral antibody and the disappearance of virus from the CNS, thereby suggesting that the immune response may be an important determinant in the outcome of infection (Kundin, 1966; Webb *et al.*, 1968a,b; Thind and Price, 1969a; Cole and Wisseman, 1969a; Weiner *et al.*, 1970). Studies utilizing procedures which modify or sup-

TABLE I

IMMUNOSUPPRESSIVE TREATMENT OF EXPERIMENTAL ANIMALS INFECTED WITH ARBOVIRUSES

Virus group	Virus	Experimental host	Method of immunosuppression	Reference
A	Venezuelan equine encephalitis	Mouse	X-Irradiation	Kundin (1966)
	Venezuelan equine encephalitis	Monkey	Cortisone	Gleiser *et al.* (1961)
	Western equine encephalomyelitis	Mouse	Cyclophosphamide	Weiner *et al.* (1971)
	Western equine encephalomyelitis	Mouse	Cyclophosphamide	Thind and Price (1969b)
	Semliki forest	Mouse	Cyclophosphamide	Cole, Bradish, and Allner (unpublished, 1969)
B	St. Louis encephalitis	Mouse	X-Irradiation	Goldberg *et al.* (1935)
	St. Louis encephalitis	Mouse	Cyclophosphamide	Thind and Price (1969b)
	St. Louis encephalitis	Hamster	Cortisone	Imam and Hammon (1957a, b)
	Japanese encephalitis	Hamster	X-Irradiation	Imam and Hammon (1957a)
	Japanese encephalitis	Hamster	Cortisone	Imam and Hammon (1957a, b)
	Japanese encephalitis	Mouse	Cyclophosphamide	Thind and Price (1969b)
	Japanese encephalitis	Mouse	Cortisone	Vollmer and Hurlburt (1951)
	Japanese encephalitis	Monkey	Cyclophosphamide	Nathanson and Cole (1970)
	Dengue-1	Mouse	Cyclophosphamide	Cole and Nathanson (1968)
	Dengue-2	Mouse	Cyclophosphamide	Thind and Price (1969b)
	West Nile	Mouse	X-Irradiation	Goodman and Koprowski (1962)
	West Nile	Mouse	Cortisone	Goodman and Koprowski (1962)
	West Nile	Mouse	6-Thioguanine	Goodman and Koprowski (1962)
	West Nile	Mouse	Cyclophosphamide	Cole, Weiner and Nathanson, (unpublished, 1968)
	West Nile	Mouse	Cyclophosphamide	Weiner *et al.* (1971)
	West Nile	Mouse	Cyclophosphamide	Thind and Price (1969b)
	West Nile	Rat	Cyclophosphamide	Cole and Nathanson (1968)
	Yellow fever	Mouse	Antilymphoid serum	Hirsch and Murphy (1967, 1968)
	Yellow fever	Mouse	Antimacrophage serum	Panijel and Cayeux (1968)
	Ilheus	Mouse	Cyclophosphamide	Thind and Price (1969b)
	Langat	Mouse	X-Irradiation	Webb *et al.* (1968b)
	Langat	Mouse	Antibody	Webb *et al.* (1968a)
	Langat	Mouse	Cyclophosphamide	Thind and Price (1969a, b, c)
	Langat	Mouse	Thymectomy	Thind and Price (1969c)
	Langat	Mouse	Antilymphoid serum	Thind and Price (1969c)
	Tick-borne encephalitis	Mouse	X-Irradiation	Malkova (1962)
Ungrouped	Vesicular stomatitis	Mouse	Antimacrophage serum	Hirsch *et al.* (1969)

press the host immunological apparatus were designed to clarify this association.

As shown in Table I, numerous reports have appeared which describe the use of various immunosuppressive procedures to alter the outcome of experimental arbovirus encephalitis. Most studies have shown that significant depression of immune reactivity is associated with enhanced virus-specific morbidity and mortality. Suppressed animals often show a prolonged viremia, elevated virus levels in target tissues, and a reduced or undetectable antibody response.

To illustrate these effects, the remainder of this section will review a series of studies in which arbovirus infection was compared in the normal and immunosuppressed host. Emphasis is placed on laboratory models of self-limiting infections of the CNS in which a single host- or virus-associated variable appears to account for the nonfatal outcome. Immunosuppression was accomplished using cyclophosphamide, a particularly potent agent (Schwartz and Borel, 1968), and one whose effect is consistently reproducible.

b. Methods. Acute immunosuppression was accomplished by initiating drug treatment 24 hours after live virus injection. Since the duration of cyclophosphamide-mediated immunosuppression is limited, one or two additional drug doses were usually given at 5- to 8-day intervals. Drug was administered by the intraperitoneal or subcutaneous route, and dosage (milligrams per kilogram body weight), was adjusted on the basis of host age and species.

c. Host Species. Certain strains of Japanese encephalitis (JE) virus have a high intracerebral neurovirulence for young adult rhesus monkeys; about 75% die, with an average survival time of 8 to 10 days (Nathanson *et al.*, 1966). In contrast, young adult spider monkeys fail to develop clinical disease following intracerebral inoculation of JE virus, although histological evidence of encephalitis is readily demonstrable. Minimal amounts of virus can infrequently be isolated from CNS tissue and blood during the first week of infection, but virus does not appear in oropharyngeal secretions.

Cyclophosphamide was given to spider monkeys on day 1 (100 mg/kg) and day 9 (50 mg) after an intracerebral inoculation of JE virus. All animals receiving drug developed acute paralytic disease within 12 to 14 days, preceded by several days of viremia and oropharyngeal shedding of virus. Histological examination of spinal cords from immunosuppressed animals revealed very severe neuronal destruction, in comparison with untreated monkeys in which cord lesions were relatively mild (Nathanson and Cole, 1970).

Of particular interest was the almost complete absence of neuronophagia even though many neurons showed severe diffuse chromatolysis. This damping of inflammatory elements was associated with drug-induced leucopenia. All immunosuppressed monkeys had virus in their spinal cords, and levels were as much as 1000 times above those seen in infected control animals. Only infected nonsuppressed monkeys developed neutralizing and hemagglutination-inhibiting antibodies, which were first detected 14 days after infection. Drug control animals remained well and were free of CNS lesions at sacrifice.

d. Host Age. The association of decreasing host susceptibility with increasing host age is described in a foregoing section. One well-studied host-virus combination, in which age-related resistance is absolute, is West Nile virus infection of rats (Sabin, 1952, 1954; ElDadah *et al.*, 1967; ElDadah and Nathanson, 1967). Suckling animals display an equal susceptibility to West Nile virus given by any route, and uniformly die from a fulminating infection of the CNS. At 16 days of age death no longer occurs, although a small percentage of rats develop transient neurological symptoms. Adult rats remain asymptomatic following intracerebral inoculation of West Nile virus, but undergo an abortive CNS infection. A limited period of viral replication can be detected in the brain by direct assay or by immunofluorescent staining, and virus disappears from the brain shortly after serum-neutralizing antibodies appear. Histologically, only minimal perivascular cuffs and focal infiltrates are present with little or no evidence of neuronal outfall.

Adult rats were given cyclophosphamide, 100 mg/kg, on day 1 and 50 mg/kg on days 8 and 14 after intracerebral inoculation of West Nile virus (Cole and Nathanson, 1968). Approximately 75% of these animals developed fatal CNS infection; virus eventually reached a level in the brain which was 100-fold or greater than that found in normal animals. Of particular significance was the fact that in both suppressed and normal rats virus growth curves and number of infected neurons in the brain were similar through day 7, indicating that immunosuppression had no direct effect on the numbers of susceptible cells or on the rate of spread of the infection. Following the appearance of serum-neutralizing antibody the amount of virus in the brain of normal animals subsequently fell to undetectable levels by the 11th day. Virus titers continued to increase in the brains of drug-treated animals, and by the 12th day reached a maximum level which remained essentially unchanged until death. An increase in the number of fluorescent cells was seen, which paralleled the increase in virus. Histologically, brains revealed severe destruction of the cerebral cortex and hippocampus, with almost total loss of neurons. Rats given drug alone showed no histological abnormalities of the CNS, but 20% died of drug toxicity.

e. Virus Strain and Passage History. As mentioned earlier, prolonged serial brain-to-brain propagation of some arboviruses can result in the emergence of a virus population with markedly enhanced neurovirulence.

Dengue-1 virus, isolated from acute phase serum from human patients, usually produces no overt symptoms when first inoculated intracerebrally in suckling mice. After 2 or 3 additional blind intracerebral passages, the virus is lethal for sucklings but innocuous for adult mice. Additional passage eventually leads to a virus strain (MP-125) capable of producing uniform mortality in mice of all ages (Cole and Wisseman, 1969a).

Infections with low-passaged dengue-1 virus (MP-3) were studied in normal and immunosuppressed adult mice, the latter receiving 150 mg/kg of cyclophosphamide on days 1, 7, and 14 after intracerebral inoculation of virus. In both groups of mice minimal levels of virus were first detectable in the CNS several days after infection. Virus persisted at a low level in the brains of normal animals, disappearing shortly after the appearance of serum antibody on the 12th day; no animals showed signs of clinical illness. In contrast, all immunosuppressed mice developed CNS disease and died 19 to 25 days after infection, without a detectable antibody response. Virus in the brain reached high levels and persisted until death. Lethal MP-3 infection in suppressed mice is characterized by slow virus replication and long incubation period, which differentiates it from lethal MP-125 infection in normal mice (Cole and Nathanson, 1968).

f. Route of Inoculation. The effect of this variable is best illustrated by employing arboviruses which exhibit a low or negligible peripheral neurovirulence, but which are highly virulent when inoculated directly into the CNS. Both dengue-1 (MP-125 strain) and West Nile virus fail to kill adult mice following intraperitoneal inoculation with very large doses, while relatively small doses given intracerebrally are lethal. Unlike dengue virus, West Nile virus gains access to the CNS following peripheral inoculation and produces a transient self-limiting infection preceded by a minimal viremia (Weiner *et al.,* 1970).

A single dose of cyclophosphamide (250 mg/kg), given 1 day after peripheral West Nile virus inoculation, completely overcomes this route-dependent resistance. Animals develop fatal CNS disease, with high levels of virus in blood and brain prior to death (Cole, Weiner, and Nathanson, unpublished, 1968). In comparison, repetitive drug doses following peripheral inoculation with dengue virus produce no effect. Dengue virus, with its minimal potential for replication in extraneural tissue (Cole and Wisseman, 1969a), lacks the ability to invade the neural compartment; resistance in this case is independent of immune responsiveness.

g. Virus Dose. The role of immune responsiveness in the relationship between virus dose and outcome of CNS infection can be readily demonstrated by titrating selected arboviruses in normal and immunosuppressed mice. Keeping host age and route of inoculation constant, the 50% lethal end points for West Nile, Langat, Semliki Forest, and Western equine encephalomyelitis viruses were all found to increase in immunosuppressed animals (Thind and Price, 1969b; Cole and Nathanson, unpublished, 1969).

C. Miscellaneous Viruses

This section reviews data on certain other experimental models of virus infection of the CNS which have been used for studies of immunosuppression. Reference is also made to problems which might be fruitfully probed with immunosuppressive techniques in future studies.

1. Picornaviruses

Encephalomyocarditis (EMC) virus. Glasgow and associates (Murphy and Glasgow, 1967, 1968; Farber and Glasgow, 1968) have reported the effect of several immunosuppressive measures upon the outcome of EMC infections in adult mice. Intraperitoneal inoculation of EMC virus produces an infection which kills a small proportion of mice (large virus dose) or no mice (small dose). Combined treatment with cyclophosphamide and thioguanine enhanced viremia and replication in target organs and over 80% of the mice died. In treated animals the onset of serum antibody was delayed by 2 days; serum interferon titers were slightly higher in treated than control mice.

Preparation of mice with 350 R whole body X-irradiation (Murphy and Glasgow, 1968) had a similar effect. Depression of neutralizing antibody induction was marked; in controls, antibody appeared on day 4 and reached titers over 1000 by day 6; at this time antibody had not appeared in treated mice. Passive administration of anti-EMC serum (recipients had a neutralizing antibody titer of 2000), to X-irradiated, EMC-inoculated mice, produced complete protection if given on the day of virus and partial protection when given up to 3 days after virus. Glasgow concluded that the immune response played a more important role than interferon in the recovery of mice from EMC infections.

Poliovirus and coxsackie virus. The sensitivity of monkeys to the minimal amounts of live poliovirus which remained in the incriminated lots of Cutter vaccine (Nathanson and Langmuir, 1963) was increased by cortisone and/or X-irradiation (Syverton *et al.* 1956; Eklund *et al.*, 1956; Bodian, 1956). It appears, from the fragmentary data in those reports, that viremia was enhanced by the treatments, but it is not clear whether there was a significant suppression of serum antibody response.

Other studies, showing that cortisone, X-irradiation, or stress enhanced susceptibility of a variety of experimental animals to poliovirus or coxsackie virus, reported higher virus titers in blood and brain, but also failed to include data on antibody (Kilbourne and Horsfall, 1951; Syverton *et al.*, 1952; Shwartzman and Fisher, 1952; Shwartzman, 1953; Melnick, 1953; Shwartzman *et al.*, 1955; Cajal *et al.*, 1959; Johnsson and Rasmussen, 1965). Smith and Cheever (1959) administered 400 R whole-body X-irradiation to weanling mice and, 24 hours later, inoculated them intraperitoneally with coxsackie virus B4; a more widespread infection was seen (apparently without death) together with a reduced neutralizing antibody response in the X-irradiated animals, in comparison to infected but untreated control mice.

2. Rabies Virus

Although, as the first animal virus isolated, rabies has received extensive study, its pathogenesis still presents some provocative problems. Wiktor, Koprowski, and associates (Fernandes *et al.*, 1964; Wiktor *et al.*, 1968; Campbell *et al.*, 1968) have demonstrated that rabies virus can produce persistent noncytocidal infections in certain tissue culture systems, and that rabies virus antiserum plus complement will cause immune lysis of such infected cells. Johnson (1965a) studied the pathogenesis of the fixed CVS strain of rabies virus in mice. After subcutaneous inoculation, high titers of virus were present in the CNS on the third day and immunofluorescent antigen was seen on the fourth day; however, little or no evidence of neuronal cytopathology or inflammation was seen up to death of mice 8 to 12 days after infection. The lack of necrotic changes in neurons infected for 4 days or more suggested that, in this experimental model, the virus may not be cytopathic.

Nonneuroadapted strains of rabies virus ("street virus") can produce subclinical infections when inoculated by extraneural routes (Johnson, 1966; Bell *et al.*, 1966). Following subclinical infection the virus may persist as a latent infection, which can be activated by stress or by administration of ACTH (Soave 1962, 1964).

Recovery from acute symptomatic rabies infection of the CNS has been studied by Bell (1964; Bell *et al.*, 1966). Disappearance from the brain of detectable infectious rabies virus is associated with appearance of rabies antibody in brain homogenates, reminiscent of Morgan's (1949a) findings for poliomyelitis and Schlesinger's (1949a,b) for arboviruses.

This brief synopsis suggests several questions regarding rabies virus-host interactions which might be explored with immunosuppression. Among these are: (*i*) What is the role of the immune response in recovery from active rabies virus infection of the CNS, or in maintaining persistent rabies infections in a latent form? (*ii*) Can rabies infection initiate an immunopathological process?

3. Herpes Viruses

The comparative virology of the herpes viruses has been reviewed by Plummer (1967), while Nahmias and Dowdle (1968) have compared types 1 and 2 (oral and genital) strains of herpes simplex virus (herpesvirus hominis) in detail. A number of these viruses (including herpes simplex virus, varicella virus, B virus, and pseudorabies virus) are capable of producing severe encephalitis and have an unusual affinity for first-order sensory neurons. Infection may be localized to one or a few sensory ganglia together with the corresponding innervation area of skin or mucous membrane. Herpes viruses often can produce persistent latent infections and it is postulated that the cell bodies of first-order sensory neurons may serve as the site of persistence of herpes simplex virus (Paine, 1964; Kibrick and Gooding, 1965; Roizman, 1965; Fenner, 1968) and of varicella virus (Weller, 1965; Hope-Simpson, 1965). The limited data available suggest that a continued low level of infectious virus may be found during latency (Schmidt and Rasmussen, 1960; Kaufman *et al.,* 1968). However, virus has not been isolated from trigeminal ganglia of patients with facial herpes (Richter, 1944).

The mechanism of activation of latent herpes simplex or herpes zoster is obscure. Activation may occur following radiation, fever, physiological and psychological disturbances, and section of the sensory root of the trigeminal nerve (Ellison *et al.,* 1959). Likewise, zoster may be associated with a variety of prior precipitating conditions. Hope-Simpson (1965) has postulated that a naturally occurring decline in antibody level may precede zoster, and it is possible that a diminished immune responsiveness due to disease (e.g., Hodgkin's disease, Sokal and Firat, 1965) or immunosuppressive therapy could be one of the precipitating causes. The activation of cytomegalovirus (Schneck, 1965; Craighead, 1969) and of herpes simplex virus (Montgomerie *et al.,* 1969) which has been reported in immunosuppressed patients is consistent with this possibility. However, it seems likely that activation of latent herpes infections is often unrelated to immune mechanisms.

At present there is only limited information on the effect of immunosuppression upon experimental herpes simplex infection. Nahmias *et al.* (1969) treated weanling mice with antithymocyte serum, before and after infection with varying doses of a type 1 herpes virus strain. Two different effects were seen. Viral inocula adequate to produce approximately 50% mortality from encephalitis were administered by intraperitoneal or intragenital routes; under these circumstances virus probably spreads through the circulation to invade the CNS, and antithymocyte serum increased mortality to 75–100%. Following intracerebral inoculation, antithymocyte serum either had no influence or decreased mortality, depending upon virus dose. The authors suggested that the latter effect might be due to inhibition of the CNS inflammatory response. In our view this hypothesis (Hirsch and Murphy, 1967), which resembles that advanced by Webb *et al.* (1968a,b), requires further testing.

4. *Parvoviruses*

Rat virus is an indigenous virus of laboratory and wild rats (Kilham, 1966; Toolan, 1968); some strains cause symptomatic (often fatal) infections in suckling rats, but only inapparent infections in adult animals. There is evidence to suggest that this virus can also produce persistent latent infections accompanied by serum antibody (Kilham and Olivier, 1959; Kilham, 1966; Robey *et al.*, 1968).

The HER strain of rat virus causes silent infections when inoculated into adult rats; however, paralytic disease develops in a significant number following drug-induced immunosuppression (Nathanson *et al.*, 1970). The HER strain was originally isolated from "normal" animals given immunosuppressive drugs only (Nathanson *et al.*, 1970; Paterson and Nathanson, unpublished, 1970); whether this represented activation of latent infection, or potentiation of a coincidental natural acute infection, has yet to be determined.

IV. Discussion and Conclusions

A. *Multifactorial Determination of the Outcome of Viral Infection*

1. *Concept of a Race between Virus and Host Defenses*

Apart from the use of immunosuppressive techniques, there are a number of observations in the literature which are consistent with the concept that the outcome of a viral infection of the CNS is determined by a race between the replicating agent and host defenses, including the immune response. If infection is visualized as a race between virus and host defenses, then the outcome is determined by the balance between factors favoring the virus and those favoring the host. Furthermore, different factors, involving quite different mechanisms, can act in concert or in opposition. Several examples illustrate this viewpoint.

a. *Intracerebral Inoculation.* Schlesinger's (Schlesinger *et al.*, 1944; Schlesinger, 1949a,b) series of investigations of Western equine encephalomyelitis (WEE) virus are particularly instructive. Guinea pigs, vaccinated with killed WEE virus, resisted homologous intracerebral challenge, although virus replication in the brain appeared to parallel that in controls for about 24 hours. After this time, virus disappeared from brains of vaccinated animals but rapidly multiplied in controls, which died 2 or 3 days after inoculation.

In a similar experiment using vaccinated mice (Schlesinger, 1949a) the outcome was dependent upon the strain of WEE virus; growth of a rapidly multiplying strain was retarded in brains of vaccinated animals, but death still occurred. In contrast, a strain which replicated relatively slowly, but which killed unimmunized animals, produced an abortive nonfatal cycle of infection in vaccinated mice, with clearance of virus by about 5 days after infection.

Studies of the protective effect of elevated body temperature offer another example. Cole and Wisseman (1969b) found that mice, incubated at 35°C (body temperature 39°C) survived an intracerebral inoculation of a strain of dengue-1 virus which killed all animals held at 22°C (body temperature 37°C). At elevated temperatures intracerebral virus replication was retarded, brain interferon levels were lower, and appearance of antibody was delayed. Approximately 20 days after infection, virus titers dropped and antibody appeared. In this instance it appears that hyperthermia had a greater inhibitory effect on virus replication (Lwoff, 1959, 1969) than on host defenses, and reversed the outcome of infection. When a more virulent dengue virus strain was used, the effect of hyperthermia was negligible and all animals died.

b. Extraneural Inoculation. For many years it has been well documented that a variety of viruses, which regularly produce lethal infections when inoculated intracerebrally, even in minimal doses, produce only sublethal (often subclinical) immunizing infections when inoculated parenterally (Lennette and Koprowski, 1944). More recently, it has become clear that, in some instances, the potentially lethal virus actually invades the CNS, where it undergoes a transient cycle of replication, reaches only low titer, and then disappears (Gleiser *et al.*, 1962; Huang and Wong, 1963; Webb *et al.*, 1968b; Thind and Price, 1969d; Doherty, 1969; Weiner *et al.*, 1970). From these circumstances it is evident that infection aborts without spreading to a large residual population of highly susceptible cells. It appears that peripheral inoculation (and extraneural infection) triggers host defenses several days prior to CNS invasion, permitting these defenses to anticipate and outrace the infectious process. The role of the immune response in interactions of this type has been described in the foregoing section on arbovirus encephalitis.

The effect of specific factors is dependent upon the mode of virus spread to the CNS. Thus, Nathanson and Bodian (1962) found that a small dose of immune globulin protected monkeys against intramuscular challenge with the highly virulent Mahoney strain of poliovirus, which invaded the CNS from the blood. However, the same treatment failed to protect against the "fixed" MV strain, which spread to the CNS by the neural route. Conversely, sciatic nerve freeze protected against gastrocnemius inoculation of the MV strain but not against the Mahoney strain (Nathanson and Bodian, 1961a).

c. Comment. These examples suggest certain generalizations which, although obvious deserve brief statement. (*i*) Virus virulence and host susceptibility are attributes which can only be characterized for specific virus-host interactions. (*ii*) The relative importance of specific mechanisms in determining the outcome of infection differs markedly in different experimental models, as well as in different instances of naturally occurring infection. (*iii*) It is simplistic to consider a single mechanism as the sole determinant of the outcome of infection, although, for purposes of analysis, it is often possible to experimentally "isolate" individual mechanisms. (*iv*) Experimental intervention designed to demonstrate the importance of a particular mechanism must be interpreted with caution. Exogenous factors (such as antibody, interferon, or immunologically competent cells), introduced into experimental animals, may produce unambiguous effects but do not necessarily prove that the factor under examination is singularly important in the outcome of unmanipulated infection. Attempts to inhibit a specific host defense may suffer from lack of specificity, since it is difficult to markedly impair a single defense mechanism without producing widespread physiological derangements.

2. Role of the Immune Response in Primary Viral Infection: Present Status and Future Directions

The evidence regarding the possible role of the immune response in recovery from primary viral infections with potentially neurovirulent viruses, can be conveniently considered under several heads, based upon differences in experimental approach.

a. Descriptive Sequential Observations. Classical descriptive studies of viral pathogenesis fall into this category. For instance, Bodian (1959) summarized the sequential evolution of poliovirus infection of primates, based upon data accumulated by many laboratories. Antibody appears between 5 and 10 days after infection, often coincident with the clearing of viremia, and about the time that spinal cord virus titers are increasing, that is, a few days prior to paralysis. Such observations may be misleading for several reasons. First, more sensitive methods of detection indicate that serum antibody can appear considerably earlier after exposure to poliovirus antigen (Svehag and Mandel, 1964) and the earliest antibody may be complexed by excess virus in the blood (Nathanson and Bodian, 1962; Melnick *et al.*, 1966). Furthermore, antibody in CNS or CSF may be more relevant than serum antibody (Morgan, 1949a,b). In any event, data of this type permit only weak inferences as to causal relationships.

Descriptive studies provide more important data when a comparison is made of models in which the outcome of infection varies. There are several studies in which naturally occurring differences in the time of appearance of serum antibody were related to the outcome of infection.

Overman and Kilham (1953) studied mumps meningoencephalitis produced by intracerebral inoculation of hamsters with the M-1 (less virulent) and M-2 (more virulent) virus strains. The M-1 strain killed newborn hamsters, while 8-day-old animals survived. Survival was associated with an earlier HI antibody response. The M-2 strain, which had a much shorter incubation period, killed 8-day-old hamsters, and Overman and Kilham suggested that the M-2 strain was able to outrace the immune response. In additional studies with mice, Overman (1954a,b) showed that an inactivated mumps vaccine elicited a more rapid HI antibody response in older mice; furthermore the greatest change in responsiveness occurred between 7 and 10 days of age, which correlated with the age of development of host resistance.

Morgan (1941) found that the response of mice to inactivated Eastern equine encephalomyelitis (EEE) virus vaccine, as measured by neutralizing antibody, increased considerably during the first 10 days of life; this was correlated with a marked reduction, during the first month of life, in the intraperitoneal LD_{50} of the virus. A similar explanation for age-specific resistance of mice to cowpox virus was advanced by Subrahmanyan (1968).

Schell (1960) studied the marked differences in susceptibility of mice of different strains to mousepox virus, and concluded that the relative resistance ofC57BL mice was correlated with their more effective immune response to this agent.

b. Passive Immunization. It is well known that passive administration of immune serum prior to infection can dramatically protect against extraneural viral infection, if viremia plays an important role in CNS invasion (Morgan, 1949b; Nathanson and Bodian, 1962). Furthermore, doses of antibody, so low that no neutralizing activity can be measured in the serum of recipients, can protect (Bodian, 1952). However, if administration is delayed until after infection, the effect is rapidly lost, depending upon the host-virus combination, and upon route of administration and dose of antibody (Murphy and Glasgow, 1968). Thus, experiments with passive antibody are suggestive, but they leave unanswered the question whether the active primary immune response of the unmanipulated host is sufficiently rapid to play a role in the outcome of infection.

c. Active Immunization. Another approach to evidence implicating the immune response is manipulation of the virus inoculum to vary the amount of antigen relative to the number of infectious particles. A classic example is the work of Schlesinger (1949b), who showed that when "lightly immunized" mice were challenged intracerebrally with varying doses of Western equine encephalomyelitis virus, death occurred following small but not large virus inocula. The paradoxical or "zone" effect which has been described for other host-virus interactions (Schlesinger, 1959), was interpreted as reflecting the greater antigenic stimulus afforded by the larger inoculum. A similar approach was exploited by Bodian (1956), who showed that incorporation of a small amount of virulent virus in a large volume of inactivated vaccine markedly reduced the subsequent frequency of paralysis following intramuscular injection.

d. Immunosuppression. The effects of immunosuppression have been detailed in an earlier section and only the essentials need be recapitulated. A variety of procedures can be used to render experimental animals unresponsive or hyporesponsive to exogenous antigens, including viruses. Application of these techniques to many virus-host models produces several effects: (*i*) The levels of virus in blood, brain, or other tissues are elevated, and virus may appear earlier and persist for longer periods. (*ii*) More cells are eventually infected (immunofluorescent observations) and, if the virus is cytocidal, a greater number are destroyed. Concomitantly, subclinical infections become symptomatic and often fatal. (*iii*) The appearance of antibody in serum or tissues is retarded, and death may intervene before antibody is detected. (*iv*) Interferon levels are often directly related to virus titer, and may be higher in tissues of suppressed animals than in infected but unsuppressed controls. (*v*) The physiological derangements produced by many immunosuppressive techniques may reduce the interferon response: cyclophosphamide, Robinson and Heath (1968); antilymphoid serum, Barth *et al.* (1969) and Sheagren *et al.* (1969); X-irradiation, DeMaeyer *et al.* (1969); cortisone, Rytel and Kilbourne (1966) and Mendelson and Glasgow (1966). However, large doses of immunosuppressive drugs do not always reduce the interferon response (Ho *et al.*, 1967).

e. Comment. The dramatic potentiation of many experimental virus infections by a variety of immunosuppressive techniques strongly suggests that the immune response, in some virus-host interactions, plays a key role in the outcome. In our view, concomitant reduced interferon responsiveness, when it occurs, is not sufficient to account for this potentiation, in light of the elevated interferon levels which regularly accompany enhanced virus titers. At present it is impossible to determine whether the effects of immunosuppressants are due, in part, to damping of host defenses other than the immune response and interferon.

f. Future Directions. To further define the role of immune mechanisms during viral infections, better methods are needed both for immunosuppression and to monitor immune status.

Greater specificity is required of immunosuppressive methodology; the goal is an animal with normal responsiveness to all but one or more selected antigens. Due in great part to the stimulus of tissue transplantation, this goal may soon be achieved.

(*i*) *Immunization-suppression.* Schwartz and Borel (1968) have reviewed evidence indicating that administration of an immunosuppressive drug, during the period of immune induction (for instance, 24 hours after antigen) may selectively destroy immunocytes responding to that antigen (Santos, 1967). Upon recovery from the acute drug effects, the animal regains normal responsiveness to antigens other than the one administered prior to drug. Although this approach has successfully been used with some inert particulate antigens, its success depends on a number of critical variables; repeated administration of the test antigen and drug, or thymectomy, may be required to maintain unresponsiveness.

Preliminary experiments in our laboratory (Weiner *et al.*, 1971) demonstrated that this approach has potential for studies of virus infection. Adult mice were given 3 intraperitoneal inoculations of formalin-inactivated West Nile (WN) or Western equine encephalomyelitis (WEE) virus vaccines, at weekly intervals. One day after each vaccination the mice received cyclophosphamide, 150 mg/kg. Ten days after the last cyclophosphamide injection, animals suppressed in this manner were again inoculated with WN or WEE vaccine; they failed to produce HI antibody to the virus to which they had been suppressed, but responded normally to the heterologous viral antigen. Since WN and WEE viruses exhibit low neurovirulence in adult mice after intraperitoneal inoculation, the specificity of immunosuppression could be further tested. Ten days after immunization-suppression, mice were challenged intraperitoneally with a large dose of WN or WEE virus; animals were killed by the virus to which they had been suppressed, but survived challenge with the heterologous virus.

(*ii*) *Passive administration of antibody* has been successfully used to suppress responsiveness to the corresponding antigen (Uhr and Moller, 1968), presumably by virtue of its ability to bind antigen. The potentiation of Langat virus infection by specific viral antibodies (Webb *et al.*, 1968a) may represent an example of this phenomenon.

Large doses of *antigen* have been shown to induce hyporesponsiveness (Dresser and Mitchison, 1968). Thus, Flick and Pincus (1963) injected inactivated concentrated vaccinia virus intramuscularly into newborn rabbits, and 4 days later challenged intradermally with live vaccinia virus. In contrast to control rabbits which developed a normal primary local vaccinia lesion, animals pretreated with viral antigen developed a generalized vaccinia infection which killed more than 50%.

(*iii*) Tests designed to provide *in vitro* assessment of *delayed hypersensitivity* to viral antigens are a major need. The variety of products released by sensitized lymphocytes *in vitro*, when exposed to the immunizing antigen (David, 1968), and the biological responses evoked by these products, suggest numerous potential *in vitro* assays. When such methods are applied to viral pathogenesis new interpretations of established phenomena may emerge.

3. Interferon as a Host Defense Mechanism

The active current interest in interferon has generated a large body of literature. Several symposium volumes provide useful general reviews (Finter, 1967a, 1970; Wolstenholme and O'Connor, 1967). *In vitro* studies of interferon are outside the scope of this discussion, but it is relevant to note the mass of data which documents marked differences between viruses, both in their activity as interferon inducers, and in their sensitivity to interferon. This, in turn, suggests that the importance of interferon will vary in different host-virus interactions.

Particularly relevant to consideration of host defenses is the review by Baron (1970).

a. Descriptive Sequential Observations. Most cells are potentially capable of interferon synthesis, and interferon production usually occurs in those tissues which are supporting virus replication. In addition, there is a tendency for local fixation of interferon (Finter, 1966). Thus, following intracerebral inoculation of adult mice with West Nile virus, virus replication and interferon production are essentially confined to the CNS (Subrahmanyan and Mims, 1966). Conversely, intravenous inoculation of interferon inducers stimulates particularly the spleen, and results in high titers of circulating interferon (Fruitstone *et al.*, 1966; Baron *et al.*, 1966a,b). Intravenously injected interferon rapidly disappears (10–60 minutes), and probably equilibrates with the extracellular fluid compartment (Baron *et al.*, 1966a; Finter, 1966; Gresser *et al.*, 1967; Ho *et al.*, 1967). However, it appears to be taken up more readily by certain tissues and organs (particularly liver) than by others (Subrahmanyan and Mims, 1966; Ho *et al.*, 1967).

Sequential descriptions of the relationship between virus, interferon, and antibody are numerous (e.g., Murphy and Glasgow, 1967, 1968; Cole and Wisseman, 1969a). In general, these show that the rise and fall of interferon follows that of virus quite closely, while antibody appears later, often about the time that virus titers begin to drop. Originally, such observations were provisionally interpreted (Baron, 1963; Isaacs, 1963) as evidence for the role of interferon in recovery from infection. The pitfalls in such an interpretation are illustrated by the comparative study of Cole and Wisseman (1969a), who observed the usual sequence of events, but found the highest interferon levels in lethal host-virus combinations, where virus titers were also highest.

b. Comparative Studies of Variable Host Susceptibility. The marked influence of *age* on susceptibility of rodents to infection with a wide variety of viruses capable of producing encephalitis has been described above. These observations provide an opportunity for assessment of the possible role of interferon in these age-specific changes in susceptibility. An early report by Heineberg *et al.* (1964), utilizing coxsackie virus B1, suggested that interferon production might be reduced in susceptible infant mice compared to resistant adults. However, subsequent studies with other models (Sindbis virus, Vilvek, 1964; West Nile virus, Subrahmanyan, 1968; dengue virus, Cole and Wisseman, 1969a) fail to suggest that interferon plays an important role in age-specific variation in host susceptibility.

In a preceding section the *genetically determined* difference in susceptibility of different strains to mice to intracerebral inoculation of group B arboviruses was described (Goodman and Koprowski, 1962). Virus replicates in brains of resistant animals, but growth is slower from the outset, indicating some quantitative difference in virus-cell interaction. *In vitro* studies (Vainio, 1963) suggest that cell cultures reflect the susceptibility of the animals from which they are derived, since susceptible cultures yielded at least 100-fold as much virus as did resistant cultures. Cultures from resistant and susceptible animals show equal ability to produce interferon (Vainio *et al.*, 1961). More recently Hanson and associates (1969) have suggested that resistant cells are more sensitive to interferon than are susceptible cells. Further exploration of this provocative finding is needed.

c. Virus Virulence. There are a number of *in vitro* studies comparing virus variants with a greater or lesser virulence, in which the more virulent strain produces less interferon or is less sensitive to interferon (Glasgow and Habel, 1962; Wagner *et al.*, 1963; Finter, 1964a; Aurelian and Roizman, 1965). However, in certain *in vivo* systems, virulent strains are as sensitive to interferon as avirulent strains (Cole and Wisseman, 1969a).

d. Protection by Passive Administration of Exogenous Interferon. Administration of pre-formed interferon to a passive recipient has repeatedly been shown to protect against a subsequent virus challenge. Finter (1966) explored the effect of interferon against intraperitoneal challenge with a strain of Semliki Forest virus which produced a lethal infection in adult mice after intraperitoneal inoculation. When a large dose of interferon was inoculated intramuscularly 3.5 hours prior to challenge with 110 mouse intraperitoneal LD_{50}, about 90% of animals survived. Interferon protection dropped rapidly with increasing virus dose; pretreatment with 2 large doses gave 80, 40, and 0% protection, respectively, against 80, 320, and 1280 LD_{50} of virus. When given after virus, interferon was much less effective. Since interferon is rapidly removed from the circulation, the doses used by Finter produced negligible serum titers in recipients.

Baron and co-workers (1966b) gave juvenile mice passive interferon intravenously, and then challenged with minimal doses (about 1–10 LD_{50}) of encephalomyocarditis (EMC) virus or vesicular stomatitis virus (VSV), by the intracerebral route. Pretreatment with large doses over the 24 hours prior to challenge protected mice completely against an EMC challenge which killed 40% of controls. A similar interferon regime reduced VSV mortality from 95 to 65%.

In evaluating these results, several comparisons should be borne in mind. The amounts of interferon used in passive experiments are undoubtedly less than those produced actively in response to viruses which are optimal interferon inducers (Baron *et al.,* 1966a). Passive protection with interferon given prior to virus challenge, when compared to that afforded by passively administered antibody, is impressive for intracerebral injection (Morgan, 1949b), but not for extraneural routes of infection. In any event, studies of this type only indicate the potential role which interferon might play in the outcome of certain virus infections.

e. Effect of Active Interferon Induction. Finter (1966) tested the effect of virus-induced interferon in protection against heterologous virus challenge of mice. Active induction of interferon with Newcastle disease virus (NDV) injected intravenously at various times from 24 to 4 hours prior to intraperitoneal challenge with 110 intraperitoneal LD_{50} of Semliki Forest virus, protected 30 to 100% of mice. Baron and associates (1966b) found that the protection afforded against intracerebral challenge with about 10 LD_{50} (95% lethal dose) of EMC virus depended on the time of induction, survival being greatest (60%) when NDV was administered 24 hours before virus challenge.

On the other hand, interferon induction has had a variable effect on the outcome of certain experimental rabies infections. Thus, while high levels of circulating interferon did not protect against intramuscular challenge of adult mice with approximately 1 LD_{50} of rabies virus (Soave, 1968; Finter, 1967b), complete protection of rabbits was achieved by a single intravenous injection of the synthetic inducer polyinosinic-polycytidylic acid (Fenje and Postic, 1970).

f. Comment. The experimental data indicate that some viruses are potent interferon inducers, and that the levels of interferon found in blood and tissues during certain virus infections are sufficient to markedly retard virus replication. Combined with the older data on viral interference (Schlesinger *et al.,* 1944), it appears likely that interferon modulates a number of infections. In some instances, interferon may be a critical determinant of the outcome. However, the lack of a method for specific blockade of the interferon aspect of host defenses, makes definitive proof difficult to attain.

4. Other Mechanisms

a. Age Effects. The age-specific decrease in susceptibility of mice to intraperitoneal or other extraneural routes of injection, in the face of relatively high susceptibility to intracerebral inoculation, has already been discussed at several points. This effect is associated with variations in viremia, which in turn reflect differences in the replication of virus in tissues that release virus into the circulation. Little attempt has been made to elucidate the underlying cellular mechanisms, with the exception of a study by Johnson (1964b) of herpes simplex virus. *In vitro,* peritoneal macrophages from suckling and adult mice were equally susceptible to herpes infection, but infected macrophages from young animals were much more efficient as a source of infection for other cells in the culture. Age may also have a decisive effect in experimental models where neural spread, rather than viremia, is operative (e.g., Sabin and Olitsky, 1937a,b). There is a need for further *in vitro* studies of age-determined susceptibility.

b. Virus Receptor Sites on Cell Surfaces. Since the pioneering work of Holland (1961) and his associates on the mechanism of the resistance of nonprimate cells or animals to human polioviruses, a great deal of information on cellular receptor sites has accumulated. In a series of studies Holland showed that while mouse cells cannot be infected with intact poliovirus, viral RNA alone, or viral RNA enclosed within the capsid of coxsackie virus B1, can enter and infect mouse cells (Holland, 1961; Cords and Holland, 1964).

Kunin (1962) found that loss of susceptibility of older mice to group B coxsackie viruses was correlated with age-specific reduction of receptor activity of brain homogenates. Originally it was thought that quantitative differences in attachment might account for more subtle effects, such as the virulence of different poliovirus strains; more recent work (Harter and Choppin, 1965) has failed to confirm earlier impressions.

c. Serum Protective Factor. Thind and Price (1968, 1969c) have described cross-protection between antigenically related group B arboviruses in mice. Protection could be passively transferred by serum from immunized mice which lacked detectable neutralizing antibody, and the activity was designated serum protective factor (SPF). SPF resembles antibody in its antigenic specificity and persistence in the serum of immunized mice; however, it differs in certain physical properties from the best characterized immunoglobulins, and its precise nature awaits further study.

d. Temperature Effects on Virus Replication. There is little information on variation in neurovirulence of virus strains, which goes beyond essentially descriptive data. The effect of temperature on virus replication is an exception. Temperature can be studied both as a virus variable, by comparing mutants with different growth temperature optima (Fenner, 1968), and as a host variable, by comparing replication of a single strain at optimal and nonoptimal temperatures (Lwoff, 1969). Furthermore, temperature characteristics tend to exert a strong influence on the outcome of infection; that is, thermoresistant mutants tend to be virulent; and elevation of body temperature tends to slow virus growth and favor host survival. Thus, Carmichael and associates (1969; Carmichael and Barnes, 1969) have correlated the high susceptibility of young puppies to canine herpesvirus with their body temperature (about 36°C) which is lower than that of adult dogs (37°–38°C); in tissue culture the virus grows optimally at 35°–36°C.

Lwoff (1959, 1961, 1969) has made an extensive study of the mechanism of temperature sensitivity, based on *in vitro* studies of the replication of poliovirus variants. At supraoptimal temperatures several events were defined (Lwoff, 1969) which contribute to the reduced accumulation of viral RNA: a ribonuclease is activated (perhaps released from lysosomes) which degrades viral RNA; and the activity of viral RNA replicase is markedly decreased.

It has been suggested (Baron, 1970) that the effects of temperature might occur (at least in some laboratory models) because hyperthermia causes a greater reduction in virus replication than in interferon production, with an inverse effect of hypothermia (Stancek, 1965). Thus, Ruiz-Gomez and Sosa-Martinez (1965) found that holding mice at 4°C enhanced their susceptibility to coxsackie virus B1, with concomitant increase in virus titers and decrease in interferon levels. On the other hand, the protection of hyperthermic mice from Sindbis or from dengue-1 virus infection (Kirn *et al.*, 1967; Cole and Wisseman, 1969b) was associated with decreased levels of both virus and interferon in the brain.

V. Summary

This review has summarized current views of the pathogenesis of virus infections of the nervous system, with particular attention to certain aspects of virus-host interactions. Following invasion of the central nervous system, infection can follow a variety of patterns, as to number and distribution of neuronal and nonneuronal cells involved. There is a corresponding diversity in the pathological lesions of the CNS produced by acute virus infection.

Infection can be pictured as a race between virus and host defenses, where many factors, acting through different mechanisms, can influence the outcome. Outcome is always determined by multiple virus and host variables, although single variables can be independently studied under experimentally controlled conditions in the laboratory. A body of evidence has evolved to indicate that, in many virus-host combinations, the immune response plays an important role in recovery from primary infections. Likewise, it is clear that an immunopathological process mediates the disease which follows certain CNS virus infections. Further refinement to produce virus-specific immunosuppression is required to strengthen the experimental evidence. Finally, *in vitro* correlates of delayed hypersensitivity are needed to delineate the relative roles of humoral and cellular aspects of the immune response in the outcome of virus infections of the central nervous system.

References

Adams, J. M., Boak, R. A., Carpenter, C. M., French, J. D., Klein, S. J., Pressman, J. J., and Smith, J. L. (1953). *J. Lab. Clin. Med.* **41,** 142.

Albrecht, P. (1960). *Acta Virol. (Prague), Engl. Ed.* **4,** 150.

Albrecht, P. (1962). *In* "Biology of Viruses of the Tick-borne Encephalitis Complex" (H. Libikova, ed.), pp. 247–257. Academic Press, New York.

Albrecht, P. (1968). *Curr. Top. Microbiol. Immunol.* **43,** 44.

Allison, A. (1967). *Perspect. Virol.* **5,** 29.

Anderson, K. (1940). *Amer. J. Pathol.* **16,** 137.

Appel, M. J. G. (1969). *Amer. J. Vet. Res.* **30,** 1167.

Armstrong, C. (1942). *Mil. Surg.* **91,** 129.

Ashe, W. K., Mage, M., Mage, R., and Notkins, A. L. (1968). *J. Immunol.* **101,** 500.

Aurelian, L., and Roizman, B. (1965). *J. Mol. Biol.* **11,** 539.

Bablanian, R., Eggers, H. J., and Tamm, I. (1965a). *Virology* **26,** 100.

Bablanian, R., Eggers, H. J., and Tamm, I. (1965b). *Virology* **26,** 114.

Baer, G. M. (1969). *In* "The Structure and Function of Nervous Tissue" (G. H. Bourne, ed.), Vol. 3, Academic Press, New York.

Baer, G. M., Shanthaveerappa, T. R., and Bourne, G. M. (1965). *Bull. W. H. O.* **33,** 783.

Bailey, O. T., Pappenheimer, A. M., Cheever, F. S., and Daniels, J. B. (1949). *J. Exp. Med.* **90,** 195.

Bang, F. B. (1942). *J. Exp. Med.* **76,** 263.

Bang, F. B. (1943). *J. Exp. Med.* **77,** 337.

Bang, F. B. (1959). *In* "The Viruses" (F. M. Burnet and W. M. Stanley, eds.), Vol. 3, pp. 63–110. Academic Press, New York.

Bang, F. B., and Luttrell, C. N. (1961). *Advan. Virus Res.* **8,** 199.

Bang, F. B., and Warwick, A. (1960). *Proc. Nat. Acad. Sci. U.S.* **46,** 1065.

Barlow, R. M., and Dickinson, A. G. (1965). *Res. Vet. Sci.* **6,** 230.

Barlow, R. M., and Gardiner, A. C. (1969). *J. Comp. Pathol.* **79,** 397.

Baron, S. (1963). *Advan. Virus Res.* **10,** 39.

Baron, S. (1970). *In* "Interferons" (N. B. Finter, ed.), North-Holland, Amsterdam.

Baron, S., Buckler, C. E., McCloskey, R. V., and Kirschstein, R. D. (1966a). *J. Immunol.* **96,** 12.

Baron, S., Buckler, C. E., Friedman, R. M., and McCloskey, R. V. (1966b). *J. Immunol.* **96,** 17.

Barth, R. F., Friedman, R. M., and Malmgren, R. A. (1969). *Lancet* **ii,** 723.

Baublis, J. V., and Payne, F. E. (1968). *Proc. Soc. Exp. Biol. Med.* **129,** 593.

Bell, J. F. (1964). *J. Infec. Dis.* **114,** 249.

Bell, J. F., Lodmell, D. L., Moore, G. J., and Raymond, G. H. (1966). *J. Immunol.* **97,** 747.

Benda, R., and Cinatl, J. (1962). *Acta Virol. (Prague), Engl. Ed.* **6,** 159.

Benson, L. M., and Hotchin, J. E. (1960). *Proc. Soc. Exp. Biol. Med.* **103,** 623.
Benson, L. M., and Hotchin, J. E. (1969). *Nature (London)* **222,** 1045.
Berge, T. O., Gleiser, C. A., Gochenour, W. S., Jr., Meisse, M. L., and Tigertt, W. D. (1961a). *J. Immunol.* **87,** 509.
Berge, T. O., Banks, I. S., and Tigertt, W. D. (1961b). *Amer. J. Hyg.* **73,** 209.
Bernhard, W. (1964). *Cell. Inj., Ciba Found. Symp., 1963,* pp. 209–243.
Blackwood, W., McMenemey, W. H., Meyer, A., Norman, R. M., and Russell, D. S. (1967). "Greenfield's Neuropathology." Williams & Wilkins, Baltimore, Maryland.
Bodian, D. (1948). *Bull. Johns Hopkins Hosp.* **83,** 1.
Bodian, D. (1952). *Amer. J. Hyg.* **56,** 78.
Bodian, D. (1954). *Amer. J. Hyg.* **60,** 358.
Bodian, D. (1956). *Amer. J. Hyg.* **64,** 92.
Bodian, D. (1959). *In* "Viral and Rickettsial Infections of Man" (T. M. Rivers and F. L. Horsfall, Jr., eds.), pp. 479–498. Lippincott, Philadelphia, Pennsylvania.
Bodian, D. (1961). *Poliomyelitis, Pap. Discuss. 5th Int. Poliomyelitis Conf., Copenhagen, 1960,* pp. 66–73.
Bodian, D. (1964). *Bull. Johns Hopkins Hosp.* **114,** 13.
Bodian, D., and Howe, H. A. (1941a). *Bull. Johns Hopkins Hosp.* **68,** 58.
Bodian, D., and Howe, H. A. (1941b). *Bull. Johns Hopkins Hosp.* **69,** 79.
Boring, W. D., ZuRhein, G. M., and Walker, D. L. (1956). *Proc. Soc. Exp. Biol. Med.* **93,** 273.
Boyse, E. A., Morgan, R. S., Pearson, J. D., and Wright, G. P. (1956). *Brit. J. Exp. Pathol.* **37,** 333.
Brightman, M. W. (1965). *Amer. J. Anat.* **117,** 193.
Brownlee, A., and Wilson, D. R. (1932). *J. Comp. Pathol.* **45,** 67.
Bruno-Lobo, M., Peralta, P. H., Bruno-Lobo, G. G., and de Paola, D. (1968). *An. Microbiol.* **15,** 53.
Bunge, R. P., and Harter, D. H. (1969). *J. Neuropathol. Exp. Neurol.* **28,** 185.
Cabasso, V. J. (1962). *Ann. N.Y. Acad. Sci.* **101,** 498.
Cairns, H. J. F. (1950). *Nature (London)* **166,** 910.
Cajal, N., Mateescu, S., and Copelovici, Y. (1959). *Acta Virol. (Prague), Engl. Ed.* **3,** Suppl., 107.
Campbell, J. B., Kaplan, M. M., Koprowski, H., Kuwert, E., Sobol, F., and Wiktor, T. J. (1968). *Bull. W. H. O.* **38,** 373.
Cancilla, P. A., and Barlow, R. M. (1968). *Res. Vet. Sci.* **9,** 88.
Cancilla, P. A., and Barlow, R. M. (1970). *J. Neuropathol. Exp. Neurol.* **29** (in press). Abstr.
Carmichael, L. E., and Barnes, F. D. (1969). *J. Infec. Dis.* **120,** 664.
Carmichael, L. E., Barnes, F. D., and Percy, D. H. (1969). *J. Infec. Dis.* **120,** 669.
Cascardo, M. R., and Karzon, D. T. (1965). *Virology* **26,** 311.
Chamberlain, R. W. (1968). *Curr. Top. Microbiol. Immunol.* **42,** 38.
Cheever, F. S., Daniels, J. B., Pappenheimer, A. M., and Bailey, O. T. (1949). *J. Exp. Med.* **90,** 181.
Choppin, P. W. (1964). *Virology* **23,** 224.
Choppin, P. W. (1968). *In* "Textbook of Immunopathology" (P. A. Miescher and H. J. Müller-Eberhard, eds.), pp. 337–349. Grune & Stratton, New York.
Coffin, D. L., and Liu, C. (1957). *Virology* **3,** 132.
Cole, G. A., and Nathanson, N. (1968). *Nature (London)* **220,** 399.
Cole, G. A., and Wisseman, C. L., Jr. (1969a). *Amer. J. Epidemiol.* **89,** 669.
Cole, G. A., and Wisseman, C. L., Jr. (1969b). *Proc. Soc. Exp. Biol. Med.* **130,** 359.
Cole, G. A., Nathanson, N., and Rivet, H. (1970). *Amer. J. Epidemiol.* **91,** 339.

Cooke, B. T., Hurst, E. W., and Swan, C. (1942). *Aust. J. Exp. Biol. Med. Sci.* **20,** 129.
Cooper, P. D. (1967). *Brit. Med. Bull.* **23,** 155.
Cooper, P. D., Johnson, R. T., and Garwes, D. J. (1966). *Virology* **30,** 638.
Cords, C. E., and Holland, J. J. (1964). *Virology* **24,** 492.
Cox, H. R. (1954). *Bacteriol. Rev.* **18,** 239.
Craighead, J. E. (1969). *Amer. J. Epidemiol.* **90,** 506.
Dalton, A. J., Rowe, W. P., Smith, G. H., Wilsnack, R. E., and Pugh, W. E. (1968). *J. Virol.* **2,** 1465.
David, J. R. (1968). *In* "Textbook of Immunopathology" (P. A. Miescher and J. H. Müller-Eberhard, eds.), pp. 111–131. Grune & Stratton, New York.
Dean, D. J., Evans, W. M., and McClure, R. C. (1963). *Bull. W. H. O.* **29,** 803.
DeMaeyer, E., DeMaeyer-Guiguard, J., and Jullien, P. (1969). *Proc. Soc. Exp. Biol. Med.* **131,** 36.
Doherty, P. C. (1969). *J. Comp. Pathol.* **79,** 413.
Downie, J. C., and Oxford, J. S. (1969). *J. Gen. Virol.* **5,** 11.
Dresser, D. W., and Mitchison, N. A. (1968). *Advan. Immunol.* **8,** 129.
Dubes, G. R., and Wenner, H. A. (1957). *Virology* **4,** 275.
Duffy, C. E. (1951). *Proc. Soc. Exp. Biol. Med.* **76,** 566.
Dulbecco, R. (1952). *Proc. Nat. Acad. Sci. U.S.* **38,** 747.
East, J., Parrott, D. M. V., and Seamer, J. (1964). *Virology* **22,** 160.
Eklund, C. M., Bell, E. J., and Hadlow, W. J. (1956). *Amer. J. Hyg.* **64,** 85.
ElDadah, A. H., and Nathanson, N. (1967). *Amer. J. Epidemiol.* **86,** 776.
ElDadah, A. H., Nathanson, N., and Sarsitis, R. (1967). *Amer. J. Epidemiol.* **86,** 765.
Ellison, S. A., Carton, C. A., and Rose, H. M. (1959). *J. Infec. Dis.* **105,** 161.
Evans, D. G., ed. (1969). *Brit. Med. Bull.* **25,** 119.
Farber, P. A., and Glasgow, L. A. (1968). *Amer. J. Pathol.* **53,** 463.
Farmer, T. W., and Janeway, C. A. (1942). *Medicine (Baltimore)* **21,** 1.
Fenje, P., and Postic, B. (1970). *Nature (London)* **226,** 171.
Fenner, F. (1968). "The Biology of Animal Viruses." Academic Press, New York.
Fenner, F., and Cairns, J. (1959). *In* "The Viruses" (F. M. Burnet and W. M. Stanley, eds.), Vol. 3, pp. 225–249. Academic Press, New York.
Fenner, F., and Sambrook, J. F. (1964). *Annu. Rev. Microbiol.* **18,** 47.
Fernandes, M. V., Wiktor, T. J., and Koprowski, H. (1964). *J. Exp. Med.* **120,** 1099.
Findlay, G. M., and Stern, R. O. (1936). *J. Pathol. Bacteriol.* **43,** 327.
Finter, N. B. (1964a). *J. Hyg.* **62,** 337.
Finter, N. B. (1964b). *Brit. Med. J.* **ii,** 981.
Finter, N. B. (1966). *Brit. J. Exp. Pathol.* **47,** 361.
Finter, N. B., ed. (1967a). "Interferons." North-Holland, Amsterdam.
Finter, N. B. (1967b). *In* "Interferon" (G. E. W. Wolstenholme and M. O'Connor, eds.), pp. 204–215. Little, Brown, Boston, Massachusetts.
Finter, N. B., ed. (1970). "Interferons." North-Holland, Amsterdam. In press.
Flexner, S. (1931). *Science* **74,** 251.
Flick, J. A., and Pincus, W. B. (1963). *J. Exp. Med.* **117,** 633.
Fraser, K. B., Nairn, R. C., McEntegart, M. G., and Chadwick, C. S. (1959). *J. Pathol. Bacteriol.* **78,** 423.
Fruitstone, M. J., Michaels, B. S., Rudloff, D. A. C., and Sigel, M. M. (1966). *Proc. Soc. Exp. Biol. Med.* **122,** 1008.
Gilden, D., Cole, G. A., and Nathanson, N. (1971). *J. Neuropathol. Exp. Neurol.* **30,** (in press). Abstr.
Gillespie, J. H. (1962). *Ann. N.Y. Acad. Sci.* **101,** 540.
Glasgow, L. A., and Habel, K. (1962). *J. Exp. Med.* **115,** 503.

Gledhill, A. W. (1967). *Nature (London)* **214,** 178.
Gleiser, C. A., Gochenour, W. S., Jr., Berge, T. O., and Tigertt, W. D. (1961). *J. Immunol.* **87,** 504.
Gleiser, C. A., Gochenour, W. S., Jr., Berge, T. O., and Tigertt, W. D. (1962). *J. Infec. Dis.* **110,** 80.
Godman, G. C. (1966). *Int. Rev. Exp. Path.* **5,** 67.
Goldberg, S. A., Brodie, M., and Stanley, P. (1935). *Proc. Soc. Exp. Biol. Med.* **32,** 587.
Goodman, G. T., and Koprowski, H. (1962). *J. Cell. Comp. Physiol.* **59,** 333.
Goodpasture, E. W. (1925). *Amer. J. Pathol.* **1,** 11.
Gorham, J. R. (1960). *Advan. Vet Sci.* **6,** 287.
Gresser, I., Fontaine, D., Coppey, J., Falcoff, R., and Falcoff, E. (1967). *Proc. Soc. Exp. Biol. Med.* **124,** 91.
Groschel, D., and Koprowski, H. (1965). *Arch. Gesamte Virusforsch.* **17,** 379.
Haas, V. H. (1954). *J. Infec. Dis.* **94,** 187.
Haas, V. H., and Stewart, S. E. (1956). *Virology* **2,** 511.
Habel, K., ed. (1955). *Ann. N.Y. Acad. Sci.* **61,** 737.
Hanaoka, M., Suzuki, S., and Hotchin, J. (1969). *Science* **163,** 1216.
Hanson, B., Koprowski, H., Baron, S., and Buckler, C. E. (1969). *Microbios* **1B,** 51.
Harbitz, F., and Scheel, O. (1907). *J. Amer. Med. Ass.* **49,** 1420.
Harter, D. H., and Choppin, P. W. (1965). *J. Immunol.* **95,** 730.
Harter, D. H., and Choppin, P. W. (1967). *Virology* **31,** 279.
Haymaker, W. (1961). *In* "Encephalitides" (L. van Bogaert, J. Radermecker, J. Hozay, and A. Lowenthal, eds.), pp. 38–56. Elsevier, Amsterdam.
Heineberg, H., Gold, E., and Robbins, F. C. (1964). *Proc. Soc. Exp. Biol. Med.* **115,** 947.
Henle, G., Dienhardt, F., and Girardi, A. (1958). *Proc. Soc. Exp. Biol. Med.* **87,** 386.
Henle, W. (1963). *J. Immunol.* **91,** 145.
Heremans, J. F. (1968). *Curr. Top. Microbiol. Immunol.* **45,** 131.
Herndon, R. M., and Rubinstein, L. J. (1968). *Neurology* **18,** Pt. 2, 8.
Hill, A. B., and Knowelden, J. (1950). *Brit. Med. J.* **ii,** 1.
Hirsch, M. S., and Murphy, F. A. (1967). *Nature (London)* **216,** 179.
Hirsch, M. S., and Murphy, F. A. (1968). *Lancet* **ii,** 37.
Hirsch, M. S., Murphy, F. A., Russe, H. P., and Hicklin, M. D. (1967). *Proc. Soc. Exp. Biol. Med.* **125,** 980.
Hirsch, M. S., Murphy, F. A., and Hicklin, M. D. (1968). *J. Exp. Med.* **127,** 757.
Hirsch, M. S., Gary, G. W., Jr., and Murphy, F. A. (1969). *J. Immunol.* **102,** 656.
Ho, M., Postic, B., and Ke, Y. H. (1967). *In* "Interferon" (G. E. W. Wolstenholme and M. O'Connor, eds.), pp. 19–35. Little, Brown, Boston, Massachusetts.
Holland, J. J. (1961). *Virology* **15,** 312.
Holmes, K. V., and Choppin, P. W. (1966). *J. Exp. Med.* **124,** 501.
Holtermann, O. A., and Majde, J. A. (1969). *Nature (London)* **223,** 624.
Hook, E. W., Luttrell, C. N., Slaten, K., and Wagner, R. R. (1962). *Amer. J. Pathol.* **41,** 593.
Hope-Simpson, R. E. (1965). *Proc. Roy. Soc. Med.* **58,** 9.
Hopper, P. K. (1959). *J. Comp. Pathol.* **69,** 78.
Hotchin, J. E. (1962). *Cold Spring Harbor Symp. Quant. Biol.* **27,** 479.
Hotchin, J. E. (1965). *In* "Slow, Latent, and Temperate Virus Infections" (D. C. Gajdusek, C. J. Gibbs, Jr., and M. Alpers, eds.), NINDB Monogr. No. 2, pp. 341–359. U.S. Govt. Printing Office, Washington, D. C.
Hotchin, J., and Weigand, H. (1961). *J. Immunol.* **87,** 675.

Hotchin, J., Benson, L. M., and Seamer, J. (1962). *Virology* **18,** 71.
Howe, H. A., and Ecke, R. S. (1937). *Proc. Soc. Exp. Biol. Med.* **37,** 125.
Huang, C. H., and Wong, C. (1963). *Acta Virol. (Prague), Engl. Ed.* **7,** 322.
Hughes, J. T. (1969). *In* "Virus Diseases and the Nervous System" (C. N. M. Whitty, J. T. Hughes, and F. O. MacCallum, eds.), pp. 29–37. Blackwell, Oxford.
Hurst, E. W. (1931). *J. Comp. Pathol.* **44,** 231.
Hurst, E. W. (1933). *J. Exp. Med.* **58,** 415.
Hurst, E. W. (1936). *Brain* **59,** 1.
Imam, I. Z. E., and Hammon, W. McD. (1957a). *Proc. Soc. Exp. Biol. Med.* **95,** 6.
Imam, I. Z. E., and Hammon, W. McD. (1957b). *Proc. Soc. Exp. Biol. Med.* **95,** 12.
Innes, J. R. M., and Saunders, L. Z. (1962). *"Comparative Neuropathology."* Academic Press, New York.
Isaacs, A. (1963). *Advan. Virus Res.* **10,** 1.
Isacson, P. (1967). *Progr. Allergy* **10,** 256.
Johnson, H. N. (1959). *In* "Viral Rickettsial Infections of Man" (T. M. Rivers and F. L. Horsfall, Jr., eds.), pp. 405–431. Lippincott, Philadelphia, Pennsylvania.
Johnson, H. N. (1966). *Proc. Nat. Rabies Symp.* pp. 25–30. National Communicable Disease Center, Atlanta, Georgia.
Johnson, K. P., and Johnson, R. T. (1968). *J. Neuropathol. Exp. Neurol.* **27,** 390.
Johnson, R. T. (1964a). *J. Exp. Med.* **119,** 343.
Johnson, R. T. (1964b). *J. Exp. Med.* **120,** 359.
Johnson, R. T. (1965a). *J. Neuropathol. Exp. Neurol.* **24,** 662.
Johnson, R. T. (1965b). *Amer. J. Pathol.* **46,** 929.
Johnson, R. T. (1968). *J. Neuropathol. Exp. Neurol.* **27,** 80.
Johnson, R. T. (1970a). *Res. Publ., Ass. Res. Nerv. Ment. Dis.* **49,** (in press).
Johnson, R. T. (1970b). *J. Infec. Dis.* **121,** 227.
Johnson, R. T., and Johnson, K. P. (1968). *J. Neuropathol. Exp. Neurol.* **27,** 591.
Johnson, R. T. and Johnson, K. P. (1969). *Exp. Mol. Pathol.* **10,** 68.
Johnson, R. T., and Mercer, E. H. (1964). *Aust. J. Exp. Biol. Med. Sci.* **42,** 449.
Johnson, R. T., and Mims, C. A. (1968). *New Engl. J. Med.* **278,** 23, 84.
Johnsson, T., and Rasmussen, A. F., Jr. (1965). *Arch. Gesamte Virusforsch.* **17,** 392.
Jungeblut, C. W., and Bautista, G., Jr. (1956). *J. Infec. Dis.* **99,** 103.
Kantoch, M., Warwick, A., and Bang, F. B. (1963). *J. Exp. Med.* **117,** 781.
Katz, M., Rorke, L. B., Masland, W. S., Koprowski, H., and Tucker, S. H. (1968). *New Engl. J. Med.* **279,** 793.
Katz, M., Rorke, L. B., Masland, W. S., Brodano, G. B., and Koprowski, H. (1970). *J. Infec. Dis.* **121,** 188.
Kaufman, H. E., Brown, D. C., and Ellison, E. D. (1968). *Amer. J. Ophthclmol.* **65,** 32.
Kibrick, S., and Gooding, G. (1965). *In* "Slow, Latent, and Temperate Virus Infections" (D. C. Gajdusek, C. J. Gibbs, Jr., and M. Alpers, eds.), NINDB Monogr. No. 2, pp. 143–154. U.S. Govt. Printing Office, Washington, D. C.
Kilbourne, E. D., and Horsfall, F. L., Jr. (1951). *Proc. Soc. Exp. Biol. Med.* **77,** 135.
Kilham, L. (1966). *Nat. Cancer Inst. Monogr.* **20,** 117–135.
Kilham, L., and Margolis, G. (1969). *Lab. Invest.* **21,** 183.
Kilham, L., and Olivier, L. J. (1959). *Virology* **7,** 428.
Kirn, A., Schieffer, A., and Tinland, R. (1967). *Nature (London)* **215,** 86.
Kohn, A. (1965). *Virology* **26,** 228.
Koprowski, H. (1962). *Amer. J. Dis. Child.* **103,** 273.
Kristensson, K., and Sourander, P. (1969). *Acta Neuropathol.* **14,** 38.
Krummel, W. M., and Uhr, J. W. (1969). *J. Immunol.* **102,** 772.

Kundin, W. D. (1966). *J. Immunol.* **96,** 49.
Kundin, W. D., Liu, C., and Gigstad, J. (1966). *J. Immunol.* **97,** 393.
Kunin, C. M. (1962). *J. Immunol.* **88,** 556.
Larsen, J. H. (1969a). *Immunology* **16,** 15.
Larsen, J. H. (1969b). *J. Immunol.* **102,** 941.
Lehmann-Grube, F. (1964). *Arch. Gesamte Virusforsch.* **14,** 344.
Lehmann-Grube, F. (1967). *Nature (London)* **213,** 770.
Lehmann-Grube, F. (1969). *Arch. Ges. Virusforsch.* **28,** 303.
Lehmann-Grube, F., Slenczka, W., and Tees, R. (1969). *J. Gen. Virol.* **5,** 63.
Lennette, E. H., and Koprowski, H. (1944). *J. Immunol.* **49,** 175.
Levey, R. H., Trainin, N., Law, L. W., Black, P. H., and Rowe, W. P. (1963). *Science* **142,** 483.
Lillie, R. D., and Armstrong, C. (1945). *Arch. Pathol.* **40,** 141.
Live Poliovirus Vaccines (1959). First International Conference on Live Poliovirus Vaccines. Panamer. Health Org. Sci. Publ. No. 44.
Live Poliovirus Vaccines (1960). Second International Conference on Live Poliovirus Vaccines. Panamer. Health Org. Sci. Publ. No. 50.
Lockart, R. Z. (1960). *Virology* **10,** 198.
Lubinska, L. (1964). *Progr. Brain Res.* **13,** 1.
Lundstedt, C., and Volkert, M. (1967). *Acta Pathol. Microbiol. Scand.* **71,** 471.
Lwoff, A. (1959). *Bacteriol. Rev.* **23,** 109.
Lwoff, A. (1961). *Poliomyelitis, Pap. Discuss. 5th Int. Poliomyelitis Conf., Copenhagen, 1960,* pp. 13–20.
Lwoff, A. (1969). *Bacteriol. Rev.* **33,** 390.
Lwoff, A., Tournier, P., Lwoff, M., and Catala, F. (1960). *C. R. Acad. Sci.* **250,** 2644.
MacDonald, F. (1952). *Aust. J. Exp. Biol. Med. Sci.* **30,** 319.
MacLeod, J. (1962). *J. Comp. Pathol.* **72,** 411.
Malkova, D. (1962). *Acta Virol. (Prague), Engl. Ed.* **6,** 475.
Marcus, P. I. (1962). *Cold Spring Harbor Symp. Quant. Biol.* **27,** 351.
Margolis, G., and Kilham, L. (1968). *Res. Publ. Ass. Res. Nerv. Ment. Dis.* **44,** 113.
Margolis, G., and Kilham, L. (1969). *Lab. Invest.* **21,** 189.
Margolis, G., and Kilham, L. (1970). *Lab. Invest.* **22** (in press).
Meicklejohn, G., England, B., and Lennette, E. A. (1952). *Am. J. Trop. Med. Hyg.* **1,** 51.
Melnick, J. L. (1953). *Adv. Virus Res.* **1,** 229.
Melnick, J. L., Proctor, R. O., Ocampo, A. R., Diwan, A., and BenPorath, E. (1966). *Amer. J. Epidemiol.* **84,** 329.
Mendelson, J., and Glasgow, L. A. (1966). *J. Immunol.* **96,** 345.
Miller, H. G., Stanton, J. B., and Gibbons, J. L. (1956). *Quart. J. Med.* **25,** 427.
Mims, C. A. (1960a). *Brit. J. Exp. Pathol.* **41,** 52.
Mims, C. A. (1960b). *Brit. J. Exp. Pathol.* **41,** 586.
Mims, C. A. (1960c). *Brit. J. Exp. Pathol.* **41,** 593.
Mims, C. A. (1964). *Bacteriol. Rev.* **28,** 30.
Miyamoto, K., and Matsumoto, S. (1967). *J. Exp. Med.* **125,** 447.
Mochizuki, H., Tomimura, T., and Oka, T. (1954). *J. Infec. Dis.* **95,** 260.
Montasir, M., Rabin, E. R., and Phillips, C. A. (1966). *Amer. J. Pathol.* **48,** 877.
Montgomerie, J. Z., Becroft, D. M. O., Croxson, M. C., Duale, P. B., and Noriti, J. D. K. (1969). *Lancet* **ii,** 867.
Morgan, I. M. (1941). *J. Exp. Med.* **74,** 115.
Morgan, I. M. (1949a). *Fed. Proc.* **8,** 618.
Morgan, I. M. (1949b). *J. Immunol.* **62,** 301.
Moulton, J. E. (1956). *Proc. Soc. Exp. Biol. Med.* **91,** 460.

Murphy, B. R., and Glasgow, L. A. (1967). *In* "Antimicrobial Agents and Chemotherapy," Proc. 9th Conf. Amer. Soc. Microbiol. (G. L. Hobby, ed.), pp. 661–666. Williams & Wilkins, Baltimore, Maryland.
Murphy, B. R., and Glasgow, L. A. (1968). *J. Exp. Med.* **127,** 1035.
Nahmias, A. J., and Dowdle, W. R. (1968). *Progr. Med. Virol.* **10,** 110.
Nahmias, A. J., Hirsch, M. S., Kramer, J. H., and Murphy, F. A. (1969). *Proc. Soc. Exp. Biol. Med.* **132,** 696.
Nathanson, N., and Bodian, D. (1961a). *Bull. Johns Hopkins Hosp.* **108,** 308.
Nathanson, N., and Bodian, D. (1961b). *Bull. Johns Hopkins Hosp.* **108,** 320.
Nathanson, N., and Bodian, D. (1962). *Bull. Johns Hopkins Hosp.* **111,** 198.
Nathanson, N., and Cole, G. A. (1970). *Clin. Exp. Immunol.* **6,** 161.
Nathanson, N., and Langmuir, A. D. (1963). *Amer. J. Epidemiol.* **78,** 29.
Nathanson, N., Goldblatt, D., Thind, I. S., Davis, M., and Price, W. H. (1965). *Amer. J. Epidemiol.* **82,** 359.
Nathanson, N., Davis, M., Thind, I. S., and Price, W. H. (1966). *Amer. J. Epidemiol.* **84,** 524.
Nathanson, N., Stolley, P. D., and Boolukos, P. J. (1969). *J. Comp. Pathol.* **79,** 109.
Nathanson, N., Cole, G. A., Santos, G. W., Squire, R. A., and Smith, K. O. (1970). *Amer. J. Epidemiol.* **91,** 328.
Nir, Y. D., and Goldwasser, R. (1961). *Amer. J. Hyg.* **73,** 297.
Notkins, A. L., Mahar, S., Scheele, C., and Goffman, J. (1966). *J. Exp. Med.* **124,** 81.
Notkins, A. L., Mage, M., Ashe, W. K., and Maher, S. (1968). *J. Immunol.* **100,** 314.
Okada, Y., and Tadokoro, J. (1962). *Exp. Cell Res.* **2,** 108.
Oldstone, M. B. A. (1970). Personal communication.
Oldstone, M. B. A., and Dixon, F. J. (1967). *Science* **158,** 1193.
Oldstone, M. B. A., and Dixon, F. (1968). *J. Immunol.* **100,** 355.
Oldstone, M. B. A., and Dixon, F. J. (1969). *J. Exp. Med.* **129,** 483.
Oldstone, M. B. A., and Dixon, F. J. (1970). *J. Exp. Med.* **131,** 1.
Overman, J. R. (1954a). *J. Immunol.* **73,** 244.
Overman, J. R. (1954b). *J. Immunol.* **73,** 249.
Overman, J. R., and Kilham, L. (1953). *J. Immunol.* **71,** 352.
Paffenbarger, R. S., and Wilson, V. O. (1955). *Ann. N.Y. Acad. Sci.* **61,** 856.
Paine, T. F., Jr. (1964). *Bacteriol. Rev.* **28,** 472.
Panijel, J., and Cayeux, P. (1968). *Immunology* **14,** 769.
Paterson, P. Y. (1969). *Annu. Rev. Med.* **20,** 75.
Perdrau, J. R. (1928). *J. Pathol. Bacteriol.* **31,** 17.
Pereira, H. G. (1961). *Advan. Virus Res.* **8,** 245.
Plotkin, S. A., Carp, R. I., and Graham, A. F. (1962). *Ann. N.Y. Acad. Sci.* **101,** 357.
Plowright, W. (1962). *Ann. N.Y. Acad. Sci.* **101,** 548.
Plummer, G. (1967). *Progr. Med. Virol.* **9,** 302.
Pollard, M., Sharon, N., and Teah, B. A. (1968a). *Proc. Soc. Exp. Biol. Med.* **127,** 755.
Pollard, M., Kajima, M., and Sharon, N. (1968b). *Perspect. Virol.* **6,** 193.
Rabin, E. R., and Jenson, A. B. (1967). *Progr. Med. Virol.* **9,** 392.
Rabin, E. R., Jenson, A. B., and Melnick, J. L. (1968). *Science* **162,** 126.
Rahman, A. N., and Luttrell, C. N. (1963). *Bull. Johns Hopkins Hosp.* **112,** 1.
Rapp, F. (1963). *J. Bacteriol.* **86,** 985.
Richards, W. P. C., and Cordy, D. R. (1967). *Science* **156.**
Richter, R. B. (1944). *J. Nerv. Ment. Dis.* **99,** 356.
Robey, R. E., Woodman, D. R., and Hetrick, F. M. (1968). *Amer. J. Epidemiol.* **88,** 139.
Robinson, T. W. E., and Heath, R. B. (1968). *Nature (London)* **217,** 178.

Roizman, B. (1962). *Cold Spring Harbor Symp. Quant. Biol.* **27,** 327.
Roizman, B. (1965). *Perspect. Virol.* **4,** 283.
Rosenau, M. J., and Andervont, H. B. (1931). *Amer. J. Hyg.* **13,** 728.
Rowe, W. P. (1954). *Nav. Med. Res. Inst. Rep.* **12,** 167.
Rowe, W. P. (1956). *Proc. Soc. Exp. Biol. Med.* **92,** 194.
Rowe, W. P., Black, P. H., and Levey, R. H. (1963). *Proc. Soc. Exp. Biol. Med.* **114,** 248.
Ruiz-Gomez, J., and Sosa-Martinez, J. (1965). *Arch. Gesamte Virusforsch.* **17,** 295.
Rustigian, R. (1966a). *J. Bacteriol.* **92,** 1792.
Rustigian, R. (1966b). *J. Bacteriol.* **92,** 1805.
Rytel, M. W., and Kilbourne, E. D. (1966). *J. Exp. Med.* **123,** 767.
Sabin, A. B. (1937). *Amer. J. Pathol.* **13,** 615.
Sabin, A. B. (1952). *Proc. Nat. Acad. Sci. U.S.* **38,** 540.
Sabin, A. B. (1954). *Res. Publ., Ass. Res. Nerv. Ment. Dis.* **33,** 57.
Sabin, A. B. (1957). *Spec. Publ. N.Y. Acad. Sci.* **5,** 113.
Sabin, A. B. (1961). *Perspect. Virol.* **2,** 90.
Sabin, A. B., and Hurst, E. W. (1935). *Brit. J. Exp. Pathol.* **16,** 133.
Sabin, A. B., and Olitsky, P. K. (1937a). *J. Exp. Med.* **66,** 15.
Sabin, A. B., and Olitsky, P. K. (1937b). *J. Exp. Med.* **66,** 35.
Santos, G. W. (1967). *Fed. Proc. Fed. Amer. Soc. Exp. Biol.* **26,** 907.
Saunders, M., Knowles, M., Chambers, M. E., Caspary, E. A., Garner-Medwin, D., and Walker, P. (1969). *Lancet* **i,** 72.
Schell, K. (1960). *Aust. J. Exp. Biol. Med. Sci.* **38,** 271.
Schlesinger, R. W. (1949a). *J. Exp. Med.* **89,** 491.
Schlesinger, R. W. (1949b). *J. Exp. Med.* **89,** 507.
Schlesinger, R. W. (1959). *In* "The Viruses" (F. M. Burnet and W. M. Stanley, eds.), Vol. 3, pp. 157–194. Academic Press, New York.
Schlesinger, R. W., and Frankel, J. W. (1952). *Amer. J. Trop. Med. Hyg.* **1,** 66.
Schlesinger, R. W., Olitsky, P. K., and Morgan, I. M. (1944). *J. Exp. Med.* **80,** 197.
Schmidt, J. R., and Rasmussen, A. F., Jr. (1960). *J. Infec. Dis.* **106,** 154.
Schneck, S. A. (1965). *J. Neuropathol. Exp. Neurol.* **24,** 415.
Schultz, G., and Delay, P. D. (1955). *J. Amer. Vet. Med. Ass.* **127,** 224.
Schwartz, R. S., and Borel, Y. (1968). *In* "Textbook of Immunopathology" (P. A. Miescher and J. H. Muller-Eberhard, eds.), pp. 227–235. Grune & Stratton, New York.
Scott, T. F. McN. (1967). *Med. Clin. N. Amer.* **51,** 701.
Scrimshaw, N. W., Taylor, C. E., and Gordon, J. E. (1968). "Interactions of Nutrition and Infection." World Health Organ. Monogr. Ser. No. 57.
Seamer, J. (1965). *Arch. Gesamte Virusforsch.* **17,** 654.
Seifried, O., and Cain, C. B. (1932). *J. Exp. Med.* **56,** 345.
Sellers, M. I., and Lavender, J. F. (1962). *J. Exp. Med.* **115,** 107.
Sever, J. L., and Zeman, W., eds. (1968). *Neurology* **18,** Pt. 2, 1.
Sheagren, J. N., Barth, R. F., Edelin, J. B., and Malmgren, R. A. (1969). *Lancet* **ii,** 297.
Shwartzman, G., ed. (1953). "The Effect of ACTH and Cortisone Upon Infection and Resistance." Columbia Univ. Press, New York.
Shwartzman, G., and Fisher, A. (1952). *J. Exp. Med.* **95,** 347.
Shwartzman, G., Aronson, S. M., Teodoru, C. V., Adler, M., and Jahiel, R. (1955). *Ann. N.Y. Acad. Sci.* **61,** 869.
Siegel, M., and Greenberg, M. (1955). *New Engl. J. Med.* **253,** 841.
Sigel, M. M. (1952). *Annu. Rev. Microbiol.* **6,** 247.

Sigurdsson, B., Pálsson, P. A., and Grímsson, H. (1957). *J. Neuropathol. Exp Neurol.* **16,** 389.
Sigurdsson, B., Pálsson, P. A., and van Bogaert, L. (1962). *Acta Neuropathol.* **1,** 343.
Silber, L. A., and Soloviev, V. D. (1946). *Amer. Rev. Sov. Med.* Spec. Suppl. p. 6.
Singer, M., and Bryant, S. V. (1969). *Nature (London)* **221,** 1148.
Smith, L. W., and Cheever, F. S. (1959). *Proc. Soc. Exp. Biol. Med.* **100,** 817.
Soave, O. A. (1962). *J. Infec. Dis.* **110,** 129.
Soave, O. A. (1964). *Amer. J. Vet. Res.* **25,** 268.
Soave, O. A. (1968). *Amer. J. Vet. Res.* **29,** 1507.
Sokal, J. E., and Firat, D. (1965). *Amer. J. Med.* **39,** 452.
Stanček, D. (1965). *Acta Virol. (Prague), Engl. Ed.* **9,** 298.
Strode, G., ed. (1951). "Yellow Fever." McGraw-Hill, New York.
Subrahmanyan, T. P. (1968). *Aust. J. Exp. Biol. Med. Sci.* **46,** 251.
Subrahmanyan, T. P., and Mims, C. A. (1966). *Brit. J. Exp. Pathol.* **47,** 168.
Svehag, S.-E. (1962). *Arch. Gesamte Virusforsch.* **12,** 363.
Svehag, S.-E., and Mandel, B. (1964). *J. Exp. Med.* **119,** 1.
Syverton, J. T., Werder, A. A., Friedman, J., Roth, F. J., Jr., Graham, A. B., and Mira, O. J. (1952). *Proc. Soc. Exp. Biol. Med.* **80,** 123.
Syverton, J. T., Brunner, K. T., Tobin, J. O'H., and Cohen, M. M. (1956). *Amer. J. Hyg.* **64,** 74.
Takemoto, K. K. (1966). *Progr. Med. Virol.* **8,** 314.
ter Meulen, V., Enders-Ruckle, G., Muller, D., and Jappich, G. (1969). *Acta Neuropathol.* **12,** 244.
Thind, I. S., and Price, W. H. (1966). *Amer. J. Epidemiol.* **84,** 193.
Thind, I. S., and Price, W. H. (1968). *Amer. J. Epidemiol.* **88,** 287.
Thind, I. S., and Price, W. H. (1969a). *Amer. J. Epidemiol.* **89,** 89.
Thind, I. S., and Price, W. H. (1969b). *Amer. J. Epidemiol.* **90,** 62.
Thind, I. S., and Price, W. H. (1969c). *J. Immunol.* **103,** 1424.
Thind, I. S., and Price, W. H. (1969d). *Amer. J. Epidemiol.* **89,** 593.
Thormar, H. (1961). *Virology* **14,** 463.
Toolan, H. W. (1968). *Int. Rev. Exp. Pathol.* **6,** 135.
Toyoshima, K., Hata, S., and Miki, T. (1960). *Biken J.* **3,** 281.
Traub, E. (1936a). *J. Exp. Med.* **63,** 847.
Traub, E. (1936b). *J. Exp. Med.* **64,** 183.
Traub, E. (1939). *J. Exp. Med.* **69,** 801.
Turnbull, H. M., and McIntosh, J. (1926). *Brit. J. Exp. Pathol.* **7,** 181.
Uhr, J. W., and Möller, G. (1968). *Advan. Immunol.* **8,** 81.
Vainio, T. (1963). *Ann. Med. Exp. Biol. Fenn.* **41,** Suppl. 1, 1.
Vainio, T., Gwatkin, R., and Koprowski, H. (1961). *Virology* **14,** 385.
van Bogaert, L., Radermecker, J., Hozay, J., and Lowenthal, A., eds. (1961). "Encephalitides." Elsevier, Amsterdam.
Vilček, J. (1964). *Virology* **22,** 651.
Volkert, M., and Larsen, J. H. (1964). *Acta Pathol. Microbiol. Scand.* **60,** 577.
Volkert, M., and Larsen, J. H. (1965a). *Progr. Med. Virol.* **7,** 160.
Volkert, M., and Larsen, J. H. (1965b). *Acta Pathol. Microbiol. Scand.* **63,** 161.
Volkert, M., and Lundstedt, C. (1968). *J. Exp. Med.* **127,** 327.
Vollmer, E. P., and Hurlburt, H. S. (1951). *J. Infec. Dis.* **89,** 103.
Vonka, V., Janda, Z., Simon, J., Adam, E., and Starch, M. (1967). *Progr. Med. Virol.* **9,** 204.
Wagner, R. R., Levy, A. H., Snyder, R. M., Ratcliff, G. A., Jr., and Hyatt, D. F. (1963). *J. Immunol.* **91,** 112.

Walker, D. L. (1964). *Progr. Med. Virol.* **6,** 111.
Walker, D. L. (1968). *In* "Medical and Applied Virology" (M. Sanders and E. H. Lennette, eds.), pp. 99–110. Green, St. Louis, Missouri.
Walker, D. L., and Boring, W. D. (1958). *J. Immunol.* **80,** 39.
Walker, D. L., and Hinze, H. C. (1962a). *J. Exp. Med.* **116,** 739.
Walker, D. L., and Hinze, H. C. (1962b). *J. Exp. Med.* **116,** 751.
Warren, J., Jensen, K., and Mason, R. (1962). *Ann. N.Y. Acad. Sci.* **101,** 520.
Webb, H. E. (1969). *In* "Virus Diseases and the Nervous System" (C. W. M. Whitty, J. T. Highes, and F. O. MacCallum, eds.), pp. 169–177. Blackwell, Oxford.
Webb, H. E., and Smith, C. E. G. (1966). *Brit. Med. J.* **ii,** 1179.
Webb, H. E., Wight, D. G. D., Platt, G. S., and Smith, C. E. G. (1968a). *J. Hyg.* **66,** 343.
Webb, H. E., Wight, D. G. D., Platt, G. S., Wiernik, G., and Smith, C. E. G. (1968b). *J. Hyg.* **66,** 355.
Webster, L. T., and Clow, A. D. (1936). *J. Exp. Med.* **63,** 827.
Weiner, L. P., Cole, G. A., and Nathanson, N. (1971). *J. Immunol.* **105** (in press).
Weiner, L. P., Cole ,G. A., and Nathanson, N. (1970). *J. Hyg.* **68** (in press).
Weissenbacher, M. C., Schmuñis, G. A., and Parodi, A. S. (1969). *Arch. Gesamte Virusforsch.* **26,** 63.
Weller, T. H. (1965), *In* "Viral and Rickettsial Infections of Man" (F. L. Horsfall, Jr., and I. Tamm, eds.), pp. 915–925. Lippincott, Philadelphia, Pennsylvania.
Wheeler, C. F., and Canby, C. M. (1959). *Arch. Dermatol.* **79,** 86.
Wiktor, T. J., Kuwert, E., and Koprowski, H. (1968). *J. Immunol.* **101,** 1271.
Wildy, P. (1967). *J. Hyg.* **65,** 173.
Wisseman, C. L., Jr., Sweet, B. H., Rosenzweig, E. C., and Eylar, O. R. (1963). *Amer. J. Trop. Med. Hyg.* **12,** 620.
Wolstenholme, G. E. W., and O'Connor, M., eds. (1967). "Interferon." Little, Brown, Boston, Massachusetts.
Woodruff, J. F. (1970). *J. Infec. Dis.* **121,** 164.
World Health Organization (1966). *World Health Organ. Tech. Rep. Ser.* **325.**
Wright, G. P. (1953). *Proc. Roy. Soc. Med.* **46,** 319.
Yamamoto, T., Otani, S., and Shiraki, H. (1965). *Acta Neuropathol.* **5,** 288.
Young, S., and Cordy, D. R. (1964). *J. Neuropathol. Exp. Neurol.* **23,** 635.
Zilber, L. A. (1962). *In* "Biology of Viruses of the Tick-Borne Encephalitis Complex" (H. Libikova, ed.), pp. 260–264. Academic Press, New York.
Zlotnik, I. (1968). *Brit. J. Exp. Pathol.* **49,** 555.

AUTHOR INDEX

Numbers in italics refer to the page on which the complete references are listed.

C

D

E

F

G

H

I

J

L

M

N

O

P

Y

Z

SUBJECT INDEX

M

N

O

P